Essentials of MATHEMATICS

Essentials of

MATHEMATICS

SECOND EDITION

RUSSELL V. PERSON

Professor of Mathematics
Capitol Institute of Technology

JOHN WILEY & SONS, INC.
NEW YORK|LONDON|SYDNEY

FIRST CORRECTED PRINTING, NOVEMBER, 1968

Library of Congress Catalog Card Number: 67-31180   GB 471 68211X
Printed in the United States of America

Preface

Although this second edition contains some significant changes from the first edition, there has been no change in the general plan, the basic subject matter, or the purpose of the book. The purpose is still to provide the elementary mathematical background needed by students preparing to enter one of the various fields of technology. The primary emphasis is still on the practical use of mathematics.

As in the first edition, the presentation of new ideas throughout follows a basic principle of education: start with the *specific* and lead to the *general*. Practically every new idea or concept begins with a specific example rather than the general form. As an example, take the matter of fractional exponents. The student first faces the form $5^{\frac{1}{2}}$: what does it mean? This sets the problem and establishes motivation. The meaning is given through the form $x^{\frac{1}{2}}$. Later comes the form $x^{\frac{2}{3}}$, and finally the general form, $N^{p/r}$. This is the natural way of learning and is all too uncommon in textbook writing.

A few important changes have been made, mostly as a result of the many excellent suggestions by users of the book:

(a) There has been a change in organization. Arithmetic still occupies the first part of the book (Part 1). Algebra has been placed as the second major part. Geometry has been moved from Part 2 to Part 3. Since geometry follows algebra, many of the formulas of geometry can now make use of the rules of algebra. The fourth and fifth parts are still logarithms and trigonometry, respectively. In logarithms, the old Chapter 3 has been incorporated in the old Chapter 2, and the whole is now Chapter 34. This was done so that the properties of logarithms could be emphasized directly in connection with computation.

(b) The following additions have been made:

1. A chapter (Chapter 7) on number bases.
2. A section on synthetic division in Chapter 10.
3. A section on determinants in Chapter 16.
4. A section on the solid angle and its unit of measurement, the square degree.
5. Sample quizzes, sometimes two forms, at the end of some topics.

(c) The following ideas have been introduced or pointed out:

1. An example of a formal proof in geometry in connection with the Pythagorean theorem.
2. Laws of real numbers: commutative, associative, and distributive.
3. Ordered pairs of numbers as coordinates of points.
4. A brief mention of the meaning of a set.
5. The use of synthetic division in finding roots of equations.

(d) Other changes:

1. Consecutive numbering of chapters throughout the book.
2. More convenient numbering of exercises, for example in Chapters 18, 19, 21, and 34.
3. To reduce verbosity, some sentences and paragraphs have been deleted or rewritten where this could be done without loss of clarity or understanding.
4. Chapter 23 on graphs and systems of quadratics is practically a complete revision of the old Chapter 16.
5. Most exercise problems have been left intact except for a few minor changes. At the same time many new problems have been added.

I express my appreciation to the users of the book for the many excellent suggestions concerning present features that have been considered good and for the changes that have been considered desirable. Many other suggestions are greatly appreciated even though they could not all be incorporated in the book at this time.

RUSSELL V. PERSON

Washington, D.C.
January 1968

Preface to the First Edition

This book was prepared as a textbook in the essentials of elementary mathematics. It consists chiefly of material I have used for the last six years in a preparatory mathematics course covering the five subjects, arithmetic, geometry, algebra, logarithms, and trigonometry.

The book presupposes very little or no previous knowledge in the fields covered, with the exception of elementary arithmetic. It contains more detailed explanation than is usually found in textbooks of this kind. One of the most difficult features of many mathematics texts, especially for the beginner, is the overabundance of symbols. It is my contention that the ideas and concepts of mathematics are not difficult. They are made difficult only when they are surrounded by and buried in a heap of symbols. In many instances a word can be used just as conveniently as a symbol and with more understanding. Even the word *equals* is sometimes preferable to the equality sign. Whenever a new concept is introduced, it is explained and defined in ordinary everyday language. Definitions are accurate without being complicated by difficult mathematical terminology.

Although written from material used in residence classes and planned for such use, the book is equally well suited to home-study courses. It is designed to enable a student to make good progress in learning mathematics without the aid of a personal instructor. It is addressed to the student earnestly and diligently seeking knowledge. Explanations are carefully given, and each step in a new process is explained and illustrated with examples. At the same time there is ample opportunity for the instructor in residence classes to vary the presentation to suit his own personal taste. The book contains an adequate supply of exercises so that selections can be made for class assignments.

The subject matter is entirely general and is equally suitable for technical and nontechnical schools. The book can be used as a text in general mathematics in any school or institute offering a course in the fields it covers. It might well form the basis for a college one-year terminal course in general mathematics for nonscience majors.

Reasoning is inductive rather than deductive. In most instances the students formulate their own rules. The emphasis is always on understanding before memorizing, on thinking rather than on the mere application of rules. Even axioms must appear reasonable.

Mathematics is not presented as something final and complete but as a fascinating field that contains opportunity for growth. The attempt is made to have students realize that there may be more than one approach to a problem and several ways of arriving at a solution. The emphasis is upon procedure and correct reasoning, not simply upon getting the right answer. The purpose is to have the student get some understanding of the power and the beauty as well as the practical utility of mathematics.

I wish to express my gratitude to all of my colleagues and to others who have given helpful comments and suggestions in the writing of this book, especially to Mr. Lattie M. Upchurch, Jr., for his encouragement, and to John Wiley and Sons for many helpful suggestions in the course of editing the manuscript.

RUSSELL V. PERSON

Washington, D.C.
January 1961

Contents

Essentials of MATHEMATICS

Part I

ARITHMETIC

1

Whole Numbers

1.1 OUR COMMON NUMBER SYSTEM

In order to get a good understanding of the various operations used in arithmetic, one should have a clear idea of the formation of our common number system. Our system of numbers makes use of only ten symbols, called *digits*: 0, 1, 2, 3, 4, 5, 6, 7, 8, and 9. By means of these ten symbols we can write a number of any size.

Each of these symbols was invented by early man to stand for a certain number of objects. The symbols were first used for counting. For instance, at one time in the prehistoric past a man may have found this many pebbles: o, o. After many years someone decided to call this many *two* and to represent them by the symbol 2. After many more years someone who had one more than two (that is, this many, o, o, o,) decided to call them *three* and to represent them by the symbol 3. He might just as well have called them *seven* and represented them by the symbol 5. Later on, this many objects, o, o, o, o, were called *four* and written 4. The other symbols up to nine (9) were invented in the same way. The zero (0) was the last of the ten symbols invented. Of course, it must be understood that the names and symbols were not exactly the same as we know them in English.

Then, when counting continued to one more than nine (such as this many pebbles, o, o, o, o, o, o, o, o, o, o, which we now call ten), there was no symbol for the number. It was decided to lump all of these objects together as one bunch and to write the digit 1 for the bunch. This 1 was placed in a position a little farther to the left. A zero was placed to the right of 1: thus 10. This is the way we now represent *ten* objects. In other words, 1 written in the second place to the left indicates a bunch of ten.

This *place value* of the digits was one of the greatest inventions in mathematics. When we write the number 27, we mean 2 bunches of ten each, and 7 single objects more, or 20 + 7. In the number 27 the 7 is in the position we call units' place and the 2 is in the position we call tens' place. By means of this place value of a digit, we can represent a number of any size, no matter how large.

When we count to 99, we have 9 bunches of ten each and 9 single objects more, or 90 + 9. Now, if we have one more object, we get *ten* bunches,

3

which we call one hundred objects. Since we have no symbol for ten, we lump the ten bunches together and call it a large bunch. We might call it a bunch of the *second order*. We write 1 one more place to the left and follow it with two zeros: 100. The 1 is said to be in hundreds' place. When we write a number such as 358 for a number of objects, we mean 3 large bunches of one hundred each, 5 small bunches of ten each, and 8 single objects more; that is, 358 means 300 + 50 + 8.

As we get larger and larger bunches, or bunches of higher orders, we move the digits for these bunches farther and farther to the left. We might say 1000000 (one million) represents 1 bunch of the sixth order. In a larger number, such as 92,000,000, the only purpose of the zeros is to place the 92 far enough to the left so that it will indicate 92 million. If the numbers are as large as ten thousand or more, we usually separate the digits by commas into groups of three, starting at the right, thus:

$$5,870,000,000,000.$$

In our common number system the first place starting at the right represents single units; the next place to the left represents tens; the third place, hundreds; the fourth place, thousands; the fifth place, ten-thousands; the sixth place, hundred-thousands; the seventh place, millions. In the United States a billion is represented in the tenth place. That is, 1 billion is a thousand millions. However, in England and in some other countries 1 billion means a million millions.

1.2 KINDS OF NUMBERS

Numbers may be classified as *integers* and *fractions*. An integer is a whole number. The positive integers, 1, 2, 3, 4, and so on, are used in counting and, are therefore, sometimes called *counting* numbers.

A *fraction* indicates a part or parts of a whole number, such as $\frac{1}{2}$, $\frac{3}{5}$, $\frac{4}{9}$, and so on. Fractions will be studied in Chapter 2.

An *even* number is a number that can be exactly divided by 2, such as the numbers 8, 14, 376, 9530, and so on. Numbers that are not exactly divisible by 2 are called *odd* numbers, such as 3, 7, 19, 61, and 847. Whether a number is odd or even is determined by the right-hand digit. In any number, if the right-hand digit is even, such as in 7936, the number itself is even and is divisible by 2. If the right-hand digit is odd, as in the number 4865, then the number itself is odd and is not divisible by 2.

1.3 ADDITION OF NUMBERS

When numbers are added, the result is called the *sum* of the numbers. The sum of 5, 7, and 4 is 16. The numbers added together are called *addends*. Addition is usually indicated by the plus sign (+).

In the addition of numbers, two laws are useful. We probably use these laws constantly without being aware of their names. The *commutative law* for addition states that two numbers may be added in either order. For example, to add 5 and 3, we may write

$$5 + 3 \quad \text{or} \quad 3 + 5$$

Now we may begin with 5 objects and add 3 to this number. However, we may begin with 3 objects and add 5 more to them. The result is 8 in both instances. The *commutative law* for addition states that

$$5 + 3 = 3 + 5$$

In general terms, if a and b represent any two numbers, respectively, then

$$a + b = b + a$$

This is the commutative law for addition.

Another law useful in adding several addends is the so-called *associative law* for addition. This law enables us to associate numbers in such a way that addition is often simplified. For example, suppose we wish to add the following numbers:

$$16 + 3 + 7$$

We might first say $16 + 3 = 19$. Then we add 7 to 19 and get 26. However, we know it is convenient to add 10 to any number. Now we might recognize that $3 + 7 = 10$. Then we can say

$$16 + 10 = 26$$

The two ways of associating the addends can be shown by parentheses. We enclose in parentheses the numbers to be added first. We indicate our first method of association as follows:

$$(16 + 3) + 7$$

The second way we indicate as

$$16 + (3 + 7)$$

This second way means that we first combine 3 and 7 and get 10. Then we add 10 to 16 and get 26. That is,

$$(16 + 3) + 7 = 16 + (3 + 7)$$

In general, if a, b, and c represent any three addends, then the *associative law for addition* states that

$$(a + b) + c = a + (b + c)$$

The commutative and associative laws enable us to pair up any combination of addends for easy calculation. For example, note the pairs of addends that make 10 in the following example:

$$6 + 7 + 3 + 5 + 8 + 5 + 2 = 36$$

$$10 \qquad 10 \quad 10$$

This pairing of addends that make 10 is very useful in column addition.

To add several numbers, we usually arrange them in column form, placing units under units, tens under tens, and so on. The sum is written below the numbers. In adding each column it is helpful to note any combinations of digits that make 10.

Example. Add $567 + 37486 + 5694 + 79$. The steps in the addition are shown here:

```
    2          32         132        1132       1132
  567        567         567         567         567
37486      37486       37486       37486       37486
 5694       5694        5694        5694        5694
   79         79          79          79          79
    6         26         826        3826       43826
```

We begin the addition by adding the digits in the units' column: thus $7 + 6 + 4 + 9 = 26$. The 6 is placed below the units' column, and the 2 indicating tens is *carried* to the top of the tens' column. Ordinarily, this *carrying* process is done mentally, although in long addition the carried digits are often written at the top of the proper column. When we add the tens' column, we get 32. This is actually 32 tens, which is 3 hundreds and 2 tens. The 2 is placed below the tens' column, and the 3 is carried to the top of the hundreds' column. Adding the hundreds' column, we get 18, which is 1 thousand and 8 hundreds. The 8 is placed below the hundreds column, and the 1 is carried to the top of the thousands' column. Adding the thousands' column, we get 13. The 3 is placed below the thousands' column, and the 1 is carried to the top of the next column, which is the ten-thousands' column. Adding this column, we get 4, which is placed at the bottom of the column. The sum 43,826 means $40000 + 3000 + 800 + 20 + 6$.

In order to be sure that your work in mathematics is correct, you should develop the habit of checking it in some way. Probably the best way to check addition is simply to add the numbers a second time. Another way is to reverse the direction of adding. If you add the columns downward the first time, then check by adding upward. However, remember, the best way to avoid errors in addition is to be sure you know instantly the sum of each of the following sets of numbers. They are called the 45 addition combinations.

2	3	4	3	9	5	7	5	3	4	8	2	1	9	4
1	2	5	4	9	2	1	3	9	7	3	9	8	1	4

6	2	6	7	9	1	8	7	6	9	5	7	4	1	5
5	4	6	3	7	6	8	5	2	5	1	6	8	4	8

3	6	2	7	9	6	1	7	4	9	3	5	7	2	6
3	9	2	8	4	8	1	2	6	8	1	5	7	8	3

1.4 SUBTRACTION OF INTEGERS

When one number is subtracted from another, the result is called the *difference* or *remainder*. The number subtracted is called the *subtrahend*. The number from which the subtrahend is subtracted is called the *minuend*.

The symbol for subtraction is the minus sign, a short horizontal line ($-$). To indicate 7 subtracted from 15, we write, $15 - 7$. This is read "15 minus 7." The minus sign means that the second number is to be subtracted from the first, not the reverse.

The result of subtracting 7 from 15 is 8; written: $15 - 7 = 8$. In this example 15 is the minuend, 7 is the subtrahend, and 8 is the remainder.

Notice that the statement $15 - 7$ means 7 is to be subtracted from 15. For this reason, in subtraction the numbers cannot be reversed. In addition $a + b$ equals the same as $b + a$. But in subtraction $a - b$ does not mean the same as $b - a$.

In subtracting numbers we begin with the units, as in addition.

Example 1.   Subtract 435 from 897.

Subtracting,

$$\begin{array}{ll} 8\,9\,7 & \text{minuend} \\ 4\,3\,5 & \text{subtrahend} \\ \hline 4\,6\,2 & \text{remainder} \end{array}$$

As a first step, we subtract 5 units from 7 units; that is, $7 - 5 = 2$. The 2 is placed in the units' column. Next, $9 - 3 = 6$. The 6 is placed in the tens' column. Here we are actually subtracting 9 tens $-$ 3 tens $=$ 6 tens. Finally, 8 hundreds $-$ 4 hundreds $=$ 4 hundreds.

Subtraction may be checked by addition. The sum of the remainder and subtrahend should equal the minuend. In the foregoing example the work may be checked by adding 435 to 462. The sum should be the minuend, 897. This checking can easily be done mentally. After subtracting,

$$\begin{array}{l} 8\,9\,7 \\ 4\,3\,5 \\ \hline 4\,6\,2 \end{array} \quad \text{add these mentally}$$

In the subtraction of numbers it is often necessary to use a process called *borrowing*. This is the opposite of *carrying* in addition.

Example 2.   Subtract 279 from 863.

```
            5        7 15      7 15
                      1          1
  8 6 3    8 6 3    8 6 3     8 6 3
  2 7 9    2 7 9    2 7 9     2 7 9
           ___      ___       ___
             4       8 4       5 8 4
```

We begin by saying 9 subtracted from 3. Since we cannot subtract 9 from 3, we borrow 1 ten from the 6 tens. This leaves only 5 tens. The 6 is crossed out and a 5 placed above it. This 10 with the 3 in units' place makes 13. The 1 borrowed can be placed before the 3 to make 13. Then we subtract 9 from 13, which equals 4.

As a second step, we say 7 from 5. Since we cannot subtract 7 tens from 5 tens, we borrow one of the hundreds from the 8 hundreds. This leaves 7 hundreds. The 8 is crossed out and a 7 is placed above the 8. The 1 hundred borrowed is changed to 10 tens and combined with the 5 tens, making 15 tens in all. Then we say 7 tens subtracted from 15 tens leaves 8 tens. The remainder, 8, is placed in the tens' place in the answer.

Finally, we say 2 hundreds subtracted from 7 hundreds leaves 5 hundreds. This makes the complete answer 5 hundreds, 8 tens, and 4 units, or 584.

There are other methods of subtraction, but the borrowing method is perhaps the most common. The actual borrowing is usually done mentally, so that the marks indicating borrowing do not appear in the work. Thus

```
        8 6 3
        2 7 9        check by addition of
        _____        remainder to subtrahend
        5 8 4
```

Zeros often appear in the minuend when borrowing is necessary. We must then borrow from the next digit to the left.

Example 3.   Subtract 7 0 4
                           2 6 9

Solution.   We cannot subtract 9 from 4. We cannot borrow 1 from zero. Then we go to the next digit, 7, which represents hundreds. We borrow 1 hundred from 7 hundreds, leaving 6 hundreds. This 1 hundred is changed to 10 tens, and one of these tens is borrowed, leaving 9 tens. The ten borrowed is changed to units. The steps in the foregoing example may be shown in the following manner:

```
            6        6 9        6 9
                      1 1        1 1
  7 0 4    7 0 4    7 0 4     7 0 4
  2 6 9    2 6 9    2 6 9     2 6 9
           ___      ___       ___
                                4 3 5
```

Of course, in actual work, the borrowing is usually done mentally.

It is sometimes convenient to subtract two numbers even when the subtrahend appears above the minuend. In each of the following exercises *the top number is subtracted from the bottom number:*

2 3 1	4 7 3	5 1 3 2	3 4 2 6	1 3 7 4	subtrahend
8 5 7	9 8 5	6 4 8 9	9 8 6 2	8 1 4 2	minuend
6 2 6	5 1 2	1 3 5 7	6 4 3 6	6 7 6 8	remainder

In a series of horizontal terms involving addition and subtraction the operations are performed in the order in which they occur. If any quantity is enclosed in parentheses, brackets, or braces, or some form of grouping, the quantity within the parentheses is to be considered as a single quantity. In such a case the operations indicated within the parentheses are to be performed first.

$$15 - 13 + 9 = 11$$
$$12 + (5 + 2) = 19$$
$$14 - (4 + 2) = 8$$
$$24 + 6 - (5 + 2) - (6 - 5) + 6 = 28$$
$$24 + (6 - 5 + 2) - 6 - (5 + 6) = 10$$

Exercise 1.1

The following exercises should be worked for practice. If you feel you need more practice, you should work the exercises several times.

Add the following:

1.	3 8 7	6 9 2	8 9 3	8 6 3	7 4 6	9 5 9	7 3 8
	2 4 6	5 0 9	7 1 5	2 7 3	4 3 9	2 4 9	4 9 3

2.	6 6 7	5 6 8	8 7 4	4 3 6	7 9 7	8 6 7	8 2 8
	5 6 9	4 7 9	3 8 4	2 7 7	5 5 6	5 9 8	6 7 9

3.	7 6 3	7 9 4	6 2 3	8 4 7	9 1 5	7 0 7	6 5 8
	7 5 5	6 8 8	4 8 9	5 8 6	5 6 7	5 8 9	5 6 9

4.	1 3 8	2 7 1	4 5 9	6 0 2	7 3 8	9 1 5	4 9 8
	7 6 3	9 2 8	6 4 7	1 9 3	9 0 2	5 9 7	3 1 4
	4 5 3	5 9 5	9 9 5	5 2 9	4 6 5	4 3 9	5 2 9
	2 8 9	7 8 2	3 0 6	9 8 7	8 9 5	3 7 6	8 6 3

5. Add 494 + 1732 + 28 + 43,560 + 365
6. Add 298 + 3872 + 596 + 14,387 + 243
7. Add 9164 + 872 + 39 + 2586 + 497
8. Add 12,056 + 205 + 3,789 + 74,607 + 894
9. Add 43 + 5986 + 307 + 63,364 + 4567
10. Add 98 + 7 + 56 + 1,347,206 + 38,965

Subtract the following:

11. 5684	1923	8488	5635	3785
4309	1042	619	978	3159
12. 7043	9804	4132	8423	9006
3897	2973	3901	7138	5842
13. 5904	2973	3601	4826	7015
4917	584	2073	2067	3960
14. 6500	1745	1032	4000	7005
2759	796	579	1809	6738

15. In each of the exercises in No. 3, under addition, subtract the bottom number from the top number.

16. Combine $24 + (8 - 5) - (7 + 2) - (6 - 4)$

17. Combine $30 - (8 + 3) - (9 - 4) + (4 - 1)$

18. Combine $27 - (16 - 9) + (3 + 2) - (6 + 8)$

19. Combine $58 + 21 - 5 - 6 - 1 + 8 - 7$

20. Combine $25 - 7 + 2 + 3 - 8 + 6 - 9$

21. In each of the following examples subtract the top number from the bottom number:

214	365	129	284	138	273	392
839	768	947	623	506	400	600

1.5 MULTIPLICATION

Multiplication is the process of taking one number two or more times. Multiplication can be considered as a shortened form of addition. For instance, if we wish to add three 7's, we can say 3×7. The symbol for multiplication is the sign $\times$. This symbol is read "times." The expression 3×7 is read, "3 times 7" and means the same as adding three 7's: thus $7 + 7 + 7$. In column form these expressions can be written

$$\begin{array}{ll} \text{Addition:} & 7 \\ & 7 \\ & \underline{7} \\ & 21 \end{array} \qquad \begin{array}{ll} \text{Multiplication:} & \\ & 7 \\ & \underline{\times 3} \\ & 21 \end{array}$$

Multiplication can be indicated in other ways. It is sometimes indicated by a raised dot placed between the numbers: thus $3 \cdot 7$ means 3×7. We may also enclose in parentheses each of the numbers to be multiplied and then place one next to the other without any sign between them: $(3)(7) = 21$. Whenever any two numbers are written in this form, they are meant to be multiplied together.

In the multiplication of two numbers, one number is called the *multiplicand* and the other is called the *multiplier*. The *multiplicand* is the number that is to be taken a given number of times. The multiplier is the number that tells how many times the multiplicand is to be taken. In many examples it makes little difference which number is taken as the multiplier and which is taken as the multiplicand. In some cases, however, it is well to distinguish between the two. For instance, suppose we have this example: what is the cost of three books at $7 each? We can get the total cost by addition; thus, $7 + $7 + $7 = $21. Using multiplication, we can say we must find $3 \times $7. Here, the number 3 is the multiplier and the $7 is the multiplicand. If we consider the numbers alone, then the multiplication can be done in any order. That is, seven 3's are equal to the same quantity as three 7's.

The answer obtained in multiplication is called the *product*. A product always implies multiplication. The numbers multiplied together are called the *factors* of the product. As an example, the factors of 21 are 3 and 7 because 3 times 7 equals 21. The product of the three numbers, 2, 3, and 5, is 30. Therefore the factors of 30 are 2, 3, and 5.

A *composite* number is a number composed of integral factors other than 1 and the number itself. For example, 15 is a composite number because it is composed of the two factors, 3 and 5. A *prime* number is a number that cannot be separated into any integral factors other than itself and 1, such as the number 17.

In addition we have already noted two laws of numbers: the *commutative* and the *associative* laws. In the multiplication of numbers we have the corresponding laws. We have said that the product of three 7's is the same as seven 3's. That is,

$$3 \times 7 = 7 \times 3$$

The *commutative law* for *multiplication* states that the multiplication of two numbers may be done in either order. That is, either number may be considered as the multiplicand and the other the multiplier. In general terms, if a and b represent any two numbers, respectively, then by the commutative law,

$$a \times b = b \times a$$

We often make use of the commutative law to check multiplication by reversing the order of multiplication. For example,

$$327 \times 453 = 453 \times 327$$

The *associative law for multiplication* enables us to associate certain factors in such a way as to simplify computation. For example, suppose we wish to multiply the following:

$$17 \times 5 \times 2$$

We might first say $17 \times 5 = 85$. Then we multiply 85 by 2 and get 170. However, we know that it is convenient to multiply any number by 10. Now we might first recognize that $5 \times 2 = 10$. Then we can say

$$17 \times 10 = 170$$

The two ways of associating the factors can be shown by parentheses. We enclose in parentheses the numbers to be multiplied first. If we first multiply 17 by 5 and then the result by 2, we indicate this by

$$(17 \times 5) \times 2$$

The second way we may indicate as

$$17 \times (5 \times 2)$$

The answer is 170 in both instances. The *associative law for multiplication* may be indicated in general, using the numbers a, b, and c:

$$(a \times b) \times c = a \times (b \times c)$$

The associative and commutative laws for multiplication together enable us to pair up any combinations of numbers that lead to easy calculation. For example, note the multiplication by 10's in the following:

$$9 \times 2 \times 5 \times 7 \times 5 \times 2 = 6300$$

$$10 \qquad\qquad 10$$

To get the answer quickly we first take 9×7 and then multiply the result by 100.

In multiplying numbers containing more than one digit each, we usually place one number above the other with the right-hand digits in line. The larger number is usually placed above and is considered as the multiplicand.

Example 1.   Multiply 394 by 7.

$$
\begin{array}{cccc}
 & 2 & 6\,2 & 6\,2 \\
3\,9\,4 & 3\,9\,4 & 3\,9\,4 & 3\,9\,4 \quad \text{multiplicand} \\
\underline{\times\,7} & \underline{\times\,7} & \underline{\times\,7} & \underline{\times\,7} \quad \text{multiplier} \\
 & 8 & 5\,8 & 2\,7\,5\,8 \quad \text{product}
\end{array}
$$

Explanation.   We begin the multiplication with the units' digits. That is, $7 \times 4 = 28$. The product, 28, means 2 tens and 8 units. The 8 units are placed in the units' place, and the 2 tens are carried over to the tens' position. The 2 is sometimes written above the 9. Any digit carried over in this manner is sometimes written above the next digit at the left in the multiplicand. Multiplying 7×9 tens, we get 63 tens, which, added to the 2 tens carried, makes 65 tens, or 6 hundreds and 5 tens. The 5 is placed in the ten's place in the answer, and the 6 hundreds are carried over to the hundreds' place. Multiplying 7×3 hundreds, we get 21 hundreds. This 21 hundreds, added to the 6 hundreds carried, makes 27 hundreds, or 2 thousands and 7 hundreds. The entire process is shown here:

$$
\begin{array}{r}
3\,9\,4 \quad \text{multiplicand} \\
7 \quad \text{multiplier} \\
\hline
2\,7\,5\,8 \quad \text{product}
\end{array}
$$

Note. The actual carrying is usually done mentally.

If the multiplier is a two-digit number, the second digit from the right represents tens, as usual.

Example 2. Multiply 543 by 96.

$$
\begin{array}{r}
5\,4\,3 \quad \text{multiplicand} \\
9\,6 \quad \text{multiplier} \\
\hline
3\,2\,5\,8 \quad \text{multiplication by 6} \\
4\,8\,8\,7 \quad \text{multiplication by 90} \\
\hline
5\,2\,1\,2\,8 \quad \text{product}
\end{array}
$$

Explanation. First, we multiply the multiplicand, 543, by 6, the same as with a single-digit multiplier. Next, we multiply by the 9 in the multiplier. However, this 9 represents tens. Therefore, when we say $9 \times 3 = 27$, we really mean 90×3. The product of $90 \times 3 = 270$, which is 27 tens, or 2 hundreds and 7 tens. In order to make adjustment for the fact that the 27 represents tens, we place 7 in the tens' place, and carry the 2 over the hundreds' place. After multiplying by each digit in the multiplier, we add the products.

If the multiplier contains three or more digits, we follow the same plan as for a two-digit multiplier. We must remember the place value of each digit in the multiplier as well as in the multiplicand.

Example 3. Multiply 573 by 648.

$$
\begin{array}{r}
5\,7\,3 \quad \text{multiplicand} \\
6\,4\,8 \quad \text{multiplier} \\
\hline
4\,5\,8\,4 \quad \text{multiplication by 8} \\
2\,2\,9\,2 \quad \text{multiplication by 40} \\
3\,4\,3\,8 \quad \text{multiplication by 600} \\
\hline
3\,7\,1\,3\,0\,4 \quad \text{product}
\end{array}
$$

If the multiplier contains a zero digit, the multiplication by this digit need not be shown, since the product of any number by zero is zero.

Example 4. Multiply 2987 by 405.

$$
\begin{array}{r}
2\,9\,8\,7 \quad \text{multiplicand} \\
4\,0\,5 \quad \text{multiplier} \\
\hline
1\,4\,9\,3\,5 \quad \text{multiplication by 5} \\
1\,1\,9\,4\,8 \quad \text{multiplication by 400} \\
\hline
1\,2\,0\,9\,7\,3\,5 \quad \text{product}
\end{array}
$$

Example 5. Multiply 967 by 840.

$$
\begin{array}{rl}
9\,6\,7 & \text{multiplicand} \\
8\,4\,0 & \text{multiplier} \\
\hline
3\,8\,6\,8\,0 & \text{multiplication by 40} \\
7\,7\,3\,6 & \text{multiplication by 800} \\
\hline
8\,1\,2\,2\,8\,0 & \text{product}
\end{array}
$$

In Example 5 the multiplier ends in zero. In such cases the multiplier is often written farther to the right, as shown here. This form is not necessary, but it is often more convenient. Although the multiplication by zero is zero, we must write the zero in units' place to make the answer correct.

Example 6. Multiply 80436 by 7050.

$$
\begin{array}{rl}
8\,0\,4\,3\,6 & \text{multiplicand} \\
7\,0\,5\,0 & \text{multiplier} \\
\hline
4\,0\,2\,1\,8\,0\,0 & \text{multiplication by 50} \\
5\,6\,3\,0\,5\,2 & \text{multiplication by 7000} \\
\hline
5\,6\,7\,0\,7\,3\,8\,0\,0 & \text{product}
\end{array}
$$

In this example notice especially the zeros in multiplicand and multiplier. Such zeros often cause students much trouble.

The best way to check multiplication is to go back over each separate step in the multiplication to make sure that no errors have been made. In some examples it may be practical to check by reversing the multiplier and the multiplicand, as shown here.

Example 7. Multiply 579 by 346.

$$
\begin{array}{cc}
 & \textit{Check:} \\
5\,7\,9 & 3\,4\,6 \\
3\,4\,6 & 5\,7\,9 \\
\hline
3\,4\,7\,4 & 3\,1\,1\,4 \\
2\,3\,1\,6 & 2\,4\,2\,2 \\
1\,7\,3\,7 & 1\,7\,3\,0 \\
\hline
2\,0\,0\,3\,3\,4 & 2\,0\,0\,3\,3\,4
\end{array}
$$

However, in an example such as $26 \times 548{,}613$ this kind of reversal is not practical.

1.6 DIVISION

Division is the process of determining how many times one number is contained in another. The symbol for division is $\div$. The expression $28 \div 4$ is read "28 divided by 4." This indicates that we are to find the number of times 4 is contained in 28. Division may also be shown as a fraction. Thus $28 \div 4$ can be written $\dfrac{28}{4}$. The number divided by another is called the *dividend*. The number divided into the dividend is called the *divisor*.

We see that $28 \div 4 = 7$. The answer obtained by division is called the *quotient*. A quotient always implies division, just as the word product always implies multiplication. In the example $28 \div 4 = 7$ the 7 is the quotient, 28 is the dividend, and 4 is the divisor. In most instances there is a *remainder* after the division. For example, $29 \div 4 = 7$ with a remainder of 1.

Division may be checked by multiplication. The quotient times the divisor should equal the dividend. If there is a remainder, the division can be checked by multiplying the quotient by the divisor and adding the remainder. The result should be the dividend.

Example 1. Divide 37,538 by 7.

In this example, the dividend is 37,538 and the divisor is 7. When the divisor is a single digit, we use a form called *short division*. The usual form is shown here:

$$\frac{5 \ \ 3 \ \ 6 \ \ 2, \text{ remainder} = 4}{7)3 \ 7 \ {}^2 5 \ {}^4 3 \ {}^1 8}$$

We begin by dividing 7 into 37, which is 5, with a remainder of 2. Here we are really dividing 7 into 37,000, which is 5000, with a remainder of 2000. The quotient, 5, is written directly above the 7 in 37, and the 2 is carried over to the 5; that is, the 2000 remaining after the first division represents 20 hundreds and is added to the 5 hundreds in the dividend. The result is 25 hundreds to be divided by 7. From here on the division follows the same procedure. Whenever there is a remainder, it is carried over and placed next to the following digit. We divide 7 into 25, which is 3 with a remainder of 4. The 4 is carried over and placed next to the 3, making 43. Then we divide 7 into 43, which is 6, with a remainder of 1. The 1 is placed next to the 8, making 18. Finally, we divide 7 into 18, which is 2, with a remainder of 4.

The answer can be checked by multiplication. If we multiply the quotient by the divisor and add to this product the remainder, the result should be the dividend.

Check:

5 3 6 2	quotient
× 7	divisor
3 7 5 3 4	multiplying
+ 4	remainder added
3 7 5 3 8	dividend

In short division the separate remainders are found mentally and are usually not shown. For instance, in the foregoing example the student should perform subtractions mentally. The work then appears as follows:

$$\frac{5 \ 3 \ 6 \ 2, \text{ remainder} = 4}{7)\ 3 \ 7 \ 5 \ 3 \ 8}$$

In division a digit is placed in the quotient for each division or attempted division. Zeros will sometimes appear in the quotient.

Example 2.   Divide 423,543 by 6.

$$7\,0\,5\,9\,0, \text{ remainder } = 3$$
$$6\overline{)4\,2\,3\,5\,4\,3}$$

In this example notice that a zero is placed in the quotient when each step in the division involves the division of 6 into a smaller number. Of course, in this example, it is not necessary to write a zero for the division of 6 into 4, the very first digit of the dividend, since this would not change the value of the answer.

Long division is the procedure of showing the subtraction and the remainder in each step of the division. Long division is not often used with one-digit divisors. Its use is confined mainly to division by divisors containing two or more digits.

In order to show the similarity between short division and long division, we shall work an example both ways.

Example 3.   Divide 43,815 by 7.

Short division form:

$$6\,2\,5\,9, \text{ remainder } = 2$$
$$7\overline{)4\,3\,8\,1\,5}$$

Long division form:

Dividing 7 into 37, we get a quotient of 6 and a remainder of 1. In long division we show the actual subtraction. We multiply the quotient, 6, by the divisor, 7, and write the result, 42, under the first part of the dividend, 43. Subtracting, we get a remainder of 1.

$$7\overline{)4\,3\,8\,1\,5}$$

$$\begin{array}{r} 6 \\ 7\overline{)4\,3\,8\,1\,5} \\ 4\,2 \\ \hline 1 \end{array}$$

In short division the remainder, 1, is written next to the following digit, 8, to indicate 18. In long division the 8 is brought down and written next to the 1, to make 18.

Next, we divide 7 into 18 and place the answer, 2, as the second digit of the quotient. Multiplying back, 2 times 7, we get 14, which is written below the 18.

Subtracting, we get 4. Then 1, the next digit of the dividend, is brought down and written next to the 4. The division is continued in the same manner until the remainder of the entire dividend is less than the divisor.

$$\begin{array}{r} 6\,2\,5\,9 \\ 7\overline{)4\,3\,8\,1\,5} \\ 4\,2 \\ \hline 1\,8 \\ 1\,4 \\ \hline 4\,1 \\ 3\,5 \\ \hline 6\,5 \\ 6\,3 \\ \hline \text{remainder} \quad 2 \end{array}$$

Although they are often readily performed correctly by habit, it is well to stop and consider each of the steps in long division, since the same general procedure is followed in long division in algebra.

As we have stated, long division is most frequently used when the divisor contains two or more digits. The following examples show a common form for long division. Each digit of the quotient should be placed directly above the last digit of the dividend used in each separate step. In Example 4 notice that 6, the first digit of the quotient, is placed directly above the 5 in the dividend, since the first division is 47 into 295.

Example 4. Divide 29,508 by 47.

    Step 1. Divide 47 into 295. Place the 6 in the quotient *directly above the 5.*

    Step 2. Multiply the divisor, 47, by the 6 and write the product, 282, below the 295.

    Step 3. Subtract, leaving 13.

    Step 4. Bring down the 0, the next digit of the dividend.

    Step 5. Divide 47 into 130 and write the result, 2, as the second digit of the quotient.

```
      6 2 7
47)2 9 5 0 8
   2 8 2
   1 3 0
     9 4
     3 6 8
     3 2 9
       3 9
```

    Step 6. Multiply the divisor, 47, by the 2 and write the product, 94, below the 130.

    Step 7. Subtract, leaving 36.

    Step 8. Bring down the 8, the next digit of the dividend, making 368.

    Step 9. Divide 47 into 368 and write the result, 7, in the quotient.

    Step 10. Multiply the divisor, 47, by the 7 of the quotient and write the product, 329, under the 368.

    Step 11. Subtract, leaving a remainder of 39.

Example 5. Divide 113,673 by 37.

Remember a digit is written in the quotient for each division or attempted division. Sometimes a zero will appear in the quotient.

```
           3 0 7 2
37)1 1 3 6 7 3
   1 1 1
     2 6 7
     2 5 9
         8 3
         7 4
 remainder 9
```

In this example notice that after the first division by the divisor, 37, and the subtraction the first remainder is only 2. When the next digit is brought down, the new dividend becomes only 26. The divisor can not be divided into the 26. Since one digit of the dividend has already been brought down at this point, a digit must be written in the quotient for this division—in this case, zero.

    Warning. An error that is sometimes made is to write too small a number in the quotient for a particular division. In the following example an error of this kind has been purposely made to point out the danger.

Example 6. Divide 58,692 by 73.

In the division shown here the first digit in the quotient has been called 7. However, when the subtraction is made, the remainder is 75, which is greater than the divisor. Therefore, the first digit in the quotient is not correct. It should be 8. The example is worked out correctly as shown.

```
          7      (wrong)
73)5 8 6 9 2
   5 1 1
     7 5

        8 0 4    (correct division)
73)5 8 6 9 2
   5 8 4
     2 9 2
     2 9 2
```

Exercise 1.2

Multiply the following:

1. 2873	3516	4867	6295	5923
49	98	59	68	76
2. 7784	4678	5308	4971	3158
76	916	897	872	936
3. 4036	6814	7459	8916	5789
902	807	609	705	801
4. 3148	4864	9617	3976	9580
936	824	193	829	705
5. 5291	10582	3737	9999	2927
42	84	333	4444	352

Divide as indicated:

6. 419,382 ÷ 6	**7.** 210,938 ÷ 7	**8.** 816,320 ÷ 8
9. 31,416 ÷ 3	**10.** 14,142 ÷ 2	**11.** 602,064 ÷ 6
12. 80,001 ÷ 9	**13.** 419,320 ÷ 4	**14.** 35,217 ÷ 43
15. 10,488 ÷ 24	**16.** 29,664 ÷ 32	**17.** 55,091 ÷ 89
18. 67,744 ÷ 73	**19.** 64,008 ÷ 84	**20.** 17,777 ÷ 29
21. 29,792 ÷ 38	**22.** 39,292 ÷ 47	**23.** 33,512 ÷ 59
24. 26,101 ÷ 43	**25.** 34,036 ÷ 67	**26.** 57,816 ÷ 72
27. 60,716 ÷ 86	**28.** 53,336 ÷ 59	**29.** 81,463 ÷ 28
30. 444,444,444 ÷ 36	**31.** 777,777,777 ÷ 63	**32.** 69,506 ÷ 89

33. On a particular construction project 30 tons of concrete are needed. The first day 5 truck loads were used, weighing, respectively, 8713, 11,604, 12,520, 9074, and 10,008 pounds. How many more pounds are needed to complete the project? (1 ton = 2000 lb.)

34. The approximate areas of the six New England states are as follows (in square miles): Maine, 33,215; New Hampshire, 9304; Vermont, 9609; Massachusetts, 8257; Connecticut, 5009; Rhode Island, 1214. What is the total approximate area of these six states?

35. Alaska has an area of approximately 586,400 sq. miles. This area is how many times the area of the six New England states?

36. The state of Hawaii contains approximately 12,855 sq. miles. By how many square miles was the area of the United States increased by the admission of the states of Alaska and Hawaii?

37. If you take a circle tour plane trip from Washington, D.C. by way of the following cities back to Washington, what is the total length of your flight: Washington to Chicago, 597 miles; Chicago to Minneapolis, 355 miles; Minneapolis to Los Angeles, 1524 miles; Los Angeles to Dallas, 1240 miles; Dallas to St. Louis, 547 miles; St. Louis to Miami, 1061 miles; and Miami to Washington, 923 miles?

38. In 1966, the five busiest airports in the United States had the following total number of operations (takeoffs and landings): O'Hare, 519,430; Van Nuys, 439,563; Opa-Locka, 425,323; Long Beach, 393,892; and Kennedy International 389,917. What was the total number of operations for these five busiest airports?

39. For the O'Hare airport, what was the average number of operations per day? Per hour? Per minute? What was the average time per operation?

40. The total attendance at the World Series baseball games for a six-year period was as follows:

Year	Attendance	Games	Year	Attendance	Games
1961	223,247	5	1964	321,807	7
1962	376,864	7	1965	364,326	7
1963	247,279	4	1966	220,791	4

What was the average attendance per year? Per game?

41. Public school enrollment of pupils in age-group 5–17 years by ten-year periods from 1910 to 1960 was as follows:

Year	Enrollment	Year	Enrollment	Year	Enrollment
1910	17,813,852	1930	25,678,015	1950	25,111,427
1920	21,578,316	1940	25,433,542	1960	36,086,771

What was the ten-year period of greatest increase? During which intervals did decreases occur and by what number of pupils? What was the average enrollment?

42. The shipping tonnage through some of the United States harbors for one year (1964) was as follows:

Harbor	Tonnage	Harbor	Tonnage
Seattle, Wash.	13,798,836	Jacksonville, Fla.	9,231,866
San Francisco, Calif.	4,500,607	Galveston, Texas	4,015,936
Charleston, S.C.	5,106,523	Savannah, Ga.	4,157,537
Duluth-Superior Lake Port	42,996,795		

By how much did the shipping through the Duluth-Superior Lake Port exceed the combined shipping through the ocean ports mentioned?

43. Sound travels at a rate of approximately 1080 ft per sec. How much farther than 1 mile will it travel in 5 sec?

44. If the sound of thunder is heard 8 sec after the flash of lightning was seen, how far away was the lightning?

45. Light travels at a rate of 186,000 miles per sec. How long will it take light to travel 2,046,000 miles?

46. How long will it take the light from the sun, about 93,000,000 miles away, to reach the earth?

47. How far will light travel in 1 yr?

48. A speed of 45 mph is how many feet in 1 sec?

2
Fractions

2.1 NEED FOR FRACTIONS

As long as people used numbers only for *counting*, they had no need for fractions. Whether he was counting pebbles or his sheep, early man did not require fractions. Counting his sheep, he could not say 1, 2, $2\frac{1}{2}$, etc.

Numbers also serve in another capacity besides *counting*. They are necessary in *measuring*. When we measure anything, whether length, weight, time, area, or electric current, we use a unit of measure. The unit is simply a small definite amount of the same kind of thing as the quantity that is to be measured. The measurement is made by noting how many times the quantity measured contains the unit.

When early man wished to measure a particular length (for example, the length of his hut), he may have picked up a stick of convenient length to use as a unit of measure. As he laid off the unit of length (the stick) along the wall of his hut, he found that the number of times he laid off the unit was not a whole number. That is, he found that he laid off the unit, perhaps five times, and then had about a half unit left over. In this way fractions and approximations came into arithmetic. If arithmetic had been used only for counting "discrete" objects, fractions would never have been needed. In all measurement we are faced with a *continuum* rather than separate and *discrete* objects.

Counting is exact; measurement is only approximate.

It is well to distinguish between the two uses of numbers: (*a*) for counting and (*b*) for measuring.

Exercise 2.1

Tell which of the two uses of numbers is employed in each of the following situations:

1. The number of hairs on your head.
2. The length of a given hair.
3. The number of leaves on a tree.
4. The number of leaves on all the trees in the world.

5. The weight of a cupful of water.
6. The number of drops in a pail of water.
7. The number of automobiles in the United States.
8. The length of a certain automobile.
9. The weight of an automobile.
10. The length of the diameter of a particular circle.
11. The length of the circumference of a circle.
12. The number of whole days in a year.
13. The time length of a year.
14. The number of pages in a particular book.
15. The number of printed characters in a book.
16. The amount of ink required to print a book.
17. The weight of a book.
18. The area of a page.
19. The length of time it takes to read a page.
20. The amount of time it takes to read an entire book.

2.2 DEFINITION OF A FRACTION

There are two ways of looking at a fraction. In arithmetic probably our first understanding of a fraction was about as follows:

Let us consider the meaning of the fraction $\frac{3}{4}$. Suppose we divide a circle into four equal parts (Fig. 2.1). Each part is called a "fourth" and is denoted by the fraction $\frac{1}{4}$. The number below the line is called the denominator because it *denominates*, or *names*, the part. It may be called the *namer*. The word *denominate* means to *name*. If we take three of these parts, or "fourths," we show this amount by the fraction $\frac{3}{4}$. The number, 3, above the line is called the *numerator* because it *enumerates*, or *counts*, the number of parts taken. It may be called the *counter*. The three fourths are shaded in the figure.

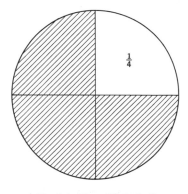

Fig. 2.1. Three "fourths."

The foregoing is the most common explanation of the meaning of a fraction. However, there is another way of looking at a fraction. A fraction can be considered as an *indicated division*. The fraction $\frac{3}{4}$ can be taken to mean 3 divided by 4, or $3 \div 4$. The horizontal line between the numerator and the denominator can be taken as a symbol of division.

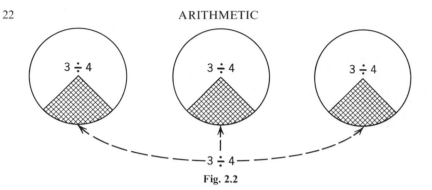

Fig. 2.2

To show this meaning of a fraction graphically, we begin with three circles instead of one. We divide the three circles into four equal parts, as shown in Fig. 2.2. You will notice that the amount indicated by the fraction $\frac{3}{4}$ is the same in both cases. However, the approach to the meaning of the fraction is different.

As another example of the two approaches, consider the meaning of the fraction $\frac{7}{10}$ of a dollar, or $\$\frac{7}{10}$. We can take the denominator, 10, to mean that one dollar is first divided into 10 parts. Each part is one *tenth* of a dollar, that is, one dime. Then the numerator, 7, means that we take 7 of these "tenths," or 7 dimes. The fraction indicates a value of 7 dimes or 70 cents.

In the second approach we look upon the fraction $\$\frac{7}{10}$ as meaning 7 dollars divided by 10. From this viewpoint, we have $\$7.00 \div 10 = \$0.70$. The value is exactly the same as before, but in this case we look upon the fraction as division. The *numerator* is the *dividend*, and the *denominator* is the *divisor*.

The two approaches may be further illustrated by lengths. Consider the meaning of $\frac{2}{3}$ foot (Fig. 2.3).
The value is the same in both cases, but the approach is different.

There is often an advantage in considering a fraction as an indicated division. From this viewpoint, $\frac{7}{9}$ means $7 \div 9$. The fraction $\frac{47}{225}$ means $47 \div 225$. Division may therefore be written as a fraction. For instance,

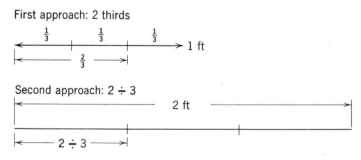

Fig. 2.3

$13 \div 4$ can be written as the fraction $\frac{13}{4}$. This view of a fraction has many advantages, expecially in algebra.

The numerator and the denominator are called the *terms* of a fraction.

A *proper fraction* is a fraction in which the numerator is less than the denominator; that is, the fraction has a value less than 1. The following are proper fractions: $\frac{1}{4}, \frac{5}{8}, \frac{5}{6}$.

An *improper fraction* is a fraction in which the numerator is equal to, or greater than, the denominator; that is, an improper fraction has a value equal to, or more than, 1. The following are improper fractions: $\frac{5}{5}, \frac{8}{7}, \frac{5}{2}, \frac{261}{43}$.

A *mixed number* is a number consisting of a whole number and a fraction. The following are mixed numbers:

$$4\tfrac{2}{3} \quad 3\tfrac{1}{4} \quad 15\tfrac{2}{7} \quad 1\tfrac{173}{489} \quad 596\tfrac{39}{56} \quad 14\tfrac{3}{1000}$$

It should be noted that a mixed number, such as $12\tfrac{4}{9}$, is really the sum of a whole number and a fraction.

$$12\tfrac{4}{9} \quad \text{means} \quad 12 + \frac{4}{9}$$

2.3 CHANGING THE FORM OF NUMBERS CONTAINING FRACTIONS

Before we work problems involving fractions, we must devise certain rules for operating with such numbers.

It is often necessary to change the form of a fraction. An improper fraction can be changed to a whole number or to a mixed number. For instance, the improper fraction $\frac{23}{6}$ can be changed to a mixed number by dividing the numerator by the denominator. We know that there are 6 sixths in each whole unit. To find the number of whole units in 23 sixths, we divide 23 by 6. $23 \div 6 = 3$ whole units and 5 sixths over. Therefore, $\frac{23}{6} = 3 + \frac{5}{6} = 3\tfrac{5}{6}$.

Rule. *To change an improper fraction to a whole number or a mixed number, divide the numerator by the denominator. The result is the whole number. Any remainder is placed over the denominator as a fraction.*

Sometimes it is desirable to change a whole number or a mixed number to an improper fraction. For instance, we might wish to change the whole number 7 into fourths. Since there are 4 fourths in each whole unit, then in 7 whole units there are (7)(4), or 28, fourths; that is,

$$7 = \frac{28}{4}$$

Rule. *To change a whole number into an improper fraction with any desired denominator, multiply the whole number by the desired denominator and place the result over the denominator.*

To change a mixed number, such as $8\frac{2}{3}$, to an improper fraction, we first change the 8 to thirds: $8 = \frac{24}{3}$. Then we add the $\frac{2}{3}$ to the $\frac{24}{3}$.

$$8\frac{2}{3} = \frac{26}{3}$$

Rule.   *To change a mixed number to an improper fraction, multiply the whole number by the denominator and to this result add the numerator of the given fraction. Place the total over the denominator.*

Exercise 2.2

Change each of the following mixed numbers to improper fractions:

1. $4\frac{2}{3}$	**2.** $3\frac{1}{4}$	**3.** $5\frac{2}{3}$	**4.** $8\frac{1}{2}$
5. $15\frac{1}{3}$	**6.** $16\frac{3}{4}$	**7.** $21\frac{2}{5}$	**8.** $14\frac{5}{6}$
9. $26\frac{1}{4}$	**10.** $38\frac{2}{3}$	**11.** $21\frac{3}{8}$	**12.** $13\frac{5}{6}$
13. $11\frac{4}{7}$	**14.** $14\frac{2}{7}$	**15.** $4\frac{4}{15}$	**16.** $16\frac{2}{3}$
17. $33\frac{1}{3}$	**18.** $66\frac{2}{3}$	**19.** $37\frac{1}{2}$	**20.** $11\frac{1}{9}$
21. $4\frac{4}{9}$	**22.** $8\frac{13}{16}$	**23.** $2\frac{17}{64}$	**24.** $5\frac{23}{32}$
25. $3\frac{11}{18}$	**26.** $9\frac{1}{11}$	**27.** $17\frac{3}{10}$	**28.** $7\frac{11}{12}$

Reduce the following improper fractions to whole numbers or mixed numbers:

29. $\dfrac{15}{4}$	**30.** $\dfrac{16}{3}$	**31.** $\dfrac{42}{5}$	**32.** $\dfrac{31}{7}$
33. $\dfrac{34}{5}$	**34.** $\dfrac{47}{6}$	**35.** $\dfrac{75}{8}$	**36.** $\dfrac{64}{11}$
37. $\dfrac{81}{3}$	**38.** $\dfrac{50}{7}$	**39.** $\dfrac{67}{9}$	**40.** $\dfrac{40}{11}$
41. $\dfrac{67}{4}$	**42.** $\dfrac{93}{10}$	**43.** $\dfrac{86}{13}$	**44.** $\dfrac{85}{17}$
45. $\dfrac{121}{8}$	**46.** $\dfrac{536}{8}$	**47.** $\dfrac{458}{5}$	**48.** $\dfrac{299}{4}$
49. $\dfrac{317}{6}$	**50.** $\dfrac{351}{8}$	**51.** $\dfrac{468}{7}$	**52.** $\dfrac{702}{9}$
53. $\dfrac{396}{12}$	**54.** $\dfrac{980}{15}$	**55.** $\dfrac{4997}{16}$	**56.** $\dfrac{3849}{9}$
57. $\dfrac{1755}{17}$	**58.** $\dfrac{5737}{30}$	**59.** $\dfrac{2367}{22}$	**60.** $\dfrac{1077}{18}$

2.4   FUNDAMENTAL PRINCIPLE OF FRACTIONS

Before considering the various operations with fractions, it is important that the following principle be thoroughly understood.

Fundamental Principle of Fractions. *If the numerator and the denominator of any fraction are multiplied or divided by the same quantity (other than zero), the value of the fraction will not be changed.*

To illustrate this principle, suppose we start with the fraction $\frac{12}{18}$. The fundamental principle states that if we *multiply* the numerator and the denominator by any number the fraction will still have the same value.

Suppose we *multiply both terms* of the fraction by the number 7. Then we get the new fraction $\frac{84}{126}$. This new fraction has the same value as $\frac{12}{18}$. Multiplying the numerator and the denominator by 7, or by any other number, does not change the value of the fraction.

You may wonder why this is true. If we multiply the fraction $\frac{12}{18}$ by 1, the value of the fraction will not change. However, the number 1 may be expressed in some form such as $\frac{3}{3}, \frac{7}{7},$ or $\frac{29}{29}$. Now let us multiply the fraction $\frac{12}{18}$ by $\frac{7}{7}$:

$$\frac{7}{7} \cdot \frac{12}{18} = \frac{84}{126}$$

When we multiply both numerator and denominator of the fraction by 7, we are only multiplying the fraction by 1. Therefore, the value of the fraction is not changed.

The fundamental principle also says that if we *divide* numerator and denominator of a fraction by the same number the fraction will still have the same value.

Suppose we *divide both terms of the fraction* $\frac{12}{18}$ by the number 3. Then we get the new fraction $\frac{4}{6}$. If we wish, we may divide numerator and denominator by 6. Then we get the fraction $\frac{2}{3}$. The new fraction has the same value as $\frac{12}{18}$. Dividing the numerator and the denominator by the same number does not change the value of the fraction.

It should be noted that if the same number (not zero) is *added to*, or *subtracted from*, both numerator and denominator of a fraction the value of the fraction *will be changed*. For example, the fraction $\frac{2}{3}$ will have a different value if we add some number such as 4 to both numerator and denominator. If we add 4 to both terms of the fraction, we get a new fraction, $\frac{6}{7}$, which has a different value from $\frac{2}{3}$.

2.5 REDUCING FRACTIONS

By use of the fundamental principle, it is possible to change the terms of a fraction without changing the value. Such a change in the terms is often necessary or desirable in working with fractions.

Changing the terms of a fraction without changing the value of the fraction itself is called *reducing* the fraction. Usually, the expression *reducing a fraction* means changing the terms to smaller numbers. Work with fractions is often simplified if the numbers are small. For example, the fraction $\frac{15}{20}$ can be changed in form by dividing both terms by 5. Then

$$\frac{15}{20} = \frac{15 \div 5}{20 \div 5} = \frac{3}{4}$$

The value of the fraction has not been changed. The new fraction, $\frac{3}{4}$, has the same value as the fraction $\frac{15}{20}$. We say the fraction is reduced to lower terms because the numbers have been made smaller.

In reducing fractions to lower terms, we divide numerator and denominator by any number contained in both an even number of times. Now the question arises: How can we tell what number can be divided into numerator and denominator? Sometimes we can tell easily by inspection. In many cases the problem is more difficult. At this point we need to know how to tell the divisibility of numbers. Here are some tests: let us test the number 131,736.

(a) A number is divisible by 2 if the last digit at the right is divisible by 2; that is, if the number is even; in the example, 6 is divisible by 2.

(b) A number is divisible by 4 if the number represented by the last two digits is divisible by 4; in the example, 36 is divisible by 4.

(c) A number is divisible by 8 if the number represented by the last three digits is divisible by 8; in the example, 736 is divisible by 8.

(d) A number is divisible by 3 if the sum of its digits is divisible by 3; in the example, $1 + 3 + 1 + 7 + 3 + 6 = 21$, divisible by 3.

(e) A number is divisible by 9 if the sum of its digits is divisible by 9; in the example, 21 is not divisible by 9, therefore the number itself is not.

(f) A number is divisible by 10 if it ends in zero; this number does not.

(g) A number is divisible by 5 if it ends in 5 or zero; this number does not.

(h) Divisibility by 7: there is no test; try it out.

(i) A number is divisible by 11 if the *difference* between the *sums* of the *alternate digits* is zero or divisible by 11; in the example, for one set of digits we have $1 + 1 + 3 = 5$; for the alternate digits, $3 + 7 + 6 = 16$. The difference is 11; therefore the number is divisible by 11.

Note. For divisibility by 3 or 9, the digits may be added until the result is only one digit. First we get 21. Then we can add $2 + 1 = 3$.

A fraction is said to be reduced to lowest terms when the numerator and the denominator do not contain a common factor. For example, $\frac{48}{60}$ can be changed to $\frac{12}{15}$ by dividing both terms by 4. However, the fraction can be reduced still further to $\frac{4}{5}$ by dividing both terms by 3. The fraction is now in its lowest terms, since the numerator and denominator do not contain a common factor. If the terms of a fraction can be first divided by 4 and again by 3, then the terms of the original fraction can be divided by (3)(4), or 12.

The expression *reducing a fraction* sometimes also refers to changing a fraction to *higher* terms. This procedure is often necessary. For instance, the fraction $\frac{3}{4}$ can be reduced to higher terms by multiplying numerator and denominator by some number.

$$\frac{3}{4} = \frac{(8)(3)}{(8)(4)} = \frac{24}{32}$$

Remember: reducing a fraction does not, and must not, change its value.

Exercise 2.3

Reduce the following fractions to lowest terms:

1. $\dfrac{18}{54}$

2. $\dfrac{27}{45}$

3. $\dfrac{30}{42}$

4. $\dfrac{54}{66}$

5. $\dfrac{36}{84}$

6. $\dfrac{36}{78}$

7. $\dfrac{84}{132}$

8. $\dfrac{75}{105}$

9. $\dfrac{72}{168}$

10. $\dfrac{108}{144}$

11. $\dfrac{105}{135}$

12. $\dfrac{72}{192}$

13. $\dfrac{140}{224}$

14. $\dfrac{105}{189}$

15. $\dfrac{180}{252}$

16. $\dfrac{192}{288}$

17. $\dfrac{168}{378}$

18. $\dfrac{135}{360}$

19. $\dfrac{54}{234}$

20. $\dfrac{288}{1056}$

21. $\dfrac{462}{616}$

22. $\dfrac{168}{840}$

23. $\dfrac{210}{672}$

24. $\dfrac{168}{1155}$

25. $\dfrac{1260}{1512}$

26. $\dfrac{1782}{2673}$

27. $\dfrac{3003}{8008}$

28. $\dfrac{2310}{3234}$

29. $\dfrac{3780}{9072}$

30. $\dfrac{7182}{7938}$

31. $\dfrac{6174}{6468}$

32. $\dfrac{4165}{7595}$

33. $\dfrac{4641}{10829}$

34. $\dfrac{14911}{47027}$

35. $\dfrac{13860}{16632}$

36. $\dfrac{63063}{111573}$

Change the fractions in each of the following sets to new fractions with higher terms and with the indicated denominator.

37. $\dfrac{3}{4}, \dfrac{2}{3}, \dfrac{3}{8}, \dfrac{7}{12}$; new denominator: 24

38. $\dfrac{3}{5}, \dfrac{7}{8}, \dfrac{5}{12}, \dfrac{11}{40}$; new denominator: 120

39. $\dfrac{2}{3}, \dfrac{6}{7}, \dfrac{4}{5}, \dfrac{8}{15}$; new denominator: 105

40. $\dfrac{4}{9}, \dfrac{8}{27}, \dfrac{7}{12}, \dfrac{31}{36}$; new denominator: 108

41. $\dfrac{7}{15}, \dfrac{11}{18}, \dfrac{17}{24}, \dfrac{21}{40}$; new denominator: 360

2.6 ADDITION AND SUBTRACTION OF FRACTIONS

If two or more fractions have the same denominators, they are added or subtracted by adding or subtracting their numerators. The result is placed over the denominator.

Example 1. $\dfrac{7}{8} + \dfrac{3}{8} = \dfrac{7+3}{8} = \dfrac{10}{8}$. The sum $\frac{10}{8}$ should be reduced to $\frac{5}{4}$.

Example 2. $\dfrac{7}{8} - \dfrac{3}{8} = \dfrac{7-3}{8} = \dfrac{4}{8} = \dfrac{1}{2}$

Example 3. $\dfrac{7}{9} + \dfrac{8}{9} - \dfrac{2}{9} = \dfrac{7+8-2}{9} = \dfrac{13}{9} = 1\frac{4}{9}$

If the denominators are different, we must first change the form of some or all of the fractions, so that all have the same denominator.

First, we must find the *lowest common denominator* (LCD), that is, the smallest number that can be divided by all the denominators. Then we change each fraction to a new fraction having the LCD as its denominator. After making this change, we proceed as usual for fractions with the *same denominator*.

Example 4.   Add $\frac{3}{4} + \frac{2}{3} + \frac{5}{8} - \frac{7}{12}$. The denominators are 4, 3, 8, and 12. By inspection, we find the LCD is 24, since this is the smallest number that can be divided by all the denominators. Now each fraction must be expressed as a fraction with a denominator of 24. To change the form of the fractions we use the *fundamental principle*. Let us first write down the denominator of the fractions:

$$\frac{}{24} + \frac{}{24} + \frac{}{24} - \frac{}{24}$$

The $\frac{3}{4}$ is changed to $\frac{18}{24}$ by multiplying numerator and denominator by 6. The fraction $\frac{2}{3}$ is changed to $\frac{16}{24}$ by multiplying both terms by 8. The fraction $\frac{5}{8}$ is changed to $\frac{15}{24}$ by multiplying both terms by 3. The fraction $\frac{7}{12}$ is changed to $\frac{14}{24}$ by multiplying both terms by 2.

Now the fractions can be added:

$$\frac{18}{24} + \frac{16}{24} + \frac{15}{24} - \frac{14}{24} = \frac{18+16+15-14}{24} = \frac{35}{24} = 1\frac{11}{14}$$

In adding mixed numbers, we might use either one of several methods. Probably the most practical way is to place the numbers in column form. Then we add whole numbers and fractions separately. To add $43\frac{1}{2}$, $59\frac{1}{4}$, $127\frac{4}{5}$, and $413\frac{7}{10}$, we place them in column form as follows:

$$\underline{\text{Short Form}} \quad \text{or} \qquad \underline{20}\,(\text{LCD})$$

	Short Form		or	20 (LCD)
$43\frac{1}{2} = 43\frac{10}{20}$	$43\frac{1}{2}$	$\frac{10}{20}$	$43\frac{1}{2}$	10
$59\frac{1}{4} = 59\frac{5}{20}$	$59\frac{1}{4}$	$\frac{5}{20}$	$59\frac{1}{4}$	5
$127\frac{4}{5} = 127\frac{16}{20}$	$127\frac{4}{5}$	$\frac{16}{20}$	$127\frac{4}{5}$	16
$413\frac{7}{10} = 413\frac{14}{20}$	$413\frac{7}{10}$	$\frac{14}{20}$	$413\frac{7}{10}$	14

$$642 \qquad + \frac{45}{20} = 644\frac{5}{20} = 644\frac{1}{4}$$

Each fraction is expressed as a new fraction with the lowest common denominator. Then the fractions and whole numbers are added separately. The sum of the whole numbers is 642. The sum of the fractions is $\frac{45}{20}$, which, reduced to a mixed number in lowest terms, becomes $2\frac{1}{4}$. This quantity is combined with 642. The total is $644\frac{1}{4}$.

In some instances it is convenient, when adding fractions, to change mixed numbers to improper fractions. This method is not practical if the whole numbers are large. However, when whole numbers are small, this method is often simple.

Example 5. Add $6 + \frac{4}{5} + 4\frac{3}{5} + 3\frac{1}{2}$.

We can change all numbers to tenths. Then we have

$$\frac{60}{10} + \frac{8}{10} + \frac{46}{10} + \frac{35}{10} = \frac{149}{10} = 14\frac{9}{10}$$

Subtraction of numbers involving fractions and mixed numbers is usually done by placing the subtrahend below the minuend as with whole numbers. However, in subtraction we often run into some difficulties. The following examples show the subtraction of fractions.

Example 6. Subtract $492\frac{7}{8} - 154\frac{1}{8}$.

This problem presents no difficulty.

$$492\frac{7}{8}$$
$$154\frac{1}{8}$$

Subtracting, $\qquad \overline{338\frac{6}{8}} = 338\frac{3}{4}$

We subtract $\frac{1}{8}$ from $\frac{7}{8}$. The result is $\frac{6}{8}$. Then we subtract the whole numbers.

Example 7. Subtract $536\frac{5}{12} - 142\frac{5}{12}$.

$$536\frac{5}{12}$$
$$142\frac{5}{12}$$

Subtracting, $\qquad \overline{394}$

In this example we subtract $\frac{5}{12}$ from $\frac{5}{12}$, which is zero. However, this zero (0) must *not* be written down below the fractions. If it is written, the entire answer would appear to be 3940, which is not correct.

Example 8.   Subtract $436\frac{5}{8} - 124$.

$$436\frac{5}{8}$$
$$\underline{124}$$
Subtracting, $$312\frac{5}{8}$$

In this example we subtract nothing from $\frac{5}{8}$. We simply bring down the $\frac{5}{8}$ as the fractional part of the remainder.

Example 9.   Subtract $436 - 124\frac{5}{8}$.

$$
\begin{array}{cc}
& 5 \\
43\cancel{6}\frac{8}{8} & 435\frac{8}{8} \\
\underline{124\frac{5}{8}} & \underline{124\frac{5}{8}} \\
& 311\frac{3}{8}
\end{array}
$$

In this example, we must take one whole unit from the 6 and change it to $\frac{8}{8}$ before we can subtract the $\frac{5}{8}$.

Example 10.   Subtract $832\frac{4}{7} - 158\frac{6}{7}$.

$$
\begin{array}{cc}
832\frac{4}{7} & 831\frac{11}{7} \\
\underline{158\frac{6}{7}} & \underline{158\frac{6}{7}} \\
& 673\frac{5}{7}
\end{array}
$$

In this example we cannot subtract $\frac{6}{7}$ from $\frac{4}{7}$. Therefore, we take one whole unit from the 2 in the minuend and change it to $\frac{7}{7}$. This quantity, $\frac{7}{7}$, combined with the $\frac{4}{7}$ already in the minuend, makes $\frac{11}{7}$. Now we subtract $\frac{6}{7}$ from $\frac{11}{7}$, which leaves $\frac{5}{7}$, as the fractional part of the answer.

2.7   FINDING THE LOWEST COMMON DENOMINATOR

We have seen that if fractions are to be added or subtracted they must have the same denominator. If the denominators are different, then the form of the fractions must be changed so that they have a common denominator. The first step in changing fractions is to determine some number that is divisible by all of the given denominators.

In some examples the LCD can be determined by inspection, which is simply a good guess. However, in many instances, we need a more systematic method of determining the LCD of two or more fractions.

It is first necessary to understand what is meant by a *multiple* of a number. A multiple of any given number is some number that is exactly divisible by the given number. The following numbers are all multiples of 8 because they are all exactly divisible by 8: 8, 16, 24, 32, 40, 48, 56, 64, 72, 80, etc. The following numbers are all multiples of 12 because they are all exactly divisible by 12: 12, 24, 36, 48, 60, 72, etc.

A *common multiple* of two or more numbers is some number that is exactly divisible by each of the given numbers. Thus the following numbers are common multiples of 8 and 12 because all can be divided exactly by 8 and 12: 24, 48, 72, 96, etc. Notice that the number 24 is the smallest number exactly divisible by both 8 and 12. Such a number is called the *lowest common multiple* (LCM) of the two numbers 8 and 12. The lowest common multiple of two or more numbers is the smallest number that is exactly divisible by each of the given numbers. When we add or subtract fractions, we first find the lowest common multiple of the denominators. This number is the lowest common denominator of the fractions.

There are several ways of determining the lowest common multiple of two or more numbers. One method is shown in the following example.

Example. Find the lowest common multiple of these numbers: 24, 45, 75, and 210.

Step 1. We write each number as a product of its prime factors. To find the prime factors of a number, we begin dividing the number by the smallest number contained in the given number. For instance, to find the prime factors of 24, we divide 24 by 2, then the result by 2, the next result by 2, and so on until the quotient is not divisible by any other factor. The method is shown at the right. The result of the divisions shows that the prime factors of 24 are 2, 2, 2, and 3. We do the same with the other numbers and then write each as a product of its factors:

$$2)\overline{24}$$
$$2)\overline{12}$$
$$2)\overline{\,6}$$
$$3$$

$$24 = 2 \cdot 2 \cdot 2 \cdot 3$$
$$45 = 3 \cdot 3 \cdot 5$$
$$75 = 3 \cdot 5 \cdot 5$$
$$210 = 2 \cdot 3 \cdot 5 \cdot 7$$

Step 2. Now, for the LCM, we write down each of the prime factors as many times as it is contained in any one of the given numbers. The factor 2 is contained three times in 24, which is the greatest number of times we find the factor 2 in any one number. Therefore, we set down $2 \cdot 2 \cdot 2$, as part of the LCM. The factor 3 is contained twice in 45. Therefore, we write down two 3's, thus $3 \cdot 3$ as part of the LCM. The greatest number of times we find 5 in any one of the given numbers is twice. Therefore, we write down two 5's. The factor 7 is found only once in any one of the given numbers. Therefore, one 7 must be used in the LCM. The entire lowest common multiple is therefore the product of the following factors:

$$2 \cdot 2 \cdot 2 \cdot 3 \cdot 3 \cdot 5 \cdot 5 \cdot 7$$

The product, 12,600, is the LCM, that is, the smallest number that will contain the numbers 24, 45, 75, and 210. If these four numbers are the denominators of four fractions, respectively, then the lowest common denominator of the fractions is 12,600.

Exercise 2.4

Find the lowest common multiple of each of the following sets of numbers:

1. 6, 8, 12 **2.** 4, 6, 3 **3.** 2, 3, 4, 5

4. 4, 6, 9, 24 **5.** 10, 15, 20 **6.** 3, 5, 7, 11

7. 6, 9, 18 **8.** 4, 5, 6, 10 **9.** 30, 42, 60

10. 24, 54, 60 **11.** 180, 84, 630 **12.** 180, 210, 315

13. 120, 180, 300 **14.** 168, 200, 270 **15.** 48, 180, 252

16. 120, 270, 720 **17.** 72, 120, 270, 600 **18.** 216, 324, 900, 1125

19. 675, 1260, 1890, 2940 **20.** 1575, 2205, 3150, 5775

21. 1260, 1500, 1875, 3250 **22.** 1080, 2772, 3600, 6930

23. 3600, 3780, 7560, 9240 **24.** 5544, 8064, 17,820, 37,800

25. (a) Add each of the following sets of mixed numbers:

$$48\tfrac{7}{8} \qquad 32\tfrac{1}{8} \qquad 431\tfrac{1}{4} \qquad 123 \qquad 57\tfrac{4}{5} \qquad 62\tfrac{4}{7}$$
$$\underline{15\tfrac{3}{8}} \qquad \underline{18\tfrac{5}{8}} \qquad \underline{53\tfrac{7}{16}} \qquad \underline{47\tfrac{5}{8}} \qquad \underline{13} \qquad \underline{39\tfrac{6}{7}}$$

(b) In each of the examples in Exercise 25(a) subtract the bottom number from the top number.

Add and subtract as indicated. Any numbers enclosed in parentheses are to be considered as a single quantity. Any operation indicated within the parentheses must therefore be performed first.

26. $7\tfrac{2}{3} + 3\tfrac{5}{8}$ **27.** $9\tfrac{3}{8} + 2\tfrac{5}{12}$ **28.** $12\tfrac{5}{7} + 7\tfrac{2}{3}$

29. $3\tfrac{5}{12} + 8\tfrac{7}{16}$ **30.** $5\tfrac{8}{9} + 1\tfrac{7}{12}$ **31.** $16\tfrac{7}{16} + 7\tfrac{11}{24}$

32. $12\tfrac{7}{36} + 9\tfrac{5}{8}$ **33.** $21\tfrac{16}{73} + \tfrac{13}{45}$ **34.** $\tfrac{7}{8} - \tfrac{5}{6}$

35. $\tfrac{3}{8} - \tfrac{3}{10}$ **36.** $79 - 45\tfrac{3}{4}$ **37.** $83\tfrac{7}{10} - 46\tfrac{4}{5}$

38. $23\tfrac{1}{9} - 7\tfrac{7}{10}$ **39.** $91\tfrac{5}{18} - 43\tfrac{7}{12}$ **40.** $63\tfrac{16}{21} - 8\tfrac{3}{14}$

41. $21\tfrac{12}{35} - 4\tfrac{8}{15}$ **42.** $17\tfrac{3}{20} - 3\tfrac{11}{15}$ **43.** $41 - 15\tfrac{3}{16}$

44. $32 - 29\tfrac{5}{8}$ **45.** $12 - 7\tfrac{5}{12}$ **46.** $17\tfrac{3}{16} - 8$

47. $210 - 17\tfrac{3}{8}$ **48.** $300 - 79\tfrac{4}{11}$ **49.** $50 - 9\tfrac{5}{12}$

50. $17\tfrac{8}{15} - 4\tfrac{17}{20}$ **51.** $11\tfrac{13}{17} - 10\tfrac{13}{17}$ **52.** $4\tfrac{5}{8} - 3\tfrac{1}{10} + 9\tfrac{7}{16}$

53. $\tfrac{3}{4} + \tfrac{2}{3} - \tfrac{3}{8}$ **54.** $5\tfrac{4}{9} + 2\tfrac{7}{12} - 4\tfrac{1}{8}$ **55.** $26\tfrac{13}{48} + 4\tfrac{7}{36} + 1\tfrac{9}{32}$

56. $7\tfrac{3}{5} - (1\tfrac{5}{21} + 2\tfrac{4}{15})$ **57.** $8\tfrac{7}{18} - (4\tfrac{5}{21} - 1\tfrac{7}{45})$ **58.** $12\tfrac{5}{36} + (3\tfrac{10}{27} - \tfrac{3}{8})$

59. $6\tfrac{5}{9} + (4\tfrac{13}{15} + 3\tfrac{7}{20})$ **60.** $9\tfrac{11}{24} - (3\tfrac{7}{8} + 1\tfrac{5}{36})$ **61.** $8\tfrac{31}{90} + 5\tfrac{43}{75} - 4\tfrac{13}{120}$

62. $6\tfrac{13}{48} - (3\tfrac{5}{36} + 1\tfrac{35}{108})$ **63.** $\tfrac{1}{60} + \tfrac{1}{80} + \tfrac{1}{150}$ **64.** $7\tfrac{17}{80} + 3\tfrac{7}{180} - 4\tfrac{19}{300}$

65. $38\tfrac{13}{16} + 63\tfrac{17}{18} - 79\tfrac{5}{24} + 84\tfrac{25}{36}$ **66.** $20\tfrac{4}{105} - 15\tfrac{15}{154} + 16\tfrac{14}{165} - 5\tfrac{17}{231}$

2.8 MULTIPLICATION OF FRACTIONS

Probably almost everyone who reads this page knows the rule for multiplying fractions.

Rule. *In multiplying fractions, multiply the numerators together for the numerator of the product and multiply the denominators together for the denominator of the product.*

Yet it is well to analyze the problem involved in such multiplication in order to understand the reason for the rule. Rules should not only be memorized; they should first be understood.

In multiplication involving fractions we encounter some new difficulties in meaning. Of course, *when multiplying a fraction by an integer,* we can consider the problem as a shortened form of addition. For instance, suppose we have the following problem in multiplication:

$$4 \times \frac{3}{5} \quad \text{often written} \quad (4) \cdot \left(\frac{3}{5}\right)$$

We can say the problem means the same as the following addition:

$$\frac{3}{5} + \frac{3}{5} + \frac{3}{5} + \frac{3}{5} = \frac{12}{5}$$

The correct answer in this example can be found *by multiplying the numerator by the integer* 4: thus

$$(4) \cdot \left(\frac{3}{5}\right) = \frac{(4) \cdot (3)}{5} = \frac{12}{5}$$

In some cases we can divide some factor or factors into numerator and denominator either before or after multiplying. As an example,

$$(6) \cdot \left(\frac{5}{12}\right) = \frac{(\cancel{6})(5)}{\cancel{12}} = \frac{5}{2}; \quad \text{or} \quad \cancel{6} \cdot \frac{5}{\cancel{12}} = \frac{5}{2}$$

As a *second type of multiplication* consider multiplying an integer by a fraction. In this case we can reverse the order of multiplication, since multiplication can be done in any order. Suppose we have the following problem:

$$\left(\frac{3}{7}\right)(5)$$

We can reverse the order, by the commutative law and write

$$(5)\left(\frac{3}{7}\right) = \frac{15}{7}$$

When we come to a *third type* of problem, multiplying a *fraction by a fraction,* we cannot use the same kind of reasoning. Suppose we have

$$\frac{2}{3} \times \frac{4}{5}$$

We cannot say this means "add $\frac{4}{5}$ two-thirds of a time." This statement has no meaning. However, let us get at the meaning in another way. First, consider the product of two fractions whose numerators are 1, such as

$$\frac{1}{5} \times \frac{1}{4} \quad \text{or} \quad \frac{1}{5} \text{ of } \frac{1}{4}$$

(In connection with fractions, the multiplication symbol, ×, has the same meaning as the word *of*.) We already know that $\frac{1}{5}$ times any quantity or $\frac{1}{5}$ of any quantity is the same as dividing the quantity by 5. For example, $\frac{1}{5}$ of $35 = 35 \div 5 = 7$. Then $\frac{1}{5} \times \frac{1}{4}$ means the same as dividing $\frac{1}{4}$ by 5. Now, if we have $\frac{1}{4}$ of a dollar (a quarter) and take $\frac{1}{5}$ of this amount, we get $\frac{1}{20}$ of a dollar, a nickel. That is,

$$\frac{1}{5} \times \frac{1}{4} = \frac{1}{20}$$

Then we have the rule: *The product of two fractions whose numerators are 1 is a new fraction having the numerator 1 and a denominator that is the product of the original denominators.*

Now we are in a position to see the meaning of the product

$$\frac{2}{3} \times \frac{4}{5}$$

We have seen that $\frac{2}{3}$ is the same as $(2)(\frac{1}{3})$, and $\frac{4}{5}$ is the same as $(4)(\frac{1}{5})$. Then we can say

$$\frac{2}{3} \times \frac{4}{5} = (2) \times \left(\frac{1}{3}\right) \times (4) \times \left(\frac{1}{5}\right)$$

Since multiplication can be done in any order, we can write

$$(2) \times (4) \times \left(\frac{1}{3}\right) \times \left(\frac{1}{5}\right) = (8) \times \left(\frac{1}{15}\right) = \frac{8}{15}$$

At this point we notice that the product of the two fractions is a new fraction whose numerator is the product of the original numerators and whose denominator is the product of the original denominators. This is exactly the rule stated at the beginning of this section. The rule can be shown to hold for all multiplication involving fractions. It can be shown in many different ways. We now apply the rule to some examples.

Example 1.   Find $\frac{7}{8} \cdot \frac{4}{9}$.

Solution.   If the numerators are multiplied together and the denominators are multiplied together, we find that a factor "4" can be divided into both terms of the answer. This "4" can be divided into a numerator and a denominator before the terms are multiplied; thus

$$\frac{7}{\underset{2}{\cancel{8}}} \cdot \frac{\cancel{4}}{9} = \frac{7}{18}$$

Example 2. Find $\frac{8}{15} \cdot \frac{5}{12} \cdot \frac{6}{7}$.

Solution. In this example three numbers can be divided into numerators and denominators; namely, 3, 4, and 5.

$$\frac{\overset{2}{\cancel{8}}}{\underset{3}{\cancel{15}}} \cdot \frac{\overset{2}{\cancel{6}}}{7} \cdot \frac{\cancel{5}}{\cancel{12}} = \frac{4}{21}$$

Example 3. Find $(3\frac{4}{7}) \cdot (6\frac{3}{10})$.

Solution. The best way to multiply mixed numbers is to change the mixed numbers to improper fractions.

$$(3\tfrac{4}{7}) \cdot (6\tfrac{3}{10}) = \frac{\overset{5}{\cancel{25}}}{\cancel{7}} \cdot \frac{\overset{9}{\cancel{63}}}{\underset{2}{\cancel{10}}} = \frac{45}{2} = 22\tfrac{1}{2}$$

Example 4. Find $(\frac{5}{8}) \cdot (496\frac{3}{7})$.

Solution. Changing a mixed number to an improper fraction sometimes leads to a large improper fraction. In some examples the multiplication may instead be done in parts, although this method is probably more susceptible to error. First we arrange the numbers to be multiplied in column form. We call the $\frac{5}{8}$ the multiplier and the $496\frac{3}{7}$ the multiplicand.

$$496\tfrac{3}{7}$$
$$\tfrac{5}{8}$$

Multiply $\frac{3}{7}$ by $\frac{5}{8}$ $\qquad\qquad \frac{15}{56}$

Multiply 496 by 5 $\qquad\qquad)2480$
Divide by 8 $\qquad\qquad\qquad 310$
Add the fraction to 310 $\qquad\quad 310\frac{15}{56}$

Example 5. Find $(285\frac{3}{8})(469\frac{2}{3})$.

Solution. Even though the change to improper fractions here leads to large numbers, this procedure is best in an example of this kind. By changing the mixed numbers to improper fractions, we get

$$\frac{\overset{761}{\cancel{2283}}}{8} \cdot \frac{1409}{\cancel{3}} = \frac{1072249}{8} = 134,031\tfrac{1}{8}$$

2.9 RECIPROCAL OF A NUMBER

Before beginning the division of fractions, we need to understand what is meant by the reciprocal of a number. The *reciprocal* of any number is defined as the result of 1 divided by the number. The reciprocal of 5 is $\frac{1}{5}$. The reciprocal of 7 is $\frac{1}{7}$. The reciprocal of 1 is $\frac{1}{1}$, or 1. The reciprocal of 487 is $\frac{1}{487}$. The reciprocal of the fraction $\frac{3}{5}$ is

$$1 \div \frac{3}{5} \quad \text{or} \quad \frac{1}{\frac{3}{5}}$$

Let us determine the result of this division. By using the fundamental principle of fractions, we can change the expression $\dfrac{1}{\frac{3}{5}}$ into a simpler form. As the fraction is written, the numerator is 1. The denominator is $\frac{3}{5}$. Now we multiply both numerator and denominator by 5.

$$\frac{(5)(1)}{(5)(\frac{3}{5})} = \frac{5}{3}$$

Therefore, the reciprocal of $\frac{3}{5}$ is $\frac{5}{3}$. We have the following rule:

Rule. *The reciprocal of a fraction can be obtained simply by inverting the fraction.* Thus the reciprocal of $\frac{4}{7}$ is $\frac{7}{4}$.

Then, by definition, the product of any number and its reciprocal is equal to 1.

2.10 DIVISION INVOLVING FRACTIONS

The division of a fraction by a whole number may be considered as the division of any denominate number. For example,

$$8\,\text{lb} \div 4 = 2\,\text{lb}$$

In the same way,

$$8\,\text{ninths} \div 4 = 2\,\text{ninths},$$

or, in fraction form,

$$\frac{8}{9} \div 4 = \frac{2}{9}$$

If the numerator is taken as a *counter* of a number of objects, then division by a whole number simply means the division of the numerator by that number.

Suppose the numerator is not exactly divisible by the whole number, as in the division,

$$\frac{3}{7} \div 4$$

then the expression can be written in another way. Dividing a number by 4 means the same as taking $\frac{1}{4}$ of the number. Therefore, the division means the same as $\frac{1}{4}$ of $\frac{3}{7}$. Now the problem is one of multiplication:

$$\frac{1}{4} \times \frac{3}{7} = \frac{3}{28}$$

To divide a fraction by a whole number, then, we have the rule: *divide the numerator or multiply the denominator* by the whole number.

However, when the divisor itself is a fraction, the problem is not quite so simple. We need a rule that applies to all situations. Take the example,

$$7 \div \frac{2}{5}$$

First, let us recall two facts: (1) any number divided by unity, 1, is the number itself, and (2) the product of any number and its reciprocal is 1. Now we write the division in the form of a fraction:

$$7 \div \frac{2}{5}$$

is written

$$\frac{7}{\frac{2}{5}}$$

By the fundamental principle of fractions we multiply both numerator and denominator of the fraction by $\frac{5}{2}$ and get

$$\frac{7 \times \frac{5}{2}}{1} = \frac{\frac{35}{2}}{1} = \frac{35}{2}$$

Therefore, we discover that

$$7 \div \frac{2}{5} = 7 \times \frac{5}{2}$$

From the foregoing example we can formulate the rule for division involving fractions:

Rule. *In dividing any number (fraction, whole number, or mixed number) by a fraction, multiply the dividend by the reciprocal of the divisor.*

There are many ways in which this rule can be shown to be true. There is one exception: *we cannot divide by zero.* Division by zero is excluded in all mathematics. Here are some illustrations of the rule:

(a) $5 \div \frac{2}{3} = 5 \times \frac{3}{2} = \frac{15}{2} = 7\frac{1}{2}$
(b) $\frac{5}{8} \div 3 = \frac{5}{8} \times \frac{1}{3} = \frac{5}{24}$
(c) $4\frac{2}{3} \div 2\frac{3}{5} = \frac{14}{3} \div \frac{13}{5} = \frac{14}{3} \times \frac{5}{13} = \frac{70}{39} = 1\frac{31}{39}$
(d) $\frac{3}{5} \div 0 =$ no answer.

The rules for the multiplication and division of fractions make it possible to simplify the work in many problems involving several multiplications and divisions. For example, in some problems we find it necessary to multiply two or more numbers together and then divide the product by one or more other numbers. The result may be a problem such as the following:

$$\frac{48 \times 35 \times 36}{63 \times 50 \times 32}$$

This example may be worked in a simple way. First, let us see what it means. The example means that the numbers 48, 35, and 36 are to be multiplied together. Then the denominator is also to be expanded by multiplication. Finally, the product obtained for the numerator is to be divided by the product obtained for the denominator.

If we perform the multiplication and division as indicated, we first get the result

$$\frac{60480}{100800}$$

This fraction can be reduced by dividing numerator and denominator by any factor common to both terms. We see at once that 10 is a common factor and can be divided into both terms. The result is

$$\frac{6048}{10080}$$

Now we can continue to reduce the fraction by dividing the terms by any other common factor.

$$\frac{6048 \div 8}{10080 \div 8} = \frac{756 \div 4}{1260 \div 4} = \frac{189 \div 9}{315 \div 9} = \frac{21 \div 7}{35 \div 7} = \frac{3}{5}$$

The work can be greatly simplified by first dividing the numerators and the denominators of the original form by common factors before multiplying. We see at once that we can divide the following factors into both numerator and denominator: 16, 7, 9, 5, 2, 2.

$$\frac{\overset{3}{\cancel{48}} \times \overset{5}{\cancel{35}} \times \overset{\overset{2}{\cancel{4}}}{\cancel{36}}}{\underset{9}{\cancel{63}} \times \underset{10}{\cancel{50}} \times \underset{\underset{5}{2}}{\cancel{32}}} = \frac{3}{5}$$

The student is warned: This method of simplifying an expression cannot be used when additions or subtractions appear in numerator or denominator or both.

In the following example, the numerator and the denominator of the expression must be expanded as indicated.

$$\frac{6 \times 8 \times 5 + 1}{12 \times 4 \times 10} = \frac{241}{480}$$

A problem can often be set up in a form suitable for reducing. All numbers that are to be multiplied together are placed as factors in the numerator. All numbers to be used as divisors can be written in the denominator separated by the *multiplication* sign.

Example. A man drives 480 miles in 12 hr. What is his average speed in feet per second?

Solution. A distance of 480 miles is equal to (480)(5280) ft. The total number of feet is not expanded but is left in factored form. The number of feet is now divided by the number of seconds in 12 hr: 12 hr are equal to (12)(60)(60) sec. Now we set up the problem.

$$\frac{480 \times 5280}{12 \times 60 \times 60} = 58\frac{2}{3} \text{ ft per sec.}$$

The answer is obtained easily by dividing numerator and denominator by any numbers contained in both.

Exercise 2.5

Multiply:

1. $\frac{2}{5} \times \frac{4}{7}$ **2.** $(9\frac{3}{7})(2\frac{1}{2})$ **3.** $(2\frac{6}{7})(\frac{3}{5})$

4. $(\frac{12}{35})(\frac{24}{37})$ **5.** $(18)(\frac{4}{9})$ **6.** $(6\frac{3}{4})(70)$

7. $(9\frac{3}{4})(6\frac{1}{2})$ **8.** $(17\frac{3}{5})(2\frac{5}{8})$ **9.** $(33)(\frac{4}{15})$

10. $(4\frac{5}{8})(36)$ **11.** $(26\frac{4}{7})(1\frac{3}{4})$ **12.** $(5\frac{5}{9})(514)$

13. $(15\frac{6}{7})(5\frac{4}{9})$ **14.** $(\frac{3}{8})(4\frac{9}{20})$ **15.** $(12\frac{16}{21})(4\frac{7}{8})$

16. $(4\frac{16}{75})(10\frac{5}{32})$ **17.** $(24)(5\frac{3}{16})$ **18.** $(384)(513\frac{5}{8})$

Divide:

19. $\frac{3}{4} \div \frac{5}{8}$ **20.** $\frac{4}{9} \div 2\frac{2}{3}$ **21.** $\frac{7}{8} \div \frac{3}{4}$

22. $\frac{16}{25} \div 1\frac{4}{5}$ **23.** $9\frac{2}{7} \div 1\frac{3}{7}$ **24.** $2\frac{5}{8} \div \frac{3}{10}$

25. $2\frac{4}{15} \div \frac{8}{11}$ **26.** $72 \div 1\frac{3}{7}$ **27.** $2\frac{8}{21} \div 4$

28. $15 \div \frac{9}{10}$ **29.** $27 \div \frac{18}{85}$ **30.** $5\frac{2}{5} \div 16$

31. $13\frac{1}{15} \div 1\frac{8}{25}$ **32.** $44 \div 10\frac{4}{5}$ **33.** $3\frac{12}{35} \div 1\frac{5}{21}$

34. $3\frac{13}{24} \div 7\frac{3}{16}$ **35.** $\frac{28}{43} \div 6$ **36.** $11\frac{2}{3} \div 15$

Simplify:

37. $(15\frac{2}{3})(8\frac{5}{16})(13\frac{4}{15})$ **38.** $(6\frac{4}{5})(8\frac{3}{4})(10\frac{4}{15})$

39. $(4\frac{8}{25})(3\frac{10}{21})(5\frac{7}{16})$ **40.** $(3\frac{48}{91})(5\frac{7}{9})(4\frac{27}{32})$

41. $(5\frac{35}{81})(4\frac{2}{7})(2\frac{4}{15})$ **42.** $(8\frac{18}{25})(6\frac{3}{16})(7\frac{20}{27})$

43. $(36\frac{3}{4})(5\frac{10}{27})(9\frac{3}{8})$ **44.** $(4\frac{5}{18})(3\frac{3}{14})(6)$

45. $(3)(\frac{5}{20}) \div (11\frac{2}{3})$ **46.** $(5\frac{5}{24})(16) \div (6\frac{2}{3})$

47. $\dfrac{28 \times 75 \times 66}{125 \times 44 \times 27}$ **48.** $\dfrac{54 \times 55 \times 98}{35 \times 18 \times 88}$

49. $\dfrac{18 \times 30 \times 77}{22 \times 42 \times 45}$ **50.** $\dfrac{12 \times 60 + 1}{48 \times 30 - 2}$

51. $\dfrac{2 + 18 \times 45}{5 + 27 \times 50}$

52. $\dfrac{40 \times 50 \times 60}{40 + 50 + 60}$

53. Five pieces, measuring, respectively, $3\frac{3}{8}$, $5\frac{1}{4}$, $4\frac{5}{16}$, $2\frac{9}{32}$, and $3\frac{15}{16}$ in., are cut from a strip of brass 2 ft, 6 in. long. How much of the strip remains if the amount of waste is $\frac{3}{32}$ in. per cut?

54. A strip of aluminum is cut into seven pieces measuring, respectively, $2\frac{3}{8}$, $3\frac{1}{16}$, $3\frac{5}{8}$, $4\frac{5}{64}$, $2\frac{17}{64}$, $3\frac{3}{4}$, and $2\frac{1}{2}$ in. If the waste for each cut is $\frac{5}{64}$ in., find the length of the original strip.

55. How many pieces, each $3\frac{7}{16}$ in. long, can be cut from a piece of metal 28 in. long if $\frac{3}{32}$ in. is allowed for each cut as waste?

56. Twelve pieces, each $1\frac{9}{16}$ in. long are cut from a strip of copper 24 in. long. How much of the strip remains if $\frac{1}{32}$ in. is allowed per cut for waste?

57. Two holes are to be drilled in a metal plate so that the distance between the holes is $1\frac{7}{8}$ in. The diameters of the holes are $\frac{3}{8}$ and $\frac{7}{32}$ in., respectively. Find the distance between the centers.

58. Find the total weight of four chickens weighing, respectively, 2 lb, 10 oz, 3 lb, $2\frac{1}{2}$ oz, 3 lb, $4\frac{1}{2}$ oz, and 3 lb, 9 oz.

59. A rectangle is $5\frac{7}{8}$ in. long and $3\frac{5}{16}$ in. wide. Find the distance around the rectangle.

60. If a man works at a job for 10 weeks, $5\frac{1}{2}$ days per week and $7\frac{3}{4}$ hr per day, how many hours does he work at the job?

61. The gasoline tank on a car holds $12\frac{3}{4}$ gal. If the car travels at an average of $16\frac{5}{8}$ miles on 1 gal, how many times will the tank have to be filled to travel 1000 miles?

62. On a blueprint of a particular house $\frac{1}{2}$ in. represents 1 ft. Find the lengths on the blueprint that will represent the dimensions of the following rooms: $11\frac{1}{2} \times 13$ ft, $18\frac{1}{4} \times 14\frac{3}{8}$ ft, $12\frac{1}{3} \times 15\frac{1}{2}$ ft, and $16\frac{3}{4} \times 12\frac{5}{8}$ ft.

3
Decimal Fractions

3.1 DEFINITION

The decimal fraction was one of the major advances in mathematics. For a long time people had used the place value of the digits to indicate the number 10 and numbers larger than 10. For instance, when we write a number such as 4444, the 4 at the extreme right, as we have said, indicates units. The 4 at the left of units place indicates *tens*; that is, the second 4 from the right has a value equal to ten times as much as the first 4. The third 4 from the right has a value ten times as much as the second 4, and so on.

Placing a digit in the second, third, fourth, or fifth place from the right multiplies its value by 10, 100, 1000, or 10,000. This place value of digits was early recognized as one of the most important ideas in arithmetic.

However, for a long time no one ever thought of placing digits at the *right* of units place. Then, less than 400 years ago, decimal fractions were invented. It was seen that a digit could be written one place to the right of units place with some mark, such as a period, between them. In this position a digit could represent one tenth as much as in units place. Thus a 4 written one place to the right of units place, as 0.4, means $\frac{4}{10}$.

The point separating the units place from the fractional part is called a *decimal point*. A fraction written with digits at the right of the decimal point is called a *decimal fraction*. If no decimal point is shown in a number, the number is understood to be an integer, and the decimal point is understood to be at the right of the number. When we write the number 63 without a decimal point, the decimal point is understood to be just at the right of the 3: thus 63.

Notice the difference in value of each of the 1's in these numbers.

1000	one thousand
100	one hundred
10	one ten

· *Note.* In some parts of the world a comma is used to separate the whole number from the decimal fraction. Then, periods are used to separate the groups of digits in the whole number. A number that we write as 92,304,571.86, would be written in some countries as 92.304.571,86.

1   one unit
0.1   one tenth
0.01   one one-hundredth
0.001   one one-thousandth
0.0001   one ten-thousandth

For each place a digit is moved to the right of the decimal point, the digit represents another division by 10, or one tenth as much as in the preceding place.

$\frac{1}{10}$ is written 0.1

$\frac{1}{100}$ is written 0.01

$\frac{1}{1000}$ is written 0.001

Annexing zeros to the right of a decimal fraction does not change the value. These fractions all have the same value:

$$0.3 = \frac{3}{10} \qquad 0.30 = \frac{30}{100} \qquad 0.300 = \frac{300}{1000}$$

In the same way, annexing zeros to the left of a whole number does not change the value. The value of 934.5 is not changed by writing it 000934.5000.

A number consisting of a whole number and a decimal fraction is sometimes called a *mixed decimal*. Thus

the numbers 0.352
and 0.0086 } are decimal fractions

the number 614.54 is a mixed decimal

The number of decimal places in a number means the number of digits to the right of the decimal point. The number 0.352 is said to have three decimal places. The number 0.0086 has four decimal places. The number 614.54 has two decimal places.

To summarize, whenever a digit is moved one place farther to the left, its value is multiplied by 10. Whenever a digit is moved one place farther to the right, its value is divided by 10. The number 3333.333 means $3000 + 300 + 30 + 3 + \frac{3}{10} + \frac{3}{100} + \frac{3}{1000}$. The number 72508.6439 means

7 ten-thousands
2 thousands
5 hundreds
0 tens
8 units
6 tenths
4 hundredths
3 thousandths
9 ten-thousandths

In reading a number the word "and" is used *only* at the decimal point. The foregoing number is read "seventy-two thousand five hundred eight *and* six thousand four hundred thirty-nine ten-thousandths."

3.2 CHANGING A COMMON FRACTION TO A DECIMAL

A common fraction such as $\frac{3}{4}$ can easily be changed to a decimal if we look upon a fraction as an indicated division. The fraction $\frac{3}{4}$ means $3 \div 4$. To find the decimal fraction equal to $\frac{3}{4}$, we perform the division $4\overline{)3}$. We place a decimal point after the 3 and add zeros at the right of the decimal point, as we divide.

$$4\overline{)3.00}$$

Place the decimal point for the answer directly above the decimal point in the dividend. After two divisions the remainder is zero.

$$
\begin{array}{r}
0.75 \\
4\overline{)3.0} \\
2\,8 \\
\hline
20 \\
20 \\
\hline
0
\end{array}
$$

Therefore, $\frac{3}{4} = 0.75$.

The answer can easily be checked by writing 0.75 as a common fraction, $\frac{75}{100}$, and then reducing the fraction. It becomes $\frac{3}{4}$.

Some common fractions do not come out even as a decimal fraction. For instance,

$$\frac{1}{3} = 0.3333\ldots \qquad \frac{3}{7} = 0.4285714285714\ldots$$

The dots indicate that the answer does not come out even.

Whenever a common fraction is changed to a decimal fraction, the result is either an even decimal or a repeating decimal, as shown in the following examples:

$$\frac{2}{5} = 0.4 \qquad \frac{1}{4} = 0.25 \qquad \frac{3}{8} = 0.375 \qquad \frac{4}{25} = 0.16$$

$$\frac{7}{16} = 0.4375 \qquad \frac{2}{3} = 0.666666\ldots \qquad \frac{5}{11} = 0.45454545\ldots$$

By a repeating decimal, we mean a decimal in which the number after a certain point has the same set of consecutive digits. In the fraction $\frac{1}{3}$ the decimal will consist of a repetition of 3's. In the fraction $\frac{5}{11}$ the decimal will consist of a repetition of the two digits, 45.

Since a decimal fraction always indicates the denominators, 10, 100, 1000, etc., it follows that many common fractions cannot be stated as exact decimals. If a common fraction has a denominator that can be changed to 10, 100, 1000, etc., then the fraction can be stated as an exact decimal. For instance, $\frac{3}{5}$ can be changed to $\frac{6}{10}$ and can therefore be written 0.6; $\frac{1}{2}$ can be stated as $\frac{5}{10}$ and can be written 0.5. However, a fraction such as $\frac{4}{7}$ cannot be changed to tenths or hundredths, etc., and cannot be written as an exact decimal.

3.3   CHANGING A DECIMAL FRACTION TO A COMMON FRACTION

It is sometimes desirable to change a fraction from decimal form to common fraction form. This is easily done by writing the entire decimal as a common fraction and then reducing it to lowest terms.

Example 1.
$$0.25 = \frac{25}{100} = \frac{1}{4}$$

$$0.625 = \frac{625}{1000} = \frac{5}{8}$$

To change a mixed decimal to a mixed number, change only the fraction part.

Example 2.
$$16.24 = 16\tfrac{24}{100} = 16\tfrac{6}{25}$$
$$485.0375 = 485\tfrac{375}{10000} = 485\tfrac{3}{80}$$

Sometimes we find a combination of a decimal and a common fraction. For instance, in the fraction, $0.87\frac{1}{2}$, the $\frac{1}{2}$ can be immediately changed to 0.5 and the 5 simply attached to 0.87. Thus

Example 3.
$$0.87\tfrac{1}{2} = 0.875 = \frac{875}{1000} = \frac{7}{8}$$

In some examples the change is a little more difficult.

Example 4.   Change to common fraction form
$$0.16\tfrac{2}{3}$$
This can first be written as a common fraction.
$$\frac{16\frac{2}{3}}{100}$$

Now multiply numerator and denominator by 3.
$$\frac{3 \times 16\frac{2}{3}}{3 \times 100} = \frac{50}{300} = \frac{1}{6}$$

Exercise 3.1

Reduce the following common fractions and mixed numbers to decimals:

1. $\frac{1}{2}$ **2.** $\frac{3}{4}$ **3.** $\frac{5}{8}$ **4.** $\frac{9}{16}$ **5.** $\frac{4}{11}$
6. $1\frac{1}{4}$ **7.** $3\frac{3}{16}$ **8.** $5\frac{3}{7}$ **9.** $6\frac{7}{8}$ **10.** $4\frac{5}{13}$
11. $8\frac{2}{5}$ **12.** $4\frac{1}{3}$ **13.** $7\frac{5}{6}$ **14.** $3\frac{7}{16}$ **15.** $1\frac{3}{32}$
16. $4\frac{7}{20}$ **17.** $9\frac{8}{9}$ **18.** $\frac{31}{15}$ **19.** $\frac{26}{3}$ **20.** $5\frac{3}{40}$
21. $9\frac{5}{32}$ **22.** $\frac{27}{8}$ **23.** $\frac{41}{32}$ **24.** $\frac{185}{9}$ **25.** $\frac{135}{16}$

Reduce the following decimal fractions to common fraction form:

26. 0.6   **27.** 0.25   **28.** 0.333   **29.** 0.16
30. 0.45   **31.** 1.2   **32.** 0.375   **33.** $0.33\frac{1}{3}$
34. 4.75   **35.** 8.05   **36.** 7.048   **37.** $3.02\frac{1}{2}$
38. 13.64   **39.** 15.075   **40.** 4.0625   **41.** 5.0375
42. 3.002   **43.** 8.005   **44.** $9.87\frac{1}{2}$ **45.** $0.300\frac{1}{2}$
46. $3.3\frac{1}{3}$ **47.** 11.08   **48.** $2.66\frac{2}{3}$ **49.** $0.00\frac{1}{7}$

3.4 ADDITION OF DECIMALS

In adding decimal fractions or mixed decimals, we place the numbers in column form with the decimal points in line.

Example. Add 25 + 48.7 + 5.724 + 864.1 + 0.0372.

```
        25
        48.7
         5.724
       864.1
         0.0372
       943.5612   sum
```

3.5 SUBTRACTION OF DECIMALS

In subtracting decimal fractions, or mixed decimals, we place one number below the other with decimal points in line.

Example 1. Subtract 145.397 − 31.729.

```
       145.397
        31.729
       113.668   remainder
```

Sometimes it is necessary to annex zeros at the right of a decimal fraction or at the right of the decimal point. This does not change the value.

Example 2. Subtract 56.4 − 13.6537.

```
       56.4000
       13.6537
       42.7463   remainder
```

Example 3. Subtract 2 − 0.53728.

$$
\begin{array}{l}
2.00000 \\
0.53728 \\
\hline
1.46272
\end{array} \quad \text{add to check}
$$

Remember that subtraction can be quickly checked by addition.

Exercise 3.2

Perform the following additions and subtractions:

1. 567.43 + 79.96 + 869.58
2. 573.9 + 958 + 1957.2
3. 7.084 + 287.6 + 0.851
4. 495 + 98.3 + 0.04074
5. 678.4 + 4.78 + 80000
6. 9.3 + 0.187 + 384.7 + 0.0937
7. 3.7 + 58.53 + 28 + 98.357
8. 78.82 + 3.8 + 0.0367 + 690
9. 3.65 + 54.28 + 0.0538 + 701
10. 42.6 + 74 + 0.0036 + 2.36794

11. From 85.73 subtract 44.67
12. From 9827 subtract 427.9
13. From 3580 subtract 29.47
14. From 780.5 subtract 31.83
15. From 719.3 subtract 9.485
16. From 576.3 take 27.486
17. From 377.4 take 188.432
18. From 80.8 take 41.9032
19. From 3.96 take 2.83914
20. From 86.4 take 0.06081

21. From 3 subtract 0.25
22. From 7 subtract 1.4963
23. From 2 subtract 0.38658
24. From 5 subtract 0.89798
25. From 1 subtract 0.06027
26. Find 5 − 1.39782
27. Find 6 − 5.42697
28. Find 3 − 1.58314
29. Find 2 − 0.63825
30. Find 1 − 0.71345

31. A family goes on a tour and drives the indicated distance during each of the first four days: Monday, 234.5 miles; Tuesday, 315.2 miles; Wednesday, 342.6 miles; Thursday, 286.1 miles. If the trip is 1400 miles in all, how many miles must they drive the fifth day to complete the trip in five days?

32. The following lengths were cut from a strip of steel (in inches): 3.75, 4, 4.25, 4.5, and 4.75. If the original strip was 24 in. and 0.05 in. was wasted in cutting each piece, what was the length of the piece remaining?

3.6 MULTIPLICATION OF DECIMAL FRACTIONS OR MIXED DECIMALS

In multiplying two numbers, (1) we place one above the other just as with whole numbers; (2) we perform the actual computation without regard to decimal points, just as though the numbers were whole numbers; (3) we place the decimal point in the answer. To place the decimal point correctly, we point off as many places from the right as there are decimal places in the multiplier and multiplicand combined.

Example 1. (2.95)(3.1).

$$
\begin{array}{r}
2.9\,5 \\
3.1 \\
\hline
2\,9\,5 \\
8\,8\,5 \\
\hline
9\,1\,4\,5
\end{array}
$$

The decimal point is now placed in proper position by counting three places from the right. The product is 9.145.

In order to see why the decimal point is determined by this rule, suppose we write the numbers as improper common fractions.

Then (2.95)(3.1) is the same as

$$
\frac{295}{100} \times \frac{31}{10} = \frac{9145}{1000} = 9.145
$$

Notice that the number 2.95 indicates a denominator of 100 and the number 3.1 indicates a denominator of 10. When the denominators are multiplied together, the denominator of the product is 100×10, or 1000. The product of the numerators is then divided by 1000, which means that we point off three decimal places.

In some cases it is necessary to add zeros at the left of the answer in multiplication.

Example 2. (0.034)(0.02).

$$
\begin{array}{r}
0.034 \\
0.02 \\
\hline
68
\end{array}
$$

In order to get the necessary decimal places in the product (that is, *five*), we must annex three zeros at the left of 68. The product is

$$
0.00068
$$

3.7 ROUNDING OFF NUMBERS

When we come to division involving decimal fractions, we are first faced with the problem of rounding off numbers. For instance, when we change the common fraction $\frac{3}{7}$ to a decimal fraction, we get the following:

$$
\begin{array}{r}
0.428571428571428571\ldots \\
\hline
7)3.0000000000
\end{array}
$$

The answer is an unending, repeating decimal. We are then faced with the problem of when to stop. Usually we stop the division at some point so that the number we have is convenient to use. In a problem such as this we would probably drop all the digits after the first four or five. The numbers we keep are called *significant* digits.

It is important to understand exactly what is meant by a *significant* digit. In any given number the first significant digit is the first digit other than zero starting at the left of the number. In a decimal fraction, such as 0.00062049, the first significant digit is 6. The first three zeros at the left are not significant digits. The decimal 0.00062049 has five significant digits. The 0 between the 2 and the 4 is a significant digit. In a whole number, such as 93,407,000, the zeros at the right do not count as significant digits unless definitely stated as such. The number 93,407,000 has five significant digits.

In the division of reducing $\frac{3}{7}$ to a decimal, as shown above, when some digits at the right are dropped, we say the number is "rounded off." In the number 0.428571428571..., if we keep the first five digits, we have 0.42857. In some cases the last digit kept is increased by 1, and in other cases it remains the same.

Suppose we say the distance from the earth to the sun at a particular instant is 93,284,716 miles. In most cases we are not interested in such a high degree of accuracy. Usually, we would say the distance is approximately 93,000,000 miles. In other words, we round off the number 93,284,716 and use only the two important (or significant) digits, 93. We sometimes say a number such as 93,000,000 is stated in round numbers. The term "rounding off" comes from the words "round numbers," which refer to the zeros used.

When we round off any number, we imply that the number we are using is only approximate, yet accurate enough for practical purposes.

In rounding off a number, if the part to be dropped represents *more than half* the digit 1 in the last place kept, then the last digit kept is increased by 1. If the part to be dropped represents *less than half* the digit 1 in the last place kept, then the last digit kept is left as it is.

In order to understand clearly the method of rounding off numbers, let us take the number 647.2. Suppose we wish to round off this number so that we shall have only three digits, beginning with 6. In this case we drop the 2 and retain the number 647. What we mean is that 647 is approximately equal to 647.2.

However, if we wish to round off the number 647.9 to three significant digits, we can say that the number 648 is approximately equal to 647.9. In this case the 7 is increased to 8 because the digit we drop (that is, the 9) is more than 5.

For rounding off numbers, we have the following rules:

1. In rounding off a number, if the first digit dropped is less than 5, then the last digit kept is left as it is.
2. If the first digit dropped is larger than 5, then the last digit kept is increased by 1.

3. If the digit dropped is exactly 5, followed only by zeros, then we need a special rule.

In the business world, when a particular cost or price or monetary item ends with one half cent, it is customary to increase the amount to the next even cent. For example, a cost of $17.825 is rounded off to $17.83. In business a number ending in one half cent is always rounded *upward*. That is, the next digit at the left is increased by 1.

However, in mathematics a number ending in 5 cannot always be rounded upward. If this were always done, then there would be an accumulation of errors upward, and the net result would be too great an error in the answer.

Therefore, for numbers ending in 5 we use a special rule that will result in rounding off such numbers *sometimes upward and sometimes downward*.

If a number ends exactly in 5, followed only by zeros, then, when the 5 is dropped, the last digit kept is not changed if it is *even*. If the last digit kept is *odd*, it is changed to the next higher *even* digit. That is, the last digit kept is always made an even digit. Remember that this special rule applies only when the digit dropped is 5 followed only by zeros.

As a result of this last rule, if we round off many numbers ending in 5, the net effect will be that we shall round off such numbers *upward* about as many times as we round them *downward*.

Numbers are rounded off not only in division but also in multiplication and, in fact, in any computation when we wish to retain only a certain number of significant digits.

Exercise 3.3

Round off each of the numbers listed below to five, four, three, and two significant digits.

1. 473529	**2.** 29.6725	**3.** 5081362	**4.** 183.935
5. 852.9217	**6.** 357261.4	**7.** 49.25004	**8.** 0.0728476
9. 0.1739651	**10.** 9172.653	**11.** 488535	**12.** 4265312
13. 9270403	**14.** 0.2610851	**15.** 3.258135	**16.** 0.000429965
17. 0.00584036	**18.** 0.860106	**19.** 57.0046	**20.** 0.03074545

3.8   DIVISION INVOLVING DECIMAL FRACTIONS

In the division of decimal fractions, most people use the following procedure.

Example 1. $0.23\overline{)97.63_\wedge 5}$.

First we mentally move the decimal point in the dividend and divisor as many places to the right as there are decimal places in the divisor. This makes the divisor a whole number. Then the decimal point is placed in the answer directly above the new position of the decimal point in the dividend. This should be done before division is

$$\begin{array}{r} 4 . \\ 0.23\overline{)97.63_\wedge 5} \end{array}$$

started. In order to be sure of the proper place for the decimal point in the answer, we place each number in the quotient directly above the number used in the dividend for each division. For instance, 23 is contained in 97 only four times. The 4 is written above the 7. Then the division is performed just as with whole numbers.

Example 2. Divide 45.837 by 3.12 and carry the answer to five significant digits.

$$\begin{array}{r} 14.6913 \\ 3.12\overline{)45.837} \\ \underline{312} \\ 1463 \\ \underline{1248} \\ 2157 \\ \underline{1872} \\ 2850 \\ \underline{2808} \\ 420 \\ \underline{312} \\ 1080 \end{array}$$

The answer, rounded off to five digits, is 14.691.

Exercise 3.4

Perform the following multiplications:

1. 91.7 × 4.8	**2.** 63.9 × 0.58	**3.** 0.948 × 8.6
4. 8.56 × 3.8	**5.** 7.85 × 0.75	**6.** 9.28 × 59
7. 7.36 × 0.089	**8.** 84.9 × 0.58	**9.** 0.748 × 3.9
10. 576 × 0.69	**11.** 97.3 × 0.042	**12.** 7.84 × 0.53
13. 0.487 × 0.538	**14.** 0.487 × 0.012	**15.** 0.023 × 0.031
16. 0.0863 × 0.074	**17.** 0.0293 × 0.054	**18.** 0.00628 × 0.39
19. 98.5 × 0.0087	**20.** 0.0279 × 0.067	**21.** 8.963 × 3.21
22. 7.368 × 0.62	**23.** 18.079 × 0.36	**24.** 918.2 × 0.809
25. 8.6734 × 1.046	**26.** 78.925 × 0.809	**27.** 4.8179 × 1.036
28. 0.09378 × 0.516	**29.** 697.82 × 0.408	**30.** 0.75806 × 0.083
31. 0.05796 × 1.007	**32.** 1087.4 × 0.816	**33.** 0.8507 × 0.0513
34. 0.00126 × 1.034	**35.** 4965.2 × 0.204	**36.** 0.00769 × 3500

Perform the following divisions:

37. 2.1044 ÷ 26	**38.** 3621.5 ÷ 54	**39.** 0.11862 ÷ 46
40. 2.3638 ÷ 0.86	**41.** 0.54532 ÷ 9.9	**42.** 8.5934 ÷ 6.7
43. 141.38 ÷ 3.9	**44.** 68.83 ÷ 0.019	**45.** 234.91 ÷ 0.28

46. 0.03301 ÷ 3.9	**47.** 6.1392 ÷ 0.76	**48.** 48613 ÷ 0.065
49. 3.1749 ÷ 4.59	**50.** 3869.3 ÷ 3.48	**51.** 3.5073 ÷ 0.082
52. 0.47602 ÷ 0.492	**53.** 0.07814 ÷ 0.057	**54.** 118.6 ÷ 0.0019
55. 55.413 ÷ 1.87	**56.** 36435 ÷ 38.2	**57.** 458.21 ÷ 0.673
58. 4394.2 ÷ 0.048	**59.** 0.00402 ÷ 58.1	**60.** 0.02002 ÷ 0.037

3.9   A FEW SHORT-CUTS

There are many so-called *short cuts* for fast computation in arithmetic. The following five rules cover a few of the most useful in multiplication and division.

Rule 1.   *To multiply any number by 10, 100, 1000, etc., move the decimal point toward the right as many places as there are zeros in the multiplier.*

Examples.
$$10 \times 48.63 = 486.3$$
$$100 \times 48.63 = 4863$$
$$1000 \times 48.63 = 48630$$
$$1{,}000{,}000 \times 0.0003724 = 372.4$$

Rule 2.   *To divide any number by 10, 100, 1000, etc., move the decimal point toward the left as many places as there are zeros in the divisor.*

Examples.
$$48.63 \div 10 \quad = 4.863$$
$$48.63 \div 100 \quad = 0.4863$$
$$48.63 \div 1000 = 0.04863$$
$$295.37 \div 1{,}000{,}000 = 0.00029537$$

Rule 3.   *To multiply a number by 5, move the decimal point one place to the right and divide by 2.*

Examples.
$$5 \times 8 \quad = \frac{1}{2} \text{ of } 80 = 40$$

$$5 \times 367 = \frac{1}{2} \text{ of } 3670 = 1835$$

Rule 3 means that we actually multiply by 10 and then divide by 2, which is equivalent to multiplying by 5. The rule can be extended to multiplication by 50, 500, etc.

Rule 4.   *To multiply a number by 25, move the decimal point two places to the right and divide by 4.*

Examples.
$$25 \times 36.8 = \frac{1}{4} \text{ of } 3680 = 920$$

$$25 \times 893 \quad = \frac{1}{4} \text{ of } 89300 = 22325$$

Rule 4 means that we actually multiply by 100 and then divide by 4, which is equivalent to multiplying by 25. The rule can be extended to multiplication by 250, 2500, etc.

Rule 5. *To multiply a number ending in $\frac{1}{2}$ by itself, multiply the whole number by one more than itself and then annex the fraction $\frac{1}{4}$.*

This is one of the most useful rules in mathematics for rapid multiplication. It is useful especially in engineering but also in other fields of mathematics, such as statistics.

Example 1. $(6\frac{1}{2})(6\frac{1}{2})$.
Take 6×7 and annex the fraction $\frac{1}{4}$. *Answer:* $42\frac{1}{4}$.

Example 2. $(19\frac{1}{2})(19\frac{1}{2})$.
Take 19×20 and annex the fraction $\frac{1}{4}$. *Answer:* $380\frac{1}{4}$.

Rule 5 can also be used when $\frac{1}{2}$ is written as a decimal, 0.5.

Example 3. $(8.5)(8.5)$.
Take 8×9 and annex the fraction 0.25. *Answer:* 72.25.

Example 4. $(24.5)(24.5)$.
Take 24×25 and annex the fraction 0.25. *Answer:* 600.25.

Rule 5 can also be used for any number ending in 5 even though it is not a decimal.

Example 5. $(245)(245)$.
Take 24×25 and annex the two digits 25. *Answer:* 60,025.

Example 6. $(125)(125)$.
Take 12×13 and annex 25. *Answer:* 15,625.

If a problem requires several multiplications and divisions involving decimal fractions, it can often be simplified in the same manner as with whole numbers. We have seen how the following example can be reduced:

$$\frac{24 \times 25 \times 49}{35 \times 28 \times 45}$$

In this example the numerator and the denominator can be divided successively by 3, 4, 5, 5, 7, and 7, and the fraction reduces to $\frac{2}{3}$.

If the numbers in the numerator and/or the denominator contain decimals, the computation can be simplified in the same way. However, in that case it is best first to multiply the numerator and the denominator by 10, 100, 1000, or by some other number of 10's so that the decimals disappear. This is done simply by *moving the decimal point the same number of places in the numerator and the denominator.*

Suppose, in arranging the work in a problem, we get the following fractional expression:

$$\frac{0.6 \times 175 \times 4.8 \times 0.12}{1.25 \times 4 \times 3.6 \times 0.028}$$

The decimals can be eliminated by multiplying numerator and denominator by 10 a sufficient number of times. In this case we multiply numerator and denominator by 1000000, so that all decimals disappear. To multiply both terms by 1000000, we simply move the decimal point a total of six places in the numerator and a total of six places in the denominator. The problem then becomes:

$$\frac{6 \times 175 \times 48 \times 1200}{125 \times 4 \times 36 \times 28}$$

All the numbers are now integers, and the fraction can easily be reduced to 120.

Exercise 3.5

Multiply each of the following numbers by 10, 100, 1000:

1. 48.6   **2.** 5.37
3. 0.0084   **4.** 0.4628
5. 2700   **6.** 0.00526
7. 1.83   **8.** 2.4
9. 0.038   **10.** 0.00005

Divide each of the numbers in Example 1 by 10, 100, and 1000.
Multiply each of the following numbers by 5 and by 25:

11. 384   **12.** 23760
13. 73519   **14.** 63.2
15. 347.06   **16.** 0.00052801

Multiply by a short method:

17. $(7\frac{1}{2})(7\frac{1}{2})$ **18.** $(11\frac{1}{2})(11\frac{1}{2})$
19. $(8.5)(8.5)$ **20.** $(23.5)(23.5)$
21. $(465)(465)$ **22.** $(2\frac{1}{2})(2\frac{1}{2})$
23. $(10\frac{1}{2})(10\frac{1}{2})$ **24.** $(9.5)(9.5)$
25. $(31.5)(31.5)$ **26.** $(635)(635)$

Simplify each of the following:

27. $\dfrac{240 \times 7.2 \times 0.36 \times 8.4}{4.8 \times 0.15 \times 168.96}$ **28.** $\dfrac{42 \times 62.5 \times 2.43 \times 0.7854}{2.64 \times 0.175 \times 270 \times 432}$

29. $\dfrac{3.1416 \times 6.45 \times 62.5 \times 8.8}{2.2 \times 1728 \times 31.5 \times 2.54}$ **30.** $\dfrac{6.28 \times 377 \times 60 \times 0.0128}{0.7854 \times 39.37 \times 62.4 \times 60}$

Exercise 3.6

Assume that measurements are approximate in all cases.

1. On an automobile trip a stop was made at each of the following towns, *A, B, C, D,* and *E.* The odometer showed the following readings:

at beginning of trip: 34,782.7   at town *C*: 34,884.5
at town *A*:   34,817.3   at town *D*: 34,942.8
at town *B*:   34,858.6   at town *E*: 35,006.1

Find each of the distances between the stops. What was the length of the entire trip? If the entire trip took 14.3 gal of gasoline, what was the average mileage per gallon? Find the cost of the gasoline used at 29.6 cents per gal.

2. A car travels the following distances on four successive days: Monday, 285.3 miles; Tuesday, 318.4 miles; Wednesday, 364.8 miles; and Thursday, 197.2 miles. Find the total number of miles traveled on the four days. What was the average number of miles per day? On the entire trip 76.2 gal of gasoline were used. What was the average mileage per gallon? Find the total cost of gasoline for the trip at 31.9 cents per gal.

3. Five chickens have the following weights, respectively: 2 lb, $7\frac{1}{2}$ oz; 2 lb, $9\frac{1}{4}$ oz; 2 lb, $13\frac{3}{4}$ oz; 3 lb, $1\frac{1}{2}$ oz; and 2 lb, $11\frac{3}{4}$ oz. Find the cost of each at 47 cents per lb.

4. The sides of a triangle are 7.3, 8.25, and 9.63 in., respectively. Find the perimeter of the triangle. (The perimeter is the distance around a figure.)

5. A rectangle has a length of 2.43 in. and a width of 1.82 in. Find its perimeter and its area.

6. A rectangular room is 21.35 ft long and 14.8 ft wide. What is the length of the molding required to reach around the room? How many square feet are there in the floor?

7. A square is 31.5 in. on a side. Find its perimeter and area.

8. Find the area and the perimeter of a room 18.8 ft long and 13.5 ft wide.

9. What must be the length of a rectangle 2.71 in. wide if it is to contain approximately 12 sq in.?

10. Three chickens weigh, respectively, $2\frac{3}{8}$, $3\frac{1}{4}$, and $2\frac{9}{16}$ lb. Change these weights to decimal fractions and then find the total weight of all three. What will be the cost of each at 47 cents per lb?

11. A beef roast weighs 4 lb, $10\frac{1}{2}$ oz. What will it cost at 85 cents per lb?

12. Two holes, one of them $\frac{7}{16}$ in. in diameter and the other $\frac{11}{32}$ in. in diameter, are to be drilled in a metal plate so that the distance between the holes is $4\frac{1}{4}$ in. Find the distance between the centers.

13. What is the total thickness of a pile of 12 metal sheets of iron, if each sheet is 0.045 in. thick?

14. A pile of 15 sheets of metal has a total thickness of 2.14 in. What is the approximate thickness of each sheet?

15. A copper wire has a diameter of 0.032 in. How many turns of the wire can be wound on a coil that is 3 in. long?

16. A piece of aluminum 4.625 in. long is cut from a strip 20 in. long. If the cut itself wastes 0.06 in., how long is the remaining strip?

17. Six strips of brass measuring, respectively, 3.275, 4.35, 2.625, 0.875, 5.125, and 4.6 in. are cut from a strip 32 in. long. How long a strip is left if 0.045 in. are wasted in each cut?

18. A strip of metal is cut into five strips of the following lengths, respectively: 4.25, 3.95, 7.3, 6.485, and 5.74 in. The waste for each cut is 0.035 in. How long was the original piece?

19. Five pieces, each measuring 1.375 in. long, are cut from a strip of silver alloy 12 in. long. If each cut wastes 0.018 in., what is the length of the remaining piece?

20. How many pieces, each 3.125 in. long, can be cut from a strip of brass if the waste for each cut is $\frac{1}{16}$ in. and the strip is 25 in. long?

21. A bar of copper is cut into 8 pieces, each $2\frac{7}{16}$ in. long. If each cut wastes $\frac{1}{32}$ in., find the length of the original bar.

22. Six pieces measuring, respectively, $2\frac{7}{16}$, $5\frac{1}{4}$, $6\frac{1}{2}$, $7\frac{5}{8}$, $3\frac{1}{8}$, and $3\frac{5}{16}$ in. are cut from a piece of aluminum, 30 in. long. If the waste is $\frac{3}{16}$ in. per cut, find the length of the remaining strip. Work first by common fractions and then by decimal fractions.

23. How many pieces, each 2.225 in. long, can be cut from a strip of brass 1 yd long if the waste is 0.04 in. per cut?

24. In May 1934 the CB&Q railroad made a record run from Denver to Chicago, a distance of 1015.31 miles, in 13 hr, 5 min, 44 sec. What was the average speed in miles per hour? What was the speed in feet per second?

25. In October of the year 1936 the CB&Q made the run from Chicago to Denver, a distance of 1017.23 miles, in 12 hr, 12 min, 27 sec. What was the average speed in miles per hour and feet per second?

26. In October 1934 the UP railroad made a record run of 9 miles in 4 min, 30 sec. What was the average speed in miles per hour and feet per second?

27. In 1966 the Burlington Zephyr had a scheduled run of 54.6 miles to be traversed in 43 min. What was the rate in miles per hour?

28. In May 1893 the New York Central made a run of 1 mile in 32 sec. What was the rate in miles per hour?

29. In June 1927 a Pennsylvania railroad train made a trip from Washington, D.C., to New York City, a distance of 224.5 miles, in 3 hr, 7 min. What was the average speed in miles per hour?

30. In July 1934 a Milwaukee railroad train made a trip of 61.4 miles in 39 min, 46 sec. Find its speed in miles per hour.

31. Charles Lindbergh made his historic flight from New York to Paris, a distance of 3610 miles, in 33 hr, 29 min, 30 sec in May 1927. What was his average speed in miles per hour?

32. In November 1957 Captain Sweet of the USAF flew from Los Angeles to New York and back to Los Angeles, a distance of 4891.8 miles, in 6 hr, 46 min, 36.23 sec. What was his average speed?

4

Percentage

4.1 DEFINITION

The expression *per cent* is so common in everyday speech that probably most adults know what is meant by "one hundred per cent," "50 per cent," or some other similar expression. The statement, "You are one hundred per cent right" means "You are completely right." When we say, "He lost 50 per cent of his money," we mean he lost half of it.

The words "per cent" mean "hundredths" or "by the hundred." The expression 25 per cent means "25 hundredths" or "25 out of every hundred." The symbol for per cent is %. When we say 25%, we mean "25 out of every hundred," $\frac{25}{100}$ as a common fraction, or 0.25 as a decimal. The expression 60% means $\frac{60}{100}$, or 0.60.

Note, especially in the example 25% that the number 25 by itself is a *whole* number, or integer; 25 alone is *not* a fraction. The expression becomes a fraction when we attach the per cent sign (%), as in 25%, when we place the denominator 100 below the 25, $\frac{25}{100}$, or when we place the decimal point before the 25, 0.25.

When we use the expression *per cent*, such as 25%, we always mean a part of *some quantity*. The expression 25% by itself means no particular quantity, such as dollars, pounds, or feet. The 25% is equivalent to the common fraction $\frac{1}{4}$. By itself, the fraction $\frac{1}{4}$ means nothing except as it is considered as the indicated part of some particular quantity. For instance, 25% of $48 means $\frac{25}{100}$ of $48, or $\frac{1}{4}$ of $48, which is $12.

4.2 RELATION BETWEEN PER CENTS AND FRACTIONS

In multiplication or division involving per cents it is first necessary to change the per cent to a decimal or common fraction before performing the multiplication or division. In most problems the decimal form is more convenient. On the other hand, in many examples, when we have found an answer in the form of a decimal or common fraction, we often wish to state it as a per cent. It is important, therefore, that we understand clearly the method of changing one

56

form of an expression to another form. The following rules and examples show how these changes are made.

Rule 1. *To change a per cent to a common fraction, omit the per cent sign (%) and write 100 below the number of per cent. Then reduce the fraction if possible.*

For instance, the expression 15% can be reduced as follows: $15\% = \frac{15}{100} = \frac{3}{20}$. The expression 20% is equal to the fraction $\frac{20}{100}$ or to 0.20. The value can be reduced to lower terms as in any fraction: $20\% = \frac{20}{100} = \frac{1}{5}$.

Examples.

$$25\% = \frac{25}{100} = \frac{1}{4} \qquad\qquad 0.5\% = \frac{0.5}{100} = \frac{5}{1000} = \frac{1}{200}$$

$$63\% = \frac{63}{100} \qquad\qquad 125\% = \frac{125}{100} = 1\tfrac{1}{4}$$

$$5\% = \frac{5}{100} = \frac{1}{20} \qquad\qquad 200\% = \frac{200}{100} = 2$$

$$1\% = \frac{1}{100} \qquad\qquad 12\tfrac{1}{2}\% = \frac{12\tfrac{1}{2}}{100} = \frac{25}{200} = \frac{1}{8}$$

Rule 2. *To change a per cent to a decimal, move the decimal point two places toward the left and then omit the per cent sign.*

It is easy to see that this rule is reasonable if we first change the per cent to a common fraction.

Examples.

$$47\% = \frac{47}{100} = 0.47 \qquad\qquad 142\% = \frac{142}{100} = 1.42$$

$$8\% = \frac{8}{100} = 0.08 \qquad\qquad 3.25\% = \frac{3.25}{100} = \frac{325}{10000} = 0.0325$$

$$3.4\% = \frac{3.4}{100} = \frac{34}{1000} = 0.034 \qquad\qquad 0.02\% = \frac{0.02}{100} = \frac{2}{10000} = 0.0002$$

Rule 3. *To change a decimal fraction to per cent, move the decimal point two places to the right and annex the per cent sign (%).* A common fraction can be changed first to a decimal fraction and the result changed to per cent.

Examples.

$0.32 = 32\%$	$0.0625 = 6.25\%$	$7.5 = 750\%$
$0.415 = 41.5\%$	$0.0001 = 0.01\%$	$10 = 1000\%$
$0.007 = 0.7\%$	$1.75 = 175\%$	$0.14\tfrac{2}{7} = 14\tfrac{2}{7}\%$
$\dfrac{3}{4} = 0.75 = 75\%$	$\dfrac{5}{16} = 0.3125 = 31.25\%$	$\dfrac{1}{32} = 0.03125 = 3.125\%$

Exercise 4.1

Change the following per cents to common fractions or mixed numbers and to decimal form:

1. 35%	**2.** 48%	**3.** $4\frac{3}{8}\%$	**4.** 7%
5. $\frac{1}{8}\%$	**6.** 10%	**7.** $37\frac{1}{2}\%$	**8.** $162\frac{3}{4}\%$
9. $14\frac{2}{7}\%$	**10.** 450%	**11.** 175%	**12.** 95%
13. 1000%	**14.** $3\frac{1}{5}\%$	**15.** $33\frac{1}{3}\%$	**16.** $\frac{1}{4}\%$
17. $1\frac{7}{8}\%$	**18.** $\frac{1}{16}\%$	**19.** $1\frac{1}{3}\%$	**20.** $5\frac{1}{4}\%$

Change the following common fractions, mixed numbers, and decimals to per cents:

21. $\frac{4}{5}$	**22.** $\frac{3}{16}$	**23.** $\frac{7}{64}$	**24.** $\frac{15}{32}$
25. $5\frac{5}{8}$	**26.** $1\frac{3}{25}$	**27.** 0.025	**28.** 0.0015
29. 1.453	**30.** 2.3	**31.** $\frac{2}{3}$	**32.** $\frac{4}{11}$
33. $3\frac{5}{9}$	**34.** 1.04	**35.** 5.1	**36.** $1\frac{35}{128}$
37. 0.0005	**38.** 0.075	**39.** 0.6	**40.** 2 .

4.3 RATE, BASE, PERCENTAGE

In a problem involving per cent three quantities must always be considered. These three quantities are called the *rate*, the *base*, and the *percentage*, respectively. In order to see the relation between these three quantities, consider the example 25% of $48 = $12. In this statement, 25% is called the *rate*, $48 is called the *base*, and $12 is called the *percentage*. The statement means one quarter of $48 = $12.

In any percentage statement the rate is the indicated fractional part of a particular quantity. As such, the rate is equivalent to a common or decimal fraction. The base is the number of which a fractional part is taken. The base usually has a name or denomination of some kind, such as dollars, objects, or measurements, such as feet or pounds.

The foregoing example can be stated by using a decimal fraction in place of *per cent* for the rate. Thus the statement 25% of $48 = $12 can be written

$$0.25 \times \$48 = \$12$$

From this example notice that the general percentage statement may be given as

$$\text{rate} \times \text{base} = \text{percentage}$$

Note especially that the *percentage* is a *product* and that the *rate* and the *base* are *factors* multiplied together. Whenever we know the two factors in any problem in multiplication, we multiply them together to form the product. Whenever we know the product and one of the factors, we can find the other factor by dividing the product by the known factor. For instance, if we know the two factors are 5 and 7, we can find the product by multiplying

5 and 7 together. The product is 35. If we know the product of two factors is 91 and one of the factors is 7, we can find the other factor by dividing 91, the product, by 7, the known factor. The other factor is 91 ÷ 7, which is 13.

4.4 FINDING THE PERCENTAGE WHEN THE RATE AND THE BASE ARE KNOWN

If the rate and the base are given, we have a problem in which the two factors are known and the product (the percentage) is to be found. If two factors are known, their product is found by multiplying the factors together. Therefore, we have the following rule:

Rule 4. *To find the percentage when the rate and the base are given, multiply the base by the rate.*
The rule may be stated as

$$\text{percentage} = \text{rate} \times \text{base}$$

The percentage has the same name or denomination as the base. We have said that 100% means $\frac{100}{100}$, or all of a particular quantity. If the rate is equal to 1 (that is, 100%), then the percentage is equal to the base. If the rate is less than 1 (that is, less than 100%), then the percentage is less than the base. If the rate is more than 1 (that is, more than 100%), then the percentage is more than the base. These three different conditions are illustrated in the following examples. Remember, rate × base = percentage.

Example 1. 100% of 80 lb = 1.00 × 80 lb = 80 lb

Example 2. 25% of 80 ft = 0.25 × 80 ft = 20 ft

Example 3. 150% of $80 = 1.5 × $80 = $120

4.5 FINDING THE RATE WHEN THE BASE AND THE PERCENTAGE ARE KNOWN

If we know the base and the percentage, we have a problem in which the product of two factors is known. The product is the percentage. One of the factors is the base. The part to be found is the other factor, which is the rate. We must then divide the product (the percentage) by the known factor (the base). Therefore, we have the following rule.

Rule 5. *To find the rate when the base and the percentage are given, divide the percentage by the base.* The rule may be stated as

$$\text{rate} = \text{percentage} \div \text{base}$$

As an example showing the use of this rule, suppose we have the following problem: a man earns $6000 a year and spends $1170 of it for food. What part or per cent of his income does he spend for food?

In this problem the rate is unknown. The regular percentage statement takes the following form: rate × base = percentage. What rate × $6000 = $1170?

Now we are to find the rate to be used so that the base multiplied by this rate will equal $1170. Here we have given the percentage, $1170, which is the *product* of two factors. One of the factors is the base, $6000. Therefore, in this problem we divide the product, $1170, by the known factor, $6000.

$$\$1170 \div \$6000 = 0.195$$

The quotient, 0.195, is the other factor, or the rate. We can check the answer by the question: does 0.195 × $6000 = $1170? If we perform the multiplication, we find the statement is true. Since the problem calls for the answer in per cent, we change the decimal 0.195 to 19.5%.

If a quantity changes by an increase or a decrease over any period of time, the question arises as to which value should be taken as the base. In computing the rate of increase or decrease, the base is usually taken as the original quantity in point of time. For example, if the population of a town increases from 4000 to 5000, the increase is 1000. To find the rate of increase, we use the original population, 4000, as the base. The rate of increase is then 25%; that is, $1000 \div 4000 = 0.25$. However, if the population decreases from 5000 to 4000, the decrease is 1000, but the rate of decrease is only 20%, that is, $1000 \div 5000 = 0.20$.

If an article cost $12 and is sold for $18, the gain is $6. To find the rate of gain, we take $6 \div 12 = 0.50$, or 50%. However, if the article cost $18 and is sold for $12, the loss is $6, but the rate of loss is $33\frac{1}{3}\%$, that is, $6 \div 18 = 0.3333$. In business dealings, it is true that gains and losses are often computed on the selling price as a base. Yet as a general rule, the rate of increase or decrease should be based on the first number in point of time.

4.6 FINDING THE BASE WHEN THE RATE AND THE PERCENTAGE ARE KNOWN

A third type of problem involves finding the base when the rate and the percentage are given in the problem. Here, again, we have the product, as well as one of the factors. The other factor, the base, is to be found. The problem requires that we divide the known product (percentage) by the known factor (rate). Therefore, we have the following rule:

Rule 6.   *To find the base when the rate and the percentage are given, divide the percentage by the rate.* The rule may be stated as

$$\text{base} = \text{percentage} \div \text{rate}$$

As an example showing the use of this rule, suppose we have the following problem: a man spends $1018, or 17.2% of his income, for rent. What is his income?

In this problem the base is unknown. In the regular percentage statement, rate × base = percentage, we have

$$17.2\% \text{ of income} = \$1018$$

or, as a decimal,

$$0.172 \times \text{income} = \$1018$$

To find the unknown factor, the income, we divide the percentage, $1018, by the known factor, the rate, which is 0.172. Thus

$$\$1018 \div 0.172 = \$5918.60$$

The answer, $5918.60, is his income, or the base.

In a problem of this kind, the answer is rounded off, since it does not come out even when the division is performed. The answer, therefore, is approximate. However, it should be remembered that it is not his income itself that is approximate. His income is an exact number of dollars and cents. The same is true with regard to the amount spent for rent. That amount is exact. The part of the problem that is approximate is the rate, 0.172.

Probably the greatest difficulty is in identifying the rate, the base, and the percentage. Here are three statements that might be remembered as a help in working percentage problems:

(1) The percentage is a product of two factors. Therefore, whenever the percentage is given, the process will be division; that is, the percentage must be divided by the given factor.

(2) The base and the percentage have the same name or denomination, such as dollars, feet, miles, pounds, objects, or quantities of any kind.

(3) The rate has no name or denomination but is simply an indicated part to be taken of some quantity. The rate may be over 100%.

One way to identify the base is to answer the question: in this problem we are dealing with a *part of* WHAT? The answer to the question WHAT? will usually be the base.

Exercise 4.2

Find the unknown part in each of the following statements:

1. 15% of $84 =

2. 25% of ____ = $16

3. ____% of $520 = $195

4. 132% of 15 lb =

5. 62.5% of 80 miles =

6. 7,654,000 people is ____% of 178,000,000 people

7. 0.0016 in. is ____% of 1.32 in.   **8.** 145% of ____ = $812

9. $60 is ____% of $48   **10.** $42\frac{1}{2}$% of ____ = $40.63

11. During one year a family received an income of $6500 and spent the following rates of it for the items mentioned. Find the amount spent for each item.

Food	19%	Medical expense	8.6%
Housing	18%	Insurance and savings	13%
Utilities	15%	Travel	6.3%
Clothing	10.4%	Miscellaneous	the remainder

12. A family receiving an income of $7400 during one year spent the amount indicated for each of the following items. Find the rate of the total income that was spent on each item.

Food	$1400	Medical expense	$640
Housing	1350	Insurance and savings	1050
Utilities	1030	Travel and amusement	650
Clothing	720	Miscellaneous the remainder	

13. One year the population census of a town was 32,400. The following year the population had increased by 6.5%. What was the population after the increase?

14. One year the population census of a town was 155,000. A year later it had decreased by 4.2%. What was the population after the decrease?

15. The population of a certain town was 48,000. A year later it had increased by 2300. What was the rate of increase and the population a year later?

16. During one year the population of a town decreased by 3100. If the original population was 65,000, what was the rate of decrease and what was the population after the decrease?

17. What is the rate of increase when the population increases from 30,000 to 40,000?

18. What is the rate of decrease when the population decreases from 40,000 to 30,000?

19. An article was bought for $48 and sold at a gain of 25%. What was the gain and the selling price?

20. An article was bought for $60 and sold at a loss of 20%. What was the loss and the selling price?

21. Find the rate of gain or loss for each of the following:
   (a) An article bought for $120 and sold for $135.
   (b) An article bought for $135 and sold for $120.

22. The price of a stock rose from $85 to $88. What was the rate of increase?

23. Find rate of decrease when the price of stock decreases from $88 to $85.

24. A baseball player's batting average for a season was 0.289. How many hits did he make if he had 429 official times at bat?

25. A baseball player made 154 hits in 506 official times at bat. What was his batting average?

26. Which of the following has a higher batting average? *A* who had 172 hits in 532 times at bat or *B* who had 118 hits in 344 times at bat?

27. After a man's weight had increased by 4.5% he weighed 167.2 lb. What was his weight before the increase?

28. A bar of iron expanded in length from 62.4 to 62.402 in. What was the per cent of expansion?

29. After an increase in salary of $7\frac{1}{2}\%$, a man received a salary of $7310. What was his salary before the increase?

5

The Metric System of Measurement

5.1 DEFINITION

The metric system of measurement is a decimal system; that is, the system is based upon the number 10, just as our number system itself is based on 10. To change the size of the units in the metric system, all we need to do is to move the decimal point to the right or left.

In order to understand the importance of such an arrangement, let us imagine what we might do if there were 10 in. in 1 ft, 10 ft in 1 yd, 10 yd in 1 rd, 10 rd in 1 furlong, and 10 furlongs in 1 mile.

35,672 in. could be changed to
3567.2 ft
356.72 yd
35.672 rd
3.5672 furlongs
0.35672 miles

Instead, in our present method, called the English system, we must perform the following divisions:

$$35,672 \div 12 = 2972.667 \quad \text{number of feet}$$
$$2972,667 \div 3 = 990.889 \quad \text{number of yards}$$
$$990.889 \div 5.5 = 180.16 \quad \text{number of rods}$$
$$180.16 \div 40 = 4.504 \quad \text{number of furlongs}$$
$$4.504 \div 8 = 0.563 \quad \text{number of miles}$$

5.2 ORIGIN OF METRIC SYSTEM

Our common English system of measurements grew up piece by piece without any definite plan. As a result there was no attempt to make it easy to convert one kind of division into another. The metric system, instead, was planned as a complete system. It was devised and set up in France in 1789 at the time of the French Revolution. At that time, the French decided to make a completely new start in setting up a logical system of measurements.

The foot measurement had originally come from a length in some way related to that of a man's foot. Instead, the French decided to start out with some measurement that was fixed in nature and not so variable as men's feet. They decided to take as a unit of length one ten-millionth of the distance from the equator to the north pole. This distance was to be the primary unit and was called one *meter* (m), meaning *measure*. The distance chosen for this length is equal to 39.37 inches in the English system, although later calculations showed that this length is not exactly one ten-millionth of the distance from the equator to the north pole. However, the relation between the English system and the metric system has been established by law, so that now

$$1 \text{ m} = 39.37 \text{ in.}$$

The meter is therefore a little longer than the English yard of 36 inches. If you have never seen a meter stick, remember that it is a little longer than a yard stick. One good way to remember a measurement of any kind is to *see* it. Measure off a distance of about $39\frac{2}{5}$ inches, and you will get an idea of the length of one meter.

5.3 UNITS OF THE METRIC SYSTEM

In the metric system all measurements of length, area, volume, and even weight are based upon the primary unit, the *meter* (m). The meter is divided into smaller divisions but not by dividing it into twelve parts as we do in the English system to change 1 foot to 12 inches. Instead, the divisions in the metric system are in *tenths*. The primary unit of length, the meter, is divided into ten parts. Each part is $\frac{1}{10}$ of a meter. The word for tenth is "deci." In fact, the word *decimal* itself means *one tenth*. Therefore, a length $\frac{1}{10}$ of a meter is called a *decimeter* (dm). A decimeter (Fig. 5.1) is equal to 3.937 inches, or approximately 4 inches.

The decimeter is further divided into ten parts. Each part, about $\frac{2}{5}$ of an inch, is called a *centimeter* (cm). The prefix "centi" means one one-hundredth.

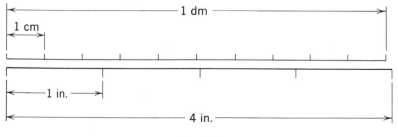

Fig. 5.1

In fact, the word for our coin, the *cent*, means $\frac{1}{100}$ of a dollar. One centimeter is $\frac{1}{100}$ of a meter, or 0.3937 inch, which is approximately $\frac{2}{5}$ of an inch. In other words, 1 inch equals approximately $2\frac{1}{2}$ centimeters. More accurately,

$$1 \text{ in.} = 2.54 \text{ cm (approximately)}$$

The centimeter is therefore a rather small measurement. However, it is much used in scientific work.

The centimeter is further divided into ten divisions, each division called *millimeter* (mm). The prefix "milli" means one one-thousandth. The millimeter is therefore $\frac{1}{1000}$ of a meter. It is a very small measurement, approximately $\frac{1}{25}$ of an inch.

In actual practice it always happens that some units of measurement are used more than others. For instance, the decimeter is not often used. Instead, the centimeter and the millimeter have quite common usage in our everyday speech. A 35-mm camera film is a film that is 35 millimeters wide. The sizes, 8 mm and 16 mm, are also used to refer to the width of films. The bores of cannon and of smaller firearms are often stated in terms of the metric system. An 8-mm rifle has approximately the same bore, or calibre, as a "30-30." A 150-mm cannon is a 6-inch gun.

In the explanation of the metric system up to this point we started with the primary unit, the meter, and moved toward smaller and smaller units, the decimeter, the centimeter, and down to the smallest, the millimeter. Now we shall move toward larger measurements.

A distance of 10 meters is called 1 *decameter* (dkm), sometimes spelled *dekameter*. (The prefix "deca" means *ten*.) A decameter is a distance of about 32.8 feet. A distance of 10 decameters is called 1 *hectometer* (hkm). (The prefix "hecto" means 100.) A hectometer is equal to 100 meters. The decameter and the hectometer are not much used in everyday speech. For instance, a sprint of 1 hectometer is called the "hundred-meter dash."

A distance of 10 hectometers is called 1 *kilometer* (km). (The prefix "kilo" means 1000.) A kilometer is equal to 1000 meters, or approximately $\frac{5}{8}$ of a mile.

The following table is a summary of the relations between the units of length in the metric system:

10 millimeters (mm)	= 1 centimeter (cm)
10 cm	= 1 decimeter (dm)
10 dm	= 1 meter (m)
10 m	= 1 decameter (dkm)
10 dkm	= 1 hectometer (hkm)
10 hkm	= 1 kilometer (km)
100 cm	= 1 m

$$1000 \text{ mm} = 1 \text{ m}$$
$$1 \text{ cm} = \tfrac{1}{100} \text{ m}$$
$$1 \text{ mm} = \tfrac{1}{1000} \text{ m}$$

Notice especially the meaning of these prefixes:

deci means $\tfrac{1}{10}$ *deca* means 10
centi means $\tfrac{1}{100}$ *hecto* means 100
milli means $\tfrac{1}{1000}$ *kilo* means 1000
micro means $\tfrac{1}{1000000}$ *mega* means 1,000,000

that is,

1 decimeter $= \tfrac{1}{10} \text{ m}$ 1 decameter $= 10 \text{ m}$
1 centimeter $= \tfrac{1}{100} \text{ m}$ 1 hectometer $= 100 \text{ m}$
1 millimeter $= \tfrac{1}{1000} \text{ m}$ 1 kilometer $= 1000 \text{ m}$
1 micron $= \tfrac{1}{1000000} \text{ m}$ 1 megameter $= 1000000 \text{ m}$

In order to change measurements from English to metric and metric to English units, we use chiefly these conversion facts:

$$1 \text{ m} = 39.37 \text{ in.}$$
$$1 \text{ in.} = 2.54 \text{ cm (approximately)}$$
$$1 \text{ km} = 0.621 \text{ mile (or approximately } \tfrac{5}{8} \text{ mile)}$$

In order to see the convenience of the metric system, consider the following example. Suppose we start with 1647832 millimeters.

$$1647832 \text{ mm} = 164783.2 \text{ cm}$$
$$= 16478.32 \text{ dm}$$
$$= 1647.832 \text{ m}$$
$$= 164.7832 \text{ dkm}$$
$$= 16.47832 \text{ hkm}$$
$$= 1.647832 \text{ km}$$

In this example the easiest conversion to the English system is by the use of the relation

$$1 \text{ m} = 39.37 \text{ in.}$$

To change 1647832 mm to English units, we first express the measurement in meters, 1647.832. Then we multiply by 39.37:

$$(1647.832)(39.37) = 64875.14584 \text{ in.}$$
$$= 64875 \text{ in.}$$
$$= 5406\tfrac{1}{4} \text{ ft}$$

Example. What is the difference in length between 60 meters and 200 feet?

Solution. The problem may be worked in several ways, and the answer may be stated in any units desired.

Let us change both measurements to inches.

$$60\,m = (60)(39.37\,in.) = 2362.20\,in.$$
$$200\,ft = (200)(12\,in.) \quad = 2400\,in.$$

The difference in length is

$$2400 - 2362.2 = 37.8\,in.$$

The answer, 37.8 in., can be changed to feet or centimeters or meters.

$$37.8 \div 12 = 3.15\,ft$$
$$(37.8)(2.54) = 96.012\,cm$$
$$= 0.96012\,m$$

One important fact here is that the difference in length between 60 m and 200 ft is fixed. The difference in length does not change regardless of whether it is expressed in inches, feet, centimeters or meters.*

Exercise 5.1

Change each of the following given linear measurements to the form indicated. Carry decimals out to a reasonable degree.

1. 34 in. to centimeters

2. 93 cm to inches

3. 268 m to feet

4. 24.3 ft to meters

5. 32.2 ft to centimeters

6. 36.4 in. to millimeters

7. 2.32 miles to meters

8. 42.1 yd to meters

9. 5.32 ft to centimeters

10. 15.3 in. to millimeters

11. 15,200 ft to meters

12. 4000 m to yards

13. 23.5 mils to inches

14. $16\frac{1}{2}$ ft to centimeters

Exercise 5.2

1. A man is 5 ft $11\frac{3}{4}$ in. tall. State his height in centimeters.

2. A rectangular mirror is 26 in. wide and 6 ft long. State its length and width in centimeters.

* The smallest practical unit of length in the English system is the *mil*, which is equal to $\frac{1}{1000}$ of an inch. This paper has a thickness of approximately 3 mils. The mil is often used in stating the measurement of the diameters of wires. A diameter of 0.0264 inch is the same as a diameter of 26.4 mils.

The smallest unit of length used in science is the *Angstrom* (A). This unit, named after Knut Ångstrom, a Swedish scientist, is equal to one ten-millionth of a millimeter. The Angstrom is used chiefly in stating the length of light waves and other extremely short waves. For example, the length of a wave of yellow light is approximately 0.00058 mm, or 5800 Angstroms.

The largest unit of length is the *parsec*. A parsec is approximately the distance light will travel in 3.258 years at a rate of 186,000 miles per second. The distance to the nearest star is a little more than 1 parsec. The North Star, Polaris, is a little more than 200 parsecs from the earth.

3. A certain camera has an 80-mm lens. How many inches is this?
4. If a ball is dropped and falls without any interference, it will fall approximately 490 cm in the first second. Change this distance to feet.
5. The world's tallest television tower is approximately 490.7 m high. Find its height in feet.
6. A certain camera takes pictures of a size stated as 5.72 cm by 8.26 cm. Change these measurements to inches.
7. A family on a vacation trip drove 210.6 miles one day. How many kilometers is this?
8. A golf drive was 173 yd. Change this measurement to meters.
9. A baseball player hit an "inside-the-park" home run. The ball hit the surrounding wall 415 ft from home plate. How many meters was this?
10. One race in the Olympic Games is the 5000-m run. How many feet is this? How many miles?
11. A football player's average advance of the ball "per carry" for one season was 4.12 m. How many yards was this?
12. A paper clip is made of wire 0.036 in. in diameter. How many mils is this? How many millimeters?
13. The thickness of some sheet metal is 0.0125 in. State the thickness in mils and in millimeters.
14. Change the following speeds to feet per second and meters per second: 15 mph; 30 mph; 45 mph; 60 mph; 80 mph.
15. An airplane flies at a height of 2.35 miles. What is the height in feet?
16. A record parachute jump made by Captain Kittinger, USAF, was approximately 76,400 ft. Change this to miles and kilometers.

5.4 SQUARE MEASURE

By a square foot we mean the amount of area contained in a square 1 foot long and 1 foot wide (Fig. 5.2). A square inch is the area equal to a square that is 1 inch long and 1 inch wide.

In order to find the number of square inches in 1 square foot, we lay off the square inch as many times as possible on the square foot of area. Since there are 12 inches in 1 foot, we shall have 12 square inches in 1 row and exactly 12 rows. Therefore, we have

$$1 \text{ sq ft} = 12 \times 12 \text{ sq in.} = 144 \text{ sq in.}$$

This is sometimes written

$$1 \text{ ft}^2 = 12^2 \text{ in.}^2$$

The exponent 2 on 12 means that 12 is *squared*, that is, multiplied by itself. To indicate square inches we can write "in.^{2}" In the same way

1 yd = 3 ft;	$1 \text{ yd}^2 = 3^2 \text{ ft}^2$;	or	1 sq yd = 9 sq ft
1 rd = 16.5 ft;	$1 \text{ rd}^2 = (16.5)^2 \text{ ft}^2$;	or	1 sq rd = 272.25 sq ft

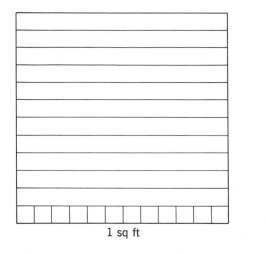

1 sq ft   1 sq in.

Fig. 5.2

In the metric system we have

1 dm = 10 cm;	1 dm² = 10² cm²,	or	1 sq dm = 100 sq cm

1 dm = 10 cm;   1 dm² = 10² cm²,   or   1 sq dm = 100 sq cm

1 cm = 10 mm;   1 cm² = 10² mm²,   or   1 sq cm = 100 sq mm

1 m   = 100 cm;   1 m² = 100² cm²,   or   1 sq m = 10000 sq cm

1 m   = 1000 mm;   1 *m²* = 1000² mm²,   or   1 sq m = 1000000 sq mm

In converting square measure in the metric system to the English system, we use the same reasoning:

1 in. = 2.54 cm;   1 in.² = (2.54)² cm²,   or   1 sq in. = 6.4516 sq cm

1 m   = 39.37 in.;   1 m² = (39.37)² in.²,   or   1 sq m = 1550.1 sq in.

Example 1.   Find the perimeter in centimeters and the area in square centimeters of a sheet of paper 11 in. long and 8.5 in. wide.

Solution.   The width and the length can first be changed to centimeters:

$$(11)(2.54 \text{ cm}) = 27.94 \text{ cm} \quad \text{length}$$
$$(8.5)(2.54 \text{ cm}) = 21.59 \text{ cm} \quad \text{width}$$

The perimeter is found by adding the two sides and the two ends together:

$$(2)(27.94 \text{ cm}) = 55.88 \text{ cm}$$
$$(2)(21.59 \text{ cm}) = \underline{43.18 \text{ cm}}$$
$$99.06 \text{ cm} \quad \text{perimeter}$$

To find the area, we multiply the length by the width:

$$(27.94 \text{ cm})(21.59 \text{ cm}) = 603.2246 \text{ cm}^2$$
$$= 603.2 \text{ cm}^2 \quad \text{(rounded off)}$$

To check the work, we first find perimeter and area in English units:

$$\text{perimeter} = 2(11) + 2(8.5) = 39 \text{ in.}$$

Now we multiply the number of centimeters in 1 inch by 39:

$$(39)(2.54 \text{ cm}) = 99.06 \text{ cm}$$

This number, 99.06 cm, checks with the first method.

To check the area, we multiply the length by the width in inches:

$$(11 \text{ in.})(8.5 \text{ in.}) = 93.5 \text{ in.}^2$$

To convert 93.5 square inches to square centimeters, we use the relation

$$1 \text{ sq in.} = 6.45 \text{ sq cm}$$

Multiplying,

$$(93.5)(6.45 \text{ cm}^2) = 603.075 \text{ cm}^2$$

The answer checks with the first method to three significant digits. This is the greatest accuracy that can be expected when we use the number 6.45 instead of 6.4516 for the number of square centimeters in 1 square inch.

In order to change square inches to square centimeters, we must use the multiplier $(2.54)^2$ or 6.45. If, in the foregoing example, we first change the length and width to centimeters, we multiply *each* of the two given measurements by 2.54. This multiplication is equivalent to multiplying by 2.54 *twice*, or by $(2.54)^2$. The length is $(11)(2.54)$ cm and the width is $(8.5)(2.54)$ cm. The area becomes

$$(11)(2.54)(8.5)(2.54) = 603 \quad \text{(rounded off)}$$

If we first find the area in square inches and then convert to square centimeters, we have

$$(11)(8.5)(2.54)^2 = 603$$

Notice that the multiplication in both cases involves the same factors.

In order to convert centimeters to inches, we use the conversion factor 2.54, but we must *divide* instead of multiply. For instance, to change 47 centimeters to inches, we divide by 2.54.

$$47 \div 2.54 = 18.5$$

Therefore,
$$47 \text{ cm} = 18.5 \text{ in.}$$

Example 2. A sheet of paper is 32.3 cm long and 24.6 cm wide. How many square inches does it contain?

Solution. This problem can be worked in two different ways. We can first express the measurements in inches and then find the area. To convert centimeters to inches, we must *divide* by 2.54.

$$32.3 \div 2.54 = 12.716 \text{ in.}$$
$$24.6 \div 2.54 = 9.685 \text{ in.}$$

If the numbers representing inches are rounded off to three significant digits, they become 12.7 and 9.69, respectively. To find the area, we multiply the length by the width.

$$(12.7 \text{ in.})(9.69 \text{ in.}) = 123.063 \text{ in.}^2$$
$$= 123 \text{ sq in.} \quad (\text{rounded off})$$

If we first multiply the length by the width expressed in centimeters, we get

$$(24.6 \text{ cm})(32.3 \text{ cm}) = 794.58 \text{ cm}^2$$

The area in square centimeters can be expressed in square inches by dividing the number of square centimeters by $(2.54)^2$, or 6.45.

$$794.58 \div 6.45 = 123.19 \text{ sq in.}$$

The area is, therefore, 123 sq in. (rounded off to three places).

The entire five-digit answer in the second case does not equal exactly the five-digit answer obtained by the first method, since the numbers used were rounded off to three significant digits. Numbers rounded off to three digits cannot be certain to produce results that are accurate to more than three significant digits.

5.5 CUBIC MEASURE

The relations between measures of volume are similar to the relations between measures of area. For volumes we take the *cubes* of linear units.

1 ft $= 12$ in.; $\quad$ 1 ft^3 $= 12^3$ in.^{3}, $\qquad$ or $\qquad$ 1 cu ft $= 1728$ cu in.

1 in. $= 2.54$ cm; $\quad$ 1 in.$^3 = (2.54)^3$ cm^3, $\quad$ or $\qquad$ 1 cu in. $= 16.387$ cu cm

Note. In chemistry, medicine, or liquid measurement the abbreviation for cubic centimeter is often "cc." One thousand cubic centimeters (1000 cc) is called one *liter* and is approximately one quart.

Example. What is the volume in cubic centimeters of a rectangular container 6 in. long, 5.5 in. wide, and 4 in. high?

Solution. We could first express each measurement in centimeters and then multiply the three measurements together. However, the work is probably simpler if we first find the volume in cubic inches.

$$(6 \text{ in.})(5.5 \text{ in.})(4 \text{ in.}) = 132 \text{ in.}^3$$
$$(132)(16.387 \text{ cu cm}) = 2163.084 \text{ cu cm}$$
$$= 2160 \text{ cu cm} \quad (\text{rounded off to three significant digits})$$

Exercise 5.3

1. A sheet of writing paper is 10.5 in. long and 8 in. wide. Find its area in square centimeters.
2. A picture measures 68.2 cm long and 46.3 cm wide. Change these measurements to inches and then find the area of the picture in square inches.
3. A rectangular tablecloth is $54\frac{3}{8}$ in. long and $34\frac{1}{2}$ in. wide. How many square centimeters are in its area?
4. A rectangular lawn is 72.25 ft long and 48.5 ft wide. Find the number of square meters in its area.
5. A building lot is 124 ft long and 52.5 ft wide. What is its area in square meters? How long a fence will it take to enclose the lot on all sides?
6. One acre contains 160 sq rd, and 1 rd is equal to 16.5 ft. How many square feet are there in 1 acre? How many square meters?
7. One *hectare* is the name given to an area equal to 10,000 sq m. How much more or less than 1 acre is 1 hectare?
8. A square table top measures 3 ft, 8 in. on a side. How many square centimeters are there in the area?
9. A chalk box has the following inside measurements: length, 5.8 in.; width, 3.9 in.; height, 3.4 in. How many cubic centimeters does it hold?
10. A suitcase has the following inside measurements: length, 72.4 cm; width, 47.2 cm; height, 18.5 cm. What is its volume in cubic centimeters?

5.6 METRIC SYSTEM OF WEIGHTS

In the English system the primary unit of weight is the *pound*. From this primary unit we get the ounce, which is $\frac{1}{16}$ of a pound, and the ton, which is equal to 2000 pounds.

In the metric system the primary unit of weight is the gram. The gram is a very small weight compared with the pound. It is equal approximately to $\frac{1}{30}$ of an ounce. For much ordinary measurement of weight, the gram is too small. Instead, a more convenient unit is the kilogram (kg), which is equal to 1000 grams. A kilogram is equal to approximately 2.2 pounds. Five kilograms of flour is approximately 11 pounds.

The gram can be changed into other units in the metric system in the same way as the meter is changed, that is, by multiplying or dividing by 10 or some power of 10. We have already mentioned the kilogram, which is equal to 1000 grams. One important small unit much used in chemistry, medicine, and other scientific fields is the milligram, which is equal to $\frac{1}{1000}$ of a gram.

The most common conversion factor between the English system and the metric system of weight is the relation

$$1 \text{ kg} = 2.2 \text{ lb (very nearly)}$$

To change kilograms to pounds, multiply the number of kilograms by 2.2.
To change pounds to kilograms, divide the number of pounds by 2.2.

For greater accuracy, we may use

1 gram = 0.03527 ounce; 1 kilogram = 2.2046 pounds

In our common English system of measurements* there is no relation between units of weight and units of length. For instance, there is no relation between one pound of weight and one foot of length. However, in the metric system there is such a relation. One gram of weight in the metric system is defined as the weight of one cubic centimeter of pure water at a temperature of 4 degrees Celsius, which is approximately 39 degrees Fahrenheit. At this particular temperature, water has its greatest density. In other words, at this temperature, a given volume of water has the greatest weight. A given weight of water occupies the least amount of space. At temperatures above or below this point water expands.

Exercise 5.4

1. A sheet of paper is $8\frac{1}{2}$ in. long and 5 in. wide. Find its area and perimeter in convenient metric measurements.
2. An envelope is 24.1 cm long and 10.6 cm wide. Find its area in square inches.
3. A house is 46 ft long and 28 ft wide. What are the dimensions in meters?

What is the difference between

4. 100 yd and 100 m?
5. 36 cm and 15 in.?
6. 80 m and 250 ft?
7. 1 km and $\frac{5}{8}$ mile?
8. 0.32 in. and 9 mm?
9. 6 sq in. and 40 sq cm?
10. 5 sq miles and 13 sq km?
11. 15 lb and 6 kg?
12. 3 oz and 80 grams?
13. 1 sq yd and 1 sq m?
14. 1 liter and 1 liquid qt (231 cu in. in 1 gal)?

Change the following weights to metric measurements:

15. 5 lb sugar
16. 10 lb flour
17. 2 lb candy
18. 25 lb potatoes
19. 3 lb butter
20. 1 lb coffee

* Some people have wondered why the units of measurement in the metric system are so extremely different in size. For instance, the primary unit of length, the *meter*, is much larger compared with the English *foot*. The size makes the unit inconvenient in much measurement in everyday life outside of scientific study. One could not conveniently carry a meter stick in his pocket as one might a foot rule. On the other hand, the primary unit of weight, the gram, is so small compared with the pound that it is too small for use in weighing many common everyday articles. For instance, one could not conveniently buy flour or sugar or coffee by the gram. The inconvenience of the size of the primary units may be one reason for the reluctance of many people to accept the system.

21. 1 lb, 10 oz salt

22. A 5-lb, $7\frac{1}{2}$-oz roast

23. A 16-lb shot

24. A 3200-lb car

25. A 180-lb man

26. What is your weight in kilograms and your height in centimeters?

Change the following measurements to convenient metric measurements:

27. 43.2 ft

28. 8.32 in.

29. 694.6 ft

30. $\frac{5}{16}$ in.

31. 3.42 miles

32. 156.4 yd

33. "A ten-foot pole"

34. "A yard wide"

35. "A grain of salt"
(1 lb = 16 oz = 7000 grains)

36. "An ounce of prevention"

37. "A pound of cure"

38. "I'd walk a mile"

39. "I'll not budge an inch"

40. "A ten-gallon hat"

41. "A fifty-yard dash"

Change these metric measurements to some convenient English measurement:

42. 13.8 cm

43. 12.7 m

44. 17.2 km

45. 4.8 dm

46. 9.2 mm

47. 100 m

48. 1500 m

49. 5000 m

50. 15-km race

Some cans of kitchen spices are marked with the number of ounces as well as the number of grams. The following sets of weights are marked on various cans. Do the weights agree?

51. $1\frac{1}{2}$ oz or 42.52 grams

52. $1\frac{1}{4}$ oz or 35.40 grams

53. $\frac{3}{8}$ oz or 10.63 grams

54. $\frac{1}{4}$ oz or 7.09 grams

55. 1 oz or 28 grams

56. $1\frac{1}{8}$ oz or 31.89 grams

57. Sound travels 1080 ft per sec. How many meters is this?

58. The wavelength for a particular radio station is 239.6 m. How many feet and yards is this?

59. Light and radio waves travel 300,000,000 m per sec. Find the difference between this and 186,000 miles.

60. If a station broadcasts on a frequency of 1,500,000 cycles (or waves) per second (cps), how many kilocycles (kc) is this? What is the length of each wave?

61. A station announces that its frequency is 960 kc. What is its wavelength?

62. Another station has a wavelength of 480 m. What is its frequency in kilocycles?

6

Square Roots of Numbers

6.1 DEFINITION

If we multiply a number by itself, we call the answer the *square*, or the *second power*, of the number. For instance, in the expression

$$7 \times 7 = 49$$

we call 49 the square of 7 or the second power of 7.

In order to indicate the multiplication of a number by itself, we often use a small number called an *exponent*.

An exponent is a small number placed at the right and a little above another number, called the base, to show how many times the base is to be used as a factor.
Thus

$$7^2 \text{ means } 7 \times 7 = 49$$

The small 2 placed near the 7 means that two 7's are to be *multiplied* together. In this example 7 is the *base* and 2 is the *exponent* of the power.

In the same way

$$5^3 \text{ means } 5 \times 5 \times 5 = 125$$

In this example 5 is the base. The 3 is the exponent of the power and means that three 5's are to be multiplied together. The 125 is called the *third power* of 5 or the *cube* of 5.

The second power of a number is called the *square* of the number. The third power of a number is called the *cube* of the number. If the exponent is larger than 3, we name the power by the exponent. Thus

5^4, or 625, is called the *fourth power* of 5
7^5 is called the *fifth power* of 7
10^6 is called the *sixth power* of 10

6.2 ROOTS OF NUMBERS

If a number is used twice as a factor to form a product, the number is called the *square root* of the product. As an example, 7 is the square root of 49 simply because $7 \times 7 = 49$. Stated in another way, *the square root of a number is one of the two equal factors of the number.*

If a number is used three times as a factor to form a product, the number is called the *cube root* of the product. As an example, 7 is the cube root of 343 simply because $7 \times 7 \times 7 = 343$. *The cube root of a number is one of the three equal factors of a number.*

Other examples:

9 is the square root of 81 because $9 \times 9 = 81$.
4 is the cube root of 64 because $4 \times 4 \times 4 = 64$.
2 is the fifth root of 32 because $2^5 = 32$.
3 is the fourth root of 81 because $3^4 = 81$.

Finding a root of a number is the opposite of finding a power. In order to find a power of a number, we multiply the number by itself. For instance, the third power of 6, that is, 6^3, is 216. The process of finding a power is called *involution.* The opposite process is called *evolution.* In the process of *evolution* we find the *root* of a number; that is, we try to find the number that has been multiplied by itself a certain number of times to produce the given number.

The symbol for a root is the sign $\sqrt{}$, called the *radical* sign. It means that a certain root is to be found. The number under the radical sign is called the *radicand* and is the number of which the root is to be found. A small number, called the *index*, is often placed in the notch of the radical sign to indicate the root to be found. Thus $\sqrt[2]{49}$ means the square root of 49, which is 7. Therefore, we write

$$\sqrt[2]{49} = 7$$

In order to indicate the cube root, we use the index number, 3. Thus $\sqrt[3]{125}$ means that the cube root of 125 is to be found, and we write

$$\sqrt[3]{125} = 5$$

Other examples:

$$\sqrt[4]{81} = 3 \qquad \sqrt[5]{32} = 2 \qquad \sqrt[3]{512} = 8$$

The index 2 is usually omitted because the square root is used most frequently.

The only roots with which we shall be concerned in this chapter are *square* roots. Our problem is how to find the square roots of numbers.

We find the square roots of some numbers by inspection. For instance, if we square all the integers from 1 to 9, we get the following squares: 1, 4, 9, 16, 25, 36, 49, 64, 81. The square roots of these numbers can be determined from memory; that is,

$$\sqrt{1} = 1 \qquad \sqrt{16} = 4 \qquad \sqrt{49} = 7$$

$$\sqrt{4} = 2 \qquad \sqrt{25} = 5 \qquad \sqrt{64} = 8$$

$$\sqrt{9} = 3 \qquad \sqrt{36} = 6 \qquad \sqrt{81} = 9$$

A few others are quite generally known and can be determined by inspection:

$$\sqrt{100} \qquad \sqrt{144} \qquad \sqrt{225}$$

$$\sqrt{121} \qquad \sqrt{169} \qquad \sqrt{400}$$

However, when we get to larger numbers, we cannot tell the square root from memory. We need some systematic method for finding the square root.

First, we need to consider what is meant by a *perfect square*. A number such as 49 is a perfect square because the square root of 49 is *exactly* 7. The square root of 169 is exactly 13, because 13×13 makes exactly 169. The number $6\frac{1}{4}$ is a perfect square. The square root of $6\frac{1}{4}$ is exactly $2\frac{1}{2}$ because $(2\frac{1}{2})(2\frac{1}{2})$ is exactly $6\frac{1}{4}$. A perfect square is a number whose square root can be stated *exactly* as a fraction or a whole number.

On the other hand, consider the number 19. There is no whole number or fraction that can be multiplied by itself to make exactly 19. The square root of 19 does not come out even as a decimal or common fraction. We can say it is approximately 4.359. If we multiply 4.359 by itself, we get a number slightly larger than 19. If we use 4.358, we get a number slightly smaller than 19. A number that cannot be expressed as a whole number or as a common fraction is called an *irrational* number. The square roots of many numbers are irrational numbers.

If the square root of a number is irrational, that is, if the square root does not come out even, we carry out the answer to as many decimal places as we need for any particular degree of accuracy. Just where to stop is a matter of good judgment.

In most cases in actual practice we find the square roots of numbers by looking them up in a table. The engineer uses a slide rule, which provides three-place accuracy. If he wants greater accuracy, he uses logarithms. There is, however, a way to work out the square root of any number. As a student of mathematics, you should understand the process and be able to use it when the need arises. The steps in the process are now shown by examples.

Example 1.   Find the square root of 1918.44.

Step 1.   Separate the number into groups of digits, two digits in a group, starting at the decimal point. Use a mark such as a prime mark, ′, not a decimal point. Draw a line over the number and place the decimal point for the answer directly above the decimal point in the number.

$$\overline{19'18'.44}$$

The answer will have one digit for each *group* of digits in the number itself. If the right group has only one digit, annex a zero. If the left group has only one digit, it is considered as one group.

Step 2. Find the largest perfect square that can be subtracted from the first group at the left. In this case, the largest perfect square in 19 is 16. The first digit in the answer will always be the square root of this perfect square; in this case it is 4. Place the 4 above the 19 for the first digit of the answer.

$$
\begin{array}{l}
4\cdot \\
\overline{19'18'.44}
\end{array}
$$

Step 3. Place the square, 16, below the 19 and subtract, leaving 3.

Step 4. Bring down the next group of digits, 18, and place them next to the 3, making 318, which we call the first remainder.

$$
\begin{array}{l}
4\cdot \\
\overline{19'18'.44} \\
\underline{16} \\
318
\end{array}
$$

At this point we know that the square root will be some number between 40 and 50, since the original number lies between 40^2 and 50^2.

Step 5. Now we double the partial answer with a zero attached. The result is 80. Divide 80 into the remainder, 318. The result is 3. Then "3" *may* be the next digit in the answer. However, this number must be considered only as a trial answer. In order to determine whether the 3 is satisfactory, we must add the 3 to 80 and then multiply the result by 3; thus

$$
\begin{array}{r}
80 \\
+\ 3 \\
\hline
83 \\
\times\ 3 \\
\hline
249
\end{array}
\qquad\qquad
\begin{array}{r}
4\ \ 3\ \ \ . \\
\hline
1918.44 \\
16 \\
\hline
318 \\
249 \\
\hline
69
\end{array}
$$

Since 249 is less than the remainder, 318, we know that 3 is the next digit in the answer. It is placed above the second group of digits, 18. The answer is therefore 43 plus some decimal fraction. The 249 is placed below the 318 and subtracted, leaving 69

Step 6. Bring down the next group of digits, 44.

Step 7. Now we proceed in the same way as in Step 5. We double the partial answer with a zero attached. The result is 860. Divide 860 into the remainder, 6944. The result is 8. This may be the next digit in the answer. However, to be sure, we first add the 8 and then multiply by 8; thus

$$
\begin{array}{r}
4\ \ 3\ .\ 8 \\
\hline
1918.44 \\
16 \\
\hline
318 \\
249 \\
\hline
6944 \\
6944 \\
\hline
\end{array}
$$

$$
\begin{array}{r}
860 \\
+\ 8 \\
\hline
868 \\
\times\ 8 \\
\hline
6944
\end{array}
$$

Since the number 6944 is not larger than the remainder, we know that 8 is the third digit in the answer. Moreover, the remainder is now zero. Therefore, the square root is exactly 43.8. To check the answer, we multiply 43.8 by itself.

Example 2. Find the square root of 13.472 to five significant digits.

Step 1. Separate the number into groups of digits.

$$
\begin{array}{l}
\cdot \\
\overline{13'47'20}
\end{array}
$$

Step 2. The first digit of the answer is 3, since the largest perfect square in 13 is 9.

Step 3. Square the "3" and subtract the result from 13, leaving 4.

Step 4. Bring down the next group of digits, 47.

```
    3 .
13.4720
 9
 447
```

Step 5. At this step in this example we run into a little trouble. We double the partial answer 3 with a zero annexed, which makes 60. We divide the 60 into 447 and get 7. However, we must add the 7 and then multiply by the 7: $60 + 7 = 67$; $67 \times 7 = 469$. The number 469 is more than the remainder 447. This means that the number "7" is too large for the second digit of the answer. Therefore, we try 6.

$$60 + 6 = 66 \qquad 66 \times 6 = 396$$

```
   3 . 6  7
13.4720
 9
 447
 396
 5120
 5089
 3100
```

Step 6. Place the "6" as the second digit in the answer directly above the 47 and subtract 396 from 447, leaving 51; then bring down the next group of digits, 20

Step 7. Double 360, which makes 720. Divide 720 into 5120. The answer is 7. We try this 7 thus:

$$720 + 7 = 727 \qquad 727 \times 7 = 5089$$

Place 5089 below the 5120 and subtract, leaving 31. We know that the third digit in the answer is 7.

To carry out the answer further, we bring down the next group of digits, which is simply two zeros. When we double the number 3670, we get 7340, which cannot be divided into the remainder 3100. Therefore, the next digit in the answer is zero. We place a zero in the answer and bring down two more zeros. Then we double 36700, which makes 73400. Dividing this number into 310000, we get 4, which is a correct fifth digit. The square root to five significant digits is 3.6704. To be sure the fifth digit is correct, we sometimes carry the work to six places.

```
   3 .  6  7  0  4
13.4720
 9
 447
 396
 5120
 5089
  310000
  293616
   16384
```

Exercise 6.1

Find the square root of each of the following numbers. If the root is irrational (does not come out even), carry the answer out to five significant digits and then round it off to four significant digits.

1. 1823.29	**2.** 7.5076	**3.** 30.6916	**4.** 14745600
5. 273800	**6.** 12110000	**7.** 6272.64	**8.** 47.4721
9. 817216	**10.** 6512.49	**11.** 10566	**12.** 1083000
13. 0.6021	**14.** 0.9083	**15.** 948.8	**16.** 2551
17. 0.026569	**18.** 0.216225	**19.** 70000	**20.** 0.00167
21. 0.000015	**22.** 0.0000034	**23.** 0.00453	**24.** 0.0503

25. If a square field contains 400 sq rd, what is the length of one side? What is the distance around the field?

26. A rectangular sheet of paper is 20 in. wide and 36 in. long. If a square is to have the same area, what is the approximate length of a side?
27. A house has a living room 14 ft wide and 22 ft long. The same house contains another room of the same area. If the second room is square, what is the length of one side?
28. A square picture contains an area of 345 sq cm. Find the length of one side.
29. A man owns two building lots having the same area. One lot is square and the other is a rectangle 110 ft long and 52 ft wide. What is the length of one side of the square lot?
30. A square lawn contains approximately 2750 sq ft of area. What is the approximate length of one side?
31. A square playground is 120 ft along one side. What is the length of one side of a playground that contains half as much area (a square)?
32. The length of one side of a square cement floor is 30 ft. What is the length of one side of a square that contains twice as much area?

6.3 SEPARATION OF RADICALS

The entire expression $\sqrt{45}$ is called a radical. The radicand is 45, and the indicated root is the square root. The symbol means that we are to find the square root of 45.

Now, there are two important principles concerning radicals that should be thoroughly understood and remembered. Suppose we consider the following example:

$$\sqrt{4 \times 9}$$

The radicand is $(4) \cdot (9)$, or 36. Then we know that the expression can be simplified into $\sqrt{36}$, which is 6. However, let us look at the problem in another way. Suppose we separate the radical into the product of two radicals. Then we might ask, is $\sqrt{4 \times 9}$ the same as $\sqrt{4} \times \sqrt{9}$? That is, is the square root of the product the same as the product of the square roots?

The square root of 4 is 2. The square root of 9 is 3. If we multiply the square roots together, we get $2 \times 3 = 6$. This is the correct answer for the square root of 36.

Let us look at another example.

Is $\sqrt{16 \times 25}$ the same as $\sqrt{16} \times \sqrt{25}$?

Is $\sqrt{400}$ equal to 4×5?

We see that this answer is also true.

The foregoing examples show an important principle.

Principle 1. *If a radicand can be separated into factors, then it is correct to take the indicated root of each factor and multiply these roots together.*

In order to see the significance of this principle, let us look at another kind of problem. Suppose we have the example $\sqrt{25}$. We know that $\sqrt{25} = 5$.

Let us look at this example in another way. Suppose we separate the radicand into two parts, $16 + 9$; that is, $\sqrt{25}$ is the same as $\sqrt{16 + 9}$. Now we might ask, is $\sqrt{16 + 9}$ the same as $\sqrt{16} + \sqrt{9}$? In other words, is the square root of the sum of 16 and 9 the same as the square root of 16 plus the square root of 9?

The square root of 16 is 4. The square root of 9 is 3. If we add these square roots, we get $4 + 3 = 7$. This is *not* the correct answer for $\sqrt{25}$. Therefore, we can say $\sqrt{16 + 9}$ is *not* the same as $\sqrt{16} + \sqrt{9}$.

Let us consider another example.

Is $\sqrt{25 - 16}$ the same as $\sqrt{25} - \sqrt{16}$? In the expression $\sqrt{25 - 16}$ the radicand is $25 - 16$, which is 9. Then the expression $\sqrt{25 - 16}$ means $\sqrt{9}$, which is 3.

However, if we take the square root of 25 and the square root of 16 and subtract the two, we get $5 - 4 = 1$. Therefore, we can say $\sqrt{25 - 16}$ is *not* the same as $\sqrt{25} - \sqrt{16}$. We can now state a second principle concerning radicals.

Principle 2.   *The square root of a sum or a difference cannot be found by taking the square root of each part. Any indicated addition or subtraction under a radical sign must be performed first.*

Example.   To find $\sqrt{49 + 36}$, we cannot simply add $7 + 6$. Instead, we must first add $49 + 36 = 85$. Then we must find the square root of 85.

6.4   A SHORT METHOD FOR FINDING ROOTS

The first principle mentioned can sometimes be used to find the square root of a number by a short method. Suppose we wish to find $\sqrt{32}$.

We separate 32, the radicand, into two *factors* such that one of the factors is a perfect square. The largest square contained in 32 as a *factor* is 16. Then we have

$$\sqrt{32} = \sqrt{(16)(2)}$$

Now, we have a right to state the expression as the product of two radicals by Principle 1; that is,

$$\sqrt{(16)(2)} = \sqrt{16} \times \sqrt{2}$$

We know that $\sqrt{16} = 4$. Then the expression reduces to $4\sqrt{2}$.

If we now remember that the square root of 2 is approximately 1.4142, we can say

$$\sqrt{32} = \sqrt{(16)(2)} = \sqrt{16} \times \sqrt{2} = 4(1.4142) = 5.6568$$

The short method depends on remembering the approximate values of a few irrational roots, especially of small integers. The following values are approximate:

$$\sqrt{2} = 1.4142 \qquad \sqrt{5} = 2.236 \qquad \sqrt{7} = 2.646 \qquad \sqrt{11} = 3.317$$

$$\sqrt{3} = 1.732 \qquad \sqrt{6} = 2.449 \qquad \sqrt{10} = 3.162 \qquad \sqrt{15} = 3.873$$

6.5 SQUARE ROOTS OF FRACTIONS AND MIXED NUMBERS

To find the square root of a common fraction or a mixed number, we first change the number to a decimal and then proceed in the usual way. For instance, to find the square root of $\frac{3}{4}$, we find the square root of 0.75. If the common fraction does not come out even as a decimal, we continue to divide to as many places as desired. For example, the square root of $\frac{3}{7}$ becomes $\sqrt{0.4285714}$. If the square root is desired to four significant digits, then the number itself should have 7 or 8 digits.

In the square root of a decimal fraction beginning with several zeros, such as $\sqrt{0.00000568}$, the answer will begin with one zero for each *group* of two zeros after the decimal point. For example, $\sqrt{0.00000568} = 0.00238$ to three significant digits.

Exercise 6.2

Find the square root of each of the following numbers to four significant digits:

1. 863.2
2. 19280
3. 28.672
4. 5423.1
5. 0.09874
6. 0.4127
7. 810000000
8. 0.008632
9. 0.0001863
10. 72900
11. 729000
12. 10240000

Find the square root of each of the following:

13. $20\frac{1}{4}$
14. $5\frac{7}{8}$
15. 13
16. $14\frac{2}{3}$
17. $1\frac{4}{7}$
18. $\frac{5}{11}$
19. $98\frac{3}{5}$
20. 3
21. $6\frac{9}{16}$
22. 156.25
23. 1562.5
24. 15625
25. 2
26. 0.9
27. 0.1

Find the following by a simple method if possible:

28. $\sqrt{18}$
29. $\sqrt{50}$
30. $\sqrt{108}$
31. $\sqrt{98}$
32. $\sqrt{200}$
33. $\sqrt{72}$
34. $\sqrt{8}$
35. $\sqrt{75}$
36. $\sqrt{45}$
37. $\sqrt{48}$
38. $\sqrt{325}$
39. $\sqrt{192}$
40. $\sqrt{180}$
41. $\sqrt{250}$
42. $\sqrt{147}$
43. $\sqrt{(16)(9)(25)}$
44. $\sqrt{(100)(4)(9)}$
45. $\sqrt{100 + 4 + 9}$
46. $\sqrt{9 + 16 + 25}$
47. $\sqrt{8^2 + 15^2}$

48. Find one side and the perimeter of a square containing 156.25 sq in.
49. A rectangle is 35.2 in. long and 8.8 in. wide. Find one side of a square containing the same area. Find the difference in the perimeters of the rectangle and the square.

50. Two square air pipes, one 8 in. on a side, the other 12 in. on a side, are joined into one large square air pipe having the same cross-sectional area as the combined area of the two smaller pipes. Find the size of the single large pipe.

51. One square ventilating pipe receives air from a rectangular opening 6 in. wide and 15 in. long. What is the size of the square pipe if it has the same cross-sectional area as the opening?

52. Find the size of a square having half the area of a 12-in. square.

7
Number Bases

7.1 INTRODUCTION

In this age of computers everyone should have some idea of number bases. We have mentioned the fact that in our common system of writing numbers, any number of any size can be expressed by the use of only ten digits, 0 through 9. When we count a number of objects one more than 9, we use the digits 1 and 0 and write 10 to express the number.

Electronic computers operate on the use of only two digits, 0 and 1. We shall see shortly how this is done. First, let us take a look at a particular base other than ten, for example, base *six*.

7.2 A PARTICULAR BASE: SIX

Suppose we decide to use only six digits: 0, 1, 2, 3, 4, and 5. When we count a number that is one more than 5 (that is, this number: o, o, o, o, o, o), we put these six objects together and call them one *bunch*. We write 1 for the bunch and then 0 for none left over. Then the symbol for *six* becomes 10. In this case, we say the number is written in *base six*. In base six notation the 1 written in the second place from the right represents one bunch of *six*.

Note that in base six we have no digit for *six*, the base. This is true for any base we might use. In base ten (our common base) we have no single digit for *ten*. In *base seven* there is no single digit for *seven*. In the same way, in using *base two*, we use only the two digits, 0 and 1, and we have no digit for *two*. However, in our explanation here, for convenience we shall use our usual digit to represent the base. For example, to refer to base *six*, we shall call it *base 6*, although in this base there is no single digit for *six*. To write a number in *base four*, we use only the four digits, 0, 1, 2, and 3, but we refer to the base as *base 4*. In writing a number in any particular base we often indicate the base by a *subscript*.

As an example in the use of base 6, consider the number of fingers on two hands. We call this number *ten* and write it 10. Now, if we wish to write this number in base 6, we would say that we have one *bunch* of 6 and an extra 4 units over. Then in base 6 we would write the number of fingers on two hands as

$$14_6$$

The subscript 6 indicates the base.

Now consider the number of days in the month of September. This number we call thirty and usually write it 30 (in base ten). The symbol means 3 bunches of 10 each and none over. Suppose now that we wish to write this number in base 6. We first see how many bunches of 6 we can get in 30. Using our common notation (base 10), we divide 30 by 6 and get 5 with no remainder. This means there are 5 bunches of 6 with none left over. Then the number of days in September written in base 6 becomes

$$50_6$$

As another example, suppose we wish to write the number 27 (base ten) in base 6. We divide 27 by 6 and get 4 with a remainder of 3. Then the number 27 (base 10) becomes, in base 6,

$$43_6; \quad \text{that is,} \quad 27_{10} = 43_6$$

Let us go one step further. Suppose we have 36 objects (say, the number of inches in one yard) and wish to write this number in base 6. When we count off 5 bunches of 6 each, we have another 6 left over, which makes another bunch. Then we have *six* bunches. But we have no digit for six. So we put the six bunches together and call it one *big bunch*, or a bunch of the *second order*. Now we write 1 for the bunch of the second order, and we write zeros for the remaining spaces. Then

$$\text{36 in base 10 becomes 100 in base 6}$$

that is,

$$36_{10} = 100_6$$

7.3 CHANGING A NUMBER FROM BASE TEN TO ANY OTHER BASE

The foregoing examples lead directly to the following rule for changing a number from base 10 to any other base:

Rule. *Divide the number (base 10) by the new base as many times as possible and write down all remainders, including zeros. The remainders are the digits of the number written in the desired base, starting with the last remainder.*

Example. Change the following numbers (base 10) to the base indicated:

(a) 461_{10} to base 6   (b) 894_{10} to base 7   (c) 187_{10} to base 2

Solution

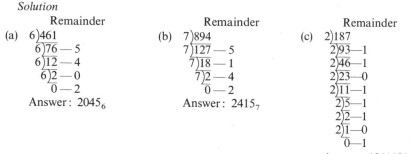

(a)
```
      Remainder
6)461
 6)76 — 5
  6)12 — 4
   6)2 — 0
    0 — 2
```
Answer: 2045_6

(b)
```
      Remainder
7)894
 7)127 — 5
  7)18 — 1
   7)2 — 4
    0 — 2
```
Answer: 2415_7

(c)
```
      Remainder
2)187
 2)93—1
  2)46—1
   2)23—0
    2)11—1
     2)5—1
      2)2—1
       2)1—0
        0—1
```
Answer: 10111011_2

7.4 CHANGING A NUMBER TO BASE TEN FROM ANY OTHER BASE

To change a number to base 10 from any other base, let us first consider the meaning of place value in any base. When we write a number such as 3724 (base 10), each of the digits, 3, 7, 2, and 4, have the following meanings. The first digit at the right, 4, represents single units. The second digit from the right, 2, represents 10's. The next digit, 7, represents the number of 10^2's, or 100's. The next digit, 3, represents 10^3's, or 1000's. The places have the following values:

$$\overline{10^3} \quad \overline{10^2} \quad \overline{10} \quad \overline{\text{units}}$$

Briefly, each place starting from the right represents successive powers of the base.

In a similar manner, when we write a number in another base, say, base 6, for instance, the digits have place values that represent successive powers of the base 6. In base 6, the places have the following values:

$$\overline{6^3} \quad \overline{6^2} \quad \overline{6} \quad \overline{\text{units}}$$

Now let us see the meaning of a number written in base 6, say, 2543_6. The digit 3 at the extreme right represents the number of units. The next digit, 4, represents the number of 6's. The next digit, 5, represents the number of 6^2's, or 36's. The next digit, 2, represents the number of 6^3's, or 216's. Now let us compute the value of the number in base 10.

The digit at the right means units:	3	
The digit 4 means 4(6), or	24	(base 10)
The next digit, 5, means $5(6^2)$, or 5(36), or	180	(base 10)
The next digit, 2, means $2(6^3)$, or 2(216), or	432	(base 10)
Adding these values (expressed in base 10), we get	639_{10}	(base 10)

Rule. *To change a number to base 10 from any other base, write down the digit at the extreme right as the number of units. Then, moving toward the left, multiply each digit by successive powers of the base. Finally, add the results.*

In base 2, used in electronic computers, the places have the following values:

$$\overline{2^8} \quad \overline{2^7} \quad \overline{2^6} \quad \overline{2^5} \quad \overline{2^4} \quad \overline{2^3} \quad \overline{2^2} \quad \overline{2^1} \quad \overline{\text{units}}$$

$$256 \quad 128 \quad 64 \quad 32 \quad 16 \quad 8 \quad 4 \quad 2 \quad 1$$

Now suppose we have the following number written in base two:

$$1\,1\,0\,1\,1\,0\,1\,1\,1$$

Let us find the value of this number expressed in our common base *ten*:

The 1 at the extreme right represents units: 1
The next 1 represents the number of 2's: 2 (base ten)
The next 1 represents the number of 4's: 4 (base ten)
The next digit, 0, means the number of 8's: 0 (base ten)
The next digit, 1, means the number of 16's: 16 (base ten)
The next digit, 1, means the number of 32's: 32 (base ten)
The next digit, 0, means the number of 64's: 00 (base ten)
The next digit, 1, means the number of 128's: 128 (base ten)
The next digit, 1, means the number of 256's: 256 (base ten)
Adding these values (in base ten), we get   439 (base ten)

Computation can also be performed in any base. However, in all cases we must take into account the base used. For example, let us multiply the following number expressed in base 6:

$$
\begin{array}{ll}
\quad 44 & 4 \times 5 = 32 \text{ (base 6)} \\
\quad 55 & 5 + 2 = 11 \text{ (base 6)} \\
\overline{\quad 352} & 5 + 4 = 13 \text{ (base 6)} \\
\quad 352 & \\
\overline{4312} &
\end{array}
$$

The multiplication can be checked by changing all numbers to base *ten* and then performing the computation:

$$44_6 = 28_{10}; \qquad 55_6 = 35_{10}; \qquad (28)(35) = 980_{10} = 4312_6$$

7.5   BASES GREATER THAN TEN; EXAMPLE: BASE TWELVE

Numbers may be expressed in bases greater than ten but then other digits are needed. For example, if we wish to use the base *twelve*, then we must have a digit for *ten* and one for *eleven*. The symbol T is sometimes used for *ten* and the symbol E for eleven. Then $5 + 5 = T$, and $7 + 4 = E$. For twelve, we write 10. The number 23 in base *ten* is written 1E in base twelve, 22 becomes $1T$, 46 becomes $3T$, and 47 is $3E$. To change a number from base ten, we divide the number by twelve (that is, 12 as we know it in base ten). Then the number 6763 in base ten becomes $3TE7$ in base twelve. Multiplying $(3)(E)$ we get 29 in base twelve.

Exercise 7.1

Each of the following numbers is expressed in base 10. Change each number to the indicated base:

1. 3699 to base 6
2. 5983 to base 7
3. 2983 to base 4
4. 2711 to base 5
5. 5044 to base 6
6. 6115 to base 8
7. 1267 to base 3
8. 6886 to base 7
9. 3638 to base 4
10. 3891 to base 9
11. 1977 to base 5
12. 5349 to base 8

Change each of the following numbers (base 10) to base 2:

13. 34
14. 36
15. 39
16. 41
17. 46
18. 49
19. 52
20. 54
21. 58
22. 279
23. 314
24. 417
25. 357
26. 443
27. 503
28. 343
29. 465
30. 327

The following numbers are written in the indicated bases. Change to base 10:

31. 3625_7
32. 4153_6
33. 2576_8
34. 12021_3
35. 23102_4
36. 30134_5
37. 22021_3
38. 20351_6
39. 35402_7
40. 43210_5

The following numbers are written in base 2; change to base 10:

41. 110101
42. 101111
43. 110011
44. 111001
45. 101011
46. 100110
47. 101101
48. 100101
49. 111011
50. 110111
51. 110110011
52. 100100111
53. 111000101
54. 101010101
55. 110011001
56. 111011010
57. 101101111
58. 100010001
59. 100110010
60. 111110001

61. Add the following numbers written in base 6:

    (a) 54
        25

    (b) 45
        54

    (c) 14
        43

62. Multiply in base 6:   (a) $(45)(35)$ (b) $(43)(25)$ (c) $(23)(45)$
63. Multiply in base 4:   (a) $(33)(22)$ (b) $(32)(23)$ (c) $(232)(123)$
64. Add in base 2:   (a) $(1011) + (1110)$ (b) $(101101) + (111101)$
65. Multiply in base 2:   (a) $(11)(11)$ (b) $(101)(111)$ (c) $(111)(11101)$

Quiz on Chapters 1–7   Form A

1. Change the following common fractions to decimals:

$$\tfrac{3}{8} \qquad \tfrac{5}{16} \qquad 2\tfrac{7}{32} \qquad 4\tfrac{9}{20} \qquad 3\tfrac{1}{5} \qquad 5\tfrac{2}{7} \qquad 4\tfrac{2}{13} \qquad 2\tfrac{7}{11}$$

2. Change the following decimal fractions to common fraction form:

$$2.15 \qquad 3.16 \qquad 4.075 \qquad 1.0375 \qquad 0.00\tfrac{1}{8} \qquad 0.28\tfrac{4}{7} \qquad 0.016\tfrac{1}{}$$

3. (a) Change 43.2 inches to centimeters.
   (b) Change 37.5 centimeters to inches.

(c) Change 141.5 square inches to square centimeters.

(d) Change 384 cm^2 to square inches.

4. A bar of steel is cut into six pieces having the following lengths (inches):

$$2\tfrac{3}{16} \qquad 3\tfrac{1}{8} \qquad 3\tfrac{3}{4} \qquad 4\tfrac{9}{16} \qquad 5\tfrac{7}{32} \qquad 6\tfrac{1}{2}$$

If $\tfrac{1}{32}$ inch is wasted for each cut, what was the length of the original piece?

5. If six pieces each 2 and $\tfrac{13}{16}$ inches long are cut from a bar of metal 20 inches long, find the length of the remaining piece if $\tfrac{1}{64}$ inch is wasted for each cut.

6. How many pieces each 3.42 inches long can be cut from a strip of brass that is 2 feet long if 0.03 inch is wasted per cut?

7. A rectangle is 15.2 inches wide and 28.4 inches long. Find the number of centimeters in the perimeter.

8. A man has an annual salary of $8600. During the year the family spent the following amounts on the items mentioned. Find the rate of his total income that was spent on each item: housing, $2020; food, $2360; clothing, $980; insurance and savings, $1120.

9. By the short method find the following square roots:

$$\sqrt{72} \qquad \sqrt{300} \qquad \sqrt{24}$$

10. (a) Change 731 (base 10) to base 2.

(b) Change 3124_5 to base 7.

Part II

ALGEBRA

8

Operations with Signed Numbers

If you are just beginning the study of algebra, the subject probably seems like a completely new language. People who hear of algebra for the first time are often confused about its meaning. It seems to them that in algebra we are adding and multiplying letters and words instead of numbers. This seems so different from arithmetic—not only different but impossible. How can you add one word to another? Or how can you multiply one word by another? Can you multiply a book by a pencil? In algebra people seem to be doing just that. Yet we shall see that this is not really so.

Algebra may be called *generalized arithmetic*. To understand this statement, suppose we ask : what is the cost of 7 books at $4 each? Here we are using arithmetic. The numbers 7 and 4 are *arithmetic* numbers. They are specific, definite numbers. The total cost of the 7 books is $28; 28 is also an *arithmetic* number.

Now, suppose we ask a general question such as this: how do you find the total cost of some books if you know the number of books and the cost of each book? The answer is: you multiply the cost of one book by the number of books. To state the rule a little more simply, we can say

(number of books) × (cost of each) = total cost

Of course, in this statement, we know that we cannot multiply *words*. The statement does not mean that at all. We know that we really multiply *numbers*. Actually, the statement is simply a rule for finding the total cost. If we wish to state the rule in a still shorter form, we may use the letter N for the number of books, the letter C for the cost of each book, and the letter T for total cost. The rule then becomes

$$N \times C = T$$

Consider another example. If a rectangle is 8 inches long and 5 inches wide, its area is 40 square inches. We find the area by multiplication: $8 \times 5 = 40$. All the numbers here used are *arithmetic* numbers.

Now, suppose we ask the general question: how do you find the area of any rectangle if you know its length and its width? The answer is: you multiply the length by the width. (Actually, what we mean is that we multiply the number of linear units in the length by the number of linear units in the width. The result gives us the number of corresponding square units in the area.) Stated as a rule, this statement becomes

$$\text{length} \times \text{width} = \text{area}$$

The statement is really simply a rule that tells how to find the area when the length and the width are known.

Here, again, the statement does not mean that we actually multiply *words*. We know that we really multiply *numbers*, not words. If we wish to state the rule in a still shorter form, we may use the letter L for length, the letter W for width, and the letter A for area. The rule then becomes

$$L \times W = A \qquad \text{or} \qquad LW = A$$

In algebra, when two or more letters representing numerical values are written next to each other without a symbol between them, their values are meant to be multiplied together.

8.2   LITERAL NUMBERS

When letters of the alphabet are used to represent numbers, as we used the letters N, C, T, L, W, and A, such letters are called *literal* numbers. *Arithmetic* numbers are numbers used only in arithmetic, such as 3, 4, 7, 12, 473, and so on. Literal numbers are letters of the alphabet that are used to represent arithmetic numbers. They are such numbers as x, y, z, n, t, w, a, and so on. For instance, the letter a is a literal number if it represents some arithmetic number. However, in the word "apple" the a is not a number at all.

Literal numbers may be called *general* numbers because they represent general values rather than specific values. Where we say $A = L \times W$, the letters represent the area, length, and width, respectively, of any rectangle; that is, a general rectangle. Algebra deals with specific arithmetic numbers and also with literal, or general, numbers. It is for this reason that algebra may be called *generalized arithmetic.*

Literal numbers cannot actually be added, subtracted, multiplied, or divided in the same way as arithmetic numbers. If we wish to find the sum of 5 and 3, we add them and get 8. If we wish to combine literal numbers in some way, such as the numbers x and y, all we can do is to indicate or express the operation and result. For instance, if we wish to add the numbers

x and y, we show the sum as $x + y$. The difference between x and y is shown as $x - y$. The product is xy. The quotient of x divided by y is $x \div y$ or x/y.

In arithmetic we generally indicate multiplication by the sign $\times$. However, since the letter x is often used as an algebraic number, the multiplication sign is usually omitted. Instead, in algebra we sometimes indicate multiplication by placing a dot between the numbers to be multiplied; thus $3 \cdot 4$. If there is no danger of confusion, we omit the multiplication sign entirely. Thus xy means x times y; $2a$ means 2 times a. Multiplication of algebraic numbers can also be indicated by placing parentheses around each of the numbers without any sign between them; thus $(x)(y)$ means x times y; $(3)(4)$ means 3 times 4.

If two literal numbers, or a literal number and an arithmetic number, are placed next to each other without a sign between them, they are always meant to be multiplied together. Of course, if we wish to indicate 3 times 4, we cannot write 34, since this means really $30 + 4$.

It often happens that we wish to indicate that the sum of two numbers, or their difference, is to be considered as a single quantity. In such cases we enclose the quantity in parentheses. Any set of numbers enclosed in parentheses must always be considered as a single quantity and is treated as such. For instance, we may wish to indicate three times the sum of x and y. The sum of x and y can be shown as $x + y$. At this point we need not use parentheses. However, suppose we wish to show three times this quantity. We then enclose the sum $x + y$ in parentheses and write a "3" before it; thus

$$3(x + y)$$

Exercise 8.1

Express the following:
1. The sum of a, b, and c
2. The product of 3 and x
3. The sum of $3x$ and $4y$
4. Seven more than x
5. A number x more than 7
6. m more than n
7. Eight less than y
8. y less than 8
9. 15 increased by n
10. c increased by x
11. 10 decreased by x
12. t decreased by y
13. The difference between a and b (if a is greater than b)
14. The difference between a and b (if b is greater than a)
15. The result of m divided by n
16. The quotient of $3n$ divided by $5x$
17. The sum of x and y divided by their product
18. The product of R and r divided by their sum
19. The sum of a and b decreased by the sum of x and y
20. Five times the sum of m and n

21. Three times the difference between h and k

22. The product of x and y added to the quotient of m divided by n

23. The product of $4a$ and $7b$

24. The sum of $5x$ and $8y$ divided by the difference between $10x$ and $4y$

8.3 NEGATIVE AND POSITIVE NUMBERS

Another way in which algebra differs from arithmetic is that in algebra we make use of what we call *negative* numbers. Negative numbers are numbers that are less than zero.

In arithmetic we did not use negative numbers. When we were learning subtraction in the first or second grade, suppose the teacher had said, "If you have 8 marbles and lose 3, how many have you left?" The answer is 5. But suppose the question had been, "If you have 3 marbles and lose 8, how many have you left?" At the time we said that is impossible.

The problem of subtracting a number from a smaller number is considered impossible in arithmetic. For that reason, for a long time negative numbers were considered to be impossible. They were called *absurd*, *ridiculous*, and "fictitious." Yet they continued to force themselves into mathematics.

We shall see that such numbers are neither impossible nor fictitious. One of the most common uses is in connection with a thermometer. When the temperature drops down to zero it can drop still lower.

Suppose we say that we shall call numbers below zero *negative* numbers. Then, when the temperature is ten degrees below zero, we can call this a *negative ten degrees*. A negative number is usually indicated by placing a minus sign ($-$) before the number. Ten degrees below zero can then be called $-10°$. If you go outdoors some day when the temperature is $-50°$, you will realize that such a temperature is not "fictitious."

Numbers that are more than zero are called *positive* numbers to distinguish them from negative numbers. A positive number can be indicated by placing a plus sign ($+$) before the number. Ten degrees above zero can be indicated by $+10°$.

When numbers are considered as positive or negative numbers, they are called *signed* numbers. If a number has no sign before it, it is considered positive. In arithmetic we work with only positive numbers.

8.4 TWO USES OF (+) AND MINUS (−) SIGNS

In arithmetic we use the signs $+$ and $-$ to indicate addition and subtraction, respectively. As *signs of operation*, they tell what mathematical operation is to be performed. However, when these signs are used to indicate positive and negative numbers, they are *signs of quality*. They indicate the *kind* of number, such as $+3$, -2, $+7$, $+10$, -5.

It might appear that it would be better to use a different pair of signs for *operation* than we use for *kinds of numbers*, but eventually you will discover that there need be no confusion at all in their meanings in any particular case.

8.5 USES FOR NEGATIVE NUMBERS

We have seen that temperatures below zero may be indicated by negative numbers, such as $-10°$, $-15°$, and so on. Negative numbers can be used in many other situations. If we indicate a distance of 3 miles *east* by a $+3$, then we may indicate a distance of 3 miles *west* by a -3. If we wish to show distances north by positive numbers, we may show distances south by negative numbers. If $+3$ (amperes) indicates a flow of electric current in a particular direction, then -3 (amperes) indicates a flow in the opposite direction.

If we represent elevation *above* sea level by a positive number, we may represent elevation *below* sea level by a negative number. For example, a town may have an elevation of 2400 feet *above* sea level. This may be represented by $+2400$. If we wish to represent the elevation of a place that is 100 feet *below* sea level, we may call its elevation -100 feet. If assets are indicated by positive numbers, then liabilities may be indicated by negative numbers. If a man has a debt of 15 dollars, we may say he has -15 dollars.

In a game we may sometimes make a score that takes us backward. We say we "get set." Such a score may be called a negative score. A score that takes us forward may be called a positive score.

8.6 A NUMBER SCALE

Positive and negative numbers may be shown on a number scale represented by a horizontal line, as shown here. Positive numbers or distances are laid off to the right of zero, negative numbers or distances to the left, as shown in Figure 8.1.

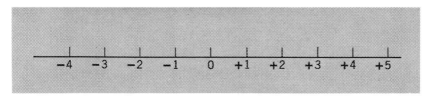

Fig. 8.1

Basically, negative numbers are counted in a direction opposite that for positive numbers. Any direction may be chosen for positive numbers, but the usual practice is to count them to the right of zero. The zero point is then the dividing point between the positive and negative numbers.

8.7 ABSOLUTE VALUE OF A NUMBER

The *absolute* value (sometimes called *numerical* value) of a number is its value without regard to the sign. The absolute value of $+10$ is the same as the absolute value of -10. The absolute value of a number is usually indicated by a pair of vertical lines, one on each side of the number, as $|-10|$. Then we can say $|+5|$ has the same value as $|-5|$.

Notice these two statements:

$$\text{This statement is not true: } 10 = -10$$
$$\text{This statement is true: } |10| = |-10|$$

We know that a $+10$ is not the same as a -10. However, their absolute values are equal. Actually, the absolute value refers to the distance from zero. The two numbers, $+10$ and -10, are the same distance from zero.

8.8 OPERATIONS WITH SIGNED NUMBERS: ADDITION

Since algebra deals with positive and negative numbers, our first problem is to formulate rules for operating with these numbers. How can we perform the operations of addition, subtraction, multiplication, and division with signed numbers so that we can always be sure to proceed correctly? First, we must devise rules that always hold. Then we must be sure to follow these rules when operating with signed numbers.

First, let us consider addition. One of the easiest and best ways to learn how to operate with signed numbers is to consider how we add scores in some games. In some games you may make a score that increases your total or a score that decreases your total; that is, you may make a score that takes you backward, in which case we say you "get set." If you use a positive number to indicate a "good" score that increases your total, then you may use a negative number to indicate a "bad" score that decreases your total. If you make a score of $+20$ and then later make a score of -15, your net, or total, score is $+5$.

Suppose, at the beginning of a game, you "get set," or go back 30 points. Your total score at that point is actually 30 points less than nothing. In a game this is sometimes called "going in the hole." You may call this a score of -30. There is nothing difficult about this idea. It simply means that if you have a score of -30 and someone else has a score of zero (0), then he is still ahead of you by 30 points. It means also that you must make 30 points before you will have a score of zero.

Suppose the following sets of scores are made. Let us find the net total score in each set. This is called "adding" the scores. If a score has no sign, it is to be considered positive. The total score is shown for each set.

Add

$+20$	$+20$	-15	-20	5	-10	-15
$+15$	-6	$+10$	-10	-15	25	4
$+35$	$+14$	-5	-30	-10	$+15$	-11

From these examples we can formulate the rule for adding signed numbers:

Rule. *To add two numbers with like signs, find the sum of their absolute values and prefix the common sign.*

To add two numbers with unlike signs, find the difference between their absolute values and then prefix the sign of the number having the greater absolute value.

If several scores are to be added, the positive scores may be combined first, then the negative scores, and finally the two combined to form the net total score.

Exercise 8.2

Add algebraically:

1.

$+17$	-28	-43	$+45$	-72	28
$+42$	$+69$	-19	-13	$+47$	-87

2.

59	-27	71	-92	0	-62
-32	$+61$	0	36	-59	62

3.

20	-70	16	-18	-23	-15
-15	$+43$	48	-4	-41	32
10	-35	-19	-42	16	-19
27	$+19$	24	-37	-56	-12
-18	-11	-21	16	15	$+14$

4.

-415	$+513$	-695	$+591$	392	-473
-107	$+624$	$+862$	-376	-505	882

5.

-57.8	$+0.596$	-81.3	-47.2	-42.9	-0.038
-0.196	$+2.68$	$+23.7$	5.81	-1.38	$+0.103$

6. 131	−213	48	153	−136	1.26
−175	407	193	−215	−249	−3.78
−243	−316	−418	84	−73	6.54
56	−526	53	−423	152	−4.08

7. −0.1615	**8.** 4.738	**9.** 0.0854	**10.** 24.3
−4.079	−1.8921	−1.7165	−17.
1.3856	−3.576	0.4739	−35.614
0.97843	−0.8325	−0.8645	7.42

8.9 SUBTRACTION OF SIGNED NUMBERS

Subtraction of signed numbers presents a little extra difficulty. Suppose you make the following scores in five trials in a game: $+20$, -15, $+12$, -8, $+4$. Your total score is 13.

Now, suppose you are told that you should have had only four trials. You are told to "erase" or "subtract" the last score. Here *subtract* means to *erase* the score.

Your total score was	$+13$	or by adding	$+13$
You subtract	$+4$	and	-4
Your net score is now	$+9$	we have	$+9$

Subtracting the $+4$ from the $+13$ is the same as adding a -4 to your score.

In another game suppose you make the following scores: $+20$, -15, $+12$, $+9$, -5. Your total score is 21.

Now suppose you are told to subtract the last score (subtract means to *erase*). If you subtract or erase the last score, which is -5, your net score becomes 26, instead of 21. Actually, subtracting the -5 increases your score by 5.

Your first score was	$+21$	or by adding	$+21$
You subtract	-5	and	$+5$
Your net score now is	26	we have	$+26$

Subtracting the -5 from the 21 is the same as adding a $+5$ to your score.

From the foregoing examples we formulate the rule for subtraction of signed numbers:

Rule. *To subtract two signed numbers, mentally change the sign of the subtrahend and then proceed as in algebraic addition.*

Note. Algebraic subtraction may be checked by addition, the same as subtraction in arithmetic. The remainder added to the subtrahend should equal the minuend.

Exercise 8.3

Subtract the bottom number from the top number:

1.	$+9$	-6	$+23$	$+43$	-56	-62
	-5	-9	$+18$	-21	$+17$	-35

2.	32	-21	$+73$	-37	-41	62
	74	54	49	56	-93	-75

3.	38	-63	-79	-23	0	0
	81	28	-54	-23	-25	74

4.	98	726	-523	-416	-917	-144
	-98	-45	127	-324	520	-300

5.	-32	-635	-322	0	315	$+558$
	-40	-847	0	-322	83	-442

In No. 6 subtract the top number from the bottom number:

6.	17	-46	35	-37	-51	14
	28	-24	16	-69	18	-48

7. Subtract the bottom number from the top in each of the following:

	-3.28	6.	-0.831	$+0.904$	$-7.$	1.
	$-5.$	1.872	7.12	$+9.801$	-0.537	4.5322

8. Add the two numbers in each of the examples in No. 7.

8.10 HORIZONTAL ADDITION AND SUBTRACTION

Suppose we have this problem in addition:

$$+6$$
$$-3$$
$$+7$$
$$-2$$

If we place these signed numbers in a horizontal line, we can indicate addition by enclosing each number with its sign in parentheses and then placing the addition sign $(+)$ between them. First, let us write

$$(+6) \text{ plus } (-3) \text{ plus } (+7) \text{ plus } (-2) = 8$$

Now, we replace the word *plus* with the sign for addition $(+)$. This sign is then the sign of operation.

$$(+6) + (-3) + (+7) + (-2) = 8$$

Here, the plus signs between the numbers are signs of operation, that is, addition. The signs inside the parentheses are the signs of positive and negative numbers.

If we drop all the plus signs of operation and omit the parentheses, we have

$$+6 - 3 + 7 - 2 = 8$$

The answer can be obtained simply by combining the signed numbers as we would in arithmetic. For horizontal addition, we have this rule:

Rule. *To add signed numbers horizontally, simply write down each number with its proper sign and omit the signs of addition. Then combine the numbers.*

To indicate subtraction in horizontal form, we enclose each number with its sign in parentheses and then place the sign of operation, a minus sign, between the numbers. For example, suppose we have this problem: from $(+12)$ subtract (-7). We first write

$$(+12) - (-7)$$

We have seen that subtracting any number is equivalent to adding the same number with its sign changed. Therefore,

$$(+12) - (-7) \quad \text{means the same as} \quad (+12) + (+7)$$

Now we apply the rule for horizontal addition and get

$$+12 + 7 = +19$$

For horizontal subtraction we have this rule:

Rule. *In horizontal subtraction, omit the signs of subtraction and simply write down each number to be subtracted with its sign changed. Then combine the terms as in horizontal addition.*

Examples. (a) $(-5) - (+4) = -5 - 4 = -9$
(b) $(+3) - (-7) = +3 + 7 = +10$
(c) $(+8) - (+3) = +8 - 3 = +5$

When horizontal additions and subtractions occur in the same problem, the signs of operation may be dropped, provided the rules for horizontal addition and subtraction are observed.

Example. $(+8) + (+7) + (-3) - (+5) - (-2) + (4) =$
$\quad +8 \quad +7 \quad -3 \quad\; -5 \quad\; +2 + \; 4 = 13$

Exercise 8.4

Combine each of the following into a single answer:
1. $(+8) + (-3) - (-4) - (+6) + (+9) =$
2. $(+5) + (+12) - (-7) + (-2) - (+8) =$
3. $(-7) - (+6) + (-13) + (+9) - (-18) =$
4. $(-12) + (+11) - (-30) + (-17) - (+26) =$
5. $(+13) - (-15) - (8) + (+16) + (-20) =$
6. $(+14) - (+9) + (+7) - (-3) + (-6) + (-3) - (-8) =$
7. $(-16) + (-3) + (9) - (-1) + (-5) - (11) - (-2) =$
8. $(-9) + (14) + (-23) - (15) - (-12) + (13) + (+8) =$
9. $(16) + (18) + (-12) - (-41) + (-9) - (14) + (-5) =$
10. $(-15) - (13) - (-7) - (32) + (-2) - (-20) + (-4) =$
11. $(12) - (-15) - (24) + (-13) - (-6) - (16) + (-3) =$
12. $(-17) - (11) + (-12) - (-5) + (18) + (3) - (-16) =$
13. $(18) + (-21) - (-73) + (-4) + (31) - (-45) - (14) =$
14. $(-312) - (-415) + (247) + (-763) - (658) - (-1234) =$
15. $(139) - (-254) - (267) + (980) + (114) + (-844) =$

8.11 MULTIPLICATION OF SIGNED NUMBERS

In multiplying signed numbers, we multiply the absolute numerical values in the same way as in arithmetic. Our main problem, then, is to determine the sign of the product.

In multiplication we call the number to be multiplied the *multiplicand.* The other number is called the *multiplier.* The answer obtained by multiplication is called the *product.*

Multiplication can be considered a short form of addition. In a problem in arithmetic, such as (3×482), the 3 is the multiplier. It shows how many times the multiplicand is to be added. As addition, the problem may be written

$$
\begin{array}{r}
482 \\
482 \\
\underline{482}
\end{array}
$$

Now suppose we have this problem in the multiplication of signed numbers: $(+3) \cdot (+4)$. Let us write one number above the other.

Example 1.   Multiply
$$
\begin{array}{r}
+4 \\
\underline{+3}
\end{array}
$$

The absolute numerical value of the product is 12. Our problem now is to determine the sign of the answer.

Let us call the $+3$ the multiplier. Suppose we consider the plus sign $(+)$ before the 3 as the sign of operation (addition). Then, since multiplication is a short form of addition, the problem means

add three "+4's"

In column addition the statement becomes

$$\begin{array}{r} +4 \\ +4 \\ +4 \\ \hline +12 \end{array}$$

If we look upon the +4's as scores in a game, the problem means

adding three +4's to your score changes your total by +12

Example 2.   Multiply
$$\begin{array}{r} -4 \\ +3 \\ \hline -12 \end{array}$$

Again, the absolute numerical value of the answer is 12. To determine the sign of the product, consider the plus sign (+) before the multiplier 3, as the sign of the operation (addition). The problem then means

add three "−4's"

Adding three −4's to your score changes your total by −12. Therefore, $(+3)(-4) = -12$.

Example 3.   Multiply $(+4)(-3)$.
Or in column form, multiply
$$\begin{array}{r} +4 \\ -3 \\ \hline -12 \end{array}$$

Again, the absolute numerical value of the answer is 12. To determine the sign of the product, consider the minus sign (−) before the multiplier, 3, as the sign of operation (subtraction). The problem then means

subtract three "+4's"

Subtracting three +4's from your score changes your total by −12. Therefore, $(-3)(+4) = -12$.

Example 4.   Multiply $(-3)(-4)$.
Or in column form, multiply
$$\begin{array}{r} -4 \\ -3 \\ \hline +12 \end{array}$$

Again, the absolute numerical value of the answer is 12. To determine the sign of the product, consider the minus sign (−) before the multiplier, 3, as the sign of operation (subtraction). Then the problem means

subtract three "−4's"

Subtracting three −4's from your score changes your total by +12. Therefore, $(-3)(-4) = +12$.

From the foregoing examples we can formulate the rule for multiplying signed numbers.

Rule. *The product of two numbers with like signs is a positive number. The product of two numbers with unlike signs is negative.*

In symbols, the rule for the signs of a product may be stated in this way:

$$(+)(+) = + \qquad (+)(-) = -$$
$$(-)(-) = + \qquad (-)(+) = - :$$

However, remember that this way of showing the rule for the multiplication of signed numbers is only symbolic and the signs themselves are not to be considered as factors.

Note. When we come to the multiplication of signed numbers under radical signs, we shall find it necessary to modify slightly the statement: $(-)(-) = +$.

Exercise 8.5

Multiply the following:

1. $(-3)(-7)(-4) =$
2. $(-5)(+4)(-6) =$
3. $(+8)(-1)(-5) =$
4. $(12)(-2)(+8) =$
5. $(-1.2)(3.5)(4.3) =$
6. $(-\frac{1}{2})(-24)(-\frac{2}{3}) =$
7. $(+36)(-0.04)(-2) =$
8. $(-7.2)(+0.13)(-3.5) =$
9. $(6.3)(-2.4)(-1)(-2) =$
10. $(-\frac{3}{5})(\frac{4}{7})(-\frac{5}{8})(+4) =$
11. $(-1)(-2)(+3)(-4)(+4) =$
12. $(2)(-3)(-1)(+2)(-2)(+3) =$
13. $(-4)(+1)(-3)(-1)(-3)(-5)(-1) =$
14. $(-1)(-2)(+3)(-5)(-2)(-6)(+2) =$
15. $(+2)(3)(-4)(-1)(+5)(-1)(-1) =$
16. $(-4)(7)(+\frac{1}{2})(-3)(-\frac{2}{3})(-\frac{3}{8}) =$
17. $(3)(-1)(-1)(4)(2)(5)(-1)(\frac{4}{15}) =$
18. $(-8)(-2)(-5)(-\frac{1}{4})(-\frac{1}{15})(10) =$
19. $(+1)(-3)(-4)(-3)(-3)(-5)(-1) =$
20. $(-4)(+3)(7)(-1)(-2)(+8)(4) =$

21.

$+62$	-81	$+124$	-98	-76	$+123$	-63
$+75$	-42	-31	$+23$	-12	-14	$+17$

22.

-114	$+13.24$	-21.3	-2.31	$-.072$	$-.472$	$+.00351$
-15	$-.27$	$-.48$	-4.3	$+.13$	5.2	$-.042$

8.12 DIVISION OF SIGNED NUMBERS

In division we have the same rules for signs as in multiplication.

Rule.   *The division of numbers with like signs gives a positive quotient.
The division of numbers with unlike signs gives a negative quotient.*

Examples.

$$(+12) \div (+4) = +3 \qquad (-12) \div (+4) = -3$$
$$(-12) \div (-4) = +3 \qquad (+12) \div (-4) = -3$$

Division may be checked by multiplication in the same way as in arithmetic; that is, the quotient multiplied by the divisor should equal the dividend. This method of checking division also applies to signs as well as to the numerical values.

In symbols, the rule for the sign of the quotient in division may be stated in this way:

$$(+) \div (+) = + \qquad (+) \div (-) = -$$
$$(-) \div (-) = + \qquad (-) \div (+) = -$$

Exercise 8.6

Divide as indicated:

1. $(+15) \div (+3) =$ **2.** $(-16) \div (-2) =$ **3.** $(-24) \div (+3) =$

4. $(36) \div (-9) =$ **5.** $(-40) \div (-8) =$ **6.** $(30) \div (5) =$

7. $(-128) \div (8) =$ **8.** $(144) \div (-6) =$ **9.** $(180) \div (-12) =$

10. $(-152) \div (-4) =$ **11.** $(-8) \div (-12) =$ **12.** $(-17) \div (+4) =$

13. $(13) \div (-5) =$ **14.** $(-20) \div (-8) =$ **15.** $(16) \div (12) =$

16. $(-\frac{5}{12}) \div (-\frac{3}{4}) =$ **17.** $(+\frac{3}{7}) \div (-\frac{6}{11}) =$ **18.** $(-\frac{4}{7}) \div (\frac{3}{5}) =$

19. $\dfrac{-936}{-8} =$ $\dfrac{-322}{+23} =$ $\dfrac{+966}{-42} =$ $\dfrac{-527}{-31} =$ $\dfrac{-0.16}{8} =$

20. $\dfrac{-0.72}{+1.2} =$ $\dfrac{-5.6}{-1.4} =$ $\dfrac{-0.3794}{-1.4} =$ $\dfrac{8.4}{-.07} =$ $\dfrac{-0.0028}{-.7} =$

21. $\dfrac{-7}{-3} =$ $\dfrac{+15}{-10} =$ $\dfrac{+0.3798}{+180} =$ $\dfrac{-48}{-60} =$ $\dfrac{-5376}{24} =$

22. A football halfback carrying the ball 7 times during a game made the following yardages for the times he carried the ball: loss 4 yards, gain 13 yards, gain 6 yards, gain 8 yards, loss 3 yards, gain 0 yards, gain 2 yards. Show his gains and losses by signed numbers and then find his total yardage. What was his average gain or loss per carry during the game?

23. A football player made the following gains and losses in a game: gain 2 yards, loss 5 yards, gain 4 yards, loss 7 yards, gain 3 yards, loss 8 yards, loss 3 yards. Show his gains and losses by signed numbers and find his total yardage gained. What was his average gain per carry?

24. An elevator operator made the following moves starting at the ground floor: up 3 floors; up 5 floors, down 2 floors, down 4 floors, up 8 floors, up 1 floor, down 9 floors, down 3 floors. Show the moves by signed numbers. Where was the operator at the end of the last move mentioned?

9
Operations with Algebraic Expressions

9.1 DEFINITIONS

A *product* is the answer obtained by multiplying two or more quantities together. For instance, in the multiplication $3 \cdot 5 = 15$, the 15 is the product of the two numbers 3 and 5. The product of 2, 2, 3, and 7 is 84. The product of $5x$ and y is $5xy$. The word *product* always implies multiplication.

The quantities multiplied together to form a product are called the *factors* of the product. The numbers 3 and 5 are factors of 15. One set of factors of $5xy$ is $5x$ and y.

Sometimes a factor can itself be further split up into factors. For instance, we can say that the factors of 60 are 6 and 10. However, the 6 and the 10 can be separated into other factors. The 6 is a product of 2 and 3. The 10 can be separated into two factors, 2 and 5. A factor that cannot be further separated into other factors except itself and 1 is called a *prime* factor. The prime factors of 60 are 2, 2, 3, and 5, since these numbers multiplied together make a product of 60. In like manner, we can say that the prime factors of $3axy$ are 3, a, x, and y, since these numbers multiplied together form the product $3axy$. The prime factors of $-ab$ are -1, a, and b.

If two numbers are multiplied together, such as in the product $3 \cdot 7$, either factor is called the *coefficient* of the other. The word *coefficient* means that the two numbers are *efficient together* in forming the product 21. In this example 3 is the coefficient of 7 and 7 is the coefficient of 3. However, both numbers are factors of 21.

It is important that you understand exactly what is meant by the words *coefficient, factor,* and *product.* In the product $5xy$

the coefficient of x is $5y$
the coefficient of y is $5x$
the coefficient of 5 is xy
the coefficient of xy is 5
the coefficient of $5y$ is x
the coefficient of $5x$ is y

The numbers 5, x, and y are the *factors* of the product $5xy$.

In the product $5xy$ the number "5" is the *numerical* coefficient. By *numerical* coefficient we mean the *arithmetic* factor. In common practice, the word *coefficient* usually refers to the numerical coefficient. If a literal number is shown without the numerical coefficient, its coefficient is always understood to be 1 (or *unity*, as mathematicians say). The numerical coefficient of xy is 1. The numerical coefficient of $-xy$ is -1.

A *term* is any algebraic expression not separated within itself by a plus or minus sign. A term consists only of factors. The following expressions are single terms:

$$3xy, \qquad 4x^2y^3, \qquad -7abcd, \qquad -2x, \qquad y, \qquad 2a^2b^2cx^4y^5z$$

A term indicates a *product*, not a sum or difference. The sign of a term is the sign preceding it. If no sign is expressed, the term is always *positive*.

Like, or *similar*, terms are terms that are exactly alike in their letter parts. The terms shown here are like terms, since the letter part is x^2y in all:

$$4x^2y, \qquad -7x^2y, \qquad -5x^2y, \qquad 15x^2y, \qquad -x^2y$$

Unlike, or *dissimilar*, terms are terms that are not exactly alike in their letter parts. The following are unlike, or dissimilar, terms:

$$4x^2y, \qquad -7xyz, \qquad -5xy^2, \qquad 3x^2z, \qquad 2x, \qquad -5y^2$$

A *monomial* is an algebraic expression consisting of only one term, such as $5xy$. A *polynomial* is an algebraic expression of more than one term. The following expressions are polynomials:

$$5x^2 + 3xy, \qquad 4xy + 7ab - x^2y, \qquad 7x^2 - 2xy + 3y^2 - 5x + 2y$$

A polynomial indicates the sum or difference of two or more terms.

A polynomial of two terms is usually called a *binomial*. A polynomial of three terms is often called a *trinomial*. The expression $5x^2 + 3xy$ is a binomial. The expression $4xy + 7ab - x^2y$ is a trinomial.

An *exponent* is a mathematical notation whose meaning must be thoroughly understood by a student of algebra. Perhaps more mistakes are made in algebra because of a misunderstanding of the meaning of *exponent* than for any other reason. To avoid errors in the use of exponents, we must understand the exact meaning of the word.

It often happens that we wish to multiply a number by itself, such as $5 \cdot 5$. To indicate this multiplication, we can write 5 with a small 2 placed at the right and a little above the 5; thus 5^2. The 2 here indicates that two 5's are to be multiplied. The 2 so placed and having this meaning is called an *exponent*. It indicates the *power* to which the 5 is to be raised. The number 5 on which the exponent is placed is called the *base*.

The expression 7^2 is called "7 squared," or "7 raised to the second power." The expression, 7^3, is read "7 cubed," or "7 raised to the third power." The exponent 3 placed on the base 7 means that the base is to be used three times as a factor; that is, $7^3 = 7 \cdot 7 \cdot 7 = 343$. If we wish to indicate the multiplication $x \cdot x \cdot x \cdot x$, we can write it x^4. This expression is read "x raised to the fourth power," or simply "x fourth."

If any number is shown without an exponent, its exponent is always understood to be 1 (unity). The number x means x^1. Also, 5^1 means 5.

From the several examples given we summarize the definition of an exponent:

An exponent is a number placed at the right and slightly above another number, the base, to show how many times the base is to be used as a factor.

9.2 ADDITION AND SUBTRACTION OF MONOMIALS

We add or subtract like terms simply by adding or subtracting their numerical coefficients. Notice that the letter part is not changed. The following examples show *addition* of monomials:

$+7$ miles	$8x^2y$	$-9x^3y^2$	$-3abc$	$6mn$	$-5xy$
$+2$ miles	$2x^2y$	$5x^3y^2$	$-2abc$	$-mn$	xy
$+9$ miles	$10x^2y$	$-4x^3y^2$	$-5abc$	$5mn$	$-4xy$

In each of the following examples the bottom monomial is subtracted from the top (recall the rule for subtraction):

$+5xy^2$	$-5a^3b$	$-3cd$	$-6xyz$	$+\ rst$	$-7h^2k^3$
$+2xy^2$	$2a^3b$	$-8cd$	$-7xyz$	$-4rst$	$-6h^2k^3$
$+3xy^2$	$-7a^3b$	$+5cd$	xyz	$+5rst$	$-h^2k^3$

If two terms are unlike, their sum or difference can only be indicated or expressed. Add the following:

7 dollars	$+8x$	$-6a$	$5x^2$
3 pesos	$+2y$	$-4b$	$-3x$
7 dollars + 3 pesos	$8x + 2y$	$-6a - 4b$	$5x^2 - 3x$

In each of the following examples the bottom monomial is subtracted from the top (recall the rule for subtraction):

$+7x$	$-4a$	$3cd$	$-5x^2y$	u
$+3y$	$+9b$	$-5mn$	$2xy^2$	v
$+7x - 3y$	$-4a - 9b$	$3cd + 5mn$	$-5x^2y - 2xy^2$	$u - v$

In horizontal addition or subtraction of monomials like terms may be combined. For example,

$$3x^2y - 4xy^2 - 3x + x^2y + 2xy^2 + 4x = 4x^2y - 2xy^2 + x$$

9.3 ADDITION AND SUBTRACTION OF POLYNOMIALS

To add or subtract polynomials, we write one polynomial under the other so that like terms fall in the same column. We then add or subtract each column separately, just as we add or subtract monomials.

Example 1. Add the following polynomials:
$$3x^2 - 4xy + 5y^2; \; 3xy - 3y^2 - x^2 + ab; \; 3x + 4x^2 - 2y^2 - 2ab.$$
Solution.
$$
\begin{array}{l}
3x^2 - 4xy + 5y^2 \\
-\;x^2 + 3xy - 3y^2 + ab \\
\underline{4x^2 - 2y^2 - 2ab + 3x} \\
6x^2 - xy - ab + 3x
\end{array}
$$

None of the terms in the sum can be combined further, since all are unlike terms.

Example 2. From $5x^2 - 3xy + 2y^2 - 2x$ subtract the polynomial $3y^2 - 2x^2 - 5y - 3xy$.
Solution.
$$
\begin{array}{l}
5x^2 - 3xy + 2y^2 - 2x \\
\underline{-2x^2 - 3xy + 3y^2 - 5y} \\
7x^2 - y^2 - 2x + 5y
\end{array}
$$

9.4 HORIZONTAL ADDITION AND SUBTRACTION OF POLYNOMIALS

The addition and subtraction of polynomials may be indicated horizontally by use of parentheses. Any terms enclosed in a set of parentheses must be considered as a single quantity. The addition of two polynomials, such as $4x^2 - 3xy - 2y^2$ and $2x^2 + 3xy - 5y^2$, can be shown by enclosing each in a set of parentheses and placing the addition sign between them:

$$(4x^2 - 3xy - 2y^2) + (2x^2 + 3xy - 5y^2)$$

You recall that when we add like terms we simply combine the terms according to the rules of algebraic addition. Since none of the signs is changed in addition, we can remove the parentheses without changing any signs and then combine like terms; thus

$$4x^2 - 3xy - 2y^2 + 2x^2 + 3xy - 5y^2 = 6x^2 - 7y^2$$

Horizontal subtraction of polynomials can be indicated by enclosing each polynomial in a set of parentheses and placing the subtraction sign, $-$, between the two quantities. For instance, if we wish to indicate the subtraction of the polynomial $2x^2 - 3x + 5$ from the polynomial $5x^2 + 2x + 5$, we can indicate the subtraction in this way:

$$(5x^2 + 2x + 5) - (2x^2 - 3x + 5)$$

Before like terms can be combined, the parentheses must be removed. Remember that in subtraction we change the sign of the number subtracted and then add algebraically. The problem can be changed to

$$(5x^2 + 2x + 5) + (-2x^2 + 3x - 5)$$

Now, if the parentheses and the sign of operation, $+$, are dropped, like terms may be combined; thus

$$5x^2 + 2x + 5 - 2x^2 + 3x - 5 = 3x^2 + 5x$$

From the foregoing examples we can formulate a simple rule for horizontal addition and subtraction of polynomials.

Rule. *If a quantity within parentheses is preceded by a plus sign* $(+)$*, this plus sign and the parentheses may be omitted without changing the sign of any term within the parentheses.*

If a quantity within parentheses is preceded by a minus sign $(-)$*, this minus sign and the parentheses may be omitted provided that the sign of each term within the parentheses is changed.*

Exercise 9.1

First add each of the following sets of monomials; then subtract the bottom monomial from top in each set.

1. $3x$ $-4x^2$ $-5st$ $+5n$ $4xy$ $-7x^2y$
     $5x$ $-7x^2$ $+\ st$ $-3n$ $-3xy$ $-3x$ x^2y

2. $-5b$ $-5n$ $3a^3$ $-6xy^2$ $-7x^3y$ $8xy^3$ $-9c^2$
     $8b$ 0 $-9a^3$ $-\ x^2y$ $4x^3y$ $-5x$ $-2c$

3. xy^3 $-3st^2$ $-7xy$ $-3xyz$ $-4m^2n$ $-9x^2y$ $-12xy$
     $7xy^3$ $-8st^2$ $+6xy$ $+3xyz$ $3m^2n$ $-9x^2y$ $-12xy^2$

4. $5a^2b^3$ $5bx^3$ $-\ 7ax$ $6m^2n$ $-\ 4x^2y^3$ $-12yz^3$ $-5a^2c^3$
     $-4a^2b^3$ $-7bx^3$ $+15ax$ $15m^2n$ $-13x^2y^3$ $-\ 8yz^3$ $6a^2c^2$

Add the following

5. $3x^2y$ **6.** ab^3 **7.** $-4x^2y^3$ **8.** $-\ bc^3d^2$
     $-5x^2y$ $-8ab^3$ x^2y^3 $6bc^3d^2$
     $7x^2y$ $4ab^3$ $-9x^2y^3$ $-5bc^3d^2$
     $-\ x^2y$ $2ab^3$ $5x^2y^3$ bc^3d^2

Horizontal addition and subtraction. Combine the following:

9. $2a + 4b + 3c - 3b + 5a - c + a - ab + 5c + 6b - 2a - b =$

10. $3x - (2y) - (-5x) + (-4z) - 3y + (6z) - (-2x) - (+3z) + 4y + z =$

11. $4x + 3y + 6 - (+3x) - (-7y) - 2 + 5z + 5x - (+4y) + (-6z) + 5 - x =$

12. $ab + 4b^2 - 5a^2 - 3ab + 3a + 2b - 2a^2 - b^2 - (-a) - (+ab) + 7 =$

Add the following polynomials:

13.
$$3x^2 - 5xy + 6y^2$$
$$x^2 + 4xy - 3y^2$$
$$-4x^2 - xy - 2y^2$$

14.
$$5x^3 - 3x^2y + 4y^3$$
$$-2x^3 + x^2y - 2xy^2$$
$$-3x^3 + x^2y - 3y^2 + 3xy^2$$

Subtract the following polynomials (bottom from the top):

15.
$$5x^2 - 4xy + 6y^2$$
$$3x^2 + xy - 5y^2$$

16.
$$-x^2 - 4xy + 3y^2 - 2x$$
$$-3x^2 - xy - 3x - 4y$$

17. Add $5x^2 + 2xy - 3y^2$ to $x^2 + 6y^2 - 4xy$.

18. Add $3x^2 - 7xy + 2y^2$ to $2xy - y^2 - x^2$.

19. Add $3nx - 5n^2 + x^2$ to $3x^2 - n^2 + 2nx$.

20. Add $y + 2xy - 4x^2 - y^2$ to $x^2 - 3y^2 - 4x - 2xy$.

21. Add $5x^2 - 3xy + y^2$, $5xy - 3x^2 + 2xy$, $5x + 4xy - 3x^2$.

22. Subtract $4x^2 - 2xy - 3y^2$ from $2x^2 - 5xy + y^2$.

23. Subtract $3x^2 - y^2 - 5xy - 3x$ from $x^2 - 2xy - 3y^2$.

24. From $5x^2y + 2x^2y^2 - 3xy^2$ take $2x^2y - 4xy^2 + 3x^2y^2$.

25. From $8x^3 - 3x^2 + 4x$ take $3x^3 + 2x^2 - 5x$.

26. Take $-2x^2 + xy + y^2$ from $x^2 + y^2$.

9.5 CHECKING THE WORK IN ALGEBRA

Since the letters we use in algebra represent arithmetic numbers, we can check our work by replacing each letter with some particular value. For example, suppose we have this example in addition:

$$3x^2 - 4xy + 5y^2$$
$$x^2 + 5xy - 4y^2$$

The sum is
$$4x^2 + xy + y^2$$

Now, if we let x equal some value, such as 2, and y equal some other value, such as 3, we then find that the first polynomial is equal to 33, the second is equal to -2, and the sum is 31, which checks with the sum.

In checking your work with particular values, you may use any arithmetic numbers for x or y. However, the numbers 1 or 0 should not be selected, since such a check would be worthless. The *best check* on your work consists of these two steps:

(a) *First, know how to do the work correctly.*

(b) *Then, do the work over again.*

10

Multiplication and Division

10.1 MEANING OF AN EXPONENT

In the multiplication and division of algebraic quantities, it is essential that we understand clearly the meaning of an exponent. In Chapter 2 we defined the word. However, at this point we need to emphasize the meaning a little more carefully.

We have seen that if we wish to indicate the multiplication of several equal factors, we can do so by the use of an *exponent*. For example, to indicate the multiplication, $5 \cdot 5 \cdot 5$, we can write the number 3 at the right and a little above the 5: thus, 5^3. The 3 used in this way is called an *exponent* and the 5 is called the *base*. The expression means that three 5's are to be multiplied together.

Let us repeat the definition of an exponent.

Definition. *An exponent is a number placed at the right and a little above another number, called the base, to show how many times the base is to be used as a factor.*

It might be pointed out that the exponent of a power was not always placed in this particular position. Its position is not significant, except that everyone today places it as shown. However, the important thing about an exponent is its *meaning*.

The expression x^4 means that four x's are to be multiplied together. To show the multiplication of five 2's together, we write 2^5. This is read "2 raised to the fifth power" or "2 to the fifth." Its value is 32. The fourth power of 7 is written 7^4, which is equal to 2401.

10.2 EXPONENTS IN MULTIPLICATION

Let us see what we mean by multiplying two powers, such as $x^4 \cdot x^3$:

$$x^4 \text{ means } x \cdot x \cdot x \cdot x$$
$$x^3 \text{ means } x \cdot x \cdot x$$

Therefore, $x^4 \cdot x^3$ means $(x \cdot x \cdot x \cdot x) \cdot (x \cdot x \cdot x)$. By using another exponent,

114

we can write the product as x^7. Therefore, we can say

$$x^4 \cdot x^3 = x^7$$

If we analyze in the same way the multiplication of two other powers, such as $n^5 \cdot n^8$, we find that the product is n^{13}. From these examples and many others we can formulate the rule for exponents in the multiplication of algebraic quantities:

Rule. *In multiplying algebraic quantities, expressed as powers, we add exponents of the same base.* (Be careful not to say simply, "when we multiply, we add." We are multiplying the *quantities*, not the exponents.)

This rule holds true for arithmetic numbers as well as for literal numbers.

$$2^5 \cdot 2^3 = 2^8 \quad \text{means } 32 \cdot 8 = 256$$
$$10^5 \cdot 10 = 10^6 \text{ means } 100,000 \cdot 10 = 1,000,000$$
$$5^3 \cdot 5^4 = 5^7 \quad \text{means } 125 \cdot 625 = 78,125$$

We state without proof the following facts:

1. The rule for adding exponents in multiplication holds true for fractional exponents: (add exponents.)

$$x^{\frac{1}{4}} \cdot x^{\frac{3}{8}} = x^{\frac{5}{8}}$$

2. The rule holds true for negative and zero exponents, as well as for positive exponents: (add exponents.)

$$(x^6)(x^{-2}) \quad = x^4$$
$$(x^{-5})(x^{-2}) = x^{-7}$$
$$(x^5)(x^0) \quad = x^5$$

3. The rule holds true also for literal exponents: (add exponents.)

$$(x^n)(x) \quad = x^{n+1} \qquad (x^a)(x^b) = x^{a+b}$$
$$(x^{2c})(x^c) = x^{3c} \qquad (2^n)(2) \quad = 2^{n+1}$$
$$(x^{a^2-3a+5})(x^{2a^2+a-2}) = x^{3a^2-2a+3}$$

If we have the multiplication of two quantities that include different bases, we add exponents of *each* base, separately.

Example. Multiply $(x^3y^2)(x^4y^3)$.
The quantity $x^3y^2 = x \cdot x \cdot x \cdot y \cdot y$
The quantity $x^4y^3 = x \cdot x \cdot x \cdot x \cdot y \cdot y \cdot y$
Therefore, $(x^3y^2)(x^4y^3) = x \cdot x \cdot x \cdot y \cdot y \cdot x \cdot x \cdot x \cdot x \cdot y \cdot y \cdot y$
Since multiplication of factors may be done in any order, the foregoing factors may be written simply as x^7y^5. Therefore, $(x^3y^2)(x^4y^3) = x^7y^5$.

When we multiply the two quantities together, we can get the product quickly by adding separately the exponents of x and the exponents of y. The exponent of x in the product is equal to the *sum* of the exponents of x in the factors. The exponent of y in the product is equal to the *sum* of the exponents of y in the factors.

10.3 MULTIPLICATION OF MONOMIALS

Example 1. Suppose we have the following problem in multiplication. $(-2x^3y^2z) \times (-5axy^4)$. To formulate a rule for multiplying monomials, let us first separate these monomials into prime factors:

$$-2x^3y^2z = (-2) \cdot x \cdot x \cdot x \cdot y \cdot y \cdot z$$
$$-5axy^4 = (-5) \cdot a \cdot x \cdot y \cdot y \cdot y \cdot y$$

The product, after rearranging factors, is

$$(-2) \cdot (-5) \cdot a \cdot x \cdot x \cdot x \cdot x \cdot y \cdot y \cdot y \cdot y \cdot y \cdot y \cdot z$$

By multiplying the factors, we get the product:

$$(-2x^3y^2z)(-5axy^4) = +10ax^4y^6z$$

In the multiplication of monomials we have the following steps:

Step 1. Determine the sign of the product by the rule for the multiplication of signed numbers.

Step 2. Multiply the numerical coefficients of the factors to get the numerical coefficient of the product.

Step 3. Multiply the literal parts by writing down all literal factors and adding the exponents of like literal factors.

Example 2. Multiply $(-3ab^2x^3)(-4a^2cx^2)(-5b^4cxy^2)$.

The product of three negative numbers is negative. The product of the numerical coefficients is $(3)(4)(5) = 60$. Adding the exponents of like literal factors,

$$a \cdot a^2 = a^3; \qquad b^2 \cdot b^4 = b^6; \qquad c \cdot c = c^2; \qquad x^3 \cdot x^2 \cdot x = x^6; \qquad y^2 = y^2$$

The final product is $-60 \ a^3b^6c^2x^6y^2$

10.4 EXPONENTS IN DIVISION

Since division is the inverse of multiplication, we should expect that division would require a procedure opposite to that of multiplication in the handling of exponents. In multiplication we *add* exponents of the same base. *In division we subtract exponents of the same base.* (The student should be careful *not* to say simply, "When we divide, we subtract." Remember we are dividing the *quantities*, not the exponents.)

The rule for exponents in division can be seen in examples. Suppose we wish to divide the quantity x^6 by the quantity x^2; that is, $x^6 \div x^2$. Let us first write the division as a fraction and then separate the quantities into prime factors:

$$\frac{x^6}{x^2} = \frac{x \cdot x \cdot x \cdot x \cdot x \cdot x}{x \cdot x}$$

If we now divide numerator and denominator by $x \cdot x$, we get

$$\frac{x^6}{x^2} = \frac{\cancel{x} \cdot \cancel{x} \cdot x \cdot x \cdot x \cdot x}{\cancel{x} \cdot \cancel{x}} = x^4$$

Stated in horizontal form, $x^6 \div x^2 = x^4$.

From the foregoing example, and others, we can formulate the rule for division:

Rule. *In dividing algebraic quantities expressed as powers, we subtract the exponent of the divisor from the exponent of the dividend.*

Examples. $\dfrac{n^9}{n^3} = n^6$; $\quad a^{20} \div a^4 = a^{16}$; $\quad x^5 \div x = x^4$.

Note. *Division may be checked by multiplication.*

We state without proof the following facts:

1. The rule for subtracting exponents in division holds true also for *fractional exponents* (subtract exponents):

$$x^{\frac{3}{4}} \div x^{\frac{1}{8}} = x^{\frac{3}{4} - \frac{1}{8}} = x^{\frac{5}{8}}$$

2. The rule holds true for *negative and zero exponents*, as well as for positive exponents (subtract exponents):

$$x^5 \div x^{-2} = x^7 \qquad x^6 \div x^0 = x^6 \qquad x^{-3} \div x^{-7} = x^4$$
$$x^3 \div x^5 = x^{-2} \qquad x^5 \div x^5 = x^0$$

3. The rule holds true also for *literal exponents* (subtract exponents):

$$x^n \div x = x^{n-1} \qquad x^p \div x^q = x^{p-q} \qquad x^{4n} \div x^n = x^{3n}$$
$$\left(x^{2a^2 - 3a + 4}\right) \div \left(x^{a^2 + a + 5}\right) = x^{a^2 - 4a - 1}$$

10.5 DIVISION OF MONOMIALS

In division the number divided by another is called the *dividend*. The number that is divided into another is called the *divisor*. The answer obtained is called the *quotient*. After the division is completed as far as possible, any part of the dividend that is left over is called the *remainder*.

Suppose we have the following problem in division:

$$(-20x^5y^4z) \div (-5x^4y^2)$$

To formulate a rule for dividing monomials, let us first separate the monomials into prime factors and write the division as a fraction:

$$\frac{-20x^5y^4z}{-5x^4y^2} = \frac{(-)2 \cdot 2 \cdot 5 \cdot x \cdot x \cdot x \cdot x \cdot x \cdot y \cdot y \cdot y \cdot y \cdot z}{(-)5 \cdot x \cdot x \cdot x \cdot x \cdot y \cdot y}$$

If we divide numerator and denominator by equal factors, we get the answer. Remember, $(-) \div (-) = +$.

$$\frac{(-) \cdot 2 \cdot 2 \cdot \cancel{5} \cdot \cancel{x} \cdot \cancel{x} \cdot \cancel{x} \cdot \cancel{x} \cdot x \cdot \cancel{y} \cdot \cancel{y} \cdot y \cdot y \cdot z}{(-) \cdot \cancel{5} \cdot \cancel{x} \cdot \cancel{x} \cdot \cancel{x} \cdot \cancel{x} \cdot \cancel{y} \cdot \cancel{y}} = +4xy^2z$$

In division of monomials we have the following steps:

1. *Determine the sign of the quotient by the rule for the division of signed numbers.*
2. *Divide the numerical coefficients to get the numerical coefficient of the quotient.*
3. *Divide the literal parts by writing down all the literal factors of the dividend and subtracting the exponents of like factors in the divisor.*

Example. Divide $-36a^2bx^3y^4z$ by $4abxy^4$.

Solution. The sign of the quotient is equal to $(-) \div (+) = -$.
Dividing the numerical coefficients, we get 9.
Subtracting the exponents of the literal factors, we get ax^2z.
Therefore, the complete quotient is $-9ax^2z$.

Note. The division of monomials can be performed without writing out the separate prime factors.

10.6 MULTIPLICATION OF A POLYNOMIAL BY A MONOMIAL

To indicate the multiplication of a polynomial by a monomial, we can place the expressions next to each other, but *the polynomial must be enclosed in parentheses.* Any expression enclosed in parentheses, braces, brackets, or other signs of grouping is to be considered as a single quantity.

For example, if we wish to indicate the multiplication of the polynomial, $5x^2 - 7xy + 4y^2$, by the monomial 3, we enclose the polynomial in parentheses and then place the 3 either before or after the polynomial as shown here:

$$3(5x^2 - 7xy + 4y^2)$$

The expression then means that the entire polynomial is to be multiplied by the monomial. For the product we multiply *each* term of the polynomial by 3 and get

$$3(5x^2 - 7xy + 4y^2) = 15x^2 - 21xy + 12y^2$$

That the product is correct can be seen if we recall that multiplication is a shortened form of addition. In addition form, the problem becomes:

$$5x^2 - 7xy + 4y^2$$
$$5x^2 - 7xy + 4y^2$$
$$5x^2 - 7xy + 4y^2$$

Adding like terms, $\qquad 15x^2 - 21xy + 12y^2$

The foregoing example is an illustration of the following rule:

Rule. *To multiply a polynomial by a monomial, multiply each term of the polynomial by the monomial.*

This rule is the application of the so-called *Distributive Law*, which states that *multiplication is distributive with respect to addition*. In general terms, the law states that $a(b + c) = ab + ac$.

Note. Be careful to observe all the rules for signs, coefficients, and letters with their exponents.

Example 1. Find the indicated product: $-3x^2y(4x^2 - 5xy - 7y^2)$.

Solution. The first term of the product is $(-3x^2y)(4x^2) = -12x^4y$. The second term of the product is $(-3x^2y)(-5xy) = +15x^3y^2$. The third term of the product is $(-3x^2y)(-7y^2) = +21x^2y^3$. The complete product is $-12x^4y + 15x^3y^2 + 21x^2y^3$.

Example 2. Find the indicated product: $x(x^3 - 4x^2 + 5x + 1)$. By the foregoing rule, the product is $x^4 - 4x^3 + 5x^2 + x$.

Example 3. Perform the indicated multiplication: $2x(3x^2 - 5xy + 8y^2)(-4y)$.

Solution. In this example the polynomial $3x^2 - 5xy + 8y^2$ is to be multiplied by $2x$ and also by $(-4y)$. Notice that $-4y$ must be enclosed in parentheses, or the meaning will not be clear.

The actual multiplying may be done in two different ways. We may first multiply the monomial $2x$ by the monomial $(-4y)$. The monomial multiplier then becomes $-8xy$. In this case we have

$$-8xy(3x^2 - 5xy + 8y^2) = -24x^3y + 40x^2y^2 - 64xy^3$$

The product could also be found by multiplying the polynomial first by $2x$. The result is $6x^3 - 10x^2y + 16xy^2$. We now multiply this polynomial by $-4y$ and get $-24x^3y + 40x^2y^2 - 64xy^3$. However, in an example such as the foregoing the simplest way to find the product is to consider the entire monomial multiplier as $(2x)(-4y)$ or $-8xy$.

10.7 DIVISION OF A POLYNOMIAL BY A MONOMIAL

Since division and multiplication are inverse processes, we have the following rule for division:

Rule. *To divide a polynomial by a monomial, divide each term of the polynomial by the monomial.*

This rule is simply a restatement of the Distributive Law, this time in reverse. In general terms,

$$ab + ac = a(b + c)$$

As in the division of monomials, be careful to observe the rules for signs, coefficients, and exponents.

Example 1. Divide the polynomial $(18x^4y - 15x^3y^2 - 12x^2y^3)$ by $(-3x^2y)$.
This division problem may also be written as a fraction:

$$\frac{18x^4y - 15x^3y^2 - 12x^2y^3}{-3x^2y}$$

Here we divide *each* term of the polynomial by the monomial $-3x^2y$ and get the quotient

$$-6x^2 + 5xy + 4y^2$$

The answer can be checked by multiplication. If we multiply the quotient by the divisor, the answer should be the dividend.

Example 2. Divide $(12ax^2 - 6a^2x^3 + 3ax) \div (3ax)$. In this example the quotient is $4x - 2ax^2 + 1$.
Let us consider carefully the division of $3ax$ into the first term of the polynomial; that is $(12ax^2) \div (3ax)$. Taking one factor at a time; we have

$$12 \div 3 = 4 \qquad a \div a = 1 \qquad x^2 \div x = x$$

If we write each part of the quotient separately, we find that the quotient of $(12ax^2) \div (3ax)$ is equal to $4 \cdot 1 \cdot x$. Whenever we find 1 as a factor with other factors, then the 1 may be omitted.

Example 3. Divide as indicated: $(5x^3 - 4x^2 + x) \div (x)$.
When each term of the polynomial is divided by the divisor, x, the quotient is $5x^2 - 4x + 1$. The correctness of the answer may be checked by multiplication.
Notice that the 1 must not be omitted in this example.

Exercise 10.1

Rewrite each of the following by the use of exponents:
1. $2 \cdot 2 \cdot 2 \cdot x \cdot x \cdot x \cdot x \cdot y \cdot y$
2. $3 \cdot a \cdot a \cdot b \cdot b \cdot b \cdot c \cdot c \cdot c \cdot c \cdot c$

3. $5 \cdot 5 \cdot 5 \cdot 5 \cdot x \cdot x \cdot x \cdot y \cdot z$
4. $7 \cdot 7 \cdot 7 \cdot a \cdot a \cdot a \cdot a \cdot a \cdot a \cdot b \cdot b \cdot c \cdot d$
5. $10 \cdot 10 \cdot 10 \cdot 10 \cdot x \cdot x \cdot y \cdot y \cdot z \cdot z \cdot z \cdot z \cdot z$
6. $3 \cdot 3 \cdot 3 \cdot 3 \cdot 5 \cdot 5 \cdot m \cdot m \cdot m \cdot m \cdot m \cdot n \cdot n \cdot n$

Multiply the following:

7. $(3x)(2x)$

8. $(-4x)(-5x^2)$

9. $(-2x^2y)(3xy^3)$

10. $(-3y^2)(y^5)$

11. $(7ax^3y)(-xy^2)$

12. $(4x^4)(5x^5)$

13. $(-3x^3)(-6x^6)$

14. $(5n^5)(n)$

15. $(5ab)(3cd)$

16. $(-c^2x^3y)(-cxy)$

17. $(-3x^2y)(-4x^3z^2)(-5xy^3z^4)$

18. $(-2ab^2c)(7a^3c^2d^4)(-3b^3cd)$

19. $(4mn^2)(-6m^2n^3)(2amn)(-2a^2)$

20. $(5r^2st)(-9rs^2)(-11rs^4t^2)$

21. $(-9xy^2z)(-7x^2z^3)(3x^3yz^4)$

22. $(-3ab)(-2a^2c)(4b^2cd)(-ab)$

23. $(-a^2b)(-a^2b^2c)(-bc^2)(-a)$

24. $-(-2x)(-4x^3y)(-3xy^2)(-y)$

25. $(-1)(-2a)(-3b)(4c)(-5d)(6e)$

26. $-(-t)(u)(-v)(-w)(x)(-y)(-z)$

27. $(3x)(4x^2 + 5xy - 2y^2)$

28. $-2x^2y(x^2y - 4x^3y^2 + x^4y^3)$

29. $2x(4x^2 - 5xy - 7y^2)yz$

30. $3a^2(4a^2 + 4ab - 5b^2)(-2b)$

31. $-4ac^2(-2a^3 + 3a^2bc - 5ab^2c^2 - 3b^3c^4)$
32. $-5xy^2(5x^3 - 3x^2y - xy^2z + y^3z^2)2z$
33. $2xy(4x^3 - 5x^2y + 4xy^2 - y^3 + 2x + 1)$
34. $xy^2z(1 - 4xy^3 - 6y^2z + 3xyz^2 + 7x - 3y)$

Divide as indicated:

35. $(20x^6y^2z^5) \div (-2xyz)$

36. $(-32a^4b^5c) \div (8a^4bc)$

37. $(14m^2n^3xy) \div (7mn^3x)$

38. $(-9ab^2c^3d) \div (6abcd)$

39. $(5x^2yz^3) \div (-5x^2yz^3)$

40. $(-50rs^2t^4) \div (-10rs^2t^4)$

41. $(42x^3yz) \div (-6xy)$

42. $(-36x^3y^4z) \div (-9x^2z)$

43. $(12x^3y^4 - 10xy^3 + 8x^2y^2) \div (-2xy)$
44. $(24ax^2y - 36a^2xy^2 + 12axy) \div (-12axy)$
45. $(8r^2s^3t^4 - 6rs^2t + 4st^3 - 5r^3s^4t^5) \div (2st)$
46. $(6x^6 - 8x^8 + 10x^{10} - 12x^{12} - 4x^4 + 2x^2) \div (2x^2)$

10.8 MULTIPLICATION OF A POLYNOMIAL BY A POLYNOMIAL

The multiplication of a polynomial by another polynomial in algebra is somewhat similar in form to the multiplication in arithmetic of a two-or-more-digit number by another similar number. As an example, consider the following multiplication problem in arithmetic: $(32)(42)$. We usually write one number above the other:

$$32$$

$$42$$

In the multiplication of two numbers, one is called the multiplicand and the other is the multiplier. The number taken a certain number of times is called the *multiplicand*. The number that indicates how many times the multiplicand is to be taken is called the *multiplier*. In arranging the numbers for multiplication, we usually consider the top number the multiplicand and the number below the multiplier.

In the foregoing example in arithmetic notice that we must make *four* separate multiplications. They are $2 \cdot 2$, $2 \cdot 3$, $4 \cdot 2$, and $4 \cdot 3$, as indicated by the arrows in the diagram at the right. The results are placed in their proper positions and added. Each digit in the multiplicand is multiplied by both digits in the multiplier.

In algebra, if we wish to multiply one polynomial by another, we place one below the other, just as in arithmetic. Suppose we have this problem:

Example 1. Multiply $(3x - 4y)(2x + 5y)$.

We use parentheses around each binomial to indicate that it is to be considered as one quantity. For multiplication, we place one binomial below the other:

$$3x - 4y$$
$$2x + 5y$$

Here we have four separate multiplications, just as we had in the arithmetic example. The four separate multiplications are shown by arrows. *Each* term of one binomial must be multiplied by *both* terms of the other.

$$3x - 4y$$
$$\uparrow$$
$$2x + 5y$$
$$6x^2$$

In algebra we begin multiplication at the left side instead of at the right as in arithmetic. The first step is to multiply $(2x)(3x)$. The first product, $6x^2$, is placed at the left just below the $2x$ of the multiplier. The *next* step is the multiplication $(2x)(-4y) = -8xy$. The result is written as the second term of the product.

$$3x \quad -4y$$
$$\uparrow \nearrow$$
$$2x + 5y$$
$$6x^2 - 8xy$$

The third step is the multiplication $(5y)(3x) = 15xy$. Since the product is a term similar to the term $-8xy$, it may be placed in the same column for convenience in adding. The fourth multiplication is $(5y)(-4y)$, which equals $-20y^2$, placed at the right. The partial products are finally combined by addition, as in arithmetic. The complete product is shown.

$$3x \quad - \quad 4y$$
$$\nwarrow \quad \uparrow$$
$$2x \ + \ 5y$$
$$6x^2 - \ 8xy$$
$$+ \ 15xy - 20y^2$$
$$6x^2 + \ 7xy - 20y^2$$

Example 2. Multiply $(4x - 7y)$ by $(3x + 5y)$.

Solution.

$$4x \ - \ 7y$$
$$3x \ + \ 5y$$
$$12x^2 - 21xy$$
$$+ \ 20xy - 35y^2$$
$$12x^2 - \ xy - 35y^2$$

Example 3. Expand $(7 - 3x^2 + 4x^3 - 5x)(2 + 3x)$.

Solution. Before beginning the actual multiplication, we shall often find it desirable to rearrange the terms of the multiplicand and the multiplier. Although the multiplication could be done without making any changes, it is usually better to arrange the terms in a descending order of powers of some letter. Therefore, we arrange the terms of multiplicand and multiplier so that each starts with the highest power of x.

Rearranging terms,	$4x^3 - 3x^2 - 5x + 7$
	$3x + 2$
Multiplying by $3x$,	$12x^4 - 9x^3 - 15x^2 + 21x$
Multiplying by 2,	$8x^3 - 6x^2 - 10x + 14$
The product is	$12x^4 - x^3 - 21x^2 + 11x + 14$

In the foregoing multiplication you will notice that each term of the multiplicand, $4x^3 - 3x^2 - 5x + 7$, is first multiplied by $3x$. Then each term of the multiplicand is multiplied by $+2$. If like terms appear in these multiplications, they are placed in the same columns and then added. If no like terms appear, each term is placed by itself since it cannot be combined with other terms. Note that like terms are added *algebraically*.

For multiplication involving two polynomials we have the following rule.

Rule. *Multiply each term of one polynomial by each term of the other, and combine any like terms that appear.*

In general terms, the rule says

$$(a + b)(c + d) = ac + ad + bc + bd$$

If like terms appear in the multiplication, they can be aligned in the same column to simplify their addition.

Exercise 10.2

Perform the indicated multiplications:

1. $(3x - 5y)(2x + 3y)$
2. $(3x^2 - 5 + 4x)(x - 3)$
3. $(2x^2 - 3xy + y^2)(3x + y)$
4. $(8 - 2x^3 + 3x)(3x - 2)$
5. $(2x^2 - 2xy - y^2)(x - 7)$
6. $(3x^2 - 4x - 5)^2$
7. $(x^2 - 2xy + y^2)^2$
8. $(x - 2)(x^2 + 4x + 8)$
9. $(2x + 1)(3x^2 - 4x - 5)$
10. $(x^2 + 3x - 7)(4 - x)$
11. $(4x^3 - xy^2 - y^3 - 3x^2y)(x - y)$
12. $(2x^3 - 5x - 2 + 4x^2)(2x - 1)$
13. $(2x - 3 + x^3 - 5x)(2 + 3x)$
14. $(3x - x^2 + 4 - x^3)(2x - 3)$
15. $(2x^2 - 2 - 4x^3 + 3x)(4 - 3x^2)$
16. $(3x - 2)^3$
17. $(3 + x^2 - 2x)(x^3 - 1 - x - 2x^2)$
18. $(2x^3 - 5 - x^2)(x^2 + 1 - 3x)$
19. $(x - 3)(2x + 5)(x - 4)$
20. $(x + 4)(2x - 1)(4 - x)(2x + 1)$
21. $(4x^2 - 6xy + 9y^2)(2x + 3y)$
22. $(x - 3)^4$
23. $(a^2 + b^2 + ab)(a^2 + ab - b^2)$
24. $(x - 2)(x - 3)(x + 2)(x + 3)$
25. $(x - 2)(x + 3)(x - 4)(x + 1)(x - 6)$
26. $(3x^2y + 4axy^2 - 7aby^3)(2a - 3b)$

27. $(x^4 - x^3y + x^2y^2 - xy^3 + y^4)(x + y)$
28. $(2r^3 - r^2t - 5rt^2 + 6t^3)(3r - 2t)$
29. $(2x^2 - 3x + 5)(4x^3 + 2x^2 - 7x - 3)$
30. $3x(2x - 5)(2x + 5)(x^2 + 2x - 3)(2y)$

10.9 DIVISION OF A POLYNOMIAL BY A POLYNOMIAL

The division of one polynomial by another polynomial in algebra is similar in form to long division in arithmetic. In fact, if you recall the separate steps in arithmetic long division, and then follow the same general steps in algebraic long division, you will be on the right track.

Suppose we have the following problem:

$$(6x^4 + 5x^3 - 12x^2 - 8x + 3) \div (3x - 2)$$

Let us now recall the steps in a problem in long division in arithmetic, for example, $(7685) \div (28)$. Let us write the two problems side by side and note the steps in each:

Arithmetic   *Algebra*

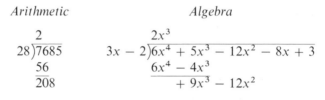

Step 1. In arithmetic we divide 28 into 76. We first consider 2 into 7. The answer is 3. However, this is too large for the first number in the quotient, so we write 2 as the quotient's first digit.

In algebra we divide $3x$ into $6x^4$. The answer is $2x^3$, which is the first term in the quotient. In algebra we do not need to "try" this answer. There is no guess work here in algebra.

The proper division of the first term of the divisor into the first term of the dividend will always result in the correct first term of the quotient.

Step 2. In arithmetic we multiply the entire divisor by the first digit of the quotient; that is, we "multiply back," taking 2 times the divisor, 28, and placing the product, 56, under the 76. Subtracting, we get 20 as a first remainder.

In algebra we multiply the entire divisor by the first *term* of the quotient; that is, we "multiply back," taking $2x^3$ times the divisor $3x - 2$. The product, $6x^4 - 4x^3$, is placed under the first part of the dividend. Subtracting, we get $9x^3$ as a remainder.

Step 3. In arithmetic we bring down 8, the next digit. In algebra we bring down $-12x^2$, the next term.

Step 4. From this point on, we continue to divide, repeating the same steps as in arithmetic. In algebra we continue until we get a remainder of zero or a remainder whose highest power of x is lower than the highest power of x in the divisor. If there is some remainder other than zero, it may be placed above the divisor as a fraction, as in arithmetic, and then added to the quotient as a fraction.

In algebra, the complete steps are as follows:

1. Divide $3x$ into $6x^4$. The result is $2x^3$.
2. Place the $2x^3$ as the first term in the quotient.
3. Multiply back, taking the $2x^3$ in the quotient times the *entire* divisor. This makes $6x^4 - 4x^3$. This quantity is placed below the first part of the dividend, as in arithmetic.
4. Subtract. The remainder is $+9x^3$ (algebraic subtraction).
5. Bring down $-12x^2$, the next term.
6. Divide $3x$, the *first* term of the divisor, into the $+9x^3$. The result is $+3x^2$.
7. Place $3x^2$ as the second term of the quotient.
8. Multiply back, taking $+3x^2$ times the entire divisor. The result, $9x^3 - 6x^2$, is placed below the new dividend, as in arithmetic.
9. Subtract. The remainder is $-6x^2$.
10. Bring down $-8x$, the next term of the dividend.
11. Continue to divide in the same way.
12. The remainder is -5.

The problems in arithmetic and algebra are shown here complete.

$$
\begin{array}{r}
274 + \frac{13}{28} \\
28\overline{)7685} \\
56 \\
\hline
208 \\
196 \\
\hline
125 \\
112 \\
\hline
13
\end{array}
$$

$$
\begin{array}{r}
2x^3 + 3x^2 - 2x - 4 - 5/(3x - 2) \\
3x - 2\overline{)6x^4 + 5x^3 - 12x^2 - 8x + 3} \\
6x^4 - 4x^3 \\
\hline
+ 9x^3 - 12x^2 \\
9x^3 - 6x^2 \\
\hline
- 6x^2 - 8x \\
- 6x^2 + 4x \\
\hline
- 12x + 3 \\
- 12x + 8 \\
\hline
- 5
\end{array}
$$

Note 1. In division it is necessary to arrange the terms of both dividend and divisor in a *descending order of powers* before beginning the division. Start with the highest power of x, or whatever the letter. If there are two letters with various powers then select one of them for the arrangement according to descending powers.

Note 2. If one of the powers is missing, it means that the coefficient of that power is zero (0). A space should be allowed in the dividend for each missing term. This vacancy may be conveniently shown by placing a $+0$ for each of the missing terms.

Example.   Divide $(3x^4 - 7 + 8x - 5x^2) \div (x - 2)$

Before beginning the division, we rearrange the terms of the dividend and divisor in a descending order of powers of x, starting with the highest power. We make allow-ance for any missing terms by placing $+0$ in the place of each missing term.

$$x - 2 \overline{)\; 3x^4 + 0 - 5x^2 + 8x - 7}$$

The completion of the division is left as an exercise for the student.

Exercise 10.3

1. $(x^2 + 8x + 15) \div (x + 3)$

2. $(2n^2 + 7n + 6) \div (n + 2)$

3. $(3x^2 + 10x - 6) \div (x + 4)$

4. $(8y^2 - 3 - 2y) \div (1 + 2y)$

5. $(6c^2 - 9d^2 - 5cd) \div (2c - 3d)$

6. $(14x + 7x^2 + 12 + x^3) \div (x + 4)$

7. $(2x^3 - 3 - 9x^2) \div (2x - 1)$

8. $(5x^2 - 15x + x^3) \div (3 + x)$

9. $(12 - 5x + 2x^3) \div (2 + x)$

10. $(x + 8x^3 - 14x^2) \div (2x - 3)$

11. $(20 + 9y^3 - 28y) \div (5 - 3y)$

12. $(1 - 11a + 18a^3) \div (3a - 1)$

13. $(4x^2 - 9) \div (2x + 3)$

14. $(14r + 5 + r^2 - 3r^3) \div (3r + 2)$

15. $(13x^2 + 12x^3 - 12x) \div (4x - 1)$

16. $(x^3 - 8) \div (x - 2)$

17. $(23n - 19n^2 + 6n^3 - 17) \div (2n - 3)$

18. $(3t^2 - 24t - 2 + 10t^3) \div (3 + 2t)$

19. $(8h^3 - 20 - 30h^2 + 38h) \div (2h - 4)$

20. $(20n^3 + 12 - 13n - 19n^2) \div (4n - 3)$

21. $(v^2 - 9v - 8v^3 + 6v^4 - 10) \div (3v + 2)$

22. $(20 + 22x^3 - 12x^4 + x^2) \div (4 - 3x)$

23. $(18x^4 - 3 - 23x + 13x^2) \div (3x - 2)$

24. $(18x - 47x^3 - 6 + 20x^4) \div (4x - 3)$

25. $(6x^3 - 37x + 8x^4 + 11) \div (4x - 5)$

26. $(9x^3 - 12x^4 + 16x^2 - 7) \div (3 - 4x)$

27. $(81 + 16x^4 - 72x^2) \div (2x - 3)$

28. $(32x^4 - 58x^2 - 2x + 3) \div (4x - 5)$

29. $(6x^2 + 4 - 6x + 15x^5 + x^3) \div (3x^2 + 2)$

30. $(12x^4 - x^3 - 23x^2 + 6x - 5) \div (3x - 4)$

31. $(6x^3 - 3x^2y - 2xy^2 + 12y^3) \div (2x - 3y)$

32. $(6a^4 + 6b^4 + 22a^3b + ab^3) \div (3a + 2b)$

33. $(6x^4 + 5x^3 - 8x^2 - 7x + 17) \div (2x^2 + 3x - 4)$

34. $(13c^2 + 3 + 7c^3 + 2c^4 + 11c) \div (2c + c^2 + 3)$

35. $(x^2y^2 - 7x^3y - 31xy^3 + 12x^4 - 15y^4) \div (2xy + 5y^2 + 3x^2)$

36. $(5y^5 - 3x^3y^2 + 6x^5 - 2xy^4) \div (y^2 + 2x^2 + 2xy)$

37. $(6x^4 - 7x^3 - 6x^2 + 2x + 2) \div (2x - 3)$

38. $(9x^4 - 8x^3 - x - 3) \div (3x - 2)$

39. $(6x^5 - 10 + 23x^2 - x - 22x^4) \div (3x - 2)$

40. $(12x^4 - 7x^3 - 3x^2 + 2x - 3) \div (2x - 3)$

41. $(4x^4 - 5x^2 - 6) \div (x^2 - 2)$

42. $(3x^6 - 5x^3 - 2) \div (3x^3 + 1)$

43. $(x^5 - 32) \div (x - 2)$

44. $(x^7 + 1) \div (x + 1)$

10.10 SYNTHETIC DIVISION

Synthetic division is a way of making long division short. This can be done by omitting much of the writing, especially the needless repetition of certain terms. Consider the following problem:

$$(3x^4 - 10x^3 + 6x^2 + 9x - 16) \div (x - 2)$$

First, let us work the problem in the usual way and note the repetition of certain terms: In the division shown, the starred terms need not be written. Note that they are simply repetitions. In each subtraction, the first remainder is always zero, so we might omit repeating the term. Also, the terms, $6x^2$, $9x$, and -16, need not be brought down. The subtraction can be done just as the terms stand.

$$
\begin{array}{r}
3x^3 - 4x^2 - 2x + 5 \\
x - 2 \overline{\smash{)}\ 3x^4 - 10x^3 + 6x^2 + 9x - 16} \\
\underline{*3x^4 - 6x^3 } \\
- 4x^3 + *6x^2 \\
\underline{- *4x^3 + 8x^2} \\
- 2x^2 + *9x \\
\underline{- *2x^2 + 4x} \\
+ 5x - *16 \\
\underline{+ 5x - 10} \\
- 6
\end{array}
$$

We may therefore omit the unnecessary repetition of terms. Moreover, we may even omit the letter x itself and write only the coefficients. Then we have the form shown at the right. In the result the starred numbers here show the quotient coefficients. To make the arrangement more compact, we move all the numbers up nearer the dividend and get

$$
\begin{array}{r}
3 \quad\ -4 \quad\ -2 \quad\ +5 \\
-2 \overline{\smash{)}3^* \ -10 \quad +6 \quad +9 \quad -16} \\
\underline{-6 } \\
-4^* \\
\underline{+8} \\
-2^* \\
\underline{+4} \\
+5^* \\
\underline{-10} \\
-6
\end{array}
$$

$$
\begin{array}{r}
3 \ -4 \ -2 \ +5 \\
-2 \overline{\smash{)}3 \ -10 \ +6 \ +9 \ -16} \\
\underline{-6 \ +8 \ +4 \ -10} \\
-4 \ -2 \ +5 \quad -6
\end{array}
$$

Note that the numbers just below the dividend came about through multiplying the divisor by each term of the quotient. Now, if we bring the first coefficient of the dividend down in line with the remainders, these numbers in the bottom row will show the coefficients in the quotient, the last number being the final remainder. Therefore, we need not write the quotient. We get

$$\underline{-2}\overline{)\begin{array}{rrrrr} 3 & -10 & +6 & +9 & -16 \\ \downarrow & -6 & +8 & +4 & -10 \\ \hline 3 & -4 & -2 & +5 & -6 \end{array}}$$

The numbers in the bottom row came about through subtraction. Now we make one more change. To avoid subtraction (and use addition instead), we change the sign of the divisor from -2 to $+2$.

Now let us summarize the steps in synthetic division, using the foregoing example:

1. With the terms of the dividend arranged in a descending order of powers, write the coefficients, including a zero for each missing power: $3 -10 +6 +9 -16$

2. Change the sign of the constant in the divisor and write this number at the *left* (some books say *right*):

$$2\overline{)3 \;\; -10 \;\; +6 \;\; +9 \;\; -16}$$

3. Leaving a working space under the dividend, draw a horizontal line below.

4. Bring down the first coefficient of the dividend:

$$2\overline{)\begin{array}{rrrrr} 3 & -10 & +6 & +9 & -16 \\ \downarrow & & & & \\ \hline 3 & & & & \end{array}}$$

5. Multiply this number by the divisor, place the product under the second term of the dividend, and *add*:

$$2\overline{)\begin{array}{rrrrr} 3 & -10 & +6 & +9 & -16 \\ \downarrow & 6 & & & \\ \hline 3 & -4 & & & \end{array}}$$

6. Multiply the result by the divisor, place the product under the third term of the dividend, and *add*

$$2\overline{)\begin{array}{rrrrr} 3 & -10 & +6 & +9 & -16 \\ & 6 & -8 & & \\ \hline 3 & -4 & -2 & & \end{array}}$$

7. Proceed in the same way to the end of the polynomial. We get

$$2\overline{)\begin{array}{rrrrr} 3 & -10 & +6 & +9 & -16 \\ & 6 & -8 & -4 & 10 \\ \hline 3 & -4 & -2 & +5 & -6 \end{array}}$$

The last term in the bottom row is the remainder, and the other terms are the coefficients of the quotient in descending powers of x. The degree of the quotient is one less than the degree of the dividend. The quotient is therefore,

$$3x^3 - 4x^2 - 2x + 5$$

with a remainder of -6.

If the final remainder is zero, the division is even, and we can say the dividend can be factored into divisor and quotient.

Example 1. Divide $(2x^4 - 11x^3 - x + 17 + 14x^2) \div (x - 3)$

Solution.

$$3\overline{)\begin{array}{rrrrr} 2 & -11 & +14 & -1 & +17 \\ & 6 & -15 & -3 & -12 \\ \hline 2 & -5 & -1 & -4 & +5 \end{array}}$$

Quotient: $2x^3 - 5x^2 - x - 4$; remainder $= 5$

Example 2. Divide: $(6 + 9x^3 - x + 4x^4) \div (x + 2)$

Solution.

$$-2\overline{)\begin{array}{rrrrr} 4 & 9 & 0 & -1 & 6 \\ & -8 & -2 & 4 & -6 \\ \hline 4 & 1 & -2 & 3 & 0 \end{array}}$$

Quotient: $4x^3 + x^2 - 2x + 3$; remainder $= 0$. Since the remainder is zero, then the binomial, $x + 2$, is a factor of the dividend.

Note. Synthetic division can be used only when the divisor is a binomial of the form, $x - c$, in which c is a constant and the coefficient of x is 1. If the coefficient of x is other than 1, such as in $3x - 4$, synthetic division may be used by making a certain adjustment in the divisor. We may first divide the divisor by the coefficient of x, in this case, 3, making it $x - \frac{4}{3}$. If we make no other adjustment, the quotient, of course, will be 3 times as large as it should be. However, to get the correct answer, we may also divide the dividend by 3. If we leave the dividend as it is, we finally divide the quotient by 3.

Example 3. Divide by synthetic division: $(12x^4 + x^3 - 12x^2 + x + 2) \div (3x - 2)$.

Solution. We change the divisor to $(x - \frac{2}{3})$. If we also divide the dividend by 3, we have

$$\tfrac{2}{3}\overline{)\begin{array}{rrrrr} 4 & \frac{1}{3} & -4 & \frac{1}{3} & \frac{2}{3} \\ & \frac{8}{3} & 2 & -\frac{4}{3} & -\frac{2}{3} \\ \hline 4 & 3 & -2 & -1 & 0 \end{array}}$$

Quotient: $4x^3 + 3x^2 - 2x - 1$; remainder $= 0$. Then $3x - 2$ is a factor of the polynomial, $12x^4 + x^3 - 12x^2 + x + 2$.

Exercise 10.4

Use synthetic division to divide each of the following polynomials by the binomials shown. In each case, write the complete quotient and the remainder. Tell in which cases the polynomial can be factored, and state the binomial factor, or factors.

1. $2x^3 - 6x^2 + 3x + 2$ divided by $(x - 1)$; $x + 1$; $x - 2$; $x - 3$; $x + 2$.
2. $3x^4 - 6x^2 + 2x + 4x^3 - 5$ divided by $x - 1$; $x + 1$; $x - 2$; $x + 2$; $x - 3$.
3. $24x - 8 + 8x^2 - 21x^3 + 6x^4$ divided by $x - 2$; $x + 1$; $x + 2$; $x - 3$; $x - 4$.
4. $10x - 9x^3 + 2x^4 - 12 + 7x^2$ divided by $x - 1$; $x + 1$; $x - 2$; $x + 2$; $x - 3$.
5. $10x^2 - 7x^3 - 12 - 8x + 3x^4$ divided by $x - 1$; $x + 1$; $x - 2$; $x - 3$; $x - 4$.
6. $5x^3 - 18x - 4$ divided by $x - 1$; $x + 1$; $x - 2$; $x + 2$; $x - 3$; $x - 5$.
7. $6 - 5x^3 + 4x^4 - 15x$ divided by $x - 1$; $x + 1$; $x - 2$; $x + 2$; $x - 3$; $x + 3$.

8. $3x^4 - 12 + 40x - 10x^3 - 9x^2$ divided by $x - 1$; $x + 1$; $x - 2$; $x + 2$; $x - 3$.

9. $3x^4 - 2x^3 + x^2 - x - 7$ divided by $x - 1$; $x + 1$; $x - 2$; $x + 2$; $x - 4$.

10. $3x^4 + 16 - 7x^2 - 12x$ divided by $x - 1$; $x + 1$; $x - 2$; $x + 2$; $x - 4$.

11. $3x^4 - 5x^3 - 9x^2 + 20x - 12$; try to find one binomial factor.

12. $2x^5 + x^4 - 31x^3 - 36x^2 + 52x + 48$; find three binomial factors.

13. $x^4 - 15x^2 + 10x + 24$; find four binomial factors.

14. $2x^4 - 11x^3 - 13x^2 + 99x - 45$; find three binomial factors.

15. $3x^4 + 4x^3 - 41x^2 - 86x - 24$; find three binomial factors.

16. Divide $x^5 - 32$ by $x - 2$.   **17.** Divide $x^7 + 128$ by $x + 2$.

18. Divide $10x^4 - 7x^3 - 18x^2 + 5x + 6$ by $2x - 3$.

19. Divide No. 14 by $2x - 1$.   **20.** Divide No. 15 by $3x + 1$.

21. Divide $3x^4 + 2x^3 - 2x^2 - 17x + 12$ by $3x - 4$.

22. Divide $10x^4 + 7x^3 - 27$ by $2x + 3$.

11

The Equation

11.1 THE EQUATION: DEFINITION

The equation is probably the most important idea in all mathematics. In fact, *algebra can be called the study of the equation.* The equation enables us to solve practical problems in everyday life. By means of equations we can find the answers to many questions in physics, chemistry, and other scientific fields, as well as in such activities as business and home economics.

Without the equation we could not solve problems. All other work in algebra would accomplish nothing by itself. So far we have studied addition, subtraction, multiplication, and division of algebraic expressions. Such manipulation of algebraic symbols would be of no value if we stopped there. All other work in algebra is pointed toward the solving of equations. It is the equation that makes algebra useful in finding answers to problems.

What, then, is an equation?

An equation is a statement of equality between two equal quantities. There are three requirements for an equation:

1. We must have *two* quantities.
2. The quantities *must be equal.*
3. We must *say* they are equal.

Let us consider the following statement: $3 + 5 = 8$. Here we have two separate quantities. One quantity is $3 + 5$. The other quantity is 8. The two quantities are equal. The equal sign ($=$) makes the statement that they are equal.

The equal sign ($=$) is one of the most important symbols in mathematics. It is the symbol that says something. It is the "verb" in grammar. Without the equal sign, nothing is stated. It is like starting a sentence such as "The man in the brown suit . . ." and then stopping. The equal sign is necessary in making the statement.

However, we must also have something after the equal sign, otherwise the statement is not complete. It is like saying, "The man in the brown suit is . . . ."

11.2 IDENTITIES AND CONDITIONAL EQUATIONS

There are two kinds of equations, *identities* and *conditional equations*. An *identity* is an equation that is true for *all values* of the letter used. A *conditional equation* is an equation that is true for *only some particular value or values* of the unknown or letter used.

Let us see whether the statement $8x - 5x = 3x$ is an identity or a conditional equation. We try some values of x to determine whether or not the statement is true for any particular value of x.

If x is equal to 7, we have $56 - 35 = 21$. This statement is true.
If x is equal to 11, we have $88 - 55 = 33$. This also is true.

If we try several other values for x, such as $x = 9$, $x = 12$, $x = 25$, or any other value, we find the statement $8x - 5x = 3x$ is true, no matter what value we use for x. This equation is therefore an *identity* because it is true for *all* values of x. For an identity we often use an equality sign consisting of three parallel lines ($\equiv$). Thus, $8x - 5x \equiv 3x$.

As another example, suppose we consider the statement, $3x + 2 = 17$. By inspection, we see that the statement is true *only* on the *condition* that x is equal to 5. We say that the number 5 *satisfies* the equation; that is, if we substitute 5 for x in the equation, the statement is true. If we try any other value for x, say $x = 4$, we shall find that the statement is not true. If $x = 4$, we have $12 + 2 = 17$, which is not true. Since the equation $3x + 2 = 17$ is true for some but not for all values of x, the equation is a *conditional equation*.

An equation may be true for more than one value of the letter and yet not be an identity. Consider the equation

$$x^2 - 5x + 6 = 0$$

Let us try some values for x in this equation. If we try $x = 1$, we find that the equation is not true. If we try the value $x = 2$, we get $4 - 10 + 6 = 0$, which is true. If we try the value $x = 3$, we get $9 - 15 + 6 = 0$, which is also true. In this equation we find that x may have two different values that make the equation true. Yet it is not an identity, since it is not true for *all* values of x.

Note. When we use the word "equation" by itself, we usually mean a *conditional equation*.

11.3 ROOT OF AN EQUATION

The *root* of a conditional equation is any value for the letter that makes the equation true. In the equation $3x + 2 = 17$, the only value for x that makes the equation true is $x = 5$. Then we say that 5 is the only root of this equation. The root is also called the *solution* of the equation.

Exercise 11.1

Tell whether each of the following equations is an identity or a conditional equation. Then find, by inspection, the root of each conditional equation.

1. $x + 5 = 13$ **2.** $2 + x = 9$ **3.** $x - 3 = 5$
4. $x - 5 = 8$ **5.** $x + 2x = 3x$ **6.** $6 - x = 1$
7. $10 = 8 + x$ **8.** $x - 6 = 0$ **9.** $2x = 16$
10. $30 = 3x$ **11.** $4x = 48$ **12.** $24 = 6x$
13. $x = 6x - 5x$ **14.** $2x + 7 = 15$ **15.** $4x - 3 = 17$
16. $x = 2x - x$ **17.** $3x = -21$ **18.** $-10 = 5x$
19. $12x = 6$ **20.** $2x = 7$ **21.** $2x + 3 = 19$
22. $3x + 4x = 14$ **23.** $4x + 3x = 7x$ **24.** $5x = 18 + 2x$
25. $15 - 2x = 9$ **26.** $6x - 5 = 19$ **27.** $5x = 60$
28. $x + 8 = 3x$ **29.** $5x - 2x = 3x$ **30.** $5x - 2x = 21$

11.4 SOLVING AN EQUATION

To *solve* an equation means to find the root. In the equation $3x + 2 = 17$ we know that the root is 5, since that is the only value for x that will make the statement a true equation.

In the foregoing equation we can easily determine the root by inspection. However, the root of an equation is not always easy to find. We need a more systematic method for solving an equation. For instance, in the equation $5x + 4 = 2x - 7$, we may have to guess a long while before finding the root.

11.5 THE EQUATION AS A BALANCED SCALE

Before beginning to solve equations, let us see how an equation resembles a balanced scale.

Suppose we have a balanced scale as shown in Fig. 11.1. On the left pan of the scale is a bag of sand of an unknown weight, x. On the right pan is an 8-ounce weight. Let us further suppose the scale is perfectly balanced. This means that we have exactly the same quantity on both sides of the scale.

An equation is like a balanced scale. The scale in Fig. 11.1 may be represented by the equation

$$x = 8$$

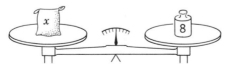

Fig. 11.1

The quantity on the left side of the scale, or equation, is *x*. The quantity on the right side of the scale, or equation, is 8. The equal sign (=) says that the quantities are equal. This is the same as saying that the scale balances.

If you will think of an equation at all times as a balanced scale, you will find many of the algebraic processes very simple. An equation can always be treated as a balanced scale.

11.6   THE AXIOMS

To solve equations we make use of several important principles called *axioms. An axiom is a general statement that is accepted as true without proof.* In order to solve equations, we need to know what the axioms mean and how they are used. The axioms are best understood if they are applied to a balanced scale.

Consider the scale in Fig. 11.1. Suppose we add a 3-ounce weight to the left side and a 3-ounce weight to the right side of the scale. (Fig. 11.2.) We feel sure that the scale will still balance. We seem to know that the following statement is true:

If we add the same quantity to both sides of a balanced scale, the scale will still balance.

The foregoing statement may be tested in a laboratory by adding various weights to one side and then always adding an equal weight to the other side. We might verify the statement with many examples. For instance, we may add 4 ounces to both sides, then 5 ounces, then 6 ounces, and so on. In each case the scale would still balance.

However, notice that the statement says that, *no matter how much is added to one side, if the same amount is added to the other side, then the scale will still balance.* To verify the statement for *all* cases is impossible. *All* cases would also have to include fractions. Yet we feel that the general statement is true for all cases. *The truth of the statement seems so obvious that it does not require proof.*

The axiom we have just illustrated with a balanced scale is called the *addition axiom.* It is often referred to as the first axiom. It is stated as follows:

Axiom 1.   *If the same quantity is added to both sides of an equation, the new equation will still be true.*

Fig. 11.2

Let us see how this axiom applies to an equation. Consider again the equation

$$x = 8$$

Now, if we add some quantity, such as 3, to both sides of the equation, we get a new equation:

$$x + 3 = 8 + 3$$

or

$$x + 3 = 11$$

Then, by Axiom 1, the new equation is also true because we have added the same quantity to both sides of the original equation. We can easily see that this is so. If we substitute 8 for x in the new equation, we get

$$8 + 3 = 11$$

which is true.

Now, consider a second possibility. Suppose we start with the balanced scale in Fig. 11.1. If we subtract the same quantity from both sides of a balanced scale, the scale will still balance. This is the basis of the *subtraction axiom*:

Axiom 2.   *If the same quantity is subtracted from both sides of an equation, the new equation will still be true.*

Let us see how this applies to the equation

$$x = 8$$

If we subtract some quantity, say 5, from both sides of the equation, we get

$$x - 5 = 8 - 5$$

or

$$x - 5 = 3$$

Then, by Axiom 2, the new equation is also true because we have subtracted the same quantity from both sides of the original equation. We can verify the new equation, for, if we substitute 8 for x, we get

$$8 - 5 = 3$$

which is true.

As a third possibility, if we start with the balanced scale in Fig. 11.1 and multiply both sides of the scale by some quantity, say 7, then each side of the scale will contain seven times as much as before, but the scale will still balance. Thus we have the *multiplication axiom*:

Axiom 3.   *If both sides of an equation are multiplied by the same quantity, the new equation will still be true.*

Let us see how this applies to the equation

$$x = 8$$

If we multiply both sides of the equation by 7, we get

$$7x = 56$$

Then, by Axiom 3, the new equation is also true because we have multiplied both sides of the original equation by the same quantity. We can verify this equation by substituting 8 for x. We get

$$7 \cdot 8 = 56$$

which is true.

As a fourth possibility, we may divide both sides of the scale by some number, say 4, and the scale will still balance. Each side of the scale will contain only one-fourth as much as the original scale, but it will still balance. This principle is known as the *division axiom. The one exception is that we cannot divide by zero.*

Axiom 4.   *If both sides of an equation are divided by the same quantity (not zero), the new equation will still be true.*

Let us apply this axiom to the equation

$$x = 8$$

If we divide both sides of the equation by 4, we get the new equation

$$\frac{x}{4} = 2$$

By Axiom 4, this equation is still true because we have divided both sides of the original equation by 4.

We can verify the new equation by substituting 8 for x. We get

$$\frac{8}{4} = 2$$

which is true.

The four axioms stated here are used in solving equations systematically. Other axioms will be needed later. All axioms may be summarized in one *general principle;*

Whatever operation is performed on one side of an equation, the same operation must be performed on the other side of the equation if the equation is to be true.

If a scale is to balance, both sides of the scale must be kept equal in value. The same is true with the two sides of an equation. We can make changes in the amount on each side of the scale, but *whatever change is made on one side of the scale the same change must be made on the other side. The same is true with regard to the equation.* Nothing must be done that will destroy the equality of the two sides of an equation. This principle is the basis of solving equations.

11.7 USE OF AXIOMS IN SOLVING EQUATIONS

The axioms are used to solve equations. To show how this is done, we begin with easy examples. Remember, guessing at the answer or finding an answer by inspection in easy examples will be of no help when you come to more difficult equations. In learning how to solve equations, the procedure is much more important than the answer itself.

Example 1. Suppose we have the following equation and we wish to solve for x; that is, find the value of x that will make the equation true:

$$x + 3 = 15$$

By use of Axiom 2, we can subtract 3 from both sides of the equation,

$$\begin{array}{r} x + 3 = 15 \\ \underline{3 \quad\quad 3} \end{array}$$

Subtracting 3 from both sides of the equation,

or
$$x = 15 - 3$$
$$x = 12$$

To check this answer, we substitute 12 for x in the original equation and ask:

$$\text{does} \quad 12 + 3 = 15? \quad \text{Yes.}$$

The statement is true, and therefore 12 is the root.

Example 2. Suppose we have the equation $x - 5 = 14$.
By use of Axiom 1, we add 5 to both sides of the equation.

Adding 5 to both sides,
$$\begin{array}{r} x - 5 = 14 \\ \underline{5 \quad\quad 5} \\ x = 14 + 5 \end{array}$$
or
$$x = 19$$

The root $x = 19$ can be checked in the same way as in the preceding example.

11.8 TRANSPOSING

In applying Axioms 1 and 2 in solving equations, we often use a "trick" called *transposing*. Although transposing is not a mathematical process, it is a shortcut that is simple, quick, and convenient if used properly. Remember, any "trick" in mathematics must be understood and used correctly. This is true even for such a trick as inverting the divisor when dividing fractions. Moreover, such "tricks" must be based on sound mathematical principles.

In the two foregoing examples notice that when a term is added to or subtracted from both sides of an equation, one term disappears from one side and reappears on the *other* side with its *sign changed*. For instance,

the equation $x + 3 = 15$
becomes $\qquad x = 15 - 3$.

When the quantity 3 is subtracted from both sides of the equation, the $+3$ disappears from the left side and reappears on the right side with its sign changed from $+$ to $-$.

the equation $x - 5 = 14$
becomes $\qquad x = 14 + 5$.

When 5 is added to both sides of the equation, the -5 disappears from the left side and reappears on the right side with its sign changed from $-$ to $+$.

A simple way to apply Axioms 1 and 2 is to transfer any term we wish from one side of an equation to the other and then change its sign. This process is called *transposing*. By *transposition* we mean that any term may be moved from one side of an equation to the other side, provided its *sign is changed*. An *entire term* must be transposed, not simply a factor.

Remember, *transposing* is only a "trick," but it is useful because it is simple, easy, and fast. It can always be used because it is based on the sound mathematical principles of Axioms 1 and 2.

Example 1.   Now let us solve the following equation by use of the axioms:

$$5x - 4 = 2x + 17$$

In solving any equation, one of our main objectives is to get all of the x terms on one side of the equation and all the other terms on the other side; that is, we isolate the terms containing x. This we do by "transposing." We transpose the -4 from the left side to the right side of the equation and change its sign to plus $(+)$. The $+2x$ is transposed from the right side to the left side and its sign is changed to minus $(-)$. The original equation is

$$5x - 4 = 2x + 17$$

Transposing, $\qquad\qquad 5x - 2x = 17 + 4$

Combining like terms, $\qquad\qquad 3x = 21$

Now we make use of Axiom 4 and divide *both* sides of the equation by 3.

We get $\qquad\qquad\qquad\qquad x = 7$

The equation is solved when we have one single x on one side of the equation. Then the root appears on the other side of the equation.

The root of the foregoing equation is 7, provided there has been no error in the solution. This means that if 7 is substituted for x in the original equation, the statement should be true.

To check the answer, we substitute the 7 in place of x in the equation, and ask

$$\text{does} \quad (5)(7) - 4 = (2)(7) + 17?$$
$$\text{does} \quad 35 - 4 = 14 + 17?$$
$$\text{does} \quad 31 = 31? \quad \text{Yes}$$

As soon as we see that one side of the equation is equal to the other side, we know we have the root of the equation. The check must result in a statement that is true.

Example 2.   Solve the equation $3x + 2 - x + 9 = 5x - 12 + x + 3$.

Solution.

Transposing,	$3x - x - 5x - x = -12 + 3 - 2 - 9$
Combining,	$-4x = -20$
Dividing both sides by -4,	$x = 5$

The check is left for the student.

Although the terms containing the unknown x are usually isolated on the left side of the equal sign, this is not essential. The x terms can just as well be transposed to the right side, and the other terms to the left side. Sometimes this may reduce the chances of error.

Example 3.   Solve $4x - 5 - 5x - 7 = x - 5 + 3x + 8$.

Solution.

Transposing, we get $\qquad\qquad -5 - 7 + 5 - 8 = x + 3x - 4x + 5x$

Combining like terms, $\qquad\qquad\qquad -15 = 5x$

Dividing both sides of the equation by 5, the coefficient of x, $\qquad\qquad -3 = x$

Therefore the root of the equation is -3. This can be checked by substituting -3 for x in the original equation.

Note.   If a term on one side of the equation is the same as a term on the other side, these terms may be dropped before transposing; that is, we subtract the term from both sides by use of Axiom 2. In the foregoing equation the -5 may be dropped, since it can be subtracted from both sides of the equation.

Exercise 11.2

Solve the following equations and check the root of each:

1. $3x + 7 = 19$ **2.** $8 = 5y - 7$

3. $1 - 3y = 10$ **4.** $3 - 4x = 29$

5. $2y - 7 = 13$

6. $7x - 15 = 13$

7. $5x = 7 + 2x$

8. $6 + 7x = 3x$

9. $5n + 11 = 3$

10. $2x - 13 = 6x$

11. $4a + 9 = a - 6$

12. $5t - 13 = 7 + t$

13. $10 - 3x = 4x - 11$

14. $2R - 9 = 7R + 21$

15. $10 - x = 3x - 4$

16. $9n + 5 = 7n - 11$

17. $15 - 2x = 1 - 5x$

18. $6y - 3 = y - 23$

19. $16 - a = 6 + 4a$

20. $7 - 5x = x + 4$

21. $7w - 9 = 5w - 9$

22. $3a + 11 = 6a - 5$

23. $7c - 5 = 11c + 25$

24. $4 - 3v = 5v - 16$

25. $1 - b = 14 - 5b$

26. $6 + k = 7 + 5k$

27. $9x + 7 = 3x + 7$

28. $2b + 24 = 3 - 7b$

29. $6x + 7 - x = 2x + 14$

30. $5y + 4 - 3y = 2y + 1 + y + 3$

31. $5t + 6 - 3t = 23 - 3t - 2$

32. $9 + 5R - 2 = 7R + 5 - R - 5$

33. $21 - 2b = 15 - b - 2 - 3b + 2$

34. $4 - 4s + 5 = 5s - 3 - 3s$

35. $a - 6 + 3a + 13 = -5a - 2$

36. $2n - 2 = 7n + 11 - 3n - 8$

37. $7x + 5 - x + 3 = 9x - x + 5 + 20$

38. $3x - 7 - 4x + 1 + 5x = 5 + x - 11 - 5x$

39. $5 + 2x - 3 - 5x = x - 5 - 2x + 7$

40. $4y + 5 - 3y - 1 = 7y + 6 - 5y - 2 - y$

11.9 PARENTHESES IN EQUATIONS

Some equations contain terms or polynomials enclosed within parentheses, such as the equation $5x - 2(4x + 3) = 7 + (3x - 2)$. In such equations the first step is to remove the parentheses. In this step we observe the following rule:

Rule. *If a quantity within parentheses is preceded by a plus sign* $(+)$, *this plus sign and the parentheses may be omitted without changing the sign of any term within the parentheses.*

If a quantity within parentheses is preceded by a minus sign $(-)$, *this minus sign and the parentheses may be omitted, provided that the sign of each term within the parentheses is changed.*

This rule is easily understood if we remember that a minus sign before parentheses is really a sign of the operation (subtraction).

Remember, if a coefficient appears before the parentheses, this coefficient is multiplied by each term within the parentheses. If no coefficient appears before the parentheses, it should be understood that the numerical coefficient is 1 (or -1 if the parentheses is preceded by a minus sign).

The foregoing rule holds true for any sign or symbol indicating a quantity, such as brackets, braces, vinculum, or for any other symbol of aggregation.

Example. Solve $4x - 3(2x - 5) - 9 + (3x + 4) = 12 - (x - 5) - 2(7 - x) - 3x$.

Solution.

Removing parentheses,
$$4x - 6x + 15 - 9 + 3x + 4 = 12 - x + 5 - 14 + 2x - 3x$$
Transposing,
$$4x - 6x + 3x + x - 2x + 3x = 12 + 5 - 14 + 9 - 15 - 4$$
Combining, $3x = -7$

Dividing both sides
of the equation by 3, the coefficient
of x,
$$x = \frac{-7}{3}$$

Note. After removing the parentheses, some like terms may be combined before transposing. However, to do so would mean an extra step, since like terms must later be combined again.

Some equations appear at first sight to be quadratics, since they contain second-degree terms; that is, terms in x^2. The study of quadratic equations will be taken up later. At this point, we simply mention that in many cases the terms in x^2 disappear in the process of solving and the equations are really simple equations; that is, they are equations in only the first degree of x.

Example 2. Solve $(x - 3)(x + 5) - (x + 2)(x - 4) = 2x - 5(x + 4)$.

Solution. In removing the parentheses, we must perform the indicated multiplication. This multiplication step may be called *expanding the products*. The minus sign between the sets of parentheses is a sign of subtraction, so that the signs of the terms following it are changed after the products are expanded.

Expanding the products, $(x^2 + 2x - 15) - (x^2 - 2x - 8) = 2x - 5x - 20$
Removing parentheses, $x^2 + 2x - 15 - x^2 + 2x + 8 = 2x - 5x - 20$.
Transposing and combining (x^2 disappears), $7x = -13$
Dividing both sides of the equation by 7, $x = \dfrac{-13}{7}$
the coefficient of x,

Check. If checking is done by substituting the value of x as found, the substitution should always be done in the *original* equation. However, *the best check is to be sure that you are using the correct method and then to be sure you do not make mistakes in the process of solving. A second check is to go over your work a second time.*

Exercise 11.3

Solve the following equations:

1. $3x + 5 = 26$
2. $6 = 2n - 7$
3. $5x - 3 = 8$
4. $8 = 3 - 5x$
5. $7y = 15 - 3y$
6. $2n + 5 = 17 - n$

7. $7 - 2c = 12 - 5c$

8. $3 + 4a = 15 + 7a$

9. $3x - 7 = x - 10$

10. $5 + 3x = 5x + 11$

11. $2x - 5 = 15 - 7x$

12. $7n + 10 = 2n - 7$

13. $4x + 3(2x - 5) = 7 + 5(3x - 7)$

14. $6y - 2(y - 8) = 9 + 4(3y - 2)$

15. $5c - 4(c + 3) = 14 - 2(c - 5)$

16. $2x + 5(x + 2) = 3x - (8 - x)$

17. $10 - 3(2 - 4t) = 9t - 2(t + 3)$

18. $8 - (3x + 4) = x - (2x - 5)$

19. $3x - 4(2x + 3) - 5 = 7 - 3(4 - 2x) - 5x$

20. $4 - (x + 3) - 3x = 2(x - 4) + 5(8 - x)$

21. $5n - 3(n + 4) + 11 = 3 - 4(2n - 1) - 6n$

22. $2(7 - n) + 3(n + 2) = 4 + 3(4n - 3) - n$

23. $3(y - 1) - (4y - 5) + 4 = 5 - 2(1 - y) - 5y$

24. $4(7v - 3) - 2(6 + 5v) + 2 = 3v - 5(v - 1) - 1$

25. $(x + 2)(x - 5) - x(3x + 2) = 2 - 2x(3 + x) + 5x$

26. $5x - (x + 3)(x - 4) + 3 = 7 - x(x - 7)$

27. $3y - y(2y - 5) + 5 = 13 + 2y(5 - y)$

28. $4 + 3c(5 - c) - 2c(3 - c) = 7 - c(c - 3)$

29. $9 - 2(3h + 1) + 2h = 3 - 4(h - 1)$

30. $7k + 4(2 - k) + 5 = 4 + 3(k + 4)$

31. $4 - (3t - 2)(t - 3) - 5t = 3t - (t - 3)(3t - 4) - 5$

32. $5y - y(2y + 3) - 7 = 6 - (5 + y)(2y - 3) - 2y$

33. $7n - 2n(2n - 3) - 2 = n - (n - 2)(4n + 3) - 8$

34. $3c - (2c - 1)(3c + 2) + 5 = 2c - 2(c - 3)(3c + 1) + 5$

35. $(2b - 1)(2b + 3) - b(b - 2) = 5b - (4 + 3b)(1 - b)$

36. $6 - 2k(4 - 3k) - 3(k - 2)(k - 3) = 5 - 3(2 - k)(2 + k)$

37. $10x - 3(x + 3)(2x - 5) = 3 - 2(4x - 7)(x + 1) - x(3 - 2x)$

38. $8x - 3(2x - 1)(3 - x) - 2x(x - 3) = 5 - 4(x + 2)(5 - x)$

39. $3 + (3x - 2)(4x + 3) - 3(3x - 1)(2x - 3) = 7x - (2x - 1)(3x + 4)$

40. $5x - (2x - 3)(x + 2) - (4x + 3)(x - 1) = 3 - (3x + 2)(2x - 3)$

41. $4x - (2x - 1)(x + 2) - x(x - 2) = 1 - 3(x - 2)(x + 1)$

12
Solving Stated Word Problems

12.1 THE IMPORTANCE OF STATED PROBLEMS

In this chapter we shall show how equations can be used to solve the so-called "stated problems" or "word problems." By this, we mean the problems that arise in connection with our work in everyday life.

Equations in algebra are used to find answers to questions that come up in connection with many kinds of work. We use algebra to solve problems concerning electric circuits, laws of motion, pressures of gases, speeds of electrons and satellites, equilibrium of forces, and many other scientific ideas. Algebra is also used to solve practical problems in business, in industry, and in the home. Solving equations enables us to find answers to practical problems not only in scientific fields but in all kinds of activity.

We do not begin with problems about unfamiliar things such as the laws of electric circuits, laws of motion, angular velocity, or efficient power supply simply because these topics are unfamiliar to most people beginning the study of algebra. Instead, we shall first solve problems dealing with familiar subject matter. We shall work problems about ages of people, speeds of cars, costs of articles, scores in games, measurements, and other everyday matters.

Remember, your purpose here is to learn how to apply the principles of algebra to the solution of problems. The kind of thinking involved in easy problems that we shall solve is exactly the same kind of thinking that must be done in solving more difficult problems in science. The approach to all problems is the same. Your purpose here should be as follows:

1. To learn the correct approach to the solution of a problem.
2. To learn to analyze a problem carefully; to look at it from every angle.
3. To learn how to write the correct equation from the information given in the problem.

If you think through the correct method for an easy problem, you can use the same approach to the more difficult problems you will encounter later.

The chief difficulty in solving word problems is that equations are not handed to us already made. We must make up the equations from the information that we find in the particular problem we are facing. In word problems, we have two chief hurdles to overcome:

1. First, we must make up an equation from the given information.
2. Then we must solve the equation.

In working word problems, students usually have most trouble making up the correct equation from the given information. This is the really difficult part of the whole process. After the equation is correctly set up, it can usually be solved without too much difficulty. If you can make up the correct equation yourself and then solve it, you can work stated problems.

12.2 EXPRESSING ALGEBRAIC QUANTITIES

In solving problems, it is necessary to express various quantities in algebraic symbols. In Chapter 8 we saw how to express the sum, the difference, the product, and the quotient of literal quantities. For instance, the sum of x and y is expressed as $x + y$.

The sum of two quantities is expressed by means of the plus sign ($+$). The difference is expressed by the minus sign ($-$). The product in many cases is expressed by writing one factor next to another if there is no confusion in meaning. The product is sometimes indicated by placing a raised dot between the factors. Division is expressed by the division sign ($\div$). Division may also be expressed in fractional form; thus $12x \div 5y$ can be written $\dfrac{12x}{5y}$.

If the sum or difference of two terms is to be considered one single quantity, it should be enclosed in parentheses. For instance, if we wish to indicate three times the sum of a and b, we should write it $3(a + b)$. The expression is read, "Three times the quantity a plus b." In reading any expression, we should state it so clearly that anyone may know from the oral statement exactly what is meant.

Exercise 12.1

Express the following:
1. The sum of $2x$ and $3y$.
2. The difference between m and n if m is greater.
3. The product of $5x$ and $7y$.
4. The quantity x plus 6 divided by 3.
5. A number 13 more than $2x$.
6. A number 5 less than $3a$.
7. Twice the sum of x and $5x$.
8. Three times the difference between $7x$ and $3y$ if x is greater than y.

9. The sum of x and y divided by their product.
10. The difference between x and y divided by the sum of a and b.
11. If A's age is x years and B is 5 years older, express B's age (years).
12. Express the sum of the ages of A and B in Problem 11.
13. If C is x years old and D is three years older than twice C's age, express D's age in years.
14. If x represents a boy's age (in years) and his father is four times as old, express the number of years in the father's age.
15. If x represents a boy's age (in years), express his age 5 years ago.
16. From Problem 14, express the father's age in years 5 years ago.
17. How many months are there in 7 years? In x years? In $(20 - x)$ years?
18. How many months are there in x years and 5 months?
19. If the cost of a radio is represented by x dollars, express the cost of a TV if the TV costs $12 more than 5 times the cost of the radio.
20. Express the total cost of the radio and TV in Problem 19.
21. Express the number of cents in the value of 23 nickels; in x nickels; in the quantity $(62 - x)$ nickels.
22. Express the number of cents in 7 dimes; in x dimes; in $(54 - x)$ dimes.
23. Express the number of cents in x quarters and $(37 - x)$ dimes.
24. Express the cost of thirteen 6-cent stamps; x 6-cent stamps.
25. Express the cost of x 8-cent stamps and $(16 - x)$ 1-cent stamps.
26. Express the value of x pounds of tea at 60 cents a pound.
27. If x is an integer (whole number), express the next consecutive integer.
28. If n is an *even* number, what is the next consecutive *even* number?
29. If x is an *odd* number, what is the next consecutive *odd* number?
30. If n is an even number, how do you express the following *odd* number?
31. If t is *any* integer, what kind of an integer is $2t$? $2t + 1$?
32. If x is an even number, and y is even, what kind of a number is $(x + y)$?
33. If c is an odd number, and d is odd, what kind of a number is $(c + d)$?
34. If c is an odd number, what are the next three consecutive odd numbers?
35. Express the number of miles driven in t hours at 35 mph.
36. At 50 mph, how many miles can be driven in $(8 - x)$ hours?
37. How many minutes are there in 5 hours? In x hours? In $(3 - x)$ hours?
38. Express the number of minutes in x hours and 15 minutes.
39. If x represents the number of inches in the width of a rectangle, express the length (in inches) if the length is 7 inches more than the width.
40. Express the perimeter of the rectangle in Problem 39.
41. In a triangle ABC, if x represents the number of degrees in angle A, express the number of degrees in angle C if C is twice as large as A.
42. Express the number of degrees in angle B (Problem 41) if angle B is 15 degrees less than angle C. Express the sum of the three angles in the triangle.
43. Using the letter x, express the sum of the scores of two football teams if one team made 19 more points than the other team.
44. Using x for the number of inches in the width of a rectangle, express the perimeter of the rectangle if the length is 5 inches less than 3 times the width.

45. A man gets a salary increase of $800 per year. If *x* represents his salary for the first year, express his salary for the 2nd, 3rd, 4th, and 5th years.

46. On a trip by car you decrease your driving 50 miles per day each day. If you drive *x* miles the first day, express your mileage the next three days.

12.3 THE APPROACH TO PROBLEM SOLVING

The first thing to remember in beginning to solve a problem is this: *never think about the answer*. If you start out trying to guess the answer, you are starting out the wrong way. Your first concern should always be with the proper approach.

Remember, at this time you are not simply looking for answers. If your only concern is the answer to the problem, you can usually find it in the back of the book or you can hire someone to work the problem for you. Instead, you are now trying to learn how to use algebra to solve problems.

Some students say: "Oh, I can work this problem by arithmetic. I can find the answer without using algebra." That is probably true in easy problems. However, do not lose sight of your purpose here. Your purpose is not only to get an answer to a problem but to learn how to apply the principles of algebra. Working an easy problem without using algebra will not furnish practice in the use of algebra.

In learning how to use algebra in solving problems, we begin with simple examples. No matter how easy it may be to get the answer to a problem, you should use algebra to solve it. That is the only way to acquire the necessary practice so that you can solve more difficult problems later on.

In solving a problem by algebra, we use some letter, say, *x*, to represent an unknown quantity. In every problem there is some quantity that is already known, sometimes several. Also, in every problem there is at least one quantity that is not known. Such a quantity is called an *unknown*. Sometimes a problem contains several unknowns.

The convenient thing about algebra is that even though we do not know a particular quantity, we can let *x* represent this unknown, and then we work with the letter just as though we knew its value. An example may help to make this procedure clear.

Let us suppose you are 23 years old. From that given fact we can tell many things:

1. Four years from now you will be 23 + 4, or 27 years old.
2. Five years ago you were 23 − 5, or 18 years old.
3. If your father is twice your age, he is (2)(23), or 46 years old.
4. If your uncle is three years older than your father, he is 46 + 3, or 49 years old.

5. If you have a sister two years younger than you, she is 23 − 2, or 21 years old.

6. If your mother is one year younger than your father, she is 46 − 1, or 45 years old.

Now, let us begin again and assume that we do not know your age. We shall say that the number of years in your age will be represented by the letter x. Then we can repeat the foregoing facts, using the letter x for your age in years.

1. Four years from now you will be $x + 4$ years old.

2. Your age (in years) five years ago can be represented by $x − 5$.

3. If your father is twice your age, his age (in years) can be represented by $2x$.

4. If your uncle is three years older than your father, his age (in years) can be represented by $2x + 3$.

5. If you have a sister two years younger than you, her age (in years) can be represented by $x − 2$.

6. If your mother is one year younger than your father, her age (in years) can be represented by $2x − 1$.

There is a definite procedure you can follow to get started on the solution of a problem. Moreover, if you start right, you will usually reach a solution. There are *five definite steps* you can follow in solving any problem. You may have some difficulty in following one or two of the steps, but you can always use these five as a guide.

Here are the "Five Golden Rules" for solving problems:

1. *Let some letter, such as x, represent one of the unknowns.* (This is usually though not necessarily the smallest.)

2. *Then, try to express the other unknowns by using the same letter.*

3. *Write a true equation from the information given in the problem. Make your equation say in symbols exactly what the problem says in words.*

4. *Solve the equation.*

5. *Check your answer to see whether it satisfies the conditions given in the problem.* Do *not* check in the equation you have made up.

If you can do the *first three* steps, the problem is practically done. Most people have trouble with the first three steps. In fact, many people have trouble with the very first step. *If you can let some letter represent one of the unknowns and if you state definitely what the letter is to represent, you have the right start.*

After the first two steps have been completed and the unknown quantities have been properly stated in terms of a letter, there is often some difficulty in analyzing the problem before the equation can be written. In this analysis between the second and third steps try to discover the different relationships between the various quantities in the problem. Try to determine whether one quantity is equal to another or whether the sum or difference of two quantities is equal to a third quantity. Then try to make the equation state this relationship.

We shall now work out several problems, following the five steps.

12.4 GENERAL PROBLEMS

Example.   A chair and a desk together cost $68. The desk cost $5 more than twice the cost of the chair. Find the cost of each.

Solution.   Here we have at least two unknowns, the cost of the chair and the cost of the desk. Your thinking should be, "I am going to let the letter x represent the number of dollars the chair cost." Begin your statement with the word "Let."

Step 1.   Let x = the number of dollars the chair cost.

Be sure you state definitely just what the letter x is to represent. Now we express the cost of the desk, using the same letter.

Step 2.   Then $2x + 5$ = the number of dollars the desk cost.

At this point, we see that the problem says that the sum of the two costs was $68. So we make that statement by means of an equation.

Step 3.   Equation: $x + (2x + 5) = 68$

If you can get this far in the problem, the rest is usually easy.

Step 4.   Solving

$$x + 2x + 5 = 68$$
$$3x = 68 - 5$$
$$3x = 63$$
$$x = 21$$

Therefore, the cost of the chair was $21 and the cost of the desk was $47, which is $5 more than twice as much as the cost of the chair.

Step 5.   *Check:*

Cost of chair	$21
Cost of desk	47
Total cost	$68

Warning.   Be sure the checking is done in the original problem, not in the equation that you have made up.

Note concerning the use of a letter x to represent a quantity. Be sure to let x (or the letter used) represent a number. A letter such as x cannot represent the length of a rectangle. Instead, it may represent the *number of inches* or the *number of feet* in the length. The letter x cannot represent a person's age. Instead, it may represent the *number of years* or the *number of months* in his age. A letter, such as x, cannot represent an amount of money. It may represent the *number of dollars*, the *number of cents*, or the *number of dimes*. It cannot represent the weight of an object. Instead, it may represent the *number of pounds*, the *number of ounces*, the *number of tons* in the weight.

Any letter may be used to represent an unknown number. We may use *x, y, z, n, t*, or any other letter. Some students often use the first letter of a word to which it refers, such as *d* for the number of dimes, *n* for the number of nickels, and so on. This is convenient provided that the letter is understood to represent a *number*. When this is done, however, students sometimes take the letter to mean something other than a number. For example, using *d* for the number of dimes, they mistake *d* for the amount of money rather than the number of coins. Some even go so far as to say that *d* must be 10 because there are 10 cents in one dime. Remember, whatever letter you use, it always represents a *number*. If you use *d* for the number of dimes, then it represents just so many pieces of money.

A good way to be sure of a correct statement is to start the problem with the form shown here:

"Let *x* = the *number* of..."

Another correct way is to say:

"Let *x* = the width of the rectangle (in inches)"

Exercise 12.2

1. One number is three times another number, and their sum is 68. What are the two numbers?
2. One number is two less than five times another and their sum is 76. What are the numbers?
3. One number is four times another and their difference is 69. What are the two numbers?
4. Divide the number 40 into two parts so that three times the smaller part is equal to twice the larger part.
5. A student bought a slide rule and a drawing set for a total of $39. The drawing set cost $8 more than the slide rule. Find the cost of each.
6. A lady bought a purse and a pair of shoes for a total cost of $34. If the shoes cost $2.50 more than the purse, what was the cost of each?
7. A fishing rod and reel together cost $28. If the reel cost $7 less than the rod, what was the cost of each?
8. A lady bought a dress, a hat, and a pair of gloves for a total of $48. The hat cost $3 less than twice the cost of the gloves, and the dress cost $12 more than the combined cost of the gloves and the hat. Find the cost of each.
9. In a football game the home team made five points less than twice the score of the visiting team. If the total score made by both teams was 52, how many points were made by each team?
10. In a certain baseball game one team made a total score of one more than four times

the score of the other team. If the total score made by both teams was 11, what score was made by each team?

11. In a certain basketball game one team made a total of 81 points. The number of field goals was five less than three times the number of free throws. How many field goals and how many free throws did the team make? (A free throw counts one point, a field goal counts two points.)

12. In a duckpin bowling match one man averaged a score of 13 points more *per game* than the other. If the total combined score of both men for three games was 611 points, what was the average score of each man *per game*?

13. A family on a tour of 820 miles in three days drove twice as many miles the second day as the first. The third day they drove 60 miles less than on the second day. Find the distance traveled each day.

14. The length of a rectangle is 6 in. greater than the width. If the perimeter of the rectangle is 50 in., how wide and how long is the rectangle? (Remember, a rectangle has four sides. The perimeter is the distance around the rectangle.)

15. A rectangular field is 23 rd longer than it is wide. If the perimeter of the field is 210 rd, find its length and its width.

16. It requires 62 ft of picture molding to reach around the four walls of a room. The length of the room is 5 ft less than twice the width. What is its length and its width?

17. A tract of land along a river is to be fenced along one side and both ends. The length of the tract is 20 rd less than three times the width. If the total length of fence required is 120 rd, find the width and the length of the tract.

18. In a certain triangle one side is $4\frac{1}{2}$ in. longer than another side, and the third side is 3 in. shorter than the sum of the other two. If the perimeter of the triangle is 34 in., what is the length of each side?

19. In a certain triangle side a is 3 in. shorter than twice the length of side b and side c is 4 in. longer than side b. If the perimeter of the triangle is 45 in., what is the length of each side?

20. Smith, Jones, and Brown invest a total of $48,000 in a business. Smith invests one and one half times as much as Jones, and Brown invests $2400 less than Smith. How much did each man invest in the business?

12.5 AGE PROBLEMS

Example. A man is three years older than four times his son's age. Five years from now, the sum of their ages will be 48 years. What are their ages now?

Solution. Let x = the number of years in the son's age *now*.

Then $4x + 3$ = the number of years in the father's age *now*.

In this problem we must analyze carefully the information given. The problem does not say the sum of their ages is 48 years *now*. Instead, the sum of their ages will be 48 years *five years from now*. Let us look at their ages five years from now. Remember, both people will be five years older then.

Five years from now the son will be $x + 5$ years, and the father will be $4x + 3 + 5$, or $4x + 8$. These are the two quantities whose sum is 48. Therefore, we write the equation which makes this statement:

Equation: $(x + 5) + (4x + 8) = 48$.

When you have once written the equation correctly, the rest of the problem is usually easy. If you solve this equation, the value you get for x will be exactly what x represents as indicated in the first statement in the solution. It will be the number of years in the son's age *now*.

Exercise 12.3

1. A man is 27 years older than his son. The sum of their ages is 45 years. How old is each?
2. A mother is three times as old as her daughter. If the sum of their ages is 52 years, how old is each?
3. Find the age of a man and the age of his son if the father is seven years older than three times the son's age and the sum of their ages is 41 years.
4. A man is now five times as old as his son. Four years hence the sum of their ages will be 47 years. How old is each one *now*?
5. Vernon is eight years older than Donald. Two years hence Vernon will be three times as old as Donald. How old is each one *now*?
6. A man is now six times as old as his son. In three years he will be four times as old as his son. How old is each one *now*?
7. A man is 21 years older than his son. Five years ago he was four times as old as his son. How old is each one *now*?
8. A man is six years older than three times his son's age. Five years hence the sum of their ages will be 56 years. How old is each one now?
9. John is six times as old as Gregory. Four years hence John will be twice as old as Gregory. How old is each one now?
10. A man is now twice as old as his son. Eighteen years ago he was 5 times as old as his son. Find the age of each.
11. A man's age is 7 years more than 3 times his son's age. Eight years hence he will be 6 times as old as his son was 2 years ago. How old is each now?

12.6 CONSECUTIVE NUMBER PROBLEMS

An integer is a whole number, such as 3, 8, 17, 546. *Consecutive integers* are integers that have no other integer between them, such as 6, 7, 8, 9. If we begin with the integer 15, then the next consecutive integer is $15 + 1$, or 16.

If we say that the letter x represents the first of a series of four consecutive integers, then the second is $x + 1$, the third is $x + 2$, and the fourth is $x + 3$.

Consecutive even integers are even integers that have no other even integer between them, such as 6, 8, 10. Notice that two consecutive even integers have a difference of 2. In a series of three consecutive *even* integers, if we let

x represent the first, then $x + 2$ will represent the second, and $x + 4$ will represent the third.

Consecutive odd integers are odd integers with no other odd integer between them, such as 7, 9, 11. Notice that two consecutive odd integers have a difference of 2. In a series of three consecutive *odd* integers, if we let x represent the first, then $x + 2$ will represent the second, and $x + 4$ will represent the third.

Example. Find four consecutive odd integers whose sum is 216.

Solution.   Let x = the first of the four consecutive odd integers.
Then $x + 2$ = the second of these odd integers.
and $x + 4$ = the third of these odd integers.
and $x + 6$ = the fourth of these odd integers.
Equation: $x + (x + 2) + (x + 4) + (x + 6) = 216$

The equation simply states that the sum of the four numbers is 216, as the problem says. When we solve the equation, the value we get for x will be the number represented by x in the first statement.

Solving the equation,

$$x + x + 2 + x + 4 + x + 6 = 216$$
$$4x = 216 - 2 - 4 - 6$$
$$4x = 204$$
$$x = 51$$

Since we let x represent the first of the four integers, this number is 51. The four consecutive odd integers are 51, 53, 55, and 57.

Check : $51 + 53 + 55 + 57 = 216$.

Exercise 12.4

1. Find three consecutive integers whose sum is 147.
2. Find four consecutive even integers whose sum is 268.
3. Find six consecutive odd integers whose sum is 372.
4. A student is assigned 78 problems that he must complete in four days. He wishes to arrange his work so that each day after the first he may work five fewer problems than on the previous day. How many should he work the first day?
5. In order to make a particular piece of furniture, a carpenter saws an 8-ft board into four pieces of different lengths. The second piece is 4 in. longer than the first, the third is 4 in. longer than the second, and the fourth is 4 in. longer than the third. Find the length of each piece.
6. A mechanic cuts five pieces of different lengths from a bar of aluminum. Each piece after the first is $1\frac{1}{2}$ in. shorter than the preceding piece. If the total combined length of the five pieces is 30 in., find the length of each piece.
7. On a vacation tour of 780 miles to be covered in four days, a family wishes to arrange their driving so that each day after the first they may drive 30 miles less than on the previous day. How many miles should they drive the first day?

8. A step ladder is to have eight steps, the longest one at the bottom, and each step above is to be $\frac{1}{2}$ in. shorter than the step immediately below it. If the steps are to be cut from a 10-ft board without any part left over, what should be the length of each piece?

9. Each year a man received a salary increase of $300 over the salary of the preceding year. His total salary for a five-year period was $26,500. What was his salary for each year of the five-year period?

12.7 COIN AND OTHER PROBLEMS ABOUT MONEY

Example 1. A collection of 71 coins, consisting of nickels and quarters, is worth $8.15. Find the number of coins of each kind.

Solution. In this problem there are two unknowns: the number of nickels and the number of quarters. Follow Steps 1 and 2:

$$\text{Let} \quad x = \text{the number of nickels in this collection}$$
$$\text{Then} \quad 71 - x = \text{the number of quarters in the collection}$$

Now, if we study the problem carefully, we see that we have used all the information except the $8.15. This is the total value. It is not the total number of coins.

To write the equation, we must remember that the total *value* of the coins is $8.15, or 815 cents. If we express the number of cents in all the coins, we can say that the total number of cents is equal to 815.

The value of x nickels is $5x$ cents.

The value of $(71 - x)$ quarters is $25(71 - x)$ cents.

The equation will simply state that the total number of cents = 815.

Equation: $5x + 25(71 - x) = 815$

When we solve this equation, the number we shall get for x will be the number of nickels in the collection, since that is the number that was represented by x in the first statement.

Example 2. A merchant has been selling one kind of candy at 90 cents a pound and another kind at 40 cents a pound. However, sales have been slow. Customers do not like to pay as much as 90 cents a pound for the one kind, and they are not satisfied with the cheap kind. Therefore, the merchant decides to make a mixture by taking some of each kind of candy, and he wishes to sell the mixture at 56 cents a pound. How many pounds of each kind should he use for 20 pounds of the mixture so that he will receive the same amount of money for the mixture as if he had sold the two kinds separately?

Solution. Let $x = $ the number of pounds of the 40-cent candy.

Then $20 - x = $ the number of pounds of the 90-cent candy.

Now we express the *value* of each kind (in cents). The sum of these values must then be equal to the total amount the merchant will receive for the mixture, which is $(20)(56$ cents$)$, or 1120 cents, or $11.20. To avoid decimal fractions, we express all values in cents. The equation becomes

$$40x + 90(20 - x) = 1120$$
$$\text{Solving the equation, we get } x = 13\tfrac{3}{5}.$$

Therefore, he should take $13\frac{3}{3}$ pounds of the 40-cent candy and $6\frac{2}{5}$ pounds of the 90-cent candy. Now we can check the answer to determine whether the number of pounds of each is correct to equal a total value of \$11.20. Remember, the check must be done in the original problem, *not* in the equation we have set up.

Exercise 12.5

1. A collection of 62 coins consisting of nickels and dimes has a value of \$4.15. Find the number of coins of each kind in the collection.

2. A collection of nickels and quarters is worth \$6.35. If the total number of coins of both kinds is 71, what is the number of each kind?

3. Forty-six coins consisting of quarters and half dollars are worth \$14.75. How many coins are there of each kind?

4. A certain collection of nickels, dimes, and quarters contains three times as many dimes as nickels. The number of quarters is seven less than the number of dimes. If the total value of the collection is \$7.05, what is the number of coins of each denomination?

5. A collection of nickels, dimes, and quarters has a total value of \$3.95. The number of quarters is one half the number of dimes, and the number of nickels is nine more than the number of quarters. How many coins of each kind are there in the collection?

6. A man buys some 3-cent stamps and some 4-cent stamps. If the total number of stamps is 77 and the total cost is \$2.76, how many of each kind did he buy?

7. A lady said, "I bought some 1-cent stamps and some 3-cent stamps, for a total cost of \$1.32. I received twelve more 1-cent stamps than 3-cent stamps." How many of each kind did she buy?

8. At a school entertainment, children's tickets were sold at 30 cents each and adults' tickets were sold at 45 cents each. If the total amount of money received was \$27.30, how many tickets of each kind were sold? (total: 80)

9. At a school play, the price of admission for adults was 60 cents and for children, 25 cents. The total paid attendance was 102. If the same amount of money was received from all the adults as from all the children who attended, how many admissions of each kind were there?

10. At a particular ball game, the price of admission was \$2 for general admission and \$3 for reserved seats. If the amount of receipts was \$37,800 for a total of 16,300 admissions, find the number of admissions of each kind.

11. A merchant has been selling one kind of nuts at 70 cents a pound and another kind at 30 cents a pound. He wishes to make a mixture of 100 lb by taking some of the good nuts and some of the poorer quality so that he can sell the mixture at 45 cents a pound and not lose money in the process. How many pounds of each kind should he use?

12. A merchant sells pecans at 90 cents a pound, cashews at 50 cents a pound, and walnuts at 80 cents a pound. Now he wishes to make a mixture of 80 pounds of the three kinds to sell at 65 cents a pound. How many pounds of each kind should he use if he wishes to use 3 times as many pounds of cashews as pecans?

13. At a ball game the price of admission was \$1.50 for general admission, \$2.50 for grandstand seats, and \$3.25 for box seats. If 19,480 tickets were sold and the total receipts were \$34,108, find the number of tickets sold at each rate if there were 4 times as many general admission tickets sold as the number of grandstand tickets.

14. A 1-dollar bill has a portrait of Washington, a 2-dollar bill has a portrait of Jefferson, and a 5-dollar bill has a portrait of Lincoln. A man has 48 bills consisting of Washingtons, Jeffersons, and Lincolns, with a total value of \$175. If the number of Lincolns is 3 more than twice the number of Washingtons, find the number of bills of each kind.

15. On a trip to Latin America a traveler picked up some *pesos* in Nicaragua worth about 11.6 cents each, some *lempira* in Honduras worth 50 cents each, and some *sucres* in Ecuador worth 7.4 cents each. On his return he found he had a total number of 425 pieces of money worth \$95.20. If he had twice as many pesos as lempira, find the number of pieces of each kind of money he had.

16. Later the traveler took a trip to northern Europe and collected some *marks* from West Germany worth about 23.8 cents each, some *kroner* from Sweden worth about 19.3 cents each, and some *gulden* from Netherlands worth about 26.3 cents each. On his return he found he had 500 pieces of money worth \$110.20 and that he had 60 more kroner than marks. How many pieces of money of each kind did he have?

17. A sand-and-gravel dealer sells sand at \$1.70 a ton, fine gravel at \$2.10 a ton, and coarse gravel at \$2.30 a ton. For a concrete preparation, he wishes to mix the three kinds to sell at \$2.00 a ton, and he wishes to use twice as much fine gravel as sand. How many tons of each kind should he use to prepare a mixture of 100 tons?

12.8 PROBLEMS IN UNIFORM MOTION

If we drive a car for a distance of 120 miles in exactly 4 hours we call the 120 miles the *distance* and the 4 hours the *time*. We can find the average *rate* of speed by dividing the distance traveled by the time of traveling. If the distance is 120 miles and the time required is exactly 4 hours, the average rate of speed is

$$120 \div 4 = 30$$

Our average rate of speed is 30 miles per hour (mph).

When we say *average speed*, we do not mean that the speed was exactly the same rate, 30 mph, during every minute of the time. It is impossible to drive at exactly 30 mph every minute for 4 hours.

In working problems in uniform motion, we assume that the speed does not change. If there is any change in the speed, we must make some adjustment for the change. We assume also that the speed was uniform even at the start. It is incorrect to say, "A car starts out from a certain town at 30 mph." A car cannot start at 30 miles per hour.

In problems in motion we assume that average speed indicated will continue at the same average. For instance, if a car travels at an average rate of speed of 45 miles per hour for 3 hours, it will travel 135 miles in all. In this example

$$45 \text{ mph is called the rate } (r)$$
$$3 \text{ hr is called the time } (t)$$
$$135 \text{ miles is called the distance } (d)$$

To find the total distance traveled in a given time at a given average rate of speed, we multiply the rate by the time. Of course, the factors must be stated in the proper units of measurements. The formula for the distance is

$$d = rt$$

Example. A car starts out from a town at 7 A.M. traveling at an average rate of 35 mph. At 10 A.M. a second car starts out from the same town traveling along the same road at an average rate of 50 mph. At what time of the day will the second car overtake the first?

Solution. In this problem several facts are unknown: the number of hours each car travels and the distance each car travels. We could let some letter such as x represent any one of these unknown quantities. However, it is probably best to let x represent the number of hours for one of the cars.

$$\text{Let} \qquad x = \text{the number of hours the first car travels}$$
$$\text{Then } x - 3 = \text{the number of hours the second car travels}$$

Let us set up a table of *values*:

	Rate (mph)	Time (hrs)	Distance (miles)
First car	35	x	$35x$
Second car	50	$x - 3$	$50(x - 3)$

We then fill in the given values. When we have expressed the number of hours each car travels, we fill in the remaining blanks. In the "distance" column we fill in the expression for the distance each car travels. This distance is found simply by multiplying the time by the rate for each car.

$$\text{The first car travels} \qquad 35x \text{ miles}$$
$$\text{The second car travels} \quad 50(x - 3) \text{ miles}$$

Now, we suddenly realize that the two cars travel exactly the same distance. This fact is stated in equation form:

$$35x = 50(x - 3)$$

The equation says exactly what is implied in the problem. An equation such as this shows the power of the symbol of equality. This symbol, the equal sign ($=$), is probably the most powerful symbol in all mathematics.

When the equation is solved for x, this value will show the number of hours traveled by the first car. However, we must be careful to answer the question asked in the problem. The question was: "At what *time of the day* will the second car overtake the first?" The answer is 5 P.M.

Exercise 12.6

1. One automobile starts out from a town at 8 A.M. and travels at an average rate of 40 mph. Two hours later a second automobile starts out to overtake the first. If the second automobile travels at an average rate of 55 mph, how long will it take the second to overtake the first?

2. Two cars travel in opposite directions, the first at an average rate of 60 mph and the second at an average rate of 45 mph. How long will it take until they are 400 miles apart?

3. Two cars start out at the same time, one from town *A*, traveling toward town *B* at an average rate of 50 mph, the other from town *B*, traveling toward town *A* at an average rate of 35 mph. How long will it be until they meet if the towns are 500 miles apart?

4. One car starts out from town *C* at 8 A.M., traveling toward town *D* at an average rate of 40 mph. A second car starts out from town *D* at 11 A.M., traveling toward town *C* at an average rate of 45 mph. At what time of day will they meet if towns *C* and *D* are 460 miles apart?

5. One car starts out at 10 A.M., traveling at an average rate of 42 mph. At 12 noon a second car starts out to overtake the first. How fast must the second car travel to overtake the first by 7 P.M.?

6. A boy returns a bicycle to his friend. He cycles at 8 mph and walks back at 3 mph, after spending an hour with his friend. If he arrives home 6 hr after he left, how far has he traveled *one way*?

7. A man takes a trip of 675 miles, part way by train at 60 mph and the rest of the way by car at 50 mph. If the entire trip takes 12 hr, how far has he traveled by each mode of transportation?

8. A bus driver makes a regular run at an average rate of 50 mph. On one particular run he finds it necessary to reduce his average speed by 10 mph, and, as a result, he is 2 hr late. How long is the trip?

9. A man starts out at 10 A.M. on a 290-mile trip and drives part of the way at an average of 40 mph. He stops $\frac{1}{2}$ hr for lunch and then finds that he must drive the rest of the way at 50 mph to finish his trip by 5 P.M. When does he stop for lunch?

10. A man makes a trip of 360 miles in a total of 12 hr. He travels the first part of the trip by motor boat at 18 mph, then transfers to a car and travels at 40 mph. The last part of the trip is by train at 55 mph. If the trip by motor boat is 2 hr longer than the trip by car, how far does he travel by each mode of transportation?

11. A jet plane flying at a speed of 525 mph makes a trip in 2 hr less time than another plane flying at a speed of 350 mph. What is the length of the trip?

Exercise 12.7 (Review)

1. The sum of two numbers is 71. The larger number is five less than three times the smaller. What are the two numbers?

2. The sum of three numbers is 89. The second number is three times the first and the third is four more than the first. What are the three numbers?

3. In a basketball game one team made twice as many points as the other. The total number of points made by both teams was 96. How many points did each team make?

4. In a baseball game the total score by both teams was 15 runs. The difference between the scores of the two teams was 3 runs. What was the score of each team?

5. In a certain basketball game the total score made by both teams was 108. The home team made 21 points less than twice the score of the visiting team. Find the score made by each team.

6. In a certain football game team *A* made 31 points more than the team *B*. The score of team *A* was 5 points less than four times the score of team *B*. Find the score made by each team.

7. In a certain basketball game a team made a score of 93 points. The number of field goals was three less than four times the number of free throws. How many field goals and how many free throws did the team make? (A field goal counts 2 points, a free throw 1 point.)

8. The total cost of a suit and a hat was $70. The suit cost $7 more than five times the cost of the hat. Find the cost of each.

9. The total cost of a house and lot together was $20,700. If the house cost $360 more than eight times the cost of the lot, find the cost of each.

10. Three assignments together contain 63 problems. The second assignment contains four problems more than the first and the third contains seven less than the first. How many problems are there in each assignment?

11. A student wishes to arrange his reading assignment so that he may read five pages less each day than the day before. He has 350 pages to read in five days. How many pages should he read the first day and how many each day thereafter?

12. A rope 20 ft long is cut into two pieces so that one piece is 5 ft longer than the other. How long is each piece?

13. A strip of aluminum 30 in. long is to be cut into six pieces. It is necessary that each piece cut off be $\frac{1}{2}$ in. longer than the piece before it. What should the length of each piece be?

14. The current through one branch of an electric circuit is 1.46 amperes more than the current through another branch. When the branches join, the total current is 3.70 amperes. Find the current in each branch.

15. Two resistors connected in series in a circuit have a total resistance of 15.7 ohms. The first has a resistance of 4.3 ohms more than the second. Find the resistance of each.

16. Suppose it is necessary that two resistors connected in series have a total resistance of 50,000 ohms. When each is used alone, one must have a resistance of 45,200 ohms more than the other. What must be the resistance of each?

17. Three resistors connected in series have a total resistance of 50.5 ohms. The first

has a resistance of 6 ohms more than the second, and the third has a resistance three times as great as the first. Find resistance of each.

18. An electric current of 0.195 amperes is branched off into two circuits so that one branch carries a current of 0.03 amperes less than twice the other. Find the current in each branch.

19. The flow capacity of a water main is 600 gal per min. The main separates into three branches. It is necessary that the second branch have three times the capacity of the first, and the third must have a capacity of 50 gal per min more than the first. Find the capacity of each branch.

20. A man is now 28 years older than his son. If the father is three times as old as his son, find the age of each.

21. A man is now three times as old as his son. Four years hence the sum of their ages will be 60 years. How old is each one now?

22. A man is 24 years older than his son. Three years hence the father will be four times as old as his son. Find the age of each now.

23. A man is now four times as old as his son. Three years ago the father was six times as old as his son. Find the present age of each.

24. A man is now three years older than four times his son's age. Five years ago the sum of their ages was 28 years. How old is each one now?

25. A certain rectangle is three times as long as it is wide. Its perimeter is 72 in. Find its length and width. (Remember a rectangle has four sides.)

26. The length of a room is 5 ft less than twice the width. Its perimeter is 71 ft. Find its dimensions.

27. A wire 58 in. long is bent to form a rectangle such that the length of the rectangle is 3 in. longer than twice the width. Find the dimensions of the rectangle.

28. The sum of the three angles of any triangle is always 180°, whatever the shape or size of the triangle. In a certain triangle angle A is twice as large as angle B and angle C is 8° more than angle A. Which angle is the smallest? Find the number of degrees in each angle. Make a sketch of the triangle.

29. In a certain triangle the first angle is 10° less than the second and the third angle is twice the first. Find the size of each angle.

30. In a certain right triangle one acute angle is twice the other. Find the size of each angle.

31. In an isosceles triangle two angles are always equal. In a particular triangle, ABC, angle A and angle B are equal. Angle C contains 12.6° more than angle A. Find the number of degrees in each angle of the triangle.

32. In a certain triangle the first side is 4.5 in. longer than the second and the third side is 10 in. shorter than twice the first. The perimeter of the triangle is 64.3 in. Find the length of each side.

33. In a certain triangle the first side is 2.3 in. shorter than twice the second and the third side is 4.2 in. longer than the second. The perimeter is 24 in. Find the length of each side.

34. The sum of four consecutive integers is 282. What are the numbers?

35. The sum of three consecutive even integers is 258. What are the numbers?

36. Find five consecutive odd integers whose sum is 455.

37. A collection of 82 coins, consisting of nickels and dimes, is worth \$5.85. Find the number of each kind.

38. A collection of 69 coins, dimes and quarters, is worth \$12.45. Find the number of coins of each kind.

39. A collection of nickels, dimes, and quarters is worth \$7.05. There are six more dimes than nickels, and the total number of coins is 50. Find the number of each.

40. A collection of nickels, dimes, and quarters is worth \$7.20. The number of dimes is three less than the number of quarters, and the number of nickels is equal to the number of dimes and quarters together. Find the number of coins of each kind.

41. At an entertainment a total of 260 tickets were sold, children's tickets at 30 cents each and adult tickets at 75 cents each. The total receipts were \$109.05. How many tickets of each kind were sold?

42. At a game 380 tickets were sold, some at 50 cents each and the rest at 90 cents each. The total amount received was \$256.80. How many tickets were sold at each price?

43. At a football game 750 tickets were sold. General admission cost \$1.60 per ticket, and reserved seats were \$2.40 each. Total receipts were \$1459.20. How many tickets of each kind were sold?

44. A merchant wishes to mix 50-cent tea with 90-cent tea so that he can sell the mixture at 65 cents a pound. How many pounds should he use of each kind for 100 lb of the mixture?

45. How many pounds of 40-cent candy and how many pounds of 80-cent candy should be mixed together to form a mixture of 60 lb to sell at 55 cents a pound?

46. How many pounds each of 70-cent coffee and \$1.20-coffee should be mixed together for 50 lb of the mixture to sell at 85 cents a pound?

47. A car starts out on a trip and travels at an average rate of 35 mph. Two hours later a second car starts out from the same point, travels the same route, and averages 50 mph. How long will it take the second car to overtake the first?

48. A man takes a trip of 960 miles, part of the way by train at 60 mph and the rest of the way by car at 45 mph. The total travel time was 18 hr. How far did he travel at each rate?

49. A messenger starts out at 7 A.M. and travels at an average speed of 35 mph. Three hours later it is found that the message must be changed, so a second messenger starts out to overtake the first. How fast must the second one travel in order to overtake the first by 5 P.M.?

50. At a certain banquet there were 76 people seated at five different tables. The tables were lettered A, B, C, D, and E. The number seated at table A was one more than the number at table D. The number at table B was two more than the number at table A. The number at table C was three less than twice the number at table A. The number at table E was four less than twice the number at table D. Find the number seated at each table.

Quiz on Chapters 8–12. Form 1.   The number in parentheses is the suggested number of points for each question.

(8)   **1.** Multiply: $(4x - 3)(5x - 2)(4x + 5)$.

(8)   **2.** Multiply: $(2x - 3)(5 - 6x^2 + x^5 - 4x^3)$ (first rearrange terms).

(10) **3.** Divide: $(3 - 5x^2 + 3x^4 - 8x^3) \div (3x - 2)$ (first rearrange terms).

(14) **4.** By synthetic division, divide the polynomial $(2x^4 - 8x^2 - 5x + 6)$ by each of the following and write quotient and remainder in each case:

(7) (a) divide by $(x - 2)$; (7) (b) divide by $(x + 1)$

(10) **5.** Solve this equation for x: $3x - 2(4x + 5) + 4 = 13 - 3(x - 4) + 5x$.

In the first five problems below, set up the form for the first three steps as shown here, but do not solve:

Let $x = $ (tell what number x is to represent) (2 points).
Then $= $ (express the other unknowns) (2 points).
After analyzing the problem, write the *equation* (4 points).

(8) **6.** Find five consecutive odd numbers whose sum is 315.

(8) **7.** A collection of 71 coins, nickels and quarters, is worth \$9.35. Find the number of nickels and the number of quarters in the collection.

(8) **8.** A man is 5 years older than 3 times his son's age. Two years ago the sum of their ages was 45 years. How old is each now?

(8) **9.** A car starts out on a trip at 8 A.M. traveling at an average speed of 35 mph. At 11 A.M. a second car starts out along the same route to overtake the first. It travels at an average rate of 55 mph. When will it overtake the first?

(8) **10.** A merchant has some tea worth 40 cents a pound, a second kind worth 60 cents a pound, and a third kind worth 90 cents a pound. How many pounds of each kind should he use for 100 pounds of the mixture of the three kinds to sell at 63 cents a pound, if he wishes to use 3 times as much of the 40-cent tea as he does of the 60-cent tea?

(10) **11.** Solve this problem: The length of a rectangle is 4 inches more than 3 times the width. Find the length and the width of the rectangle if the perimeter is 52 inches.

Quiz on Chapters 8–12. Form 2. The number in parentheses is the suggested number of points for each question.

(8) **1.** Multiply: $(3x - 4)(2x + 7)(3x + 4)$.

(8) **2.** Multiply: $(3x - 2)(4x - 3x^4 + x^5 - 2x^3)$ (first rearrange terms).

(10) **3.** Divide: $(x + 2x^4 + 9 - 7x^3) \div (2x - 3)$ (first rearrange terms).

(14) **4.** By synthetic division, divide the polynomial $(3x^4 - 6x^3 - 2x^2 + 3)$ by each of the following and write quotient and remainder in each case:

(7) (a) divide by $(x - 2)$; (7) (b) divide by $(x + 1)$

(10) **5.** Solve this equation for x: $4x - 3(2x + 3) + 2 = 12 - (x - 4) + 7x$.

In the first five problems below, set up the form for the first three steps as shown here, but do not solve:

Let $x = $ (tell that number x is to represent) (2 points).
Then $= $ (express the other unknowns) (2 points).
After analyzing the problem, write the *equation* (4 points).

(8) **6.** Find five consecutive even numbers whose sum is 290.

(8) **7.** At an entertainment, 130 tickets were sold, some at 25 cents and the rest at 60 cents. How many of each kind were sold if the total receipts were $47.55?

(8) **8.** The length of a rectangle is 7 inches less than 3 times the width. Find the width and the length of the rectangle if the perimeter is 62 inches.

(8) **9.** A man takes a trip of 355 miles. Part of the way he travels by car at an average rate of 45 mph. The rest of the way he travels by train at an average rate of 60 mph. If his total travel time was 7 hours, how far did he travel at each rate?

(8) **10.** A collection of 90 coins, nickels, dimes. and quarters, is worth $10.35. If the number of nickels is twice the number of quarters, how many coins of each kind are there in the collection?

(10) **11.** Solve this problem: A man is 2 years older than 5 times his son's age. Three years hence the sum of their ages will be 47 years. How old is each now?

13
Special Products and Factoring

13.1 DEFINITION

Multiplication occurs so often in algebra that we should be able to do it quickly. In many cases multiplication can be done by *inspection*; that is, it can be done mentally and the product written down at once.

A product that can be found by inspection may be called a *special product*. We shall study several of these products. Remember, a special product does not give us a different answer. Any such product may be found by the usual long method of multiplication. The only thing unusual about a special product is that we find the product quickly. It may be called a "short-cut."

13.2 MULTIPLICATION OF MONOMIALS BY INSPECTION

In multiplying monomials we take note of three things:

1. *The sign of the product, observing the rule for signs in multiplication.*
2. *The product of the numerical coefficients.*
3. *The literal numbers (letters), adding exponents of the same letter.*

Example. Multiply $(-5x^3y^2z)(-4x^2y)(-3yz^3)$.

For the sign of the product we have the product of three negative numbers, which is negative. For the coefficients we have: $(5)(4)(3) = 60$. Adding the exponents of like letters we get the product

$$(-5x^3y^2z)(-4x^2y)(-3yz^3) = -60x^5y^4z^4$$

Exercise 13.1

Multiply the following:

1. $(-2x)(4x^2y)(-3xy^2z)$
2. $(-4a)(-2a^2b^3c)(-ac)$
3. $(5mn)(-3m^2n^3)(4mn^2)$
4. $(3x)(-x^2)(-x^3y)(4y^3)$
5. $(-xy)(-3y^2)(-2x)(-x^3y)$
6. $(xy)^2(-x)^2(-x^2)(-x^2y^3)$
7. $(-7ab^2)(-3a^2c)(-8a^4bc^5)$
8. $(abc)^2(a^2c)^2(-bc^2)(-3ac^2d)$
9. $(-3x^2y)^3(-4xy^3)(x^3y)(-5)$
10. $(a^2b^3c)(-2a^3bc^2)(-4ac)(-b)$

11. $(-9x)(-3x^2yz)(-4a^3b)^3$ **12.** $(-3xy)(-6abc)(-4mn)(-yz)$

13. $(-2r^2s)(-3xy^2)^3(-r^2st)^2$ **14.** $(rt)(-st)^2(-rs^3)(3r^2st^3)$

13.3 FACTORING MONOMIALS

Factoring is the reverse of multiplication. If two or more quantities are multiplied together, the answer is called a *product*. Each of the quantities multiplied is called a *factor* of the product. For instance, if we multiply the two numbers 5 and 7, we get the product 35; 5 and 7 are the factors of 35.

It is often necessary to find the factors of a given product. When we say, "Find the factors of 323," we mean to find two numbers that can be multiplied to produce 323. In arithmetic we can often tell the factors at sight. For instance, the factors of 21 are 3 and 7. Of course, if we are told one of the factors of a certain product, we can find the other factor by division. If we know that one of the factors of 323 is 17, we can find the other factor by division.

It must be remembered that some quantities cannot be factored. The number 37 is *prime* and cannot be factored. Just so, the expression $3x^2 - 7xy + 3y^2$ cannot be factored in terms of real rational factors.

13.4 PRIME FACTORS

A *prime factor* is a factor that cannot be further separated into any factors except itself and 1. The factors of 120 can be considered to be 10 and 12. However, 10 and 12 can be further separated into factors. The prime factors of 120 are 2, 2, 2, 3, and 5.

In algebra a monomial can easily be separated into its prime factors simply by writing all factors separately. As an example,

$$30x^3y^4z = 2 \cdot 3 \cdot 5 \cdot x \cdot x \cdot x \cdot y \cdot y \cdot y \cdot y \cdot z$$

However, in most work in algebra a monomial is not usually separated into its prime factors in this manner.

13.5 MULTIPLICATION OF A POLYNOMIAL BY A MONOMIAL

We have already mentioned (Chapter 10) that multiplication can be considered as a shortened form of addition. For instance, if we wish to find three times the quantity $7x^2 + 5x - 4$, we could write down the quantity three times and then add, as shown here:

$$
\begin{array}{r}
7x^2 + 5x - 4 \\
7x^2 + 5x - 4 \\
7x^2 + 5x - 4 \\
\hline
21x^2 + 15x - 12
\end{array}
$$

Here we see that each term of the polynomial $7x^2 + 5x - 4$ is multiplied by 3. If we wish to indicate three times the polynomial, we can write 3 next to the polynomial. However, we must then enclose the polynomial in parentheses to indicate that it is to be taken as a quantity; thus

$$3(7x^2 + 5x - 4)$$

If parentheses are omitted and the 3 is placed next to the first term of the polynomial, the meaning will be changed. The expression $3 \cdot 7x^2 + 5x - 4$ means that only the first term, $7x^2$, is to be multiplied by 3.

Compare the following two expressions and you will see the extreme importance of parentheses to indicate the intended meaning.

$$3 \cdot 7x^2 + 5x - 4 = 21x^2 + 5x - 4$$
$$3(7x^2 + 5x - 4) = 21x^2 + 15x - 12$$

For this kind of product we have the following rule:

Rule. *To find the product of a monomial and a polynomial, multiply each term of the polynomial by the monomial. Such a product may be written down at sight.*

Example 1. Multiply $3(4x + 5y) = 12x + 15y$.

Example 2. Multiply $3xy(4x - 5xy + 2y) = 12x^2y - 15x^2y^2 + 6xy^2$.

Example 3. Multiply $2x^2(3x^3 - 4xy + 5y^2)yz =$

In Example 3 part of the monomial precedes the polynomial and part follows it. However, the entire monomial multiplier is the quantity $2x^2yz$. The product is $6x^5yz - 8x^3y^2z + 10x^2y^3z$.

Exercise 13.2

Multiply the following by inspection:

1. $2(3x - 5y + 2z)$
2. $-7x(2 - 3x - x^2)$
3. $4(5x - 7y + 3)$
4. $2x(3 - 7x - xy)$
5. $-3n(5n^2 - 9)2$
6. $5x^2(6x^2 - 3xy - 1)$
7. $-2xy^2(3x - 4y)$
8. $4x(2x - 5y + 1)$
9. $-5x^2y(x^3 - y^2)$
10. $-4x(5x^2 - 3x + 1)$
11. $4x^2y(1 + 2zy^3 - 3x^3y^2)$
12. $(1 - 3x^2 + 4y^2)x^2y$
13. $(2xy + 3x^2 - 5y^3 - 1)(-4x^2y)$
14. $5x(4x^3y^2 - x^2 + 2y^3 - x)y^3$
15. $x^2(5x^3y + 4x^2y^2 - z^2 + 1)yz^3$
16. $3m(7m^2n - mn^2 + 2n - 1)n$
17. $h^2(5h - 3hk - 4k)3k$
18. $rs^2(3r^2s - rt^2 + 5s^2t - 5t)t$
19. $-a(2ab^2c^3 - 9ab^2 + 4b^3x - 2)bc$
20. $(x^2y - 3xz^2 + 5y^2z + xy)(-2xyz^2)$

13.6 FACTORING BY TAKING OUT A COMMON FACTOR

If we multiply the polynomial $5x + 4y$ by the monomial $3x^2$, we get the product $15x^3 + 12x^2y$. Therefore, we know the quantity $15x^3 + 12x^2y$ is a product and can be separated into factors. One factor is the monomial $3x^2$, and the other factor is the binomial $5x + 4y$.

It is often necessary to factor an expression such as $20x^4 - 15x^2y$. If we are told that one factor is the monomial $5x^2$, we can find the other factor by division. It is $4x^2 - 3y$.

When we divide the factor $5x^2$ into the binomial $20x^4 - 15x^2y$, we must divide the monomial into *each* term of the polynomial. We know that $5x^2$ and the binomial $4x^2 - 3y$ are the factors of the expression $20x^4 - 15x^2y$ because they can be multiplied together to produce that expression. That is the real test for factors.

The factor $5x^2$ is called a *common factor* because it can be divided into each term of the polynomial. To factor expressions of this kind, our problem is, first, to find a common factor that can be divided into each term of the polynomial. For this kind of factoring, we have the following rule:

Rule. *Inspect the terms of the polynomial to determine the greatest common factor that is contained in each term. This common factor is one factor of the given expression.*

Divide this common factor into each term of the polynomial. The quotient is the other factor.

Example 1. Factor $6x^3y^2 + 9x^2y^3 - 12xy^4$.

Solution. The greatest common factor contained in each of the terms is $3xy^2$. This is one factor of the expression. Dividing this factor into each term of the polynomial, we get the quotient $2x^2 + 3xy - 4y^2$. This is the other factor. The factors are usually written to indicate multiplication; thus

$$6x^3y^2 + 9x^2y^3 - 12xy^4 = 3xy^2(2x^2 + 3xy - 4y^2).$$

Example 2. Factor $5x^2 + x$.

Solution. The common factor is x. For the other factor, we divide each term by x.

$$5x^2 + x = x(5x + 1)$$

Exercise 13.3

Find the factors of the following expressions:

1. $3x + 12$	**2.** $20 - 4x$	**3.** $18 + 9x$
4. $-24x + 6$	**5.** $30x^3 - 20x^2$	**6.** $10x + 6x^2$
7. $24x - 8y$	**8.** $15x - 40ax$	**9.** $-32mn + 6n^2$

10. $12x + 12x^3$ **11.** $-14y^2 + 7y^3$ **12.** $22x^2y - 33xy$

13. $12x^4y - 8x^3y^2$ **14.** $15x^2y^3 + 15xy$ **15.** $35rs^2t - 10st$

16. $64R^2h - 25r^2h$ **17.** $\pi R^2h - \pi r^2h$ **18.** $\dfrac{4\pi R^3}{3} - \dfrac{4\pi r^3}{3}$

19. $12x^2 - 9xy + 6y^2$ **20.** $5x^4 - 5x^3 + 10x^2$

21. $6x^3 + 8x^2 + 2x$ **22.** $3x^2y + 9x^3y^2 + 6xy$

23. $5xy - 10x^2y^2 - 15x^3y$ **24.** $10a^2b - 8ab^2 - 2ab$

25. $x^3 - x^2 + x - x^4$ **26.** $8r^2t - 16rt^2 - 2t$

27. $20x^4y^3 - 4x^2y + 12xy^2$ **28.** $-24x^3 + 12x^2 + 4x$

29. $10n^2 + 15n^3 - 35n$ **30.** $xy^2z^3 - x^2y^3z^4$

31. $3p^2q + 7pq^2 - 5pq$ **32.** $6x^7y^6 - 3x^5y^3 + 9x^2y^4$

33. $6x^2y + 12x^3y^3 - 15x^4y^5 + 9x^2y^2$ **34.** $14x^2y^2 - 21xy + 7x - 35x^3y^5$

35. $4a^5b^2 - a^4b^3 + 3a^3b^4 + a^2b^5$ **36.** $15m^2n + 10m^3 - 5mn^2 + 20m^3n^2$

37. $124r^2 - 31rt + 62rt^2 + 93r^3t^3$ **38.** $51x^3y^6 + 34x^2y^4 + 17xy^2$

39. $18h^5k^2 - 16h^3k^3 + 12h^2k - 2hk$ **40.** $x^5 - 2x^4 + 3x^3 - 4x^2 + x$

41. $am + bm - cm + 3m$ **42.** $a(x - y) + b(x - y) - c(x - y) + 3(x - y)$

43. $5(a + b) + x(a + b) + 2(a + b)$ **44.** $(x - y)^3 + (x - y)^2 + 5(x - y)$

45. $(m + n)^2 - (m + n)$ **46.** $(c - d) + 3(c - d)^2 - 4(c - d)^3$

13.7 A SPECIAL PRODUCT: THE SUM OF TWO NUMBERS TIMES THEIR DIFFERENCE

Suppose we multiply the two binomials: $3x + 5$ and $3x - 5$.

$$
\begin{array}{r}
3x + 5 \\
3x - 5 \\
\hline
9x^2 + 15x \\
-15x - 25 \\
\hline
9x^2 \qquad - 25
\end{array}
$$

Notice that the two binomials are exactly alike except for one sign. The first binomial may be called the sum of two numbers; the second binomial may be called their difference.

The product contains only two terms. These two terms are the squares of the first term, $3x$, and the second term, 5. The two squares are separated by a minus sign. The product is the difference between the squares.

If we multiply the *sum* of any two quantities, such as $a + b$, by their *difference*, $a - b$, we always get a product that is the difference between the squares. The a and b represent any two quantities.

For this kind of special product we have the following rule:

Rule.   *The product of the sum of two numbers times their difference is equal to the difference between their squares.*

Stated as a formula, this rule is

$$(a + b)(a - b) = a^2 - b^2$$

Since this rule is true for any and all values of a and b, it is an identity. All special product rules are identities.

As an example of this rule, $(7x - 6)(7x + 6) = 49x^2 - 36$.

Exercise 13.4

Multiply the following by inspection:

1. $(x + 3)(x - 3)$
2. $(5 - y)(5 + y)$
3. $(4x - 3y)(3y + 4x)$
4. $(7r + 5s)(7r - 5s)$
5. $(3x - 8a)(8a + 3x)$
6. $(x^2 - 5)(x^2 + 5)$
7. $(5x - 11y)(5x + 11y)$
8. $(x^3 + c)(x^3 - c)$
9. $(7 - 6x^5)(7 + 6x^5)$
10. $(5y + \frac{1}{4})(5y - \frac{1}{4})$
11. $(4x + \frac{1}{3})(4x - \frac{1}{3})$
12. $(1 - 9x)(1 + 9x)$
13. $(5 + 4x)(4x - 5)$
14. $(7xy - 10)(7xy + 10)$
15. $(3a - 5bc)(3a + 5bc)$
16. $(4x^2y^3 - z)(4x^2y^3 + z)$
17. $(24n - 17)(24n + 17)$
18. $(40 + 1)(40 - 1)$
19. $(89)(91)$
20. $(3x + 4)(3x - 2)$

13.8   FACTORING THE DIFFERENCE BETWEEN TWO SQUARES

From the multiplication we have just seen, we know that any expression that represents the difference between two squares can be factored; that is, the expression must have two quantities with a minus sign ($-$) between them, and each quantity must represent the square of some number.

For example, suppose we have the expression

$$9x^2 - 16y^2$$

This binomial represents the difference between two squares. Then we know that it can be factored into two binomial factors. We indicate the two factors by first setting down the parentheses:

$$(\quad)(\quad)$$

Now we take the square root of each term of the given binomial. The square root of $9x^2$ is $3x$, which becomes the first term of each factor:

$$(3x \quad)(3x \quad)$$

The square root of the second term, $16y^2$, is $4y$, which becomes the second term of each factor:

$$(3x \quad 4y)(3x \quad 4y)$$

We connect the square roots with a plus sign $(+)$ for one factor, and with a minus sign $(-)$ for the other factor. Then we have the two factors:

$$9x^2 - 16y^2 = (3x + 4y)(3x - 4y)$$

We can check the factoring by multiplication.

Note. It is immaterial which factor is written first.

To factor an expression which represents the difference between two squares, we have this rule:

Rule. *Find the square root of each quantity. Connect the square roots with a plus sign for one factor and with a minus sign for the other factor.*

Factoring the difference between two squares is one of the most important and useful types of factoring. It should be thoroughly understood and remembered. The type might be represented in this way:

$$(\text{Quantity})^2 - (\text{quantity})^2$$

or in symbols:

$$(Q)^2 - (q)^2 = [Q + q][Q - q]$$

The rule applies not only when we have the squares of single terms, but also when we have the squares of entire quantities.

Example 1. $4x^2 - 25 = (2x - 5)(2x + 5)$.

Example 2. Factor the expression $(x - 3)^2 - (y + 2)^2$.

Solution. Here we have the squares of entire quantities. Following the rule, we take the square root of each quantity and connect the square roots as directed. It is well to keep each square root in parentheses the first time around as shown here. We get

$$[(x - 3) + (y + 2)][(x - 3) - (y + 2)]$$
$$= [x - 3 + y + 2][x - 3 - y - 2]$$
$$= [x + y - 1][x - y - 5]$$

Example 3. Factor $121x^6 - 169y^2$.

Solution. Note that the square root of x^6 is x^3. Then we get

$$121x^6 - 169y^2 = (11x^3 - 13y)(11x^3 + 13y)$$

Exercise 13.5

Factor the following expressions, if possible:

1. $x^2 - 25$ **2.** $16 - c^2$ **3.** $h^2 - 36$
4. $R^2 - r^2$ **5.** $9x^2 - 49y^2$ **6.** $36n^2 - 121$

7. $64x^2 - 1$ **8.** $1 - 144t^2$ **9.** $9x^2 - \frac{1}{4}$

10. $100t^2 - 289$ **11.** $81z^2 - 16y^2$ **12.** $196a^6 - 25$

13. $x^2y^2 - z^2$ **14.** $225n^2 - \frac{1}{9}$ **15.** $9x^2 - 36$

16. $16n^2 - 64$ **17.** $18x^2 - 50$ **18.** $100x^2 - 15626$

19. $80^2 - 1$ **20.** $(x + y)^2 - n^2$ **21.** $(a + b)^2 - (c - d)^2$

22. $25n^2 - 0.16$ **23.** $(a - b)^2 - 25$ **24.** $(2x + 5)^2 - (3y - 4)^2$

25. $x^2 - 5$ **26.** $x^2 - (y + 3)^2$ **27.** $(x - 1)^2 - (y + 3)^2$

28. $n^2 - 2$ **29.** $(5 - x)^2 - (2 - y)^2$ **30.** $(3x - 2)^2 - (2y + 5)^2$

13.9   THE SQUARE OF A BINOMIAL: A SPECIAL PRODUCT

If we multiply two binomials that are exactly alike, we call the product the *square of a binomial.* Usually we indicate such multiplication by only one factor and the exponent 2. For instance,

$$(3x + 5)(3x + 5) \text{ is usually written } (3x + 5)^2$$

This expression indicates a perfect square. By a perfect square, we mean a product of two factors that are exactly alike. The number 36 is a perfect square, since it is the product of the two identical factors, 6 and 6.

The expression $(3x + 5)^2$ indicates a perfect square, since we have two identical factors. If we multiply the two factors by the usual long method of multiplication, we get the product

$$(3x + 5)^2 = 9x^2 + 30x + 25$$

The product, $9x^2 + 30x + 25$, is called the square of a binomial.

Let us see how we may write out the square of a binomial by inspection. You will notice that the product has *three* terms. The *first* and *third* terms of the product are simply the *squares* of the two terms of the binomial. The middle term of the product is *twice the product of the two terms of the binomial.*

If the binomial indicates the difference between two numbers, such as $3x - 5$, then, by long multiplication, we find that

$$(3x - 5)^2 = 9x^2 - 30x + 25$$

If we square the binomial $3x - 5$, just as we squared the binomial $3x + 5$, we find the product is the same except for the sign of the middle term. The expression $(3x + 5)^2$ is called the square of the *sum,* and the expression $(3x - 5)^2$ is called the square of the *difference* between two numbers. The products are exactly alike except for one sign, the sign of the middle term.

For the squares of binomials, we have these rules:

Rule 1.   *The square of the sum of two quantities, such as $(a + b)^2$, is equal to the square of the first term, plus twice the product of the two terms, plus the* *square of the second term. Stated as a formula, this rule is*

$$(a + b)^2 = a^2 + 2ab + b^2$$

Rule 2. *The square of the difference between two quantities, such as* $(a - b)^2$, *is equal to the square of the first term, minus twice the product of the two terms, plus the square of the second term. Stated as a formula, this rule is*

$$(a - b)^2 = a^2 - 2ab + b^2$$

Exercise 13.6

Multiply the following by inspection:

1. $(x + 7)(x + 7)$	**2.** $(x - r)^2$	**3.** $(2n + 3)^2$
4. $(3xy - 4)^2$	**5.** $(5r - 6s)^2$	**6.** $(7n + 8)^2$
7. $(3 - 10x)^2$	**8.** $(1 + 9c)^2$	**9.** $(3x^2 - 1)^2$
10. $(9mn - 13)^2$	**11.** $(6x + \frac{1}{2})^2$	**12.** $(9x^2 + \frac{1}{3})^2$
13. $(5ab^3 + 0.1)^2$	**14.** $(16R - 25)^2$	**15.** $(30 - 19n)^2$
16. $(R - r)^2$	**17.** $(50n + 1)^2$	**18.** $(4x + \frac{1}{8})^2$
19. $(x^3y^2 + \frac{2}{3})^2$	**20.** $(5x - 0.2)^2$	**21.** $(20 - x^4)^2$
22. $(60 + 1)^2$	**23.** $(89)^2$	**24.** $(399)^2$
25. $[(a + b) - c]^2$	**26.** $[(x - 3) + y]^2$	**27.** $[x - (y - 2)]^2$
28. $[(2x - 5) - y]^2$	**29.** $[x - (3 - 2y)]^2$	**30.** $[(x - a) - b]^2$

Write the squares of the following binomials:

31. $5x - 7$	**32.** $8x + 3$	**33.** $3x - 10$	**34.** $6 - 5y$
35. $3c + d$	**36.** $4n - 9t$	**37.** $x^3 + y^5$	**38.** $1 + 2xy$
39. $2a^2b - 3c$	**40.** $4x + \frac{1}{4}$	**41.** $3n - \frac{1}{6}$	**42.** $c^2 - 5a$
43. $25 - 12xy$	**44.** $b^2 - 4ac$	**45.** $5s + 0.1t$	**46.** $3x + \frac{5}{6}y$
47. $2.5s + 0.2$	**48.** $10 - 0.5x$	**49.** $a^2b^3 - c^4$	**50.** $8x + \frac{1}{16}$

Square both sides of each of the following equations:

51. $x = 2a + 3$	**52.** $4x + 3 = a$	**53.** $3x - 5 = am - 6n$
54. $\sqrt{x} = 7$	**55.** $\sqrt{x + 5} = 6$	**56.** $\sqrt{3x - 2} = 4$

13.10 FACTORING TRINOMIALS THAT ARE PERFECT SQUARES

We have seen that the square of the binomial $3x + 5$ is $9x^2 + 30x + 25$. Therefore, we know that the trinomial $9x^2 + 30x + 25$ can be factored. Moreover, the two factors will be exactly alike, and the trinomial therefore is a perfect square.

Our problem is this: how can we recognize that a certain given trinomial is a perfect square? Suppose we have the trinomial $16x^2 + 40x + 25$. Our questions are, first, can the expression be factored and, second, if so, is the expression a perfect square? That is, will the two factors be exactly alike?

Perfect squares can often be recognized by inspection, and the factors can be written down at once. First of all, we know the expression must be a trinomial; that is, it must contain three terms. Moreover, the first and the third terms must be perfect square terms.

Look again at the trinomial $16x^2 + 40x + 25$. The first and third terms are perfect squares; they are the squares of the quantities $4x$ and 5.

However, before we can be sure the entire expression is the complete square of a binomial, we must be sure the middle term is the proper term for such a square. The middle term must be *twice* the product of the *square roots* of the other terms. In this case we have twice the product of $4x$ and 5, which makes $40x$. This means that the given expression is a perfect square of the binomial $(4x + 5)$. Therefore, we can say

$$16x^2 + 40x + 25 = (4x + 5)(4x + 5) \quad \text{or} \quad (4x + 5)^2$$

In some perfect squares the middle term is negative. You will recall that the square of the binomial $3x - 5$ is the trinomial $9x^2 - 30x + 25$. This is exactly like the square of $3x + 5$ except for the sign of the middle term.

In the trinomial $9x^2 - 30x + 25$ we notice that the first and third terms are perfect squares of the quantities $3x$ and 5, respectively. However, we recall that the square root of 25 is either a $+ 5$ or a $- 5$, and twice the product of the two square roots is a $- 30x$ if we choose the $- 5$. The expression is therefore a perfect square of a binomial:

$$9x^2 - 30x + 25 = (3x - 5)(3x - 5) \quad \text{or} \quad (3x - 5)^2$$

The factors of $9x^2 - 30x + 25$ can also be $(5 - 3x)^2$.

Example. $x^2 - 8x + 16 = (x - 4)(x - 4)$ or $(x - 4)^2$. The factors of $x^2 - 8x + 16$ can also be $(4 - x)^2$.

Note. Although the first and third terms are positive and perfect squares, the entire expression is not always a perfect square. Before we can be sure of having a perfect square, the middle term must be checked. The following expression is not a perfect square: $x^2 + 9x + 16$.

Exercise 13.7

Determine which of the following expressions are perfect squares. Then factor the perfect squares and write the two factors as the square of the binomial:

1. $9x^2 + 48x + 64$	**2.** $4y^2 - 12y + 9$
3. $c^2 - 12c + 16$	**4.** $k^2 + 10k + 25$
5. $4x^2 + 26x + 49$	**6.** $25n^4 - 40n^2 + 16$
7. $49 + 60r^3 + 16r^6$	**8.** $9x^2 + 2x + \frac{1}{9}$
9. $25p^4 + 20p + 4$	**10.** $t^2 - 15t + 16$

11. $25x^2 + 20x + 15$

12. $x^2 + x + \frac{1}{4}$

13. $y^2 - 34y + 64$

14. $64 - 16x + x^2$

15. $4n^2 - n + \frac{1}{4}$

16. $16x^2 - 2x + \frac{1}{16}$

17. $81 + 9x + \dfrac{x^2}{4}$

18. $225x^2 + 30x + 1$

19. $144t^2 + \frac{1}{9} - 8t$

20. $169T^2 + 100 - 280T$

21. $x^2y^2 + 3cxy + \frac{9}{4}c^2$

22. $x^8 + 18x^4 + 81$

23. $x^2y^4 - 16xy^2z^3 + 64z^6$

24. $9h^6k^2 + 42h^3k + 49$

13.11   FINDING A MISSING MIDDLE TERM OF A PERFECT SQUARE

Suppose we have given the two end terms of a perfect square, such as $25x^2 \cdots + 16y^2$. Our problem may be to determine the proper middle term for a perfect square trinomial. To find the necessary term, we first take the square roots, $5x$ and $4y$, of the two given terms. Then, the middle term must be twice the product of these two terms: $(2)(5x)(4y)$, or $40xy$. This middle term may be either positive or negative. If we call the middle term positive, we have

$$25x^2 + 40xy + 16y^2 = (5x + 4y)(5x + 4y) \quad \text{or} \quad (5x + 4y)^2$$

If we call the middle term negative, we have

$$25x^2 - 40xy + 16y^2 = (5x - 4y)(5x - 4y) \quad \text{or} \quad (5x - 4y)^2$$

Exercise 13.8

Supply a proper middle term to make each of the following expressions a perfect square. Then factor each expression and write as the square of a binomial:

1. $x^2 + \cdots + 9$

2. $y^2 + \cdots + 36$

3. $n^2 - \cdots + 64$

4. $a^2 - \cdots + 64$

5. $4x^2 + \cdots + 9$

6. $9n^2 - \cdots + 16$

7. $25x^2 + \cdots + 1$

8. $49y^2 - \cdots + 4$

9. $16x^2 + \cdots + 81$

10. $x^2y^2 - \cdots + \frac{1}{9}$

11. $36x^2 + \cdots + 25$

12. $121 - \cdots + 36x^2$

13. $9x^2 - \cdots + \frac{1}{9}$

14. $4r^2 + \cdots + \frac{1}{16}$

15. $a^2b^4 - \cdots + 9$

16. $16 + \cdots + 49t^2$

17. $x^2 - \cdots + \frac{1}{4}$

18. $n^2 + \cdots + 324$

19. $9x^2 - \cdots + \frac{1}{4}$

20. $\frac{4}{9} - \cdots + 25x^2$

21. $144 + \cdots + 4x^2$

22. $25 - \cdots + 9i^2$

23. $F^2 + \cdots + 400$

24. $I^2 - \cdots + 361$

13.12   COMPLETING A SQUARE BY ADDITION OF A THIRD TERM

In some expressions it happens that we have the first two terms of a perfect square. As an example, suppose we have the expression $x^2 - 6x$. Our problem in many cases is to determine what number should be added to the expression to produce a perfect square. This process is called *completing the square*. The device of completing a square is very useful in much work in mathematics.

If we remember that the middle term is *twice* the product of the two square roots of the end terms, respectively, we see that this product is $-6x$. Therefore, the product itself of the two square roots is $-3x$. Since the square root of the first term is x, the square root of the last term must be -3. Therefore, the last term is 9.

For completing the square, in some cases it may be a little more difficult to determine the number to be added. Take the example $9x^2 + 30x\ldots$. Here, the $30x$ is twice the product of the square roots, so that the product itself is $15x$. Now, the square root of the first term is $3x$. Therefore, the square root of the last term must be 5. The number to be added is the square of 5, which is 25.

For completing a square, we have the following rule:

Rule. *If the coefficient of x^2 is 1, take one-half the coefficient of x and square this number. The result is the number to be added.*

If the coefficient of x^2 is something other than 1, take one-half the coefficient of x, divide this by the square root of the coefficient of x^2, and square the result. This is the number to be added.

Exercise 13.9

Supply the missing term that will make each of the following expressions a perfect square. Then express each as the square of a binomial.

1. $x^2 + 10x \cdots$
2. $y^2 - 12y \cdots$
3. $4x^2 + 28x \cdots$
4. $9n^2 - 6n \cdots$
5. $x^2 + 16x \cdots$
6. $y^2 - 18y \cdots$
7. $x^2 + x \cdots$
8. $25x^2 + 90x \cdots$
9. $16x^2 - 32x \cdots$
10. $9x^2 - 2x \cdots$
11. $\cdots + 13x + 36x^2$
12. $9x^4 - 12x^2 \cdots$
13. $x^2 + \dfrac{x}{2} \cdots$
14. $9x^2 + 3x \cdots$
15. $4x^2 - 5x \cdots$
16. $16x^2 - 7x \cdots$
17. $49n^2 + 42n \cdots$
18. $64c^2 - 24c \cdots$
19. $100t^2 - 50t \cdots$
20. $4x^2 + 9x \cdots$

13.13   A SPECIAL PRODUCT: $(x + a)(x + b)$

If we have the two factors $(x + 3)(x + 4)$ to be multiplied, we notice that this set of factors is different from the kinds of sets we have already considered.

If we multiply these two factors by the usual long method, we get

$$(x + 3)(x + 4) = x^2 + 7x + 12$$

Note that the first term of the product is simply x^2. The third term is the product of the last two terms of the binomials; that is, $(3)(4)$. The coefficient of x is equal to the *sum* of the two terms, $+3$ and $+4$.

Such a product may be quickly written from inspection. As an example, suppose we have the two factors

$$(x + 7)(x + 5)$$

The first term of the product is, of course, x^2. The last term of the product is $(+7)(+5)$, or 35. The middle term has the sum of $+7$ and $+5$ as the coefficient of x. The product is therefore

$$(x + 7)(x + 5) = x^2 + 12x + 35$$

As a problem of this kind, we can say that

$$(x + a)(x + b) = x^2 + (a + b)x + ab$$

The signs, plus and minus, must be carefully observed in multiplication by inspection. Consider the problem

$$(x - 7)(x + 4)$$

In the product the first term is x^2. The last term is $(-7)(+4)$, or -28. To get the middle term, we take the sum of (-7) and $(+4)$, which is -3, as the coefficient of x. The complete product is: $x^2 - 3x - 28$.

Rule. *The first term of the product is the product $(x)(x)$, which is x^2.*
The second term is a term in x. The coefficient of x is the algebraic sum of the two last terms of the binomials.
The third term is the algebraic product of the last two terms of the binomials.

Exercise 13.10

Multiply by inspection:

1. $(x - 3)(x - 4)$	**2.** $(x - 5)(x - 2)$	**3.** $(y + 6)(y + 2)$
4. $(n + 12)(n + 1)$	**5.** $(a - 3)(a + 4)$	**6.** $(h + 6)(h - 9)$
7. $(c - 4)(c - 7)$	**8.** $(x + 8)(x + 1)$	**9.** $(a - 7)(a - 8)$
10. $(y - 4)(y + 13)$	**11.** $(n - 12)(n + 2)$	**12.** $(x^2 + 3)(x^2 - 7)$
13. $(b - 13)(b + 3)$	**14.** $(n - 6)(n + 5)$	**15.** $(8 + x)(9 - x)$
16. $(x - 17)(x - 5)$	**17.** $(x - 5)(x + 5)$	**18.** $(x + 20)(x + 3)$
19. $(n^3 - 5)(n^3 + 1)$	**20.** $(y + 48)(y - 3)$	**21.** $(x - 13)(x - 4)$

22. $(2 - n)(11 + n)$ **23.** $(h + 10)(h - 9)$ **24.** $(n + 7)(n - 12)$
25. $(E - 15)(E + 3)$ **26.** $(I + 14)(I - 6)$ **27.** $(x - 9)(x + 9)$
28. $(R - 7)(R - 3)$ **29.** $(n + 4)(n - 21)$ **30.** $(x + \frac{1}{2})(x + \frac{1}{3})$

13.14   FACTORING EXPRESSIONS OF THE TYPE $x^2 + px + q$

To find the factors of trinomials of this type, we write x as the first term of each factor: $(x \quad)(x \quad)$. Then we find two factors of the q term whose algebraic sum is p.

Example 1.   Factor the trinomial $x^2 - 4x - 12$.

Solution.   We set down x as the first term of each factor:

$$(x \quad)(x \quad)$$

Now we must find two factors of -12 whose algebraic sum is -4. By inspection, we see that these factors are -6 and $+2$. These numbers are the second terms of the binomials. The factors of the trinomial are

$$x^2 - 4x - 12 = (x - 6)(x + 2)$$

If the third term in a trinomial of this kind is positive, the factors of this term must have the same sign ; *both* may be positive *or both* negative. Consider the example

$$x^2 - 5x + 6 = (\quad)(\quad)$$

The factors of $+6$ must have the same sign. Since their algebraic sum is -5, the factors must be -3 and -2. Then the factors of the trinomial are

$$x^2 - 5x + 6 = (x - 3)(x - 2)$$

Note.   If there are no factors of the third term whose sum is equal to the coefficient in the middle term, then the trinomial cannot be factored in rational terms. If the two required factors of the third term are exactly alike, the two factors are identical, and the trinomial is a perfect square.

Example 2. $x^2 + 9x + 16$. This trinomial cannot be factored.

Example 3. $x^2 + 10x + 25 = (x + 5)(x + 5)$, a perfect square.

Exercise 13.11

Factor the following if possible. Tell which are perfect squares.

1. $x^2 + 7x + 12$ **2.** $x^2 - 5x + 6$ **3.** $x^2 - 5x - 6$
4. $n^2 + 6n + 9$ **5.** $y^2 - 4y - 5$ **6.** $c^2 + 4c - 12$
7. $d^2 - 5d - 14$ **8.** $n^2 - 12n + 36$ **9.** $x^2 - 14x + 49$
10. $x^2 - 13x + 12$ **11.** $t^2 + 6t - 16$ **12.** $x^2 + 8x - 12$

13. $n^2 - 10n + 16$ **14.** $t^2 - 11t + 24$ **15.** $I^2 + 44I + 84$
16. $w^2 + 3w - 40$ **17.** $16 - 8x + x^2$ **18.** $16 - 15x - x^2$
19. $x^2 - 8x - 48$ **20.** $x^2 + 8x - 84$ **21.** $n^2 - 13n - 48$
22. $b^2 - b - 72$ **23.** $x^2 - 2x - 2$ **24.** $h^2 + 18h - 40$
25. $R^2 - 21R - 84$ **26.** $N^2 - 13N - 90$ **27.** $E^2 + 30E + 81$
28. $x^2 + 40x + 144$ **29.** $n^2 - 16n - 36$ **30.** $Z^2 - 37Z + 160$

13.15 A MORE DIFFICULT SPECIAL PRODUCT: $(ax + b)(cx + d)$

We now come to a special product of two binomials that is more difficult than those heretofore mentioned. Suppose we have the two factors $(3x - 4)(5x + 2)$. If we perform the multiplication by the usual long method, we find that the product is $15x^2 - 14x - 8$.

$$
\begin{array}{r}
3x - 4 \\
5x + 2 \\
\hline
15x^2 - 20x \\
+ \ 6x - 8 \\
\hline
15x^2 - 14x - 8
\end{array}
$$

Our problem now is to see how this product may be found quickly by inspection. Let us see how each of the three terms in the answer is obtained from the two binomials.

In the answer obtained you will notice that the *first* term of the product, $15x^2$, is obtained by multiplying the first terms of the two binomials: $(3x)(5x)$.

The *third* term of the product is found by multiplying the second terms of the binomials: $(-4)(+2)$, which is -8.

The *middle* term of the product, $-14x$, is the algebraic sum of the *cross products*: $(5x)(-4)$ and $(3x)(2)$. If we write the two factors in horizontal form, we can show these cross products by arrows in this way:

$$(3x - 4)(5x + 2)$$

The middle term of the product is the sum of these *cross products*:

$$
\begin{array}{r}
-20x \\
+6x \\
\hline
-14x
\end{array}
$$

For the multiplication of two binomials of this form, we have the following rule:

Rule. *The first term of the answer is the product of the first terms of the binomials.*

The middle term of the answer is the algebraic sum of the cross products.
The third term of the answer is the product of the second terms of the binomials.

Exercise 13.12

Multiply the following by inspection:

1. $(2x + 3)(3x + 4)$ **2.** $(3x - 4)(2x - 5)$
3. $(4x + 3)(3x - 2)$ **4.** $(5n - 2)(4n + 1)$
5. $(6x + 5)(x - 2)$ **6.** $(5h - 4)(3 + 8h)$
7. $(5 - 9y)(1 + 4y)$ **8.** $(8c + 3)(4 + c)$
9. $(4 + 7b)(3b - 4)$ **10.** $(3n - 5)(2n - 5)$
11. $(4c + 7)(5c - 3)$ **12.** $(7E - 2)(5E + 3)$
13. $(8a - 5)(3a + 2)$ **14.** $(6x - 7)(x + 4)$
15. $(4x + 1)(x - 8)$ **16.** $(2x - 3y)(4x + 3y)$
17. $(5x - 7)(5x - 7)$ **18.** $(3x + 8)(3x + 8)$
19. $(11t - 7)(3t + 2)$ **20.** $(12x + 1)(x - 12)$
21. $(8 - xy)(5 + 4xy)$ **22.** $(4x - 9)(9x + 1)$
23. $(3x^2 + y)(2x^2 - 9y)$ **24.** $(4ab + 3c)(3ab - 4c)$

13.16   FACTORING A TRINOMIAL OF THE TYPE $ax^2 + bx + c$

This kind of trinomial is one of the most difficult to factor. The method is shown by an example.

Example 1.   Factor the expression $3x^2 - 7x + 2$.

Solution. Factoring a trinomial of this type is largely a matter of trial and error. At first we may have some difficulty in finding the correct set of factors. However, there is a definite approach that we can follow.

We first write down the form of the binomial factors by the use of parentheses:

$$3x^2 - 7x + 2 = (\qquad)(\qquad)$$

The first terms of the binomials must be factors of the first term $3x^2$. The only possible factors are $3x$ and x. So we write them as the first terms of the binomial factors:

$$3x^2 - 7x + 2 = (3x\qquad)(x\qquad)$$

The only possible factors of the last term 2 are 2 and 1. Both factors must be plus $(+)$ or both minus $(-)$, in order to make the product $+2$, as the last term of the trinomial.

To determine the proper factors of the trinomial, we must match up the factors of the first term, $3x$ and x, with the factors of the last term in such a way that the sum of the cross products will be equal to the middle term $-7x$. After some trial, we find that the factor -2 must be placed with the x term and the factor -1 with the $3x$ term:

$$3x^2 - 7x + 2 = (3x - 1)(x - 2)$$

Matching up the terms in any other manner would not produce the middle term $-7x$. Remember, the middle term must be the sum of the *cross products*.

Example 2. Factor $4x^2 - 5x - 6 = ($ $)($ $)$.

Solution. We know that the first terms of the factors must be factors of $4x^2$. One pair of such factors is the set $2x$ and $2x$. Another set is $4x$ and x.

To determine the proper factors of the trinomial, we must match up the factors of the first term, $4x^2$, with the proper set of factors of the last term, -6, in such a way that the sum of the cross products will be $-5x$. After some practice, we are usually able to select the proper sets of factors without too much difficulty. However, in a problem of this kind it is well at first to write down all possible combinations.

In each of the following sets of factors the first terms are factors of $4x^2$ and the second terms are factors of -6.

$(4x - 6)(x + 1)$	$(4x - 2)(x + 3)$	$(2x - 3)(2x + 2)$
$(4x - 1)(x + 6)$	$(4x + 2)(x - 3)$	$(2x + 3)(2x - 2)$
$(4x + 6)(x - 1)$	$(4x - 3)(x + 2)$	$(2x - 6)(2x + 1)$
$(4x + 1)(x - 6)$	$(4x + 3)(x - 2)$	$(2x + 6)(2x - 1)$

In all of these sets of factors only one has the correct arrangement to make the middle term $-5x$. This is the set $(4x + 3)(x - 2)$

At first you may have difficulty in selecting the correct set of factors in some examples of this type. With practice you will be able to find the correct set rather quickly.

As a help in factoring, you might remember one important point. If the original expression has no common factor, then there cannot be a common factor in any one of the separate factors. This fact enables us to omit many possible pairs immediately. Note the common factor 2 in eight of the pairs of factors we have set down. These pairs can be omitted at once because the original expression has no such common factor.

Exercise 13.13

Factor, if possible. Identify perfect squares.

1. $2x^2 - 5x - 12$	**2.** $3n^2 + 11n - 4$
3. $6c^2 - 5c - 6$	**4.** $4x^2 - 15x + 9$
5. $4n^2 - 12n + 9$	**6.** $3r^2 - 10r - 8$
7. $5x^2 + 11x + 6$	**8.** $6y^2 + y - 12$
9. $12p^2 + p - 20$	**10.** $40n^2 - 17n - 12$
11. $2 - 7x - 4x^2$	**12.** $12E^2 - 23E - 24$
13. $18n^2 - 3n - 10$	**14.** $4x^2 + 28x + 49$
15. $6b^2 - 23b + 20$	**16.** $6h^2 + 56h + 49$
17. $16k^2 + 56k + 49$	**18.** $4x^2 + 10x + 25$
19. $36 + 25x - 25x^2$	**20.** $4x^2 - 3x - 1$
21. $24a^2 - 7ab - 6b^2$	**22.** $48R^2 + 10R - 3$
23. $25x^2 - 40xy + 16y^2$	**24.** $20I^2 - 12I - 27$
25. $9x^2 - 13x + 4$	**26.** $48x^2 + 119x - 24$
27. $16x^2 + 26x + 9$	**28.** $36y^2 - 100x + 25$

13.17   FACTORING THE SUM AND THE DIFFERENCE OF TWO CUBES

If we divide the expression $a^3 + b^3$ by the quantity $a + b$, we get the quotient $a^2 - ab + b^2$. Therefore, we know that

$$a^3 + b^3 = (a + b)(a^2 - ab + b^2)$$

Also, if we divide $a^3 - b^3$ by $a - b$, we get the quotient $a^2 + ab + b^2$. Therefore,

$$a^3 - b^3 = (a - b)(a^2 + ab + b^2)$$

The best way to learn to factor the sum or difference of two cubes is to become thoroughly familiar with the pattern of the factors. In either case one factor contains *two* terms, the other factor contains *three* terms. Notice that the binomial factor is made up of the *cube roots* of the two cubes. The sign between them is the same as the sign between the cubes.

The second factor, the trinomial, in each case is made up of the squares of the cube roots, with the product of the cube roots as the middle term. In either case the two factors have only one minus $(-)$ sign. If you forget the second factor, you can always find it by long division.

Exercise 13.14

Factor the following:

1. $x^3 - 8$	**2.** $125 - n^3$	**3.** $T^3 + 1000$
4. $216x^3 + 1$	**5.** $x^6 - 27$	**6.** $x^3 + \frac{1}{8}$
7. $343t^3 - 64$	**8.** $X^{15} + 216$	**9.** $x^9 - 1$
10. $R^3 - r^3$	**11.** $8y^3 + 125$	**12.** $27x^3 - \frac{1}{27}$
13. $64n^3 - 729$	**14.** $(a + b)^3 + 8$	**15.** $(x + y)^3 - (a - b)^3$

*13.18   FACTORING THE SUM OR DIFFERENCE OF TWO EQUAL POWERS

The difference between equal powers (odd or even) of two numbers, such as $a^5 - b^5$ or $a^6 - b^6$, is always divisible by the difference between the numbers $a - b$. Therefore, in factoring such expressions we may take the difference between the numbers as one of the factors. The best way to get the other factor is by long division:

$$x^5 - y^5 = (x - y)(x^4 + x^3y + x^2y^2 + xy^3 + y^4)$$

However, if the powers are even powers, such as $x^8 - y^8$, we should first factor the expression as the difference between two squares.

* *Optional.*

The *sum* of equal powers of two numbers, such as $a^n + b^n$, is divisible by the sum of the numbers, *provided* the powers are *odd* powers. Thus

$$x^5 + y^5 = (x + y)(x^4 - x^3y + x^2y^2 - xy^3 + y^4)$$

The second factor is obtained by long division.

The *sum* of two *even* powers cannot be factored unless the powers can also be shown to be odd powers of some quantities. Thus $x^4 + y^4$ is not factorable: $x^6 + y^6$ can be called the sum of two cubes $(x^2)^3 + (y^2)^3$, and therefore the expression can be factored.

Exercise 13.15

Factor if possible:

1. $x^4 - y^4$ 2. $x^5 + 32$ 3. $x^7 - y^7$
4. $n^{12} + 1$ 5. $y^4 + 16$ 6. $x^8 - 1$
7. $x^2 + y^2$ 8. $x^{10} - 1$ 9. $x^6 - 64$

13.19 FACTORING BY VARIOUS METHODS OF GROUPING

Factoring by grouping of terms is shown here by examples.

Example 1.   Factor $2x + ax - 2y - ay$.

Solution.   Grouping terms: $(2x + ax) - (2y + ay)$.
Common factors: $x(2 + a) - y(2 + a)$.
Now, we take out the common factor $(2 + a)$.
The factors are $(2 + a)(x - y)$.

Example 2.   Factor $x^2 + 2xy + y^2 - x - y$.

Solution.   We write the first three terms as a perfect square and enclose the remaining terms in parentheses. We get

$$(x + y)^2 - (x + y)$$

We now take out the common factor $x + y$:

$$(x + y)(x + y - 1)$$

Example 3.   Factor $x^2 + 6x + 9 - c^2$.

Solution.   We write the first three terms as a perfect square:

$$(x + 3)^2 - c^2$$

We now factor the entire expression as the difference between two squares:

$$(x + 3 - c)(x + 3 + c)$$

Example 4.   Factor $x^4 + 5x^2 + 9$.

Solution. If we add and then subtract the same quantity from the expression, the value will not be changed. Let us add and subtract the quantity x^2. Then we get

$$x^4 + 5x^2 + 9 + x^2 - x^2$$

The first four terms taken together form a perfect square:

$$(x^2 + 3)^2 - x^2$$

The expression can now be factored as the difference between two squares:

$$(x^2 + 3 - x)(x^2 + 3 + x)$$

Exercise 13.16

Find the prime factors of the following. Always take out a common factor first if possible. If any factor is itself a product, it should be separated into prime factors.

1. $36x^2 - 81$ **2.** $3x^4 + 81x$ **3.** $16y^5 - 2y^2$

4. $x^6 - x^2y^4$ **5.** $256n^2 - 4n^4$ **6.** $8x^3 + 72x$

7. $x^{12} - 1$ **8.** $9t^4 - 0.25t^2$ **9.** $64y^4 - 4y^8$

10. $n^6 - 81n^4$ **11.** $250y + 2y^4$ **12.** $3x^7 - 96x^2$

13. $n^9 + n^2$ **14.** $x^4 - 169x^2$ **15.** $a^2h^2 - a^2k^2$

16. $25R^3 - 0.01R$ **17.** $3x^3 - 3x^2 - 36x$ **18.** $2n^3 - 2n^2 - 60n$

19. $4y^4 + 44y^3 - 48y^2$ **20.** $t^5 - t^4 - 42t^3$ **21.** $2x^3 - 18x^2 - 24x$

22. $9x^2 - 72x + 90$ **23.** $120x^4 + 3x^3 - 45x^2$ **24.** $36r^4 - 6r^3 - 20r^2$

25. $2x^3y - 46x^2y + 84xy$ **26.** $3h^3x + 9h^2x - 210hx$

27. $4x^3y^2 - 112x^2y^2 - 240xy^2$ **28.** $4n^4 - 20n^3 - 144n^2$

29. $12x^3y^2 - x^2y^3 - 20xy^4$ **30.** $40h^3 + 84h^2 - 40h$

31. $16x^3y - 66x^2y + 54xy$ **32.** $35k - 16H^2k - 26Hk$

33. $24xy^2 - 45y^2 + x^2y^2$ **34.** $14x^2y^3 - 4x^3y^2 + 44xy^4$

35. $66x^2 - 180x + 36x^3$ **36.** $16E^2x^3 + 124Ex^3 + 240x^3$

37. $a^2 - 6ab + 9b^2 - x^2$ **38.** $16y^2 - x^2 + 16 - 8xy$

39. $6x + 4y^2 - 9 - x^2$ **40.** $4x^4 + 3x^2 + 9$

41. $x^2 - y^2 + 2x + 6y - 8$ **42.** $x^2 - y^2 - 10x + 4y + 21$

43. $x^2 - 9y^2 + 4x + 12y$ **44.** $4x^2 - 9y^2 - 8x + 18y - 5$

45. $(x - y)^3 + 8$ **46.** $(x + y)^3 - 5(x + y)^2 + 6(x + y)$

47. $x^5 - x^3 + 8x^2 - 8$ **48.** $x^3 - 3x^2 - 9x + 27$

Quiz on Chapter 13, Factoring. Form 1. Factor each expression into prime factors.

1. $b^2 - 144$ **2.** $8n^4 - 50n^2$ **3.** $2x^7 - 2x^3$

4. $y^2 + y - 56$ **5.** $x^3 - x^2 - 20x$ **6.** $2x^2 - 6x - 56$

7. $x^2 + 9x - 52$ **8.** $y^2 - 16y - 80$ **9.** $x^2 + 13x - 30$

10. $n^2 - 9n - 90$ **11.** $x^2 + 10x - 96$ **12.** $64x^3 + 27t^3$

13. $8a^3b^3 - 1$ **14.** $3x^2 - 7x + 2$ **15.** $16x^2 + 56x + 49$

16. $24x^2 - 25x - 25$ **17.** $9x^2 + 26x + 16$ **18.** $25x^2 - 30x - 16$

19. $a^6 - b^6$ **20.** $x^8 - 1$ **21.** $x^2 - y^2 + 6x + 9$

22. Tell the difference between these two expressions and state the factors of each: $m^3 + n^3$ and $(m + n)^3$.

Add the proper number to each of the following expressions to form a perfect square and then factor the result and express it as a square:

23. $x^2 + 16x + \cdots$　　　**24.** $4x^2 - 28x + \cdots$　　　**25.** $25x^2 + 3x \cdots$

Factor each of the following:

26. $x^3 + 2x^2 - 9x - 18$　　**27.** $x^4 - 5x^2 + 9$　　　**28.** $x^2 - y^2 - 8x - 2y + 15$

Quiz on Chapter 13, Factoring. Form 2. Factor each expression into prime factors.

1. $a^2 - 121$　　　　　　**2.** $27x^4 - 12x^2$　　　　**3.** $3n^6 - 48n^2$
4. $x^2 - 7x - 42$　　　　**5.** $y^3 + 6y^2 - 30y$　　　**6.** $3x^2 + 6x - 72$
7. $x^2 - 10x - 56$　　　**8.** $n^2 + 17n - 60$　　　**9.** $x^2 - 18x - 40$
10. $y^2 - 11y - 80$　　　**11.** $x^2 + 8x - 84$　　　**12.** $8x^3 - 125y^3$
13. $27c^3d^3 + 1$　　　　**14.** $2x^2 - 5x - 3$　　　**15.** $25x^2 - 70x + 49$
16. $32x^2 + 40x - 25$　　**17.** $16x^2 - 30x + 9$　　**18.** $36x^2 - 25x - 25$
19. $x^6 - 1$　　　　　　　**20.** $c^{12} - 1$　　　　　　**21.** $a^2 - b^2 - 8a + 16$
22. Tell the difference between these two expressions and state the factors of each:
$x^3 - y^3$ and $(x - y)^3$

Add the proper number to each of the following expressions to form a perfect square and then factor the result and express it as a square:

23. $x^2 - 10x + \cdots$　　　**24.** $9x^2 + 30x + \cdots$　　　**25.** $16x^2 + 5x + \cdots$

Factor each of the following:

26. $x^3 - 5x^2 - 4x + 20$　　**27.** $x^4 + 7x^2 + 16$　　　**28.** $x^2 - y^2 + 6x - 4y + 5$

14
Fractions

14.1 DEFINITION

In algebra, as in arithmetic, it often happens that we must operate with fractions. In order to understand clearly how to perform the operations with fractions, let us recall some of the facts about fractions in arithmetic.

From arithmetic we know that a common fraction consists of two numbers, one written above the other, with a horizontal line between them: thus $\frac{3}{4}$. The number above the line is called the *numerator*. The number below the line is called the *denominator*. *The numerator and the denominator are called the terms of a fraction.*

The meaning of a fraction may be explained from two different viewpoints. In the first place, in a fraction such as $\frac{3}{4}$ we can say the number, 4, below the line indicates that a whole quantity has first been divided into four parts. Each part is called a "fourth." We indicate this fourth by the fraction $\frac{1}{4}$. The number, 4, below the line is called the *denominator* because it *denominates*, or names, the kind of part. The word "denominate" means to *name*.

Now, if we wish to take three of these parts, we write 3 above the line. The 3 is called the *numerator* because it *enumerates*, or counts, the number of parts to be considered.

There is a second explanation of the meaning of a fraction. A fraction may be considered as an *indicated division*. The line separating the numerator from the denominator can be called a sign of division. This second meaning of a fraction is often more desirable and convenient than the first. From this second viewpoint, the fraction $\frac{3}{4}$ means $3 \div 4$.

There are many advantages, especially in algebra, in considering a fraction as an indicated division. From this viewpoint, the fraction $\frac{13}{20}$ means $13 \div 20$.

Division may be indicated in either form.

The division $45 \div 285$ can be written as a fraction: $\frac{45}{285}$.

The fraction $\frac{150}{37}$ can be written as division: $150 \div 37$.

The division $2x \div 3y$ can be written as a fraction: $\dfrac{2x}{3y}$.

184

The fraction $\dfrac{x^2 - 5x + 6}{x - 2}$ can be written as division:

$$(x^2 - 5x + 6) \div (x - 2)$$

14.2 FUNDAMENTAL PRINCIPLE OF FRACTIONS

Before we consider the different operations with fractions, it is important that we thoroughly understand the following principle:

Fundamental Principle of Fractions. *If the numerator and the denominator of any fraction are multiplied or divided by the same quantity (other than zero), the value of the fraction will not be changed.*

To illustrate this principle, suppose we start with the fraction $\frac{12}{18}$. The fundamental principle says that if we multiply the numerator and the denominator of this fraction by any number whatever, the new fraction will still have the same value as the original fraction $\frac{12}{18}$.

Suppose we multiply both terms of this fraction by the number 7. We get the new fraction $\frac{84}{126}$. This new fraction still has the same value as the original fraction $\frac{12}{18}$; that is, multiplying the numerator and the denominator by the same number, 7, does not change the value of the fraction.

You may wonder why this is true. Let us try to see why. We know that any number multiplied by 1 is equal to the number itself. For instance, 1 times 12 is 12. If we multiply the fraction $\frac{12}{18}$ by 1, there is no change in the value.

However, the number 1 may be expressed in some other form, such as $\frac{3}{3}$, $\frac{5}{5}$, or $\frac{7}{7}$. Now let us multiply the fraction $\frac{12}{18}$ by $\frac{7}{7}$:

$$\frac{7}{7} \cdot \frac{12}{18} = \frac{84}{126}$$

As a result, we get the new fraction $\frac{84}{126}$, which has the same value as the original fraction $\frac{12}{18}$. When we multiply both terms of a fraction by the same number, we are only multiplying the fraction by 1.

As another example, let us consider the algebraic fraction

$$\frac{3x - 4}{5y + 2}$$

If the numerator and the denominator of this fraction are multiplied by the same quantity, say, $7x$, the new fraction will still have the same value:

$$\frac{7x \cdot (3x - 4)}{7x \cdot (5y + 2)} = \frac{7x(3x - 4)}{7x(5y + 2)} = \frac{21x^2 - 28x}{35xy + 14x}$$

The resulting fraction has the same value as the original fraction.

The fundamental principle also says that if we divide numerator and denominator of a fraction by the same number, the fraction will still have the same value. Suppose we start again with the fraction $\frac{12}{18}$. If we divide numerator and denominator by any number, say, 3, then we get the new fraction $\frac{4}{6}$. This new fraction has the same value as the fraction $\frac{12}{18}$.

If we wish, we may divide both terms of the foregoing fraction by 6. Then we get the new fraction $\frac{2}{3}$. Dividing both numerator and denominator by the same number, 6, does not change the value of the original fraction.

As another example, let us consider the algebraic fraction

$$\frac{15ax^2y}{20ax^3}$$

If the numerator and the denominator of this fraction are divided by the same quantity, say, $5ax^2$, the new fraction will still have the same value.

$$\frac{15ax^2y \div 5ax^2}{20ax^3 \div 5ax^2} = \frac{3y}{4x}$$

The resulting fraction has the same value as the original fraction.

Note. Remember that multiplying both numerator and denominator of a fraction by some number, for instance, 7, is *not* the same as multiplying the fraction itself by that number. For instance,

$$\frac{7}{7} \cdot \frac{2}{3} = \frac{14}{21}$$

Here the value of the fraction, $\frac{2}{3}$, is not changed. However, this is not the same as multiplying the fraction by 7:

$$7 \cdot \frac{2}{3} = \frac{14}{3}$$

It should be noted that if the same number (not zero) is *added* to, or *subtracted from*, both terms of a fraction the *value* of the fraction *will be changed*. As an example, the fraction $\frac{2}{3}$ does not have the same value if some number, such as 4, is added to both numerator and denominator. If we add 4 to both terms of the fraction $\frac{2}{3}$, we get the new fraction $\frac{6}{7}$. The fraction $\frac{2}{3}$ does not have the same value as $\frac{6}{7}$.

14.3   REDUCING FRACTIONS TO LOWEST TERMS

A fraction is said to be reduced to *lowest terms* when the numerator and the denominator have been made as small as possible by dividing each by some factor found in both.

To reduce fractions to lowest terms, we make use of the fundamental principle by dividing the numerator and denominator by some common factor. In some fractions we can tell at a glance what number is a divisor of both numerator and denominator. In the fraction $\frac{21}{35}$ we see at once that the numerator and denominator are divisible by 7. One way to show this is to factor numerator and denominator:

$$\frac{21}{35} = \frac{3 \cdot \cancel{7}}{\cancel{7} \cdot 5} = \frac{3}{5}$$

We cross out the "7" in numerator and denominator to show that both have been divided by 7.

In reducing fractions, some students use the word "cancel." In the foregoing example we cross out the "7" to show that numerator and denominator have been divided by 7. We sometimes say, incorrectly, we "cancel" the 7. *Cancel* is not a proper word to use in this connection. However, the word does have one correct use in mathematics. *Cancel* means to nullify, to neutralize, or to make void, as when we say we *cancel* an order. A payment of $10 will cancel a debt of $10. In the form of an equation, $-10 + 10 = 0$. In an equation such as this, $x = 12 + 5 - 5$, the $+5$ and -5 cancel each other. This is the correct use of the word.

The word *cancel* often causes students much trouble. In connection with reducing fractions, if we say "cancel" a factor in numerator and denominator, we really mean that we *divide numerator and denominator by the same factor*. The word *cancel* should not be used in reducing fractions. Students of algebra can save themselves a lot of trouble and mistakes if they will consider carefully the actual procedure involved in the so-called "cancelling" in reducing fractions.

In some fractions it may not be easy to determine the common divisor of numerator and denominator. Consider the following fraction:

$$\frac{119}{323}$$

We can easily reduce the fraction if we first factor the numerator and the denominator as shown here:

$$\frac{119}{323} = \frac{7 \cdot 17}{17 \cdot 19}$$

Now we see at once that numerator and denominator can be divided by 17, and the reduced fraction becomes $\frac{7}{19}$.

A common mistake in working with fractions is to cross out any *term* that appears in both numerator and denominator. For example, take the fraction

$$\frac{x^2 + 5x + 6}{x^2 - 9}$$

A mistake sometimes made is to cross out the "x^2" in numerator and denominator. This error happens often when we use the word "cancel." In fact, some people cross out any two things that look alike wherever they are found. Crossing out the "x^2's" in this fraction would be somewhat like crossing out the "3's" in a fraction such as $\frac{34}{37}$, which would, of course, be incorrect.

Remember, any quantity in numerator or denominator cannot be split up by crossing out a separate term if the term is connected to another term by a plus ($+$) or a minus ($-$). Only *factors* can be divided into numerator and denominator. Do not cross out separate terms unless the entire term or quantity is a *factor* of the numerator and the denominator.

However, the algebraic fraction shown may be reduced to lower terms if the numerator and denominator are factored:

$$\frac{x^2 + 5x + 6}{x^2 - 9} = \frac{(x + 3)(x + 2)}{(x - 3)(x + 3)} = \frac{x + 2}{x - 3}$$

We see that numerator and denominator are each made up as a product of factors. The binomial $x + 3$ is a factor of both numerator and denominator. This shows that both can be divided by the quantity $x + 3$. The factor $x + 3$ can be crossed out by a slanted line to show that numerator and denominator are both divided by the quantity $x + 3$.

To avoid mistakes, follow these steps.

Steps in reducing fractions:

1. *Factor numerator and denominator into prime factors.*
2. *Divide numerator and denominator by any factor or factors found in both.*

To show how algebraic fractions may be reduced, we shall work out a few examples. If the numerator and denominator of a fraction consist of only monomial factors, the prime factors need not be written out separately, since no additions or subtractions are involved.

Examples.   Reduce the fraction

$$\frac{18x^3y^2z}{24ax^4y}$$

We shall first write out all the prime factors separately and then later show that this need not be done in such fractions. Writing the prime factors of numerator and denominator, we have

$$\frac{18x^3y^2z}{24ax^4y} = \frac{2 \cdot 3 \cdot 3 \cdot x \cdot x \cdot x \cdot y \cdot y \cdot z}{2 \cdot 2 \cdot 2 \cdot 3 \cdot a \cdot x \cdot x \cdot x \cdot x \cdot y} = \frac{3yz}{4ax}$$

Prime factors that appear in both numerator and denominator are crossed out to show that these factors have been divided into both numerator and denominator. The remaining factors are multiplied together to form the reduced fraction.

The foregoing fraction might have been reduced simply by dividing numerator and denominator by common factors of each: thus

$$\frac{\overset{3}{\cancel{18}}\ \overset{y}{\cancel{x^3}}\ \cancel{y^2}\ z}{\underset{4}{\cancel{24}}\ a\ \underset{x}{\cancel{x^4}}\ \cancel{y}} = \frac{3yz}{4ax}$$

First we divide numerator and denominator by the common numerical factor 6. Next, we divide numerator and denominator by the quantity x^3. Finally, we divide numerator and denominator by the common factor y.

If the numerator or the denominator, or both, consists of more than one term, then we must first find the prime factors of each. Suppose we have the fraction

$$\frac{3x^2 + 7x - 6}{3x^2 + 5x - 12}$$

In this fraction we first factor the numerator and denominator. Then we divide the numerator and denominator by any factor found in both:

$$\frac{3x^2 + 7x - 6}{3x^2 + 5x - 12} = \frac{(3x - 2)\cancel{(x + 3)}}{(3x - 4)\cancel{(x + 3)}} = \frac{3x - 2}{3x - 4}$$

We see that the factor $x + 3$ is found in the numerator and denominator. Therefore, each may be divided by this factor. The final reduced fraction, as shown, *cannot* be further reduced.

Note. As a student of mathematics, you should always remember one important fact: the correct procedure is more important than getting the right answer. This is true in all mathematics. Consider the fraction

$$\frac{x^2 - 9}{x - 3}$$

The correct way to reduce this fraction is to factor the numerator and denominator and then to divide each by any common factor: thus

$$\frac{x^2 - 9}{x - 3} = \frac{\cancel{(x - 3)}(x + 3)}{\cancel{x - 3}} = x + 3$$

The factor $x - 3$ is divided into both numerator and denominator and we get the correct answer.

One student reduced the foregoing fraction in this way:

$$\frac{\overset{x}{\cancel{x^2}}\ \overset{+}{\diagup}\ \overset{3}{\cancel{9}}}{\underset{x}{\cancel{x}}\ \underset{-}{\diagup}\ \underset{3}{\cancel{3}}} = x + 3$$

His "cancellation" method was as follows: x into x^2 is x, 3 into 9 is 3, and minus $(-)$

into a minus $(-)$ is plus $(+)$. When he got the correct answer, he wondered why he should not be given credit for working the problem. He was told that the work was no more correct than to cancel the 6's in the fraction $\frac{16}{64} = \frac{1}{4}$. Although the answer is correct, the work is entirely wrong. A correct answer from a wrong procedure is of no value whatever.

The numerator and denominator of a fraction may contain monomial factors as well as others. The first step in factoring is to take out any common factor, as shown in this example:

$$\frac{9x^4 - 36x^2}{6x^3 - 30x^2 + 36x} = \frac{9x^2(x^2 - 4)}{6x(x^2 - 5x + 6)}$$

$$= \frac{9x^2(x - 2)(x + 2)}{6x(x - 3)(x - 2)} = \frac{3x(x + 2)}{2(x - 3)}$$

Exercise 14.1

Reduce the following fractions to lowest terms:

1. $\dfrac{15x^2y^3}{25xy^5}$ **2.** $\dfrac{35an^2y^3}{42bn^2y^3}$ **3.** $\dfrac{16c^2n^3x^5y}{24cn^5xyz}$

4. $\dfrac{36a^3bc^2}{45a^2c^3d}$ **5.** $\dfrac{60x^5y^3z}{80x^4y^4ab}$ **6.** $\dfrac{14R^2h}{28r^2h}$

7. $\dfrac{18m^2n^3}{12amn}$ **8.** $\dfrac{26x^5y^3z}{13x^3y^2z}$ **9.** $\dfrac{15a^2bc^3}{15a^2bc^3}$

10. $\dfrac{51r^2t}{85rs^3}$ **11.** $\dfrac{4ab}{12a^2b^2x}$ **12.** $\dfrac{20x^3yz^4}{-4x^3z^4}$

13. $\dfrac{-7a^2m^3n}{7a^2m^3n}$ **14.** $\dfrac{87u^4vw}{203u^3vw^2}$ **15.** $\dfrac{12x^3(x - 5)^2}{8x^2(x - 5)}$

16. $\dfrac{x^2 - 16}{x - 4}$ **17.** $\dfrac{c^2 - 25}{5 - c}$ **18.** $\dfrac{(x - 1)^4}{(x - 1)^3}$

19. $\dfrac{x^2 - 9}{x^2 - 6x + 9}$ **20.** $\dfrac{2x^2 - 50}{3x^2 - 3x - 60}$

21. $\dfrac{2x^3 + 6x^2 - 8x}{4x^3 + 4x^2 - 8x}$ **22.** $\dfrac{n^5 - 9n^3}{n^4 - 2n^3 - 3n^2}$

23. $\dfrac{n^2 - 4}{n^3 - 8}$ **24.** $\dfrac{4a^3 + 12a^2 + 9a}{9a + 6a^2}$

25. $\dfrac{a + b}{a^2 + 2ab + b^2}$ **26.** $\dfrac{3y^3 + 3y^2 - 18y}{6y^4 + 24y^3 - 72y^2}$

27. $\dfrac{4x^3y - 4x^2y - 48xy}{6x^3 + 6x^2 - 36x}$ **28.** $\dfrac{8ax^2 - 10ax - 12a}{72bx^2 - 42bx - 72b}$

29. $\dfrac{3n^2x - 108x}{2n^2y - 6ny - 36y}$

30. $\dfrac{12abx^2 - 28abx + 8ab}{54ax^3 - 6ax}$

31. $\dfrac{20nx - 20nx^2 - 75nx^3}{90x^2 - 40}$

32. $\dfrac{(a + b)^2 + a + b}{(a + b)^2}$

33. $\dfrac{ax + 3x + ay + 3y}{a^2 - a - 12}$

34. $\dfrac{3x^3 + 15x^2 - 18x}{6x^2y + 42xy + 36y}$

35. $\dfrac{3c^4 - 12c^3 + 12c^2}{3c^2 - 18c + 24}$

36. $\dfrac{10n^5 + 5n^4 - 30n^3}{2n^3 - 2n^2 - 12n}$

37. $\dfrac{u^4 - uv^3}{2u^4 - u^3v - u^2v^2}$

38. $\dfrac{9c^2 - 30c + 25}{3c^2 - 11c + 10}$

39. $\dfrac{36n^2 + 24n - 45}{30n^2 + 25n - 30}$

40. $\dfrac{a^2 - b^2 - a - b}{a^2 - 2ab + b^2 - 1}$

41. $\dfrac{x^2 - a^2 - 6x + 9}{3x^3 - 15x^2 + 18x}$

42. $\dfrac{n^4 + 5n^2 + 9}{3n^3 - 3n^2 + 9n}$

43. $\dfrac{x^2 - y^2}{x^5 - y^5}$

44. $\dfrac{x^6 - 1}{x^4 - 1}$

45. $\dfrac{x^3 - 1}{x - 1}$

46. $\dfrac{(x - 1)^3}{(x - 1)^2}$

47. $\dfrac{(x - 1)^3}{x^3 - 1}$

48. $\dfrac{R^2 - r^2}{R^2 - 2Rr + r^2}$

49. $\dfrac{x^2 - 2xy + y^2}{y^2 - x^2}$

50. $\dfrac{x^2 - 5x + 6}{12 - 4x - x^2}$

14.4 MULTIPLICATION OF FRACTIONS

In multiplication and division of fractions we also often use the word "cancel." Actually, here, again, we mean "divide" the numerator and denominator of the fraction by the same quantity. Let us take an example from arithmetic:

$$\frac{12}{35} \cdot \frac{25}{8} \cdot \frac{21}{4} =$$

We know from arithmetic that we can get the product of these fractions by multiplying all the numerators together for the numerator of the product.

However, before we do the multiplication, we usually look for common factors in numerator and denominator. We see that the factor 4 can be divided into a numerator and a denominator. We can also divide numerator and denominator by the numbers 5 and 7.

$$\frac{\overset{3}{\cancel{12}}}{\underset{\cancel{7}}{\cancel{35}}} \cdot \frac{\overset{5}{\cancel{25}}}{8} \cdot \frac{\overset{3}{\cancel{21}}}{\cancel{4}} = \frac{45}{8}$$

In this example if we first write the product of all numerators and the product of all denominators and then reduce the fraction, we get the same answer: thus

$$\frac{12}{35} \cdot \frac{25}{8} \cdot \frac{21}{4} = \frac{\overset{3}{\cancel{12}} \cdot \overset{5}{\cancel{25}} \cdot \overset{3}{\cancel{21}}}{\underset{\cancel{7}}{\cancel{35}} \cdot 8 \cdot \underset{1}{\cancel{4}}} = \frac{45}{8}$$

Of course, it is much simpler to divide common factors into numerators and denominators *before* going on to the product.

Example 1. Multiply $\dfrac{8x^2y^3}{15a^2c} \cdot \dfrac{9a^3b}{16cd^2} \cdot \dfrac{4ac^3d}{21bx^3y^2} \cdot (5x)$

Solution.

$$\frac{\overset{}{\cancel{8}} \, \overset{}{x^2} \, \overset{y}{y^3}}{\underset{\cancel{8}}{\cancel{15}} \, a^2 \, \cancel{c}} \cdot \frac{\overset{\cancel{3}}{\cancel{9}} \, \overset{a}{a^3} \, \cancel{b}}{\underset{2}{\cancel{16}} \, \cancel{c} \, d^2} \cdot \frac{\cancel{4} \, a \, \overset{2}{c^3} \, \cancel{d}}{\underset{7}{\cancel{21}} \, \cancel{b} \, x^3 \, y^2} \cdot \frac{\overset{}{\cancel{5}} \, \overset{c}{\cancel{x}}}{1} = \frac{2a^2cy}{7d}$$

Example 2. Multiply

$$\frac{3x^2 - 12}{2x^3 + 2x^2 - 24x} \cdot \frac{2x^5 - 6x^4}{x^2 + 2x - 8} \cdot \frac{x^2 + 8x + 16}{9x^3 + 54x^2}$$

Solution. First find prime factors:

$$\frac{\cancel{3}\,(\cancel{x-2})(x+2)}{2\cancel{x}(\cancel{x-3})(\cancel{x+4})} \cdot \frac{\overset{x}{2x^4}(\cancel{x-3})}{(\cancel{x-2})(\cancel{x+4})} \cdot \frac{(\cancel{x+4})(\cancel{x+4})}{9\overset{}{x^2}(x+6)}_{3} = \frac{x(x+2)}{3(x+6)}$$

This answer cannot be further reduced.

14.5 DIVISION OF FRACTIONS

In division involving algebraic fractions, we follow the same rule as in division in arithmetic. That is, we multiply the dividend by the *reciprocal* of the divisor. Remember, the divisor is the quantity that *follows* the division sign.

When multiplications and divisions of fractions occur in the same problem, these operations are performed *in the order in which they occur* unless otherwise indicated by parentheses (including brackets, braces, or other forms indicating a quantity).

Example 1. Simplify $\dfrac{15}{28} \div \dfrac{5}{21}$.

Solution. $\dfrac{15}{28} \div \dfrac{5}{21} = \dfrac{15}{28} \cdot \dfrac{21}{5} = \dfrac{9}{4}$

Example 2. Simplify $\dfrac{9a^2x}{20by^2} \div \dfrac{6ax^2}{25by^3}$.

Solution. $\dfrac{9a^2x}{20by^2} \div \dfrac{6ax^2}{25by^3} = \dfrac{9a^2x}{20by^2} \cdot \dfrac{25by^3}{6ax^2} = \dfrac{15ay}{8x}$

Example 3. Simplify $\dfrac{8x^3}{15y^2} \cdot \dfrac{3ay}{4bx} \div \dfrac{12bx}{5cy}$.

Solution. $\dfrac{8x^3}{15y^2} \cdot \dfrac{3ay}{4bx} \cdot \dfrac{5cy}{12bx} = \dfrac{acx}{6b^2}$

Example 4. Simplify $\frac{4}{15} \div \frac{5}{16} \cdot \frac{5}{8}$.

Solution. In this example we invert only the fraction $\frac{5}{16}$.

$$\tfrac{4}{15} \cdot \tfrac{16}{5} \cdot \tfrac{5}{8} = \tfrac{8}{15}$$

Example 5. Simplify $\frac{8}{15} \div \frac{2}{5} \div \frac{6}{7}$.

Solution. In this example we invert both fractions, $\frac{2}{5}$ and $\frac{6}{7}$.

$$\tfrac{8}{15} \cdot \tfrac{5}{2} \cdot \tfrac{7}{6} = \tfrac{14}{9}$$

Example 6. Simplify $\frac{10}{21} \div (\frac{2}{3} \div \frac{4}{5})$.

Solution. In this example we perform the operation within the parentheses first.

$$\tfrac{10}{21} \div (\tfrac{2}{3} \div \tfrac{4}{5}) = \tfrac{10}{21} \div (\tfrac{5}{6}) = \tfrac{10}{21} \cdot \tfrac{6}{5} = \tfrac{4}{7}$$

Exercise 14.2

Perform the indicated operations:

1. $\dfrac{8x^2y^3}{21abc} \cdot \dfrac{15ax^2}{16b^2} \cdot \dfrac{14ac^2}{25x^3y}$

2. $\dfrac{15xy^2}{28ac^2} \cdot \dfrac{7c^3}{10xy} \div \dfrac{3cy}{8a}$

3. $\dfrac{26xyz^2}{35abc^3} \div \dfrac{8yz}{9b^2c^2} \cdot \dfrac{14a^2bc}{39x^2z}$

4. $\dfrac{16a^2}{21x^2} \cdot \dfrac{3x}{2ab} \div 4ac$

5. $\dfrac{5ac^2}{8xy^3} \div \left(\dfrac{9bc}{4x^2y} \cdot \dfrac{25ac^2}{6by}\right)$

6. $\dfrac{8x^2}{15a^3} \div \dfrac{12c}{5b} \div \dfrac{4bx}{3a^2}$

7. $\dfrac{3ab}{8xy} \div \left(\dfrac{15x^2}{32y^3} \div \dfrac{5ax}{24by}\right)$

8. $\dfrac{25by^3}{26ax^2} \div \dfrac{35by^2}{39x} \cdot \dfrac{14ax}{15y}$

9. $\dfrac{2x^2 - 18}{x^3 - 25x} \cdot \dfrac{3x - 15}{2x^2 - 6x}$

10. $\dfrac{x^2 - 4}{4x + 32} \cdot \dfrac{x^2 + 2x - 48}{x^2 - 2x}$

11. $\dfrac{x^2 - 7x + 10}{x^2 - 10x + 25} \div \dfrac{x + 12}{x - 5}$

12. $\dfrac{n^2 + 13n + 12}{n^2 - 8n + 15} \div \dfrac{n + 12}{n^2 - 5n}$

13. $\dfrac{x^2 - 3}{x^3 - 4x} \div \dfrac{x^4 - 9}{x^2 - 4x + 4}$

14. $\dfrac{2c^2 + 4c + 2}{c - 1} \cdot \dfrac{c - 1}{(c + 1)^2}$

15. $\dfrac{a + 2}{a^2 + 8a - 9} \cdot (2a + 18)$

16. $(3x + 6) \cdot \dfrac{x + 1}{x^2 - 6x - 16}$

17. $(4x^2 - 1) \cdot \dfrac{2x - 1}{4x^2 - 4x + 1}$

18. $(x^2 - 4x + 4) \div \dfrac{x^2 - 4}{x}$

19. $(a^2b^2 - 4) \div \dfrac{6ab + 12}{ab - 1}$

20. $\dfrac{9c^2 - 16}{c + 1} \div (3c + 4)$

21. $\dfrac{x - 3}{x^2 + 2x - 3} \cdot \dfrac{x^2 - 2x + 1}{x^2 - 2x - 3} \div \dfrac{x^2 - 9}{x^2 - 1}$

22. $\dfrac{x^2 - 5x + 4}{x^2 + 5x + 6} \div \dfrac{x^2 + 3x - 28}{x^2 - x - 20} \cdot \dfrac{x^2 - 3x - 18}{x^2 - 6x + 5}$

23. $\dfrac{4r^2 - 12r + 9}{r^2 - 9r + 8} \cdot \dfrac{r^2 - 1}{4r^2 - 9} \div \dfrac{r^2 - 8r - 9}{(2r + 3)^2}$

24. $\dfrac{x^2 + x - 6}{x^2 + 3x - 10} \div \dfrac{x^2 - x - 12}{x^2 + 4x - 5} \div \dfrac{x^2 + 5x - 6}{x^2 - 8x + 12}$

25. $\dfrac{n^2 - 13n + 12}{n^2 - 144} \div \left(\dfrac{n^2 + 8n - 9}{n^2 + 15n + 36} \div \dfrac{n^2 - 81}{n^2 - 9}\right)$

26. $\dfrac{25y^2 - 10y + 1}{25y^2 + 10y + 1} \div \dfrac{30y^2 - 6y}{40y^2 + 8y} \cdot \dfrac{5y^2 - 5}{25y^2 - 1}$

27. $\dfrac{n^3 - 16n}{n^2 - 3n - 10} \div \left(\dfrac{n^3 + n^2 - 12n}{n^2 + 5n + 6} \cdot \dfrac{n^2 - 4}{n^2 - 9}\right)$

28. $\dfrac{x^3 - 1}{(a - b)^2} \div \dfrac{3x^2 - 2x - 5}{ax - a - bx + b} \cdot \dfrac{a^2 - b^2}{(x - 1)^2}$

14.6 SIGNS IN A FRACTION

Before beginning the study of adding and subtracting fractions, it is necessary to consider the signs in a fraction. In connection with any fraction, there are three signs that must be considered.

1. The sign of the numerator.
2. The sign of the denominator.
3. The sign of the fraction itself.

If any *two* of the three signs mentioned are changed, the value of the fraction will not be changed. Therefore, it is permissible to change any two of these signs without changing in any way the value of the fraction. We show this by an example:

$$+\frac{+8}{+2} = +\frac{-8}{-2} = -\frac{+8}{-2} = -\frac{-8}{+2} = +4$$

If the numerator and/or denominator are polynomials, a change in sign means a change in *all* the signs of the polynomial. Changing the sign of a polynomial is equivalent to multiplying or dividing it by -1. Consider this fraction:

$$-\frac{x^2 - 4x - 7}{3x - 5 - x^2}$$

This fraction may be written in any of the following ways:

$$-\frac{7 + 4x - x^2}{x^2 - 3x + 5} = +\frac{x^2 - 4x - 7}{x^2 - 3x + 5} = +\frac{7 + 4x - x^2}{3x - 5 - x^2}$$

In the first fraction the signs of numerator and denominator have been changed. In the second the signs of the fraction and the denominator have been changed. In the third the signs of the fraction and the numerator have been changed.

However, suppose a polynomial is stated in factored form. Then, if we change the signs of two factors, we are, in effect, multiplying by $(-1) \cdot (-1)$, which is equivalent to $+1$. Therefore, changing the signs of *two factors* does not change the sign of their product. If we wish to change the signs of a polynomial in factored form, we must change the signs of an *odd* number of factors.

14.7 ADDITION AND SUBTRACTION OF FRACTIONS

You will recall from arithmetic that in order that fractions may be added or subtracted they must have the *same* denominator. If two or more fractions have the *same* denominator, they are added or subtracted simply by combining the numerators and then placing the combined numerator over the common denominator: thus

$$\frac{3}{7} + \frac{5}{7} - \frac{2}{7} = \frac{3 + 5 - 2}{7} = \frac{6}{7}$$

As another example, the following fractions can be combined into one fraction simply by combining the numerators and placing the result over the denominator:

$$\frac{3x + 1}{5x} + \frac{x - 3}{5x} - \frac{2x - 7}{5x} = \frac{(3x + 1) + (x - 3) - (2x - 7)}{5x}$$

$$= \frac{3x + 1 + x - 3 - 2x + 7}{5x} = \frac{2x + 5}{5x}$$

Notice that the minus sign ($-$) before the third fraction brings about a change in the signs of the numerator. Each fraction must be considered as one quantity, and the effect is the same as though the fraction were enclosed in parentheses.

If we wish to add or subtract fractions with different denominators, we must first state all the fractions with the same denominator. Suppose we wish to add the two fractions $\frac{3}{5} + \frac{4}{7}$. We must first change both fractions to a new form having the *same* denominator. In this case the lowest common denominator is 35. Therefore, we change each fraction to a new fraction having 35 as a denominator.

To change $\frac{3}{5}$ to 35ths, we multiply numerator and denominator by 7. The fraction $\frac{3}{5}$ then becomes $\frac{21}{35}$. We change the fraction $\frac{4}{7}$ to $\frac{20}{35}$ by multiplying both numerator and denominator by 5.

It should be carefully noted that when we change a fraction to higher terms we do *not* change the value of the fraction. The fraction $\frac{21}{35}$ is still equal in value to $\frac{4}{7}$.

After two or more fractions have been stated with the same denominator, they are added or subtracted by combining the numerators and placing the combined numerator over the common denominator.

$$\frac{3}{5} + \frac{4}{7} = \frac{21}{35} + \frac{20}{35} = \frac{21 + 20}{35} = \frac{41}{35}$$

In adding fractions in algebra, we follow the same procedure as in arithmetic. If you will always recall the following steps from arithmetic and then try to follow the same steps in algebra, you will be on the right track:

1. *Find the lowest common denominator (LCD) of the fractions.*
2. *Rewrite each fraction with the LCD as its denominator.*
3. *Combine the numerators and place over the LCD.*

Finding the lowest common denominator. To find the LCD, first factor all denominators into prime factors. The LCD must contain all the *different* factors found in all the denominators. If a certain factor is found *twice* in any *one* denominator, it must be used *twice* in the LCD. If a certain factor is found only *once* in any *one* denominator, it is used only *once* in the LCD. Do not use any factor more times than it is found in any *one* denominator.

Briefly, the LCD is the product of all the *different* factors found in all the denominators, and each factor is used only as many times as it is found in any *one* denominator. Remember, the LCD must be such that it is divisible by each one of the given denominators.

Example 1. Combine $\dfrac{7x}{10} + \dfrac{3x+1}{12} + \dfrac{5x}{18}$.

Solution. To find the LCD, we first separate each denominator into prime factors.

$$10 = 2 \cdot 5$$
$$12 = 2 \cdot 2 \cdot 3$$
$$18 = 2 \cdot 3 \cdot 3$$

The LCD must contain all the different factors, 2, 3, and 5. However, we must use each factor as many times as it is found in any one denominator. The factor 2 is found twice in 12 and the factor 3 is found twice in 18. Therefore, for the LCD, we have

$$2 \cdot 2 \cdot 3 \cdot 3 \cdot 5$$

which is equal to 180. Now we change each fraction to a new fraction having a denominator of 180.

$$\frac{7x}{10} = \frac{126x}{180} \qquad \frac{3x+1}{12} = \frac{15(3x+1)}{180} \qquad \frac{5x}{18} = \frac{50x}{180}$$

The original expression then becomes

$$\frac{126x}{180} + \frac{15(3x+1)}{180} + \frac{50x}{180}$$

At this point it should be carefully noted that the value of each fraction has *not* been changed. Each fraction has simply been changed to a new form having exactly the *same value* as before.

We now write all the numerators over the LCD. Then we remove the parentheses and combine like terms.

$$\frac{126x + 15(3x+1) + 50x}{180} = \frac{126x + 45x + 15 + 50x}{180}$$

$$= \frac{221x + 15}{180}$$

Example 2. Combine $\dfrac{3x+2}{4} - \dfrac{x-3}{5} - \dfrac{4x-3}{20}$.

Solution. Notice the minus $(-)$ signs before some fractions. This means that when the numerators of such fractions are placed over a common denominator, the numerators must be considered as quantities.

In this example the LCD is 20. All the fractions are changed to new fractions having the denominator 20. They are

$$\frac{5(3x + 2)}{20} - \frac{4(x - 3)}{20} - \frac{4x - 3}{20}$$

$$= \frac{5(3x + 2) - 4(x - 3) - (4x - 3)}{20}$$

$$= \frac{15x + 10 - 4x + 12 - 4x + 3}{20} = \frac{7x + 25}{20}$$

Example 3.   Combine $\dfrac{5}{3x} + \dfrac{3x - 1}{2x^2} - \dfrac{x + 2}{x^3}$.

Solution.   The LCD is $6x^3$, since this denominator is great enough to contain all of the given denominators by division. The fractions are changed to new forms having the denominator $6x^3$:

$$\frac{10x^2}{6x^3} + \frac{3x(3x - 1)}{6x^3} - \frac{6(x + 2)}{6x^3} = \frac{10x^2 + 3x(3x - 1) - 6(x + 2)}{6x^3}$$

$$= \frac{10x^2 + 9x^2 - 3x - 6x - 12}{6x^3} = \frac{19x^2 - 9x - 12}{6x^3}$$

Example 4.   Combine $\dfrac{4}{x - 3} + \dfrac{x + 2}{x^2 - 9} - \dfrac{5x - 2}{x^2 - 6x + 9}$.

Solution.   In this example the LCD is $(x + 3)(x - 3)(x - 3)$, which may be written $(x + 3)(x - 3)^2$. We must use the factor $(x - 3)$ *twice* because it is contained *twice* in one of the given denominators. The fractions are changed to new forms having the LCD as the denominators:

$$\frac{4(x - 3)(x + 3)}{(x + 3)(x - 3)^2} + \frac{(x + 2)(x - 3)}{(x + 3)(x - 3)^2} - \frac{(5x - 2)(x + 3)}{(x + 3)(x - 3)^2}$$

$$= \frac{4(x - 3)(x + 3) + (x + 2)(x - 3) - (5x - 2)(x + 3)}{(x + 3)(x - 3)^2}$$

$$= \frac{4x^2 - 36 + x^2 - x - 6 - 5x^2 - 13x + 6}{(x + 3)(x - 3)^2} = \frac{-14x - 36}{(x + 3)(x - 3)^2}$$

The denominator is usually left in factored form. The numerator should also be factored, if possible, to determine whether the fraction can be reduced.

Example 5.   Combine $\dfrac{7}{x - 5} - \dfrac{x - 3}{5 - x}$.

Solution.   These fractions cannot be combined as they stand, since the denominators are not identical. However, they may be made identical by changing the sign of the second fraction and its denominator:

$$\frac{7}{x-5} + \frac{x-3}{x-5}$$

Now the numerators are combined and the result is placed over the common denominator. The sum is $\frac{7+x-3}{x-5}$, or $\frac{x+4}{x-5}$.

Example 6. Combine $5x - 2 - \frac{2x-1}{3} - \frac{3x+2}{2}$.

Solution. The LCD is 6. If the terms $5x$ and -2 are to be placed over the LCD, 6, they must be multiplied by 6 for the numerator. The complete solution is left for the student.

Exercise 14.3

Perform the indicated operations:

1. $\dfrac{x}{3} + \dfrac{x}{4}$

2. $\dfrac{3x}{4} - \dfrac{5x}{8} + 3$

3. $\dfrac{y+2}{3} + \dfrac{y-5}{4} + y$

4. $\dfrac{2n+5}{4} - \dfrac{3n-4}{5} + 1$

5. $\dfrac{2x}{y} + \dfrac{5}{x} + \dfrac{3}{y} - 2x$

6. $\dfrac{n}{2x} + \dfrac{3}{nx} - \dfrac{x^2}{n} - 3n$

7. $\dfrac{3}{a^2} + \dfrac{4}{a} - \dfrac{5}{2a^3}$

8. $\dfrac{5}{2x^2} - \dfrac{6x}{v} + \dfrac{3}{x} + 2v$

9. $\dfrac{2}{3ab} + \dfrac{3b}{a^2} - \dfrac{4a}{b^2}$

10. $\dfrac{3n}{2xy} - \dfrac{ny}{5x^2} - \dfrac{4nx}{3y^2}$

11. $\dfrac{x+3}{4} + \dfrac{x-2}{2} - \dfrac{3x}{8}$

12. $\dfrac{3x+4}{3} - \dfrac{5x}{6} - \dfrac{x-3}{12} - 3x$

13. $\dfrac{2x}{3} - \dfrac{3x-1}{4} + \dfrac{2x-5}{6} + 2x - 3$

14. $\dfrac{2x+5}{3} + \dfrac{6x-5}{15} - \dfrac{4-3x}{2} - \dfrac{3x}{10}$

15. $\dfrac{x+1}{x} - \dfrac{x-2}{y} - \dfrac{x+3}{xy} + 5$

16. $\dfrac{4x}{x-3} + \dfrac{2x}{x+4}$

17. $\dfrac{4x}{x^2-9} - \dfrac{3}{x-3}$

18. $\dfrac{2}{x+4y} - \dfrac{5}{x+2y}$

19. $\dfrac{7}{x-5} - \dfrac{3x}{x+2} + \dfrac{4}{x}$

20. $\dfrac{3x+5}{x^2+6x+9} + \dfrac{x-2}{x+3}$

21. $\dfrac{4}{x+3} - \dfrac{4x-3}{x^2+3x} - \dfrac{5}{x}$

22. $\dfrac{7}{x-3} - \dfrac{2x}{3-x}$

23. $\dfrac{5}{x} + \dfrac{x+3}{x-4} + \dfrac{x-3}{4-x}$

24. $\dfrac{2x-7}{x-5} - \dfrac{3}{x} - 4x - 2$

25. $\dfrac{2x-3}{x-2} - \dfrac{4}{x} - 3x - 4$

26. $\dfrac{4x+3}{x-4} - \dfrac{3}{x} - 5x - 3$

27. $\dfrac{x-2}{x-3} - \dfrac{1}{x} - x - 2$

28. $\dfrac{3x-5}{x+3} - \dfrac{4}{x} - (2x-3)$

29. $\dfrac{4-3x}{x-3} - \dfrac{5}{x} - (3x+2)$

30. $\dfrac{3x-1}{2x-3} - 3x - \dfrac{5}{x} - 6$

31. $\dfrac{3x}{x-5} + \dfrac{5x+2}{5+x} - \dfrac{2x-3}{x^2-25}$

32. $\dfrac{3}{x+y} + \dfrac{5}{x-y} - \dfrac{2}{x^2-y^2} + 1$

33. $\dfrac{x+3}{x} - \dfrac{x-8}{x+2} + \dfrac{3x-4}{x^2} - 5$

34. $\dfrac{3x^2-2x+1}{x^2+3x-10} - \dfrac{2x}{x+5} + \dfrac{1}{2-x}$

35. $\dfrac{5x+2}{x+7} + \dfrac{4x}{x-3} - \dfrac{2x+3}{x^2+4x-21} + 3$

36. $\dfrac{2x}{x-5} + \dfrac{5x^2-3x+2}{25-x^2} - \dfrac{3x-1}{x+5}$

37. $\dfrac{9}{x+2} + \dfrac{3x}{2-x} - \dfrac{5x+2}{4-x^2}$

38. $\dfrac{x+2}{9-x^2} + \dfrac{5+x}{x-3} - \dfrac{7}{3+x}$

39. $\dfrac{5+3x}{x+4} + \dfrac{x+3}{16-x^2} - \dfrac{x-2}{x-3}$

40. $\dfrac{2x}{x-2} - \dfrac{3x^2}{x+2} - \dfrac{x^2+4}{x-1}$

14.8 COMPLEX FRACTIONS

A *complex fraction* is a fraction whose numerator or denominator, or both, also contain fractions. In fact, the division of two fractions may be shown as a complex fraction.

Example 1. The indicated division, $\frac{3}{4} \div \frac{5}{7}$, may be written as the complex fraction:

$$\frac{\dfrac{3}{4}}{\dfrac{5}{7}}$$

The heavy line separating the two fractions indicates division. Of course, in working out the division, we usually use the regular division form:

$$\frac{3}{4} \div \frac{5}{7} = \frac{3}{4} \cdot \frac{7}{5} = \frac{21}{20}$$

Example 2.

$$\frac{\dfrac{4}{9}}{\dfrac{5}{6}} = \frac{4}{9} \div \frac{5}{6} = \frac{4}{9} \cdot \frac{6}{5} = \frac{8}{15}$$

Sometimes a numerator or denominator, or both, contain several fractions.

Example 3.

$$\frac{\dfrac{3}{4} + \dfrac{7}{8} - \dfrac{1}{2}}{\dfrac{2}{3} - \dfrac{5}{6} + \dfrac{1}{2}}$$

To work out the expression, we may first combine all the fractions of the numerator into a single fraction; then we combine all the fractions of the denominator into a single fraction and divide the numerator by the denominator.

$$\frac{\dfrac{3}{4} + \dfrac{7}{8} - \dfrac{1}{2}}{\dfrac{2}{3} - \dfrac{5}{6} + \dfrac{1}{2}} = \frac{\dfrac{6 + 7 - 4}{8}}{\dfrac{4 - 5 + 3}{6}} = \frac{\dfrac{9}{8}}{\dfrac{2}{6}}$$

The answer is found by

$$\frac{9}{8} \div \frac{2}{6} = \frac{9}{8} \cdot \frac{6}{2} = \frac{27}{8}$$

Another method that is sometimes simpler is to make use of the fundamental principle of fractions. In the fraction shown in Example 3 we may multiply the *entire numerator* and the *entire denominator* of the original fraction by 24, which is the LCD of all denominators that appear anywhere in the fraction. Multiply entire numerator and denominator of the fraction by 24:

$$\frac{24) \; \dfrac{3}{4} + \dfrac{7}{8} - \dfrac{1}{2}}{24) \; \dfrac{2}{3} - \dfrac{5}{6} + \dfrac{1}{2}} = \frac{18 + 21 - 12}{16 - 20 + 12} = \frac{27}{8}$$

Exercise 14.4

Simplify the following complex fractions:

1. $\dfrac{2 + \dfrac{1}{3}}{4 - \dfrac{5}{6}}$

2. $\dfrac{\dfrac{2}{3} + \dfrac{4}{9}}{\dfrac{5}{6} - \dfrac{1}{2}}$

3. $\dfrac{3x - \dfrac{x}{4}}{5 - \dfrac{2}{3x}}$

4. $\dfrac{\dfrac{x}{a} + \dfrac{x}{b}}{\dfrac{3x}{ab}}$

5. $\dfrac{4x - \dfrac{9}{x}}{2 + \dfrac{3}{x}}$

6. $\dfrac{\dfrac{1}{x} + \dfrac{1}{y}}{\dfrac{x}{y} - \dfrac{y}{x}}$

7. $\dfrac{2x - 3 - \dfrac{4x}{5}}{4x + 5 - \dfrac{2x}{3}}$

8. $\dfrac{\dfrac{1}{2x - 3} + 3}{\dfrac{10}{3x + 1} - 2}$

9. $\dfrac{\dfrac{9}{x} - 4x}{\dfrac{4x}{3} + 4 + \dfrac{3}{x}}$

10. $\dfrac{2 - \dfrac{3x + 4}{5}}{3x - \dfrac{2 + 5x}{2}}$

11. $\dfrac{1 - \dfrac{5x - 4}{3}}{2 - \dfrac{x + 3}{4}}$

12. $\dfrac{\dfrac{1}{9} - \dfrac{2}{x} + \dfrac{5}{x^2}}{3 - \dfrac{x^2}{3}}$

13. $\dfrac{3x + 4}{2 - \dfrac{5x}{x - 2}}$

14. $\dfrac{\dfrac{x}{x - 2y} - 1}{1 - \dfrac{x}{x + 2y}}$

15. $\dfrac{\dfrac{2x}{2x - 3y} - 2}{\dfrac{9x}{x + 2y} - 3}$

15
Fractional Equations

15.1 DEFINITION

A *fractional equation* is an equation containing a fraction. The fraction may be either a common fraction or a decimal fraction. The denominator may or may not contain the variable x.

Let us recall the definition of an equation. *An equation is a statement of equality between two equal quantities.* To be an equation, the expression must contain an equal sign ($=$) with some quantity on each side of it. Of course, on one side we may have only a zero (0).

If we simply indicate the sum of several fractions, the expression is not an equation. This is not an equation:

$$\frac{3x + 2}{4} + \frac{x - 3}{5} - \frac{3x}{2}$$

All we can do with these fractions is to combine them and simplify the expression. We cannot solve for x because the expression is not an equation.

On the other hand, this expression is a fractional equation:

$$\frac{3x + 2}{4} + \frac{x - 3}{5} - \frac{3x}{2} = 0$$

It can be solved.

Here are some examples of fractional equations:

(a) $\dfrac{2x}{3} = 8$

(b) $\dfrac{2x}{5} + 6 = 4x - \dfrac{3}{4}$

(c) $\dfrac{3}{x} + \dfrac{2}{x - 1} = \dfrac{12}{x^2 - x}$

(d) $\dfrac{5x + 2}{4} + 3 = \dfrac{2x + 1}{3} - x$

(e) $\dfrac{3}{x+3} - \dfrac{5x+2}{x-4} - \dfrac{x-3}{x^2-x-12} - 2 = 0$

(f) $0.23x - 15 = 1.3x + 2.4$

The expression "fractional equation" is sometimes restricted to refer only to equations in which the unknown (such as x) appears in the denominator, such as in the equation

$$\frac{3x}{x-2} + \frac{5}{x-3} = 3$$

Then the expression is not used to refer to equations having only constant denominators. However, we make no such distinction here since the same procedure is used in solving both types.

15.2   USE OF MULTIPLICATION AXIOM

As a general rule, the best procedure to follow in solving a fractional equation is to get rid of the denominators first; that is, first clear the equation of fractions. As a first step, therefore, we multiply both sides of the equation by the lowest common denominator (LCD). The LCD may be called a "multiplying operator."

This first step is simply the application of the multiplication axiom. This axiom, or rule, says:

If both sides of an equation are multiplied by the same quantity, the equation is still true.

In some instances it may be possible to solve simple fractional equations without first eliminating denominators. However, as a general rule, the *best first step* is to clear the equation of fractions.

It is important to see exactly what happens when both sides of an equation are multiplied by some quantity.

Example 1.
$$\frac{2x}{3} = 8$$

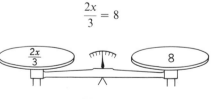

Fig. 15.1

Suppose we think of this equation as a balanced scale, as shown in Fig. 15.1. In order to eliminate fractions, we multiply both sides of the equation by 3. If we multiply the left side by 3, we get $2x$; that is, *three times* $2x/3 = 2x$. If we multiply the right side by 3, we get 24. As a new equation, we have

$$2x = 24$$

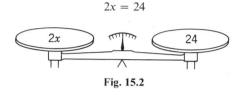

Fig. 15.2

We can also represent this new equation by a scale (Fig. 15.2). This new scale is *not* exactly the same as the original scale. The second scale has *three times as much* on each side as the original; that is, the equation

$$\frac{2x}{3} = 8$$

is not exactly the same as

$$2x = 24$$

Each side of the original equation has been made three times as much. However, we know that if the original equation is true, then the new equation is also true. The new equation can now be solved in the usual way.

$$2x = 24$$

Dividing both sides by 2, $\qquad x = 12$

To check the correctness of 12 as a root, we substitute 12 for x in the *original* equation to see whether the resulting statement is true. Check: Ask the question

$$\text{does } \frac{(2)(12)}{3} = 8?$$

$$\text{does } \frac{24}{3} = 8? \quad \text{Yes.}$$

As soon as we see that one side of the equation is equivalent to the other, we can say our answer is correct.

Example 2. Solve for x: $\dfrac{2x}{5} + 6 = 4x - \dfrac{3}{4}$.

Solution. Multiplying each term on both sides of the equation by the LCD 20, we get

$$8x + 120 = 80x - 15$$

Transposing, $\qquad 120 + 15 = 80x - 8x$

Combining, $\qquad\qquad 135 = 72x$

Dividing both sides of the equation by 72 and reducing,

$$\frac{15}{8} = x$$

When checking an answer, remember the check must always begin with the original equation.

Check: Ask the question

$$\text{does} \quad \frac{(2)(\frac{15}{8})}{5} + 6 = 4(\tfrac{15}{8}) - \frac{3}{4}?$$

$$\text{does} \quad \frac{\frac{15}{4}}{5} + 6 = \frac{15}{2} - \frac{3}{4}?$$

$$\text{does} \quad \frac{3}{4} + 6 = \frac{30}{4} - \frac{3}{4}?$$

$$\text{does} \quad \frac{27}{4} \quad = \frac{27}{4}? \quad \text{Yes.}$$

The check shows that $\frac{15}{8}$ satisfies the equation and is therefore the root.

For solving a fractional equation, we have the following steps:

Step 1.   Multiply both sides of the equation by the lowest common denominator. This will clear the equation of fractions.
Step 2.   Solve the equation as usual for a simple equation.

Some simple fractional equations may be solved without eliminating the denominators.

Example 3.   Solve for x:

$$\frac{3x}{4} - \frac{5}{2} = \frac{2x}{3} + x + 13$$

We shall solve this equation first without eliminating denominators.

Solution.   First Method.   Transposing,

$$\frac{3x}{4} - \frac{2x}{3} - x = 13 + \frac{5}{2}$$

Changing to common denominators,

$$\frac{9x}{12} - \frac{8x}{12} - \frac{12x}{12} = \frac{26}{2} + \frac{5}{2}$$

Combining,

$$\frac{9x - 8x - 12x}{12} = \frac{26 + 5}{2}$$

or

$$\frac{-11x}{12} = \frac{31}{2}$$

Dividing both sides by $-\frac{11}{12}$,

$$x = \frac{31}{2} \div \left(-\frac{11}{12}\right)$$

$$x = -\frac{186}{11} \quad \text{or} \quad -16\tfrac{10}{11}$$

Solution. *Second Method.* Starting with the equation,

$$\frac{3x}{4} - \frac{5}{2} = \frac{2x}{3} + x + 13$$

Multiplying both sides by 12, $\qquad 9x - 30 = 8x + 12x + 156$

Transposing, $\qquad\qquad 9x - 8x - 12x = 156 + 30$

Combining, $\qquad\qquad\qquad -11x = 186$

Dividing both sides by -11, $\qquad\qquad x = -\dfrac{186}{11}$

The second method is almost always preferable.

Exercise 15.1

Solve each of the following equations for the unknown and check in the original equation.

1. $\dfrac{4x}{3} = 24$

2. $72 = \dfrac{3y}{4}$

3. $\dfrac{5n}{2} = n + 6$

4. $b + 4 = \dfrac{7b}{3}$

5. $\dfrac{2c}{5} = c - 3$

6. $\dfrac{5x}{2} = x - 6$

7. $15 - y = \dfrac{2y}{3}$

8. $\dfrac{4m}{7} = m - 6$

9. $2a - 18 = \dfrac{7a}{5}$

10. $\dfrac{3x}{10} + \dfrac{9}{2} = x$

11. $10 = 3 - \dfrac{7x}{4}$

12. $1 - \dfrac{3v}{5} = 2$

13. $\dfrac{8u}{3} + 2 = -6$

14. $5x - 20 = \dfrac{5x}{9}$

15. $\dfrac{5n}{8} = n - \dfrac{1}{4}$

16. $16 - t = \dfrac{t - 1}{4}$

17. $\dfrac{3x}{2} + x = \dfrac{x}{3} + 13$

18. $8 + \dfrac{c}{4} = \dfrac{c}{3} + 5$

19. $x + 3 = \dfrac{3x}{4} - \dfrac{x}{2}$

20. $\dfrac{4n}{3} - \dfrac{5n}{6} - \dfrac{3n}{5} - 1$

21. $6 - \dfrac{2n}{3} = \dfrac{5n}{6} - n$

22. $\dfrac{R}{5} + 4 = \dfrac{R}{2} + 7$

23. $10 + \dfrac{4r}{3} = \dfrac{r}{2} + 65$

24. $\dfrac{4s}{15} + 2 = \dfrac{s}{10} - 1$

25. $4 - \dfrac{h}{3} = \dfrac{h - 3}{15}$

26. $2 + k = \dfrac{k + 5}{7}$

27. $\dfrac{2x}{5} + \dfrac{3x}{10} + 40 = \dfrac{11x}{15}$

28. A man spent $\frac{3}{4}$ of his money for a house and one-eighth of his money for a car and then has \$3000 left. How much had he at first?

29. One-fourth of a particular street was paved the first week and three-sixteenths the following week. If the remainder left to be paved was 1350 feet, what was the total length of the street to be paved?

30. A young lady went to a store and spent five-eighths of her money for a dress and one-tenth for a hat. If she had $22 left, how much did she have when she went to the store?

31. The width of a rectangle is two-thirds of the length, and the perimeter is 60 in. Find the width and the length of the rectangle.

32. One fraction is $\frac{2}{3}$ as much as another and their sum is equal to $\frac{5}{8}$. What are the two fractions?

15.3 SOLVING FRACTIONAL EQUATIONS VS. COMBINING FRACTIONS

It is important to see the difference between solving a fractional equation and simply combining fractions by addition or subtraction. Let us take the following two expressions and note the similarity and the difference between the two.

Example 1.

(a) $\dfrac{5x + 7}{2} + \dfrac{4x - 1}{3}$ (b) $\dfrac{5x + 7}{2} + \dfrac{4x - 1}{3} = 2$

The first expression is not an equation. There is nothing at the right of the equal sign ($=$). The expression cannot be solved for x. All we can do is to combine the fractions into a new fraction.

The second expression is an equation. An equation must have something on each side of the equal sign. It may have only a zero (0) on one side.

Now, notice what happens in the addition of fractions in Example 1(a):

$$\frac{5x + 7}{2} + \frac{4x - 1}{3}$$

In order to combine (add or subtract) fractions, we must have a common denominator. We change the fractions into new fractions with 6 as the lowest common denominator. However, each new fraction must have the same *value* as the original fraction. The fractions

$$\frac{5x + 7}{2} + \frac{4x - 1}{3}$$

are changed to the new fractions

$$\frac{3(5x + 7)}{6} + \frac{2(4x - 1)}{6}$$

Now we can add the fractions, since they have a common denominator. We add them by combining the numerators and placing them over the common denominator. Note that *we do not lose the denominator*. Combining the fractions, we get

$$\frac{3(5x + 7) + 2(4x - 1)}{6} = \frac{15x + 21 + 8x - 2}{6} = \frac{23x + 19}{6}$$

When we add the two fractions, we get the new fraction $\dfrac{23x + 19}{6}$. This is the answer to the problem. It *cannot* be solved for x.

In the case of adding fractions notice that the new fraction $\dfrac{3(5x + 7)}{6}$ has exactly the same value as the original fraction, $\dfrac{5x + 7}{2}$. We have not changed the value of either fraction; we have only changed its form.

Now let us consider the equation in Example 1(b):

$$\frac{5x + 7}{2} + \frac{4x - 1}{3} = 2$$

Here the multiplying operator, the LCD, is 6. When we multiply both sides of the equation by 6, the quantity on each side becomes six times as much as in the original equation. Multiplying each term in the equation by 6, we have

$$\text{six times the first fraction} = 3(5x + 7)$$
$$\text{six times the second fraction} = 2(4x - 1)$$
$$\text{six times the "2"} = 12$$

Therefore, by multiplying both sides of the equation by 6, we get the new equation

$$3(5x + 7) + 2(4x - 1) = 12$$

The denominator has *disappeared*. The equation can now be solved as we solve any simple equation.

Removing parentheses, $\qquad\qquad 15x + 21 + 8x - 2 = 12$
Transposing and combining, $\qquad\qquad\qquad\quad 23x = -7$

Dividing by 23, $\qquad\qquad\qquad\qquad\qquad\qquad x = -\dfrac{7}{23}$

The check is left for the student.

As another example, consider these two expressions:

Example 2.

(a) $\dfrac{5x - 2}{3} - \dfrac{2x - 9}{4} =$ $\qquad$ (b) $\dfrac{5x - 2}{3} - \dfrac{2x - 9}{4} = 0$

First, let us summarize the situation with respect to each expression. For the first expression (a), we can say

(1) It is *not* an equation.
(2) It *cannot* be solved for x.
(3) When we combine the fractions, the denominator (LCD) *remains*.

For the second expression (b), we can say

(1) It *is* an equation.
(2) It *can* be solved for x.
(3) When we solve the equation, the denominators *disappear*.

To combine the fractions in Example 2(a), we change the fractions to new fractions with 12 as a common denominator. We get

$$\frac{4(5x - 2)}{12} - \frac{3(2x - 9)}{12} = \frac{4(5x - 2) - 3(2x - 9)}{12} = \frac{20x - 8 - 6x + 27}{12} = \frac{14x + 19}{12}$$

This expression cannot be solved for x.

Now let us solve the equation in Example 2b:

$$\frac{5x - 2}{3} - \frac{2x - 9}{4} = 0$$

Multiply both sides of the equation by 12:

> twelve times the first fraction $= 4(5x - 2)$
> twelve times the second fraction $= 3(2x - 9)$
> twelve times the zero on the right $= 0$

The denominators disappear, and we get

$$4(5x - 2) - 3(2x - 9) = 0$$

Removing the parentheses, $20x - 8 - 6x + 27 = 0$

Transposing and combining, $14x = -19$

Dividing both sides by 14, $x = -\dfrac{19}{14}$

Example 3. Solve for x:

$$0.23x - 15 = 1.3x - 2.4$$

Solution. If we write the decimal fractions as common fractions, we see that the lowest common denominator of the fractions is 100. Therefore, we multiply both sides of the equation by 100 and get

$$23x - 1500 = 130x - 240$$

Transposing, $-1500 + 240 = 130x - 23x$

Combining, $-1260 = 107x$

Dividing both sides by 107, $-\dfrac{1260}{107} = x$

The answer may be changed to a mixed number or to a mixed decimal:

$$x = -11\tfrac{83}{107} \quad \text{or} \quad -11.78 \quad \text{(rounded off)}$$

If the value -11.78 is used in checking the work, the two sides of the equation will not be identically equal in value, since the answer is rounded off. However, if the check shows the two sides of the equation very nearly equal, the answer can be considered correct.

Exercise 15.2

Solve each of the following equations for the unknown, and check each equation whose number is divisible by 3:

1. $\dfrac{3x + 2}{4} + 5 = \dfrac{x - 9}{3} - x$

2. $\dfrac{2x - 5}{3} - x = 1 + \dfrac{x - 8}{5}$

3. $1 + \dfrac{2x - 3}{5} = \dfrac{3x - 2}{10} + x$

4. $\dfrac{3x}{4} - 2x + 1 = \dfrac{7 - 2x}{2}$

5. $x + \dfrac{x + 3}{3} = \dfrac{x + 7}{6} + 1$

6. $\dfrac{2x + 1}{5} + 2 = x + \dfrac{4 - 3x}{4}$

7. $\dfrac{2n + 3}{5} + \dfrac{n - 5}{6} + \dfrac{n}{3} = n + \dfrac{n - 1}{15}$

8. $\dfrac{y - 6}{4} + \dfrac{7 - y}{12} - \dfrac{2y}{3} = \dfrac{y + 5}{2} + 3$

9. $\dfrac{3a - 1}{6} = \dfrac{4a}{3} + 2a - 5 + \dfrac{a - 1}{2}$

10. $7 + \dfrac{2x - 7}{5} = \dfrac{4 - 3x}{10} + \dfrac{x - 4}{2}$

11. $0.3x + 2 = 1.2 - 0.5x$

12. $0.15n - 0.3 = 0.4n - 0.55$

13. $0.32y - 0.7 = 0.26 + 0.2y$

14. $0.22 + 0.4c = 0.48c - 0.5$

15. $1.375P - 3.6 = 3.15 + 0.25P$

16. $2 - 4.25R = R - 0.625$

17. $0.2x - 1.4 = 1.1x - 7.6$

18. $1.25 + 0.3y = 0.05y - 3$

19. $1.3 + 0'6x = 0.375x - 0.05$

20. $4.5n + 7.5 = 30 + 4.8n$

21. $0.125I - 0.0875 = 0.1 - 0.25I$

22. $0.8 - 0.66x = 5 - 0.24x$

15.4   A FRACTION AS AN INDICATED QUANTITY

If a fraction is preceded by a minus $(-)$, we must remember that this sign makes the *entire fraction negative*. The fraction must always be considered as a *quantity*. The fraction line separating the numerator from the denominator can be considered a vinculum, or the sign of grouping. If you are in doubt about the meaning in any expression, you may enclose a fraction in a set of parentheses.

As an example, consider the following equation:

Example 1.   Solve for x:

$$\frac{3x - 2}{5} - \frac{2x + 7}{4} = 8$$

Solution.   Multiplying both sides of the equation by 20, we get

$$4(3x - 2) - 5(2x + 7) = 160$$

At this point we can easily see that in the next step, the -5 before the parentheses will cause a change in the sign of each term within the parentheses. Removing the parentheses, we get

$$12x - 8 - 10x - 35 = 160$$

The rest of the solution is left to the student.

Example 2.   This example shows one of the great danger spots in working with fractions, whether we are simply combining fractions or solving fractional equations. Solve for x:

$$\frac{4x + 3}{5} - \frac{x + 4}{3} - \frac{2x - 1}{15} = 2$$

Solution.   As a first step, we multiply both sides of the equation by the LCD, 15. We get $3(4x + 3) - 5(x + 4) - (2x - 1) = 30$. Note the minus signs before the second and the third fractions. The entire fraction after each sign is to be considered as a quantity, and the minus signs can be considered as signs of operations (subtraction). The net result is that the signs of the terms in their numerators will eventually be changed. Continuing the solution,

$$3(4x + 3) - 5(x + 4) - (2x - 1) = 30$$
$$12x + 9 - 5x - 20 - 2x + 1 = 30$$

Transposing, $$12x - 5x - 2x = 30 - 9 + 20 - 1$$
Combining, $$5x = 40$$
Dividing both sides by 5, $$x = 8$$

The check is left for the student. Remember, it must be started in the original equation and both sides worked out in fraction form.

Exercise 15.3

Solve the following equations. Check any five.

1. $\dfrac{3x + 1}{4} - \dfrac{x - 3}{8} = \dfrac{2x - 5}{2} - 1$

2. $\dfrac{5 - 2x}{2} - \dfrac{1 - 3x}{3} - \dfrac{2x - 3}{6} = 4$

3. $\dfrac{2x}{3} - \dfrac{x - 5}{5} = 2 - \dfrac{5 + 3x}{15}$

4. $\dfrac{4x - 5}{10} - \dfrac{x - 2}{4} = \dfrac{x}{20} - 1$

5. $\dfrac{2x - 7}{3} - \dfrac{3x + 5}{12} + \dfrac{x - 3}{4} = 0$

6. $\dfrac{5x}{4} + \dfrac{x - 2}{6} - \dfrac{5 - x}{12} = 0$

7. $\dfrac{x - 3}{4} + \dfrac{2x - 1}{5} - \dfrac{5x - 3}{20} = 1$

8. $\dfrac{4 - x}{2} - \dfrac{2(7 - 2x)}{5} - \dfrac{3(x - 2)}{4} = 1$

9. $\dfrac{5x - 1}{3} - \dfrac{x - 2}{21} - \dfrac{2x + 3}{7} = 0$

10. $\dfrac{2x}{15} - \dfrac{x - 4}{9} - \dfrac{3x + 1}{45} = 0$

11. $\dfrac{2(x + 5)}{15} - \dfrac{3(x + 4)}{2} - \dfrac{4(3 - x)}{3} = 0$

12. $\dfrac{3(2x + 1)}{4} - \dfrac{2(3x - 2)}{3} - \dfrac{3 - 2x}{12} = 0$

13. $3(0.06x + 4) = 0.05(1800 + x)$

14. $0.04n - 0.08(3000 - n) = 15$

15. $0.075y - 0.05(9000 - y) = 24$

16. $0.0425t + 0.06(3500 - t) = 168$

17. $0.06x + 0.03(1800 - x) = 67.5$

18. $0.04x - 0.07(8400 - x) = 83$

19. $0.15S - 0.35(400 - S) = 1.5$

20. $0.045(6000 - N) - 0.06N = 133.5$

15.5 FRACTIONS CONTAINING VARIABLE DENOMINATORS

In the examples at the beginning of this chapter some fractions have variable denominators. This often happens in fractional equations. To solve such equations we proceed in the same way as we do with other fractional equations. We first multiply both sides of the equation by the LCD.

Example 1. Solve for x:

$$\frac{3}{x} + \frac{2}{x - 1} = \frac{12}{x^2 - x}$$

Solution. If we factor the third denominator, we see that it consists of the two other denominators as factors. Therefore, $x(x - 1)$ is the lowest common denominator. We multiply both sides of the equation by the multiplying operator $x(x - 1)$. We get

$$3(x - 1) + 2x = 12$$
Solving,
$$3x - 3 + 2x = 12$$
$$5x = 15$$
$$x = 3$$

Example 2. Solve for x:

$$\frac{5x}{x + 3} - \frac{3x + 2}{x - 4} - \frac{x - 3}{x^2 - x - 12} - 2 = 0$$

Solution. The trinomial denominator can be factored into the factors $(x + 3)(x - 4)$. This denominator is the LCD, since it is divisible by all the denominators. Therefore, we use $(x + 3)(x - 4)$ as a multiplying operator. Multiplying both sides of the equation by $(x + 3)(x - 4)$, we get

$$5x(x - 4) - (3x + 2)(x + 3) - (x - 3) - 2(x + 3)(x - 4) = 0$$
$$5x^2 - 20x - (3x^2 + 11x + 6) - x + 3 - 2(x^2 - x - 12) = 0$$
$$5x^2 - 20x - 3x^2 - 11x - 6 - x + 3 - 2x^2 + 2x + 24 = 0$$
$$21 = 30x$$

$$\frac{7}{10} = x$$

The check must be started in the original equation.

Example 3. Solve for x:

$$\frac{3}{x + 2} = \frac{1}{x - 2} - \frac{4}{x^2 - 4}$$

Solution. Multiplying both sides of the equation by the lowest common denominator, $x^2 - 4$, we get

$$3(x - 2) = x + 2 - 4$$

Removing parentheses, $3x - 6 = x + 2 - 4$

Transposing, $3x - x = 6 + 2 - 4$

Combining, $2x = 4$

Dividing both sides by 2, $x = 2$

The answer, $x = 2$, seems like a very logical one to this problem. The procedure is entirely correct. Yet, when we check the answer in the original equation, we get zero in a denominator. In fact, in this example the check produces a zero for each of two denominators.

Whenever the check of a solution produces a denominator of zero, that solution must be discarded. The foregoing equation, therefore, has *no solution*. If we carelessly say that a number divided by zero is equal to infinity, we are no better off. We might be inclined to write the check as follows:

$$\frac{3}{2 + 2} = \frac{1}{2 - 2} - \frac{4}{4 - 4}$$

$$\frac{3}{4} = \frac{1}{0} - \frac{4}{0}$$

$$\frac{3}{4} = \infty - \infty \qquad \text{(wrong)}$$

The result proves that we cannot operate in this manner with infinity. The important fact here is that we cannot divide any number by zero and that the expression $1 \div 0$ is *not* equal to infinity.

Exercise 15.4

Solve the following equations for the unknowns. Check each problem whose number is divisible by 3.

1. $\dfrac{x - 2}{x + 2} = 5$

2. $\dfrac{n + 6}{n - 1} - 8 = 0$

3. $\dfrac{y + 5}{y - 3} = 3$

4. $7 - \dfrac{2x - 3}{x - 4} = 0$

5. $\dfrac{n - 4}{n + 5} - 4 = 0$

6. $\dfrac{4y - 3}{y + 4} = 3$

7. $\dfrac{3x - 1}{2x + 1} - \dfrac{4}{3} = 0$

8. $\dfrac{2t - 7}{3t + 2} = \dfrac{3}{2}$

9. $\dfrac{4}{x + 5} - \dfrac{8}{x - 8} = 0$

10. $\dfrac{4a}{2a + 1} = \dfrac{2a + 3}{a}$

11. $\dfrac{3n - 2}{n - 2} = \dfrac{3n}{n - 1}$

12. $\dfrac{x - 2}{x + 5} = \dfrac{2x}{x + 2} - 1$

13. $\dfrac{2x}{x + 5} + 1 = \dfrac{3x}{x - 4}$

14. $\dfrac{x}{x + 4} + 3 = \dfrac{4x}{x - 1}$

15. $\dfrac{5x}{x + 2} - \dfrac{7x + 1}{x + 3} + 2 = 0$

16. $\dfrac{3x}{x + 3} - \dfrac{2x - 1}{x - 3} = 1$

17. $\dfrac{4x + 3}{x} - 4 - \dfrac{2}{x - 5} = 0$

18. $\dfrac{5}{x} - \dfrac{3}{x - 3} - \dfrac{2}{x + 3} = 0$

19. $\dfrac{2x}{x - 2} + 2 = \dfrac{4x}{x + 1}$

20. $\dfrac{x - 1}{x - 3} - \dfrac{x + 2}{x - 2} - \dfrac{3x + 7}{x^2 - 5x + 6} = 0$

21. $\dfrac{x - 4}{x - 2} - \dfrac{3}{x + 2} = 1 - \dfrac{8}{x^2 - 4}$

22. $\dfrac{3x}{x + 3} - \dfrac{2}{x - 1} = 3 - \dfrac{8}{x^2 + 2x - 3}$

23. $\dfrac{x}{x + 3} - \dfrac{x - 3}{3x} = \dfrac{5x + 2}{2x^2 + 6x} + \dfrac{2}{3}$

24. $\dfrac{3x - 1}{2x} - \dfrac{x - 3}{x - 5} = \dfrac{x^2 + 2x - 1}{2x(x - 5)}$

25. $\dfrac{2}{x^2 - 4} = \dfrac{3x - 1}{x + 2} - \dfrac{x + 4}{x - 2} - 2$

26. $\dfrac{x - 3}{x - 5} - \dfrac{3x + 7}{x - 2} + 2 = 0$

27. $\dfrac{4}{x - 3} - \dfrac{6}{3 - x} = \dfrac{5}{x - 4}$

28. $\dfrac{y - 4}{y + 2} = 2 - \dfrac{y - 1}{y + 5}$

29. $\dfrac{3x + 5}{2x + 1} - \dfrac{x}{2x - 3} - 1 = 0$

30. $\dfrac{x + 2}{x - 3} - \dfrac{2x - 3}{x^2 - 9} - 1 = 0$

31. $\dfrac{5}{m + 2} - \dfrac{3}{m - 2} - \dfrac{2}{m} = 0$

32. $\dfrac{2v + 5}{v + 2} - \dfrac{v + 4}{v - 3} - \dfrac{1 - 3v}{v^2 - v - 6} = 1$

33. $\dfrac{h + 1}{h + 2} - \dfrac{h - 1}{3h - 6} - \dfrac{2 - 5h}{h^2 - 4} = \dfrac{2}{3}$

34. $\dfrac{2x + 1}{x + 4} - \dfrac{2 - 3x}{x - 3} - 5 + \dfrac{3}{x^2 + x - 12} = 0$

35. $\dfrac{2x - 3}{x - 1} + \dfrac{x - 1}{x + 2} - 3 - \dfrac{4x - 5}{x^2 - 5x - 14} = 0$

15.6 LITERAL EQUATIONS

A *literal equation* is an equation in which constants are represented by letters of the alphabet; that is, letters appear where we would expect arithmetic numbers. This is a literal equation: $ax = b$.

In general, a literal equation is solved in the same way as any other equation. Let us first look at a simple equation such as those we have already solved.

Example 1. Solve for x: $3x = 19$.

Solution. To find the value of x, we divide both sides of the equation by 3, which is the coefficient of x. We get

$$x = \frac{19}{3}$$

Now, suppose we have a literal equation in which we find other letters in place of 3 and 19.

Example 2. Solve for x: $ax = b$.

Solution. Our problem is to solve for the value of x. Again we divide both sides of the equation by the coefficient of x. Dividing both sides by a,

$$x = \frac{b}{a}$$

The equation is now solved for x. The quantity b/a is the root of the equation.

If an equation has several terms containing the unknown, x or whatever unknown we wish to find, then all the terms containing the unknown are first isolated, just as in any other equation. To see the similarity to equations we have already solved, let us first solve an equation with arithmetic constants.

Example 3. Solve the equation for x:

$$7x - 4 = 21 - 5x$$

Solution. We first transpose to isolate the terms in x.

$$7x + 5x = 21 + 4$$

Combining like terms, $\qquad 12x = 25$

Dividing both sides by 12, $\qquad x = \dfrac{25}{12} \qquad$ the root

Example 4. Solve this literal equation for x:

$$ax - 4 = b - 8x$$

Solution. Transposing to isolate x terms, $ax + 8x = b + 4$. We cannot combine the x terms into a single term. However, by factoring the expression $ax + 8x$ into two factors, $x(a + 8)$, we see that the coefficient of x is the binomial $a + 8$. Therefore, we divide both sides of the equation by $(a + 8)$:

$$x = \frac{b + 4}{a + 8}$$

This answer cannot be reduced to lower terms.

In some literal equations it may be necessary to clear the equation of fractions.

Example 5. Solve for y:

$$\frac{ax + 2y}{b} - c = \frac{y - 5}{4} + x$$

Solution. To solve for y, we must isolate all the terms in y so that the final step shows y alone on one side of the equation and no term containing y on the other side. The first step is to multiply both sides of the equation by the LCD, $4b$; we get

$$4(ax + 2y) - 4bc = b(y - 5) + 4bx$$

Removing parentheses, $\qquad 4ax + 8y - 4bc = by - 5b + 4bx$

Transposing, $\qquad\qquad\qquad 8y - by = 4bx - 4ax + 4bc - 5b$

Dividing both sides by $(8 - b)$, $\qquad y = \dfrac{4bx - 4ax + 4bc - 5b}{8 - b}$

Note. The same equation may be solved for x by isolating the x terms. In fact, the equation may be solved for any letter we wish by isolating all the terms containing that particular letter and then dividing both sides of the equation by its coefficient. This is called "changing the subject of the formula" and is important in much work in connection with formulas.

Example 6. Solve the following formula for n:

$$I = \frac{nE}{R + nr}$$

Solution. Multiplying both sides of the equation by $R + nr$,

$$I(R + nr) = nE$$

Removing parentheses, $\qquad\quad IR + Inr = nE$

Isolating terms in n, $\qquad\qquad\quad IR = nE - Inr$

Factoring to show coefficient of n, $\quad IR = n(E - Ir)$

Dividing both sides by $E - Ir$, $\qquad \dfrac{IR}{E - Ir} = n$

Exercise 15.5

Solve each formula for the letter indicated at the right of each.

1. $V = LWH$ $\qquad\qquad\qquad (W)$ $\qquad\qquad$ **2.** $P = 2L + 2W$ $\qquad\quad (L)$

3. $\dfrac{d}{r} = t$ $\qquad\qquad\qquad\quad (r)$ $\qquad\qquad$ **4.** $V = \pi r^2 h$ $\qquad\qquad\quad (h)$

5. $y = Ax + B$ $\qquad\qquad\quad (x)$ $\qquad\qquad$ **6.** $A = \dfrac{ab}{2}$ $\qquad\qquad\quad (b)$

7. $A = 2\pi r h$ (r)

8. $Ax + By = C$ (x)

9. $I = \dfrac{E}{R + r}$ (r)

10. $F = \dfrac{9}{2}C + 32$ (C)

11. $\dfrac{1}{f} = \dfrac{1}{a} + \dfrac{1}{b}$ (a)

12. $\dfrac{W_1}{W_2} = \dfrac{L_2}{L_1}$ (W_2)

13. $A - P = Prt$ (P)

14. $x = \dfrac{y - b}{m}$ (y)

15. $F = K\dfrac{M_1 M_2}{d^2}$ (M_1)

16. $C = \dfrac{5}{9}(F - 32)$ (F)

17. $S = N\dfrac{(A + L)}{2}$ (A)

18. $A = 2\pi r(h + r)$ (h)

19. $\dfrac{a}{a + b} = \dfrac{c}{c + d}$ (b)

20. $A = \dfrac{h}{2}(B + b)$ (B)

21. $L = a + (n - 1)d$ (n)

22. $\dfrac{1}{T} = \dfrac{1}{a} + \dfrac{1}{b} + \dfrac{1}{c}$ (c)

23. $S = \dfrac{a - rL}{1 - r}$ (r)

24. $V = \dfrac{1}{3}\pi r^2 h$ (h)

25. $\dfrac{E}{e} = \dfrac{R + r}{r}$ (r)

26. $\dfrac{x}{a} = b(x - c)$ (x)

27. $a^2 = b^2 + c^2 - 2bx$ (x)

28. $V = \pi R^2 h - \pi r^2 h$ (h)

29. $a = \dfrac{bd}{bc + d}$ (d)

30. $Z_t = \dfrac{Z_1 Z_2}{Z_1 + Z_2}$ (Z_2)

31. $L = \dfrac{mt - g}{t}$ (t)

32. $T = \dfrac{1}{a} + t$ (a)

33. $A = 2r(h + r)$ (h)

34. $y^2 - 4x + 6y = 8$ (x)

35. $C = K\dfrac{ab}{b - a}$ (a)

36. $p = \dfrac{m}{d - L} - \dfrac{m}{d + L}$ (m)

37. $S = Vt + \dfrac{1}{2}gt^2$ (g)

38. $\dfrac{a}{x} - C(a - b) = \dfrac{b}{x}$ (x)

39. $x = \dfrac{x_1 + rx_2}{1 + r}$ (r)

40. $B - 2 = \dfrac{BC - A}{A - 1}$ (A)

41. $m = \dfrac{y_2 - y_1}{x_2 - x_1}$ (x_1)

42. $\dfrac{r_1}{r_1 + r_2} = \dfrac{r_3}{r_3 + r_4}$ (r_3)

43. $ax - 2b = bx - 2a$ (x)

44. $3ax + b^2 = a^2 - 3bx$ (x)

Exercise 15.6

1. The difference between two numbers is 3. If five times the smaller number is divided by the larger, the quotient is 4. What are the numbers?

2. The numerator of a fraction is 5 less than the denominator. If the numerator is decreased by 2 and the denominator is increased by 3, the value of the new fraction is $\frac{1}{3}$. Find the original fraction.

3. The denominator of a fraction is 3 more than the numerator. If the denominator is increased by 2 and the numerator is decreased by 2, the value of the new fraction is $\frac{7}{8}$. Find the original fraction.

4. Find two consecutive integers such that $\frac{2}{3}$ of the first added to $\frac{3}{5}$ of the second becomes 7 more than the first.

5. Frank can mow a lawn alone in 6 hr and Joe can mow it alone in 8 hr. If each gets a lawn mower and both work at the same time, how long should it take them?

Solution. Before we can work the problem, we must assume that they work at the same rate as when each is working alone. We cannot make allowance for their getting into each other's way, which actually might happen. Assuming that the work goes along steadily,

let x = the number of hours it will take them working together

Since Frank can mow the lawn alone in 6 hr, he can mow $\frac{1}{6}$ of it in 1 hr. Since Joe can mow the lawn alone in 8 hr, he can mow $\frac{1}{8}$ of it in 1 hr. Note that the part done in 1 hr is simply the *reciprocal* of the number of hours. Then $1/x$ is the part both can do together in 1 hr. Therefore, we can write the equation to show the total part of the work done in 1 hr:

$$\frac{1}{6} + \frac{1}{8} = \frac{1}{x}$$

The equation can be solved for x, and this value will be the number of hours it will take both working together.

6. A water tank is being filled through two pipes. One pipe alone can fill the tank in 8 hr, the other can fill the tank alone in 12 hr. How long will it take to fill the tank when both pipes are used?

7. A certain tank can be filled with water through one pipe in 6 hr. It can be filled through a second pipe alone in 4 hr. How long will it take to fill the tank if both pipes are used?

8. A swimming pool can be filled in 15 hr through one opening near the top and through a second opening in 12 hr. How long will it take to fill the pool if both openings are used?

9. In Problem 8 a third opening which can fill the pool alone in 20 hr is sometimes used. How long will it take to fill the pool if all three openings are used?

10. The pool in Problem 8 can be drained in 18 hr through a hole in the bottom of the pool. One day when the pool was empty it was decided to fill the pool by using the same two openings mentioned in Problem 8. However, someone had left the drain hole open. How long would it take to fill the pool under these conditions?

11. A businessman finds it necessary to get out a number of form letters. He has three typists. Doris can type them all alone in 6 hr, Emily can type them alone in $7\frac{1}{2}$ hr, and Lilas can type them alone in 8 hr. How long should it take them all working at the same time?

12. The width of a certain rectangle is $\frac{2}{3}$ of the length. If the width is decreased by 3 and the length increased by 3, the area is 36 sq in. less than the original rectangle. Find the dimensions of the original rectangle. What change takes place in the perimeter?

13. A rectangle is $\frac{3}{5}$ as wide as it is long. If the width is increased by 2 and the length decreased by 3, the area remains unchanged. Find the dimensions of the original rectangle. What change takes place in the perimeter?

14. If 5 is added to a certain number, $\frac{3}{4}$ of the result is 1 less than the number. What is the number?

15. If a certain number is subtracted from the numerator and twice the number is subtracted from the denominator, of the fraction $\frac{12}{19}$, the resulting fraction is equal to $\frac{2}{3}$. What is the number?

16. What number must be subtracted from the numerator and from the denominator of the fraction $\frac{17}{19}$ so that the resulting fraction will be equal to the value $\frac{3}{4}$?

17. What number must be subtracted from the numerator and the denominator of the fraction $\frac{15}{4}$ so that the value will be equal to $\frac{1}{2}$?

18. What number must be added to the numerator and the denominator of the fraction $\frac{3}{8}$ to make the new fraction equal in value to $\frac{4}{7}$?

19. A man has $4000 invested, part of which brings him a return of 3% a year and the remainder a return of 7% a year. If his total annual return on these two investments is $180, what is the amount invested at each rate?

Solution. Let x = the number of dollars invested at 3%
Then $4000 - x$ = the number of dollars invested at 7%
The income in each case equals the amount of money invested multiplied by the rate:

$$\text{income} = \text{rate} \times \text{amount invested}$$

The income from the 3% investment is $0.03x$ dollars per year. The income from the 7% investment is $0.07(4000 - x)$ dollars per year. Since the total income from both investments is $180, we write

$$0.03x + 0.07(4000 - x) = 180$$

To eliminate the fractions, both sides of the equation are multiplied by 100. The equation is then easily solved.

20. A man has $7800 invested, part of which brings him an income of 4% and the other an income of 6% per year. If the two incomes are equal, find the amount of money invested at each rate.

21. In Problem 20 find the amount of each investment if the 4% investment brings a return of $12 more per year than the 6% investment.

22. A solution of 24 gal of alcohol and water contains 15% alcohol. How much pure alcohol should be added to the 24 gal to produce a new solution testing 25% alcohol? (Disregard the very slight solubility of alcohol in water.)

Solution. In a problem of this kind keep one important principle in mind : the total amount of alcohol in the final solution will be equal to the amount of alcohol in the original solution, plus the actual amount of alcohol added ; that is,

$$\left\{\begin{array}{c}\text{alcohol in}\\ \text{original solution}\end{array}\right\} + \left\{\begin{array}{c}\text{amount of}\\ \text{alcohol added}\end{array}\right\} = \left\{\begin{array}{c}\text{total alcohol in}\\ \text{final solution}\end{array}\right\}$$

Let $x = $ the number of gallons of pure alcohol to be added

Then $24 + x = $ the total amount of the new solution

Now we investigate the amount of alcohol. The original solution already contains some alcohol: 15% of 24 gal $= 3.6$ gal. Since x gal of alcohol are added, the total amount of alcohol in the final solution is $3.6 + x$ gal. We simply state that this amount is 25% of the entire final solution :

$$3.6 + x = 0.25(24 + x)$$

The value of x obtained in solving the equation is the amount of pure alcohol that must be added.

23. How much pure alcohol must be added to 50 gal of a 10% solution to make a new solution testing 24% alcohol?

24. How many quarts of an 80% solution must be added to 15 qt of a 12% solution to make a new solution testing 30%?

25. How much water should be added to 15 qt of a 30% solution to produce a new solution testing 20%?

26. How much pure silver must be added to 20 oz of an alloy now testing 15% silver to produce an alloy testing 35%?

27. How many cubic centimeters of water must be added to 10 cc. of a solution of 80% carbolic acid to make a 1.5% solution?

28. A creamery has a vat containing 500 gal of milk testing 2.5% butterfat. How many gallons of 30% cream must be added to the milk to make the milk test 3.2% butterfat?

29. An automobile radiator contains 18 qt of a 10% solution of alcohol. How many quarts should be drained out and replaced with pure alcohol to make the solution test 25%?

30. After a 20% reduction in price, a coat was sold for $68. What was the price before the reduction?

31. One year the population census of a city was 162,000. If this was an increase of 8% over the population of the preceding year, what was the population of the preceding year and what was the increase?

32. After a lady's weight decreased 6%, it was 117.5 lb. What did she weigh before the decrease?

33. On a particular trip a man averages a speed of 45 mph. On the return trip his average speed is 36 mph and the trip requires 1 hr longer. How long was his trip (one way)?

34. A man has a motor boat that travels 12 mph. The current of a particular river has a rate of 4 mph. How far down the stream can he travel so that he can be back at his starting point in 6 hr?

35. A man and his wife walk up a moving escalator. The man walks twice as fast as his wife. When he arrives at the top, he has taken 28 steps. When she arrives at the top, she has taken 21 steps. How many steps are visible in the escalator at any one time?

Exercise 15.7

The principles used in solving fractional equations should be thoroughly understood and the procedure should be followed correctly. If you feel that you need more practice in applying the rules for solving fractional equations, you might solve some or all of the following exercises:

1. $\dfrac{3x}{5} = 6$

2. $10 - \dfrac{5x}{3} = 0$

3. $\dfrac{3x}{4} = 5 - \dfrac{x}{2}$

4. $\dfrac{x}{2} - 4 - \dfrac{x}{3} = 0$

5. $\dfrac{5x}{3} = \dfrac{3x}{2} - 2$

6. $5 = \dfrac{3x}{4} - \dfrac{2x}{3}$

7. $\dfrac{4}{x} - \dfrac{3}{2x} - \dfrac{5}{x^2} = 0$

8. $\dfrac{5}{x} - \dfrac{7}{3x} = \dfrac{2}{x^2}$

9. $\dfrac{4}{x^2} = \dfrac{7}{5x} - \dfrac{5}{3x}$

10. $\dfrac{2x}{3} - \dfrac{4x}{5} + \dfrac{3}{5} = 1$

11. $\dfrac{n}{3} - \dfrac{3}{2} = \dfrac{2n}{5} - \dfrac{11}{6}$

12. $\dfrac{15}{4} - \dfrac{y}{2} = \dfrac{3}{5} - \dfrac{3y}{20}$

13. $\dfrac{5}{2} - \dfrac{2v}{3} + \dfrac{v}{6} = 2$

14. $\dfrac{3a}{4} - \dfrac{2a}{5} = \dfrac{a}{3} + 2$

15. $\dfrac{x + 2}{4} - \dfrac{3 - x}{6} = 2 + \dfrac{x}{3}$

16. $\dfrac{2x - 3}{5} + x - \dfrac{5x - 2}{4} - 2 = 0$

17. $\dfrac{x}{3} - \dfrac{x + 4}{4} = 4 - \dfrac{x - 4}{2}$

18. $3 - \dfrac{n - 4}{10} + \dfrac{n - 3}{5} = \dfrac{n}{2}$

19. $\dfrac{3x - 4}{6} + 2 - \dfrac{2x + 6}{9} = -\dfrac{3}{2}$

20. $\dfrac{c + 3}{5} - \dfrac{3c - 2}{4} + \dfrac{c}{2} = 1$

21. $\dfrac{3d + 2}{4} - \dfrac{d - 3}{5} - \dfrac{2d - 1}{3} = 2$

22. $\dfrac{e + 3}{5} - \dfrac{2e + 1}{7} = 1 - \dfrac{e - 3}{7}$

23. $\dfrac{2t - 3}{5} + 1 = \dfrac{3t + 5}{4} - \dfrac{t - 1}{2}$

24. $\dfrac{3}{z} + \dfrac{4}{5} - \dfrac{z + 1}{z} = 0$

25. $\dfrac{2r + 3}{2r} - \dfrac{r + 8}{r} = 7$

26. $\dfrac{2u - 3}{4} - \dfrac{u + 2}{3u} - \dfrac{u - 1}{2} = 0$

27. $\dfrac{5w - 3}{w} - \dfrac{w - 1}{w + 3} - 4 = 0$

28. $\dfrac{3x + 4}{x + 3} - 2 - \dfrac{2x - 5}{2x} = 0$

29. $\dfrac{2x + 6}{x} - \dfrac{x}{x + 3} = 1$

30. $\dfrac{x + 5}{x + 6} - \dfrac{2}{3} - \dfrac{x - 1}{3x} = 0$

31. $\dfrac{x}{x - 1} + \dfrac{2x}{x + 6} - 3 = 0$

32. $\dfrac{3x - 4}{x - 2} = 5 - \dfrac{2x + 7}{x - 3}$

Quiz on Chapters 14–15. Form 1. The number in parentheses is the suggested number of points for each question.

(10) **1.** Combine the fractions at the right into a single fraction:
$$\dfrac{3x - 5}{4} - \dfrac{4x - 3}{7} - \dfrac{2x - 3}{28}$$

(10) **2.** Combine into a single fraction:
$$\dfrac{5x - 4}{x - 2} - \dfrac{2x - 5}{x + 3} - 3$$

(8) **3.** Simplify the complex fraction at the right
$$\dfrac{1 - \dfrac{3x + 2}{2x^2}}{x - \dfrac{4}{x}}$$

(10) **4.** Combine into a single fraction:
$$\dfrac{3x - 4}{x - 5} - \dfrac{6}{x} - 3x - 2$$

(16) **5.** Simplify the following expression by first factoring numerator and denominator; then write the result as a single fraction reduced to lowest terms:
$$\dfrac{x^2 - 2x - 3}{2x^4 - 72x^2} \cdot \dfrac{x^3 - 4x^2 - 12x}{x^2 - 4x + 3} \div \dfrac{2x^2 + 5x + 2}{4x^3 + 20x^2 - 24x}$$

(10) **6.** Solve the equation at the right for x:
$$\dfrac{2x + 3}{5} - \dfrac{4x - 1}{6} - \dfrac{5x - 2}{30} = 2$$

(10) **7.** Solve for x:
$$\dfrac{4x - 3}{x - 3} - \dfrac{2x + 3}{x + 4} - 2 = 0$$

(8) **8.** Solve the literal equation at the right for B:
$$C - 2 = \dfrac{AD - B}{B + 3}$$

(9) **9.** A man has $7200 invested in two investments, part of it at a 4% annual return, and the rest at 7%. If his income from the two investments is the same, how much has he invested at each rate?

(9) **10.** How much of a 15% solution and how much of a 50% solution of alcohol should be mixed together to form 80 gallons of a solution that is to test 25%?

Quiz on Chapters 14–15. Form 2. The number in parentheses is the suggested number of points for each question.

(10) **1.** Combine the fractions at the right into a single fraction:
$$\dfrac{2x - 5}{3} - \dfrac{3x - 7}{8} - \dfrac{2x - 1}{24}$$

(10) **2.** Combine into a single fraction:

$$\frac{4x - 3}{x - 3} - \frac{3x + 5}{x + 2} - 2$$

(8) **3.** Simplify the complex fraction at the right:

$$\frac{1 - \dfrac{7x + 6}{3x^2}}{x - \dfrac{9}{x}}$$

(10) **4.** Combine into a single fraction:

$$\frac{3x - 5}{x - 3} - \frac{5}{x} - 2x - 9$$

(16) **5.** Simplify the following expression by first factoring numerator and denominator; then write the result as a single fraction reduced to lowest terms:

$$\frac{x^2 - 3x - 4}{3x^4 - 75x^2} \cdot \frac{6x^3 - 24x^2 - 30x}{x^2 - 6x + 8} \div \frac{2x^2 + 3x + 1}{x^3 + 3x^2 - 10x}$$

(10) **6.** Solve the equation at the right for x:

$$\frac{2x - 3}{4} - \frac{3x - 4}{5} - \frac{5x - 6}{20} = 3$$

(10) **7.** Solve for x:

$$\frac{5x - 4}{x - 2} - \frac{2x + 3}{x + 3} - 3 = 0$$

(8) **8.** Solve the literal equation at the right for A:

$$B + 3 = \frac{CD + 2A}{A - 2}$$

(9) **9.** A man has $6500 invested, part of it at 5% annual return, and the rest at 7%. If his total annual income is $371, how much has he invested at each rate?

(9) **10.** What number must be added to the numerator and subtracted from the denominator of the fraction $\frac{6}{7}$ to make the resulting fraction equal to $\frac{2}{3}$?

16
Systems of Equations

16.1 INDETERMINATE EQUATIONS

We have solved equations such as $3x + 2 = 17$. This equation is true only on the condition that $x = 5$. Therefore, the value 5 is the root or solution of the equation. Remember that a solution is any number that makes an equation true.

Let us now consider a different kind of equation in which there are two unknowns. Suppose we have the equation

$$x + y = 11$$

This equation is true if $x = 8$ and $y = 3$. The pair of numbers may be written in parentheses as (8, 3), if we always understand that the first number, 8, is the x-value, and the second number, 3, is the y-value. However, x and y may have other values. The equation is also true if $x = 10$ and $y = 1$; that is, for the pair (10, 1). There are also other pairs of values that make the equation true. We list several such pairs in the table at the right. Any one of these pairs of numbers will satisfy the equation. If we accept fractions and negatives, then there is an infinite number of pairs of values for x and y that will satisfy this equation.

If $x =$	$y =$
8	3
10	1
4	7
11	0
14	-3
3.5	7.5
-2	13

To get a pair of values for this equation, we first give one letter any value we choose. Then we compute the value of the other letter by using the equation. For example, if we first say x shall be 4, then from the equation we find that y must be 7. Of course, if we wish, we may first assign a value to y and then compute the corresponding value of x.

In such an equation as $x + y = 11$, the numerical value of one letter cannot be determined without affecting or being affected by the other letter value. Such an equation is called an *indeterminate equation* (sometimes called a *Diophantine* equation). In an indeterminate equation, all we can do is to find pairs of values that make the equation true.

In an equation of this kind, the algebraic numbers, x and y, are called *variables* because they may take on more than one value. The values of x and

225

y are dependent upon each other. It is customary to call one the *independent* variable and the other the *dependent* variable. The independent variable is one that is first assigned a specific value. This is usually taken to be *x*. Then *y* becomes the dependent variable.

Let us consider another indeterminate equation:

$$x - y = 3$$

Here, again, we can find pairs of numbers that make the equation true. For example, if $x = 10$, $y = 7$. If $x = 15$, $y = 12$. Again, *x* and *y* are variables. The value of either is dependent upon the value of the other. The numerical value of one cannot be given without affecting or being affected by the value of the other. All we can do is to find pairs of values for *x* and *y* that constitute a solution of the equation. Again, this equation has an infinite number of solutions. Some of the pairs of values are listed in the table at the right.

If x =	y =
10	7
4	1
14	11
5.4	2.4
−1	−4
28	25
9.15	6.15

16.2 SYSTEMS OF EQUATIONS

Let us consider these two equations together:

$$x + y = 11 \qquad \text{and} \qquad x - y = 3$$

Suppose it is required that both equations be true for the same pair of values for *x* and *y*. Then we call these equations a *system* of equations.

If we try a pair of values for the first equation, such as $x = 9$ and $y = 2$, we find that this pair does not satisfy the second equation. On the other hand, if we take a pair that satisfies the second equation, such as $x = 10$ and $y = 7$, we find that this pair does not satisfy the first equation. After some trial and error, we find that one particular pair will make both equations true. This is the pair $x = 7$ and $y = 4$. The pair of numbers that satisfies both equations can be written in parentheses as (7, 4), *in that order*. For this system of equations the order cannot be reversed. It is an *ordered pair*.

Our problem in solving a system of equations is to find a pair of values for the two unknowns that will make both equations true. Such a pair of numbers is called a *solution* of the system.

In this chapter we consider equations containing terms in only the first power of *x* and *y*. Such equations are called *first degree* equations or *linear* equations. At this time we shall not be concerned with equations containing terms in x^2 or y^2 or terms with higher powers of the variables.

Note.   A system of equations is sometimes called a set of "simultaneous" equations. The name *simultaneous* is not a good term to use in this connection since the word *simultaneous* means "being at the same time." It is *not* the idea of *time* that is involved here. We do not mean that the equations must necessarily be true only at some particular time, such as today, tomorrow, or at 10.30 A.M. What we mean is that the *same pair of numbers* for x and y will make the equation true *at any time*. It is therefore better to call the two equations a *system*.

16.3 SOLVING A SYSTEM OF EQUATIONS BY ADDITION OR SUBTRACTION

In the foregoing system we found a solution by inspection: $x = 7$, $y = 4$. However, we need a systematic method for solving systems of equations. There are several methods that can be used for this purpose. One of the most convenient is the method called *addition or subtraction*.

Let us consider again the two equations $x + y = 11$ and $x - y = 3$. If we consider an equation to be a balanced scale, we can show a scale for each equation. For the equation $x + y = 11$, we have the scale in Fig. 16.1a. For the equation $x - y = 3$, we have the second scale (Fig. 16.1b).

If we add the two left-hand pans of the scales and also add the two right-hand pans, we get a new scale that may be represented by the third diagram (Fig. 16.1c). This scale will also balance because of the addition axiom.

You will note on the combined scale that the entire quantity on the left results in $2x$, whereas the total quantity on the right is 14. So we see that x must have a value of 7.

These scales may be shown in equation form. When the two equations are added, the y terms drop out.

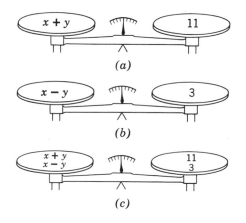

(a)

(b)

(c)

Fig. 16.1

First scale: $x + y = 11$
Second scale: $x - y = 3$
Adding the two equations, we get $2x = 14$
Solving for x (division axiom), $x = 7$
Now we find the value of y by
substituting 7 for x in either equation: $y = 4$

In this example we might have subtracted the two equations instead of adding them. If we place one equation below the other, as in addition, and then subtract one equation from the other, we get $2y = 8$.

$$x + y = 11$$
$$x - y = 3$$
Subtracting, $2y = 8$
Solving for y, $y = 4$
Then $x = 7$

The answers are the same whether we add or subtract the two equations. Notice that in either case one letter is *eliminated* in the process. The purpose of adding or subtracting the equations is to *eliminate* one letter so that the resulting equation has only one unknown.

In solving a system of equations by the method of addition or subtraction, we sometimes run into some complications. Consider these two equations:

$$5x - 3y = 7$$
$$4x + y = 9$$
Adding, $9x - 2y = 16$

If we add the two equations, we get $9x - 2y = 16$. This is a perfectly legal operation in mathematics, but it does not lead to a solution. If we subtract the two equations, we are no better off. The new equation still contains both x and y terms. By adding or subtracting the equations, we hope to eliminate one of the letters. This can happen only if the two *coefficients of one letter have the same numerical value*.

In the foregoing set of equations we can make the two coefficients of y numerically equal by multiplying the second equation by 3 (Axiom 3). The second equation then becomes $12x + 3y = 27$. This result is written below or above the first equation. The two equations are then added.

First equation: $5x - 3y = 7$
Multiplying the second equation by 3, $12x + 3y = 27$
Adding the two equations, $17x = 34$
Solving for x, $x = 2$
Then $y = 1$

After the value of x has been found, this value is substituted for x in any one of the equations. From the resulting equation, we compute the value of y.

To check the set of values for x and y, the values must be checked in *both* of the original equations. It is entirely possible to get some pair of values for x and y that will satisfy one equation but not the other. To be a correct solution, the set of answers must satisfy *both* equations.

It should be remembered that checking a pair of values must *always* be done in the *original* equations.

In solving a system of equations by the method of addition or subtraction, it is often necessary to multiply *each* of the given equations by some factor, as in the example shown here.

$$3x + 2y = 7$$
$$4x - 5y = 13$$

Multiplying the first equation by 5, $\quad 15x + 10y = 35$

Multiplying the second equation by 2, $\quad 8x - 10y = 26$

Adding the two equations, $\qquad 23x \qquad = 61$

$$x = \tfrac{61}{23}$$

To find the value of y in the foregoing equations, we may substitute the known value of x in any one of the equations. However, when such substitution is difficult because of fractional values, we may begin again with the original equations and equalize the coefficients of a different variable.

Multiplying the first equation by 4, $\quad 12x + 8y = 28$

Multiplying the second equation by 3, $\quad 12x - 15y = 39$

Subtracting the equations, $\qquad\qquad +23y = -11$

Solving for y, $\qquad\qquad\qquad y = -\tfrac{11}{23}$

Steps in solving systems of equations by addition or subtraction.

1. *Multiply one or both of the given equations, if necessary, by some factor, or factors, that will make the coefficients of one variable numerically equal.*
2. *Eliminate this variable by addition or subtraction.*
3. *Solve the resulting equation for one variable.*
4. *Find the value of the other variable by substituting the known value of one variable in one of the equations. (The second variable may be found in the same way as the first.)*

Exercise 16.1

Solve by addition or subtraction:

1. $3x + 2y = 8$
   $x - 4y = 5$

2. $2x - 3y = 19$
   $5x + 4y = 13$

3. $4x - 7y = -2$
   $3x + 4y = 17$

4. $5x + y = 1$
$x + 2y = 11$

5. $2r - 5s = 13$
$7r - 3s = 2$

6. $4m - 3n = 11$
$7n + 3m = -1$

7. $3c + 4d = -5$
$7d + 4c = -10$

8. $4h + 5k = -3$
$7k = 3h - 8$

9. $7x + 3y = 9$
$7y - 3x + -8$

10. $3y - 7z = 3$
$5z - 7y = 10$

11. $3x + 5y = -11$
$7x - y = 6$

12. $7x - 10y = 20$
$11x - 15y = 30$

13. $3x - 4y = 7$
$2x - 7y = -3$

14. $3E - 5e = 4$
$2E + 7e = -8$

15. $3I + 2i = -9$
$4I - 7i = 1$

16. $24\alpha + 15\beta = 40$
$15\alpha - 24\beta = 40$

17. $4R - 5r = 10$
$3R - 2r = 10$

18. $3a - 8b = 7$
$5a - 12b = 3$

19. $5R - 6r = 7$
$9r + 4R = 10$

20. $2y + 7x + 6 = 0$
$5x + 3y - 1 = 0$

21. $12x - 11y = 25$
$15y + 16x = 80$

22. $2.3x + 7.2y = 10$
$5.1x - 4.3y = 10$

23. $21.3\lambda - 9.5\omega = 6$
$9.5\lambda + 21\omega = 0$

24. $3.2R + 1.5r = 25$
$2.1R - 2.5r = 5$

25. $50I + 15i = 80$
$15I + 25i = 80$

26. $1.3R + 1.5r = 6$
$1.5R + 1.3r = 8$

27. $ax + by = e$
$cx + dy = f$

28. $bx - ky = a$
$cx + ky = n$

29. $mx + ny = 5c$
$nx - my = 3b$

30. $2\pi\alpha - 3\mu\beta = 4$
$5\mu\alpha - 4\pi\beta = 15$

16.4 SOLVING SYSTEMS OF EQUATIONS BY SUBSTITUTION

Substitution is another method for solving systems of equations. This method can sometimes be used to advantage, although it is perhaps not so practical as addition or subtraction. One advantage of this method is that it can often be used to solve equations of *higher degree*, as we shall see later.

Steps in solving by the substitution method.

1. *Solve one of the equations immediately for one letter in terms of the other letter.*
2. *Substitute this value for its equal in the other equation.*
3. *Solve the resulting equation for the value of one variable.*
4. *Find the value of the second variable as usual.*

Example 1. Solve by substitution: $3x - 4y = 5$
$5x + y = 16$

Solution.

Solving the second equation for y, $\qquad\qquad y = 16 - 5x$

Substitute $(16 - 5x)$ for y in the
other equation: $\qquad\qquad\qquad\qquad\qquad 3x - 4(16 - 5x) = 5$

Solve the resulting equation for x: $\qquad\qquad\qquad\qquad x = 3$

Then $\qquad\qquad\qquad\qquad\qquad\qquad\qquad\qquad\qquad y = 1$

To find the value of y, we may use the equation, $y = 16 - 5x$.

Note that in the second step, one variable is eliminated.

Example 2. Solve by substitution: $4x - 3y = 11$
$$5x + 4y = 6$$

Solution. Solve one of the equations for one letter in terms of the other.
Suppose we solve the first for x: $\qquad\qquad\qquad 4x = 11 + 3y$

Here, x is equal to a fraction: $\qquad\qquad\qquad x = \dfrac{11 + 3y}{4}$

Substitute this fraction for x in the $\qquad\qquad 5\left(\dfrac{11 + 3y}{4}\right) + 4y = 6$
other equation:
The resulting equation is now solved $\qquad\qquad\qquad y = -1$
for y. Then the value of x is found. $\qquad\qquad\qquad x = 2$

Exercise 16.2

Solve by substitution:

1. $3x + y = 2$
$\ 5x + 3y = 10$

2. $a - 3b = 9$
$\ 4a + 5b = 2$

3. $5m - 3n = -12$
$\ m + 4n = -7$

4. $2x - y = 5$
$\ 3x - 4y = 24$

5. $5x + 4y = 9$
$\ 3x - y = 4$

6. $2\alpha - 5\beta = 6$
$\ 5\alpha - \beta = 7$

7. $3A - 2B = 8$
$\ 4A - B = -3$

8. $7c - 5y = 17$
$\ 5c + y = 3$

9. $3x + 2y = 14$
$\ 4x + 5y = 21$

10. $3\beta + 2\alpha = 3$
$\ 3\alpha - 2\beta = 11$

11. $5x + y = 7$
$\ 7x + 3y = 9$

12. $6x - 5y = 2$
$\ 5x + y = -4$

13. $x - 3y = 9$
$\ 5x + 7y = 2$

14. $4a - 3b = 3$
$\ a + 4b = -5$

15. $3m + 4n - 8 = 0$
$\ 5m - 2n - 9 = 0$

16. $4x - 3y = 9$
$\ 5y - 3x + 4 = 0$

17. $7R - 5r = 7$
$\ 4r - 5R = -2$

18. $6h - 5k - 4 = 0$
$\ 3k + 7h - 9 = 0$

19. $5c - 4d = 0$
$\ 3c - d = 7$

20. $3E + 5e = 13$
$\ 4E - 3e = 7$

21. $1.7x + 3.2y = 6$
$\ 2.3x + 4y = 7$

16.5 SOLVING SYSTEMS OF EQUATIONS BY COMPARISON

This method may sometimes be used to advantage. In the method of *comparison* we solve both equations for the same variable and then equate the resulting expressions. Again note that we eliminate one variable.

Example. Solve by comparison: $4x - 3y = 11$
$$5x + 4y = 6$$

Solution. Solve both equations for one letter. Suppose we solve both for x.

From the first equation, we get $\qquad\qquad\qquad x = \dfrac{11 + 3y}{4}$

From the second equation, we get $\qquad\qquad\qquad x = \dfrac{6 - 4y}{5}$

Since x must have the same value in both equations, we set one fraction equal to the other:

$$\frac{11 + 3y}{4} = \frac{6 - 4y}{5}$$

Solving the resulting *fractional* equation for y, we get $y = -1$

Then $x = 2$

Steps in solving by comparison method.

1. *Solve each of the equations for the same letter.*
2. *Set the two values obtained equal to each other.*
3. *Solve the resulting equation for one unknown.*
4. *Find the remaining unknown by the usual method.*

Exercise 16.3

Solve by the *comparison method* the first fifteen exercises in the preceding section on the substitution method.

Solve the following systems of equations by the three different methods discussed: addition or subtraction, substitution, and comparison. Be sure to check answers in the *original* equations.

1. $3x - 2y = 5$
   $5x - 3y = 7$

2. $5x + 3y = 7$
   $5y - 3x = -6$

3. $7x - 5y = 4$
   $3x + 4y = -5$

4. $2r + 5s = 1$
   $3r - 4s = 8$

5. $4a + 6b = -3$
   $3a - 2b = 5$

6. $6I + 5i = 12$
   $5I + 3i = 9$

7. $\dfrac{x - 3}{2} - \dfrac{y - 2}{3} = 3$

   $\dfrac{x - 5}{3} - \dfrac{y + 3}{4} = 0$

8. $\dfrac{x + 2}{3} + \dfrac{y - 4}{5} - 2 = 0$

   $\dfrac{5 - x}{2} + \dfrac{2 - y}{7} = 1$

9. $\dfrac{3x - 2}{4} + \dfrac{y + 3}{5} = 0$

   $\dfrac{x + 5}{3} - \dfrac{3y - 5}{8} = -1$

10. $1 - \dfrac{x + 3}{3} + \dfrac{3y - 1}{5} = 0$

    $\dfrac{2 - 3x}{4} - \dfrac{y + 3}{6} = 5$

16.6 SYSTEMS OF EQUATIONS IN THREE OR MORE UNKNOWNS

Three equations in three unknowns may be solved by methods similar to those used for two equations. This is also true for equations containing more than three unknowns. One of the best methods to use for such equations is addition or subtraction.

If we have three unknowns (that is, three different letters) in a set of equations, then we must have three independent equations. In general, the number of independent equations must be the same as the number of unknowns.

In solving a system of equations containing several unknowns, we try to eliminate one unknown by addition or subtraction. If the coefficients of one letter are *numerically* equal in two equations, then that letter may be eliminated by adding or subtracting the two equations.

To solve a system of three equations in three unknowns, we have the following steps:

1. *Eliminate* one *letter using a set of two equations. The result is a new equation containing, at most, two letters.*

2. *Eliminate the* same *letter using another set or combination of the given equations. The result is another new equation containing, at most, two letters.*

3. *Solve the two new equations obtained in Steps 1 and 2.*

4. *When the value of one letter has been found, work backward through the equations to find the other values.*

Example 1. Solve the following system of three equations. Call the equations A, B, and C, for convenience.

$$\text{(A)}\ 2x + 5y + 3z = 7$$
$$\text{(B)}\ \ x - 2y + 5z = 15$$
$$\text{(C)}\ 3x - y - z = 8$$

Solution. Suppose we decide to eliminate z in all three equations. First we select any two equations, say, A and C.

Then we write equation A: $\qquad$ (A) $2x + 5y + 3z = 7$

Multiply equation C by 3 to make the z coefficients numerically equal: $\qquad 9x - 3y - 3z = 24$

Adding, we get a new equation we might call D. This new equation contains only two letters. The z term has been eliminated. $\qquad$ (D) $\qquad 11x + 2y = 31$

Now, we eliminate the same letter z, using another combination of equations. Suppose we use equations B and C.

We write equation B as it is: $\qquad x - 2y + 5z = 15$

Next, we multiply equation C by 5: $\qquad 15x - 5y - 5z = 40$

Adding these two equations, we get another equation we may call E: $\qquad$ (E) $16x - 7y = 55$

We now have two new equations, D and E, from which the z has been eliminated. $\qquad$ (D) $11x + 2y = 31$
$\qquad$ (E) $16x - 7y = 55$

Solving these two equations just as we solve any system of two equations, we get values for x and y:

$$x = 3 \quad \text{and} \quad y = -1$$

After we have found two of the unknowns, we go back to any previous equations in three unknowns and substitute the known values. Let us substitute the known values in equation A to find z.

$$6 - 5 + 3z = 7$$

Solving for z, $z = 2$

We now have all the values of the unknowns. Checking should always be done in the original equations.

Example 2. Solve the following system of equations:

Solution. Since the second equation has no y term, we eliminate y, using A and C:

(A) $2x + 3y - 4z = 15$
(B) $3x + 7z = -6$
(C) $5x - y + 3z = 1$

We write equation A:

$2x + 3y - 4z = 15$

Multiplying equation C by 3,
$15x - 3y + 9z = 3$

Adding, we get a new equation:
(D) $17x + 5z = 18$

We now solve this equation with B:
(B) $3x + 7z = -6$

The complete solution is left as an exercise for the student. The answers to the problem are 2, $-\frac{3}{2}$, and $\frac{3}{2}$, although these answers are not necessarily in the same order as the unknowns.

Exercise 16.4

Solve the following systems of equations. The answers are given for some, although not necessarily in the same order as the unknowns.

1. $2x + 3y - z = 11$
   $3x - y + 2z = 4$
   $4x + 2y + 3z = 8$
   (Answers: 1, 3, -2)

2. $x - 2y + 4z = -4$
   $3x + 4y - 5z = 25$
   $5x - 3y + 2z = 12$
   (Answers: -1, 2, 4)

3. $3x + 2y + 4z = 9$
   $4x + 3y - 2z = 6$
   $5x + 4y - 3z = 8$
   (Answers: 4, 1, -1)

4. $3r + 4s - 2t = -2$
   $5r + 7t = -1$
   $2r - 3s = 23$
   (Answers: 4, -5, -3)

5. $3a - 3b + 4c = 0$
   $3b - 5c + 2a = 13$
   $5a - 3c - 4b = 27$
   (Answers: 2, -3, -2)

6. $3x - 2y + 4z = 8$
   $y - z + 5x = 5$
   $2z + 2x - 3y = 4$
   (Answers: fractions)

7. $3x + 4y - 5z = 16$
   $2z + 4z + 3y = 8$
   $x - 2y - 3z = -4$
   (Some halves)

8. $5x - 2y + 3z = 12$
   $2z - 4x - 3y = -5$
   $3y - 4z - 2x = -7$
   (Two answers: -1, 2)

9. $c + 3d - 4e = 6$
$4e - 3c - 3d = -8$
$2d - e - 5c = -9$
(Fractions)

10. $5x - 3y + 4z = 10$
$2y - 4x - 5z = 10$
$3z - 2x - 4y = 0$

11. $2w - 3x + 4y - 2z = 5$
$3w + x - 3y + 4z = 8$
$w - 2x + y - 3z = 7$
$4w + 3x - 2y + 5z = 11$
(Answers: 1, -2, 4, -1)

12. $3r + 2s + 4t - 5u = 8$
$2r - 3s - 2t - 3u = 4$
$4r - 5s + 3t - 2u = 22$
$5r + 4s + 5t + 4u = -6$
(Three answers: 3, -3, -1)

13. $3a + 2b - 3c + d = 14$
$2a - 3b + 4c = -3$
$3d - 2c + 4a = 12$
$5b - 5c + 4d = 2$
(Answers: -1, 13, 3, -2)

14. $3w - 2x - z = 4$
$2w - 3y + 3z = 5$
$x + y - 2z = 0$
$4w + 3x + 2y = 6$

15. $3w - 4z - 2x = 4$
$3z - 3y + 2w = 6$
$2z - 4y - 5x = -9$
$5y - 3x + 4w = 11$

16. $2a - 4c + d + 3b = 9$
$c - 3d + 3a - 2b = 7$
$4b + 5a - 4d - 3c = 8$
$2d - c + 3b - a = -6$

17. $x - 3y + 4z - 2t = 7$
$2x + 5y - 3z - 5t = -1$
$3x - y + z + t = 9$
$x + y - 2z - 3t = 0$

18. $3A + 2B - C - 3D = 5$
$A - 3B + 2C - 5D = 7$
$2A - B + 3C + D = 6$
$A + 3B - 2C - D = -2$

19. $a - 3b + c + 2d - e = 5$
$a + b - 2c - d - 3e = 4$
$2a - b - 3c + 2d - 2e = 3$
$3a + 2b - c + 3d + e = 9$
$2a + 4b + c - d + e = 0$

20. $u + v + 2x + 3y + 2z = 5$
$u - v + 3x - 2y + z = 16$
$2u - 3v - x + y - 2z = 4$
$2u + 3v - 2x - y + z = -6$
$3u - 2v + x - 3y - 3z = 13$
(Answers are integers)

21. $3R_1 - 5R_2 + 7R_3 = 20$
$8R_2 - 3R_3 = 17$
$6R_3 - 5R_1 = 13$

22. $5.3E_1 + 4.1E_2 - 8.4E_3 = 12.4$
$7.5E_1 + 5.4E_3 = 8$
$6.3E_2 - 1.3E_3 = 3.2$

23. $21.5I_1 + 30I_2 - 15.4I_3 = 40$
$13.4I_1 - 22I_2 + 31.2I_3 = 40$
$15.2I_1 - 31.5I_2 - 24.21I_3 = 0$

16.7 EQUATIONS: DEPENDENT OR DERIVED, INCONSISTENT, INDEPENDENT

Let us consider the following equation in two unknowns:

$$3x - 5y = 11$$

If we multiply both sides of this equation by some quantity, say, 4, we get a new equation:

$$12x - 20y = 44$$

The new equation is called a *derived equation*, since it is derived from the first by the use of one of the axioms. If the second equation is given, we can obtain the first by dividing both sides of the equation by 4. In either case, we can say that one of these two equations is derived from the other. The two equations may be called *dependent* equations.

If we have two given equations, and if it is possible to obtain one of them from the other simply by use of one or more of the four axioms, then we can say the equations are *dependent*.

Two dependent equations may be reduced to one. Therefore, any set of values for x and y that satisfies one equation will also satisfy the other. For instance, the values $x = 7$ and $y = 2$ will satisfy both of the foregoing equations.

Let us see what happens when we attempt to solve a set of dependent equations. Try to solve the following:

$$3x - 2y = 7$$
$$7x - 21 = 6y - 2x$$

Transposing in the second equation, $\quad 7x + 2x - 6y = 21$

Combining, $\qquad\qquad\qquad\qquad\quad 9x - 6y = 21$

Multiplying the first equation by 3, $\quad 9x - 6y = 21$

Subtracting, $\qquad\qquad\qquad\qquad\qquad\quad 0 = 0$

Such an answer indicates a pair of dependent or derived equations. A set of dependent equations has an infinite number of solutions, since any set of values that satisfies one equation will also satisfy the other. The result we get, $0 = 0$, is true, but it offers no help in finding the answer to a practical problem.

Now, let us consider another set of equations. Let us see what happens when we attempt to solve this system:

$$2x + 5y = 21$$
$$4x + 10y = 37$$

Multiplying the first equation by 2, $\quad 4x + 10y = 42$

Subtracting from the second equation, $\qquad 0 = -5$

Since the answer is impossible, the set of equations is called a pair of *inconsistent* equations. A set of inconsistent equations has *no* common solution. There is no set of values for the letters that will satisfy both equations.

In order to solve a system of equations, the equations must be *independent* and they must *not be inconsistent*. Almost all equations encountered in practical work are independent and can be solved. If two dependent or derived equations appear in practical work, then the problem must be analyzed more carefully to determine another *independent* equation or the problem cannot be solved. If two inconsistent equations appear in the course of the solution of a practical problem, the two describe an impossible condition, and the problem must be further analyzed for errors in the setting up of the equations.

To summarize:

1. Dependent equations have an infinite number of pairs of values for x and y that will satisfy both equations.
2. Inconsistent equations have no common solution.
3. Independent equations have a particular pair, or pairs, of values that satisfy the equations. In the case of linear equations there is one and only one pair of values for the unknowns that will satisfy the independent equations.

Exercise 16.5

Try to solve the following sets of equations. Tell whether each set is inconsistent, whether the equations are dependent, or whether they are independent. Solve the systems containing independent equations.

1. $3x - 5y = 7$
   $6x - 4y = 13$
2. $4x - 5y = 8$
   $10y + 15 = 8x$
3. $2x + 7y = 6$
   $3x - 5y = 9$
4. $3x + 4y = 13$
   $6x = 26 - 8y$
5. $x - 3y = 5$
   $6y - 2x = 7$
6. $10x - 3y = 24$
   $40 + 5y = 7x$
7. $3a - 6b = 21$
   $2a - 14 = 4b$
8. $4y + 3x = -3$
   $5x - 3y = 14$
9. $4y = 12 - 7x$
   $3x = 6 - 2y$
10. $3x = 16 + 2y$
    $4y = 6x - 32$
11. $5x - y = 13$
    $2y + 18 = 10x$
12. $2x + 15 = 4y$
    $6x + 8y = 30$
13. $2x - 5y + 3z = 13$
    $5z + 4x - 10y = 17$
    $2y - 4z - 3x = -4$
14. $x - 4z + 3y = 11$
    $6y - 5z + 2x = 7$
    $9y + 6 + z = -3x$
15. $4x - 3z + 5 = 2y$
    $2z - 5y - 2x = 7$
    $y + 2x - 3z = 0$
16. $x + 3y - 2z = 3$
    $y - 4z + 2x = 7$
    $3x + 4y - z = 8$

16.8 PROBLEM SOLVING BY USING TWO OR MORE UNKNOWNS

In solving stated problems by the use of two or more unknowns, we use a different letter to represent each unknown. For example, we may use x to represent one unknown, and y to represent a second unknown.

Next, from the information given in the problem, we write equations relating the unknowns. If we use two unknowns, we must write two independent equations. For three unknowns, we must have three independent equations. The number of independent equations must be as many as the number of unknowns.

To be certain that the equations we write are independent, we make use of *different information* for each equation. If we use the same information for setting up two equations, then the two are derived or dependent equations.

When the necessary equations have been set up, they are solved as a system. The method will be shown by examples.

Example 1. At an entertainment, one group of people purchased 4 adults' tickets and 9 children's tickets for $6.55, while another group purchased 5 adults' tickets and 7 children's tickets for $6.70. Find the price of each kind of ticket.

Solution.   Let x = the price (in cents) of an adult's ticket.
            Let y = the price (in cents) of a child's ticket.

To avoid decimal fractions we express all costs in cents. Now we must write two independent equations from the given information. The cost of 4 adults' tickets at x cents each is $4x$ cents. The cost of 9 children's tickets at y cents each is $9y$ cents. The cost of the first purchase is 655 cents. Then we have the first equation (for the first purchase):

$$4x + 9y = 655$$

For the second purchase we have the equation

$$5x + 7y = 670$$

We can consider the two equations as a *system* because they are both based on purchases at unchanging prices. Multiplying the first equation by 7 and the second by 9, we get

$$28x + 63y = 4585$$
$$45x + 63y = 6030$$

Subtracting the first equation from the second, we get

$$17x = 1445; \quad \text{or} \quad x = 85, \quad \text{and} \quad y = 35$$

Therefore the two kinds of tickets cost 85 cents and 35 cents each, respectively.

Example 2.   In a certain triangle, ABC, angle A is equal to one-third of the sum of angle B and angle C; angle B is 30° more than angle C. Find the number of degrees in each angle.

Solution.   Let A = the number of degrees in angle A.
            Let B = the number of degrees in angle B.
            Let C = the number of degrees in angle C.

Now we need three independent equations. For one equation we have the information that angle A is one-third of the sum of angles B and C. That is

$$A = \tfrac{1}{3}(B + C) \qquad \text{(Equation 1)}$$

For another equation we have the information that angle B is 30° more than angle C. That is,

$$B = C + 30 \qquad \text{(Equation 2)}$$

Now we need a third equation. At this point we might be tempted to write the third equation:

$$B - C = 30$$

This equation is true, but we are making use of information already used in Equation 2. The two equations are dependent; that is, one can be derived from the other. Then, again, we might write

$$3A = B + C; \quad \text{or} \quad 3A - B - C = 0$$

However, these equations are derived from Equation 1.

We must search for other information from which we can write a third independent equation. Suddenly we recall that the sum of the three angles of any triangle is 180°. Now we have the three equations

$$A + B + C = 180$$
$$3A - B - C = 0$$
$$B - C = 30$$

Solving these as a system, we get $A = 45°$; $B = 82.5°$; $C = 52.5°$. All conditions of the problem are satisfied.

Note. In most actual work in stated problems, such as those encountered in technology, the answers often turn out to be fractions instead of integers. In such problems it is best to leave answers in the form of common fractions instead of decimals until all answers have been found. Then they may be changed to decimal form if it is so desired.

Checking answers by substitution of values in the original equations becomes difficult when answers are complicated fractions or decimals. If unending decimals are involved, checking will be only approximate. The best check in such problems is to go over each step in the work carefully to see that no error has been made in working toward the solution.

Exercise 16.6

Solve the following problems by the use of two or more unknowns.

1. A collection of 87 coins, consisting of nickels and dimes, is worth $5.65. Find the number of coins of each kind in the collection.

2. A collection of 73 coins, nickels and quarters, is worth $12.85. Find the number of coins of each kind in the collection.

3. A man has a total of $7200 invested, part of it at 3% and the remainder at 7%. Find the amount invested at each rate if his total annual income from the two investments is $396.

4. A man has $6500 invested, part of it at 6% and the rest at 9%. Find the amount invested at each rate if the return on the two investments is the same.

5. How much of a 15% solution of alcohol and how much of a 40% solution should be mixed together for 50 gallons of a solution to test 25%?

6. A chemist has two solutions, one testing 8% and the other testing 50% of a certain chemical. How much of each should be mixed together to produce 10 pints of a 23% solution?

7. How many pounds of 50-cent tea and how much of 90-cent tea should be mixed together for 70 pounds of the mixture to sell at 65 cents a pound?

8. A merchant has some coffee selling at 55 cents a pound and other coffee selling at $1.00 a pound. He wishes to make a mixture of 50 pounds to sell at 70 cents a pound. How many pounds of each kind should he use?

9. Find two complementary angles whose difference is 15°.

10. Find two supplementary angles that differ by 125°.

11. A man takes a trip of 580 miles. Part of the way he travels by car at an average rate of 45 mph and the rest of the way by train at an average rate of 65 mph. If his total travel time is 10 hours, how far does he travel at each rate?

12. A motorboat travels downstream for a distance of 60 miles in 4 hours and makes the return trip in 6 hours. Find the rate of the current and the rate of the boat in still water. (Hint: Let x = rate of boat, in mph; and let y = rate of current, in mph. Then, for the rate downstream, the rates are added; for the rate upstream, the rates are subtracted.)

13. An aeroplane makes a trip of 640 miles in 2.5 hours with the advantage of a tail wind. On the return trip the plane requires 3 hours flying against the same wind speed. Find the speed of the wind and the speed of the plane in still air.

14. A plane requires 5 hours for a trip of 2700 miles against a wind, and only 4.5 hours for the return trip flying with the wind. Find the speed of the air current and the speed of the plane in still air.

15. A plane requires 5.5 hours for a trip of 2200 miles against a wind, and only 5 hours for the return trip. Find the speed of the wind and the speed of the plane in still air.

16. A collection of 93 coins, nickels, dimes, and quarters, is worth $9.15. The number of dimes is 4 more than twice the number of nickels. Find the number of coins of each kind in the collection.

17. A certain collection of nickels, dimes, and quarters is worth $3.95. The number of quarters is half the number of dimes, and the number of nickels is 9 more than the number of quarters. Find the number of each kind.

18. At a ball game a total of 1545 tickets were sold, some at $1.20 each, some at $1.80 each, and reserved seats at $2.50 each. The number of $1.80 tickets was 125 more than the $1.20 tickets sold. If the total receipts was $2715, find the number of tickets sold at each price.

19. A grocer has three kinds of tea worth, respectively, 90 cents, 80 cents, and 50 cents a pound. He wishes to use some of each kind for a mixture to sell at 65 cents a pound. Moreover, he wishes to use twice as much of the 50-cent tea as of the 90-cent tea. How many pounds of each kind should he use for 100 pounds of the mixture?

20. In a certain triangle, ABC, angle A is 20° more than one-half of the sum of angles B and C; angle B is 5° less than twice angle C. Find the size of each angle.

21. A man has $12,000 invested in three investments. On the first investment he receives an income of 4% per year, on the second he receives an income of 7% per year, and on the third he receives a 9% return. His total annual income from the three investments is $691. If the first two investments had been reversed, he would have received $780 a year. How much has he invested at each rate?

16.9 DETERMINANTS

We have already solved systems of equations such as the following:

$$ax + by = e \qquad (1)$$
$$cx + dy = f \qquad (2)$$

This system can be solved by any one of several methods, one of which is subtraction. We shall see that the system can also be solved conveniently by the use of *determinants*.

Before considering the method of determinants, let us first see just what is done in solving the system by subtraction. In these equations the letters a, b, c, d, e, and f are constants. To solve for x, we first equalize the y-coefficients and then subtract one equation from the other. We multiply equation (1) by d, and equation (2) by b, so that the coefficients of y become equal. Then we subtract and get

$$adx + bdy = de$$
$$bcx + bdy = bf$$

Subtracting,
$$adx - bcx = de - bf$$

Solving for x,
$$x = \frac{de - bf}{ad - bc}$$

In a similar manner, equalizing x-coefficients, we get

$$y = \frac{af - ce}{ad - bc}$$

Note that the denominators are the same for both values.

Let us see now what is meant by a determinant. Let us begin with an array of numbers called a *matrix*. A matrix is often denoted by enclosing the numbers, called elements, in a pair of braces or parentheses:

$$\begin{Bmatrix} 5 & 4 \\ 2 & 3 \end{Bmatrix} \qquad \begin{pmatrix} 5 & 4 \\ 2 & 3 \end{pmatrix}$$

This symbol for a matrix does *not* indicate any operation upon the elements.

Now suppose we wish to indicate a particular operation upon the numbers. We use a pair of vertical lines, one on each side of the array. The arrangement then denotes a *determinant*:

$$\begin{vmatrix} 5 & 4 \\ 2 & 3 \end{vmatrix}$$

The *determinant* is a symbol that indicates a specific rule for operating upon the numbers in the array. Now let us see how this operation must be done.

Note that this determinant has two *rows*, the first row consisting of the elements 5 and 4; and the second row, of the elements 2 and 3. It has two *columns*, the first consisting of the numbers 5 and 2, and the second column, of 4 and 3. The *principal diagonal* is the diagonal extending from *upper left* to *lower right*. In this example the principal diagonal consists of the numbers 5 and 3.

A determinant is expanded according to the following rule, as shown by the arrows in this array:

$$\begin{vmatrix} 5 & 4 \\ 2 & 3 \end{vmatrix}$$

First, we find the product of the elements along the *principal* diagonal. In this example, this product is $(5)(3) = 15$. Next, we find the product of the elements along the other diagonal extending from *lower left* to *upper right*. In this case, this product is $(2)(4) = 8$. This second product must be *subtracted* from the first product. This is the meaning of the symbol of the determinant. The result in this example is $15 - 8 = 7$. The following expression shows how the determinant is expanded:

$$\begin{vmatrix} 5 & 4 \\ 2 & 3 \end{vmatrix} = (5)(3) - (2)(4) = 15 - 8 = 7$$

The value of this determinant is 7.

In a determinant the products must be taken *in exactly the order shown*. If some of the elements are negative, we must be especially careful to observe algebraic signs of the products. As an example,

$$\begin{vmatrix} 2 & -3 \\ -4 & -1 \end{vmatrix} = (2)(-1) - (-4)(-3) = -2 - (+12) = -2 - 12 = -14$$

In general terms, let us expand the following determinant:

$$\begin{vmatrix} a & b \\ c & d \end{vmatrix} = ad - bc$$

Note that the expanded determinant is exactly the *denominator* we obtained in solving the following system of equations:

$$ax + by = e$$
$$cx + dy = f$$

Recall that the solution of this system is

$$x = \frac{de - bf}{ad - bc} \quad \text{and} \quad y = \frac{af - ce}{ad - bc}$$

Each answer in the solution can be written in the form of a fraction having one determinant for the numerator and another for the denominator:

$$x = \frac{\begin{vmatrix} e & b \\ f & d \end{vmatrix}}{\begin{vmatrix} a & b \\ c & d \end{vmatrix}} \qquad y = \frac{\begin{vmatrix} a & e \\ c & f \end{vmatrix}}{\begin{vmatrix} a & b \\ c & d \end{vmatrix}}$$

Our problem now is this: How can the constants, a, b, c, d, e, and f, be set up in the proper array for the determinants so that we shall have immediately the correct expressions for the solution? Note that in each case the *denominator* consists of the coefficients of x and y; that is, a, b, c, and d, in the same order as they appear in the equations:

$$\begin{vmatrix} a & b \\ c & d \end{vmatrix}$$

This is called the *determinant of the system.*

The *numerators* are the same as the denominator *except* for one difference. In the solution for x, the numerator is the same as the denominator *except* that the x-coefficients are replaced with the constant terms, e and f. In like manner, in the solution for y, the numerator is formed by replacing the y-coefficients with the constant terms, e and f.

When the coefficients and constants are set up in this proper form in the numerators and in the denominator, the expansion of the determinants gives the solution of the system. This procedure is known as *Cramer's Rule.*

Example 1. Solve by determinants: $5x + 4y = 9$
$$2x + 3y = 6$$

Solution. The denominator for both values is formed by writing the coefficients of x and y as they appear in the equations. This becomes the *determinant of the system*:
$$\begin{vmatrix} 5 & 4 \\ 2 & 3 \end{vmatrix}$$

The numerator determinants are exactly the same as the denominator *except* that the constant terms, 9 and 6, replace a column of coefficients: in each case the coefficients of the letter whose value we wish to find.

$$x = \frac{\begin{vmatrix} 9 & 4 \\ 6 & 3 \end{vmatrix}}{\begin{vmatrix} 5 & 4 \\ 2 & 3 \end{vmatrix}} = \frac{27 - 24}{15 - 8} = \frac{3}{7}; \qquad y = \frac{\begin{vmatrix} 5 & 9 \\ 2 & 6 \end{vmatrix}}{\begin{vmatrix} 5 & 4 \\ 2 & 3 \end{vmatrix}} = \frac{30 - 18}{15 - 8} = \frac{12}{7}$$

Example 2. Solve by determinants: $3x - 5y + 4 = 0$
$$4y - 7x + 2 = 0$$

Solution. First, we arrange the terms so that the letters appear on the left side in the same order in both equations, and the constant terms on the right side:

$$3x - 5y = -4$$
$$-7x + 4y = -2$$

Then

$$x = \frac{\begin{vmatrix} -4 & -5 \\ -2 & 4 \end{vmatrix}}{\begin{vmatrix} 3 & -5 \\ -7 & 4 \end{vmatrix}} = \frac{-16 - 10}{12 - 35} = \frac{26}{23} \qquad y = \frac{\begin{vmatrix} 3 & -4 \\ -7 & -2 \end{vmatrix}}{-23} = \frac{-6 - 28}{-23} = \frac{34}{23}$$

Note that when the denominator determinant is once expanded, its value can be written immediately as the denominator for the value of y.

Two special cases should be mentioned here. If the numerator and the denominator in the solution are both zero, the system of equations has an infinite number of solutions, and the two equations are dependent. The following system is an example of this case:

$$2x + 3y = 5$$
$$4x + 6y = 10$$

Another special case is that in which the denominator is equal to zero but the numerator is not equal to zero. The equations are then inconsistent and they have no common solution. The following is an example of this case:

$$2x + 3y = 5$$
$$4x + 6y = 8$$

Exercise 16.7

Solve the systems in Exercises 16.1 and 16.2 by determinants.

16.10 THIRD-ORDER DETERMINANT

A system of three equations in three unknowns can also be solved by determinants. First we must know how to expand a third-order determinant.

A *third-order determinant* is one that contains three rows and three columns. The expansion of such a determinant is considerably more complicated than that of a second-order determinant. You will recall that the expansion of a determinant with two rows and two columns involves the multiplication along *two* diagonals. There are just two separate multiplications. On the other hand, the expansion of a determinant with three rows and three columns involves multiplication along *six* diagonals. There are six separate multiplications. The proper expansion is shown by an example. Suppose we have the following third-order determinant:

$$\begin{vmatrix} 8 & 5 & 9 \\ 2 & 1 & 4 \\ 6 & 3 & 7 \end{vmatrix}$$

To expand this determinant, we first rewrite the first and the second column at the right of the given determinant as shown here:

$$\begin{vmatrix} 8 & 5 & 9 & 8 & 5 \\ 2 & 1 & 4 & 2 & 1 \\ 6 & 3 & 7 & 6 & 3 \end{vmatrix}$$

Now, starting with the three elements, 8, 5, and 9, in the top row of the determinant, we have three diagonals extending *downward to the right*, as shown by arrows. Each diagonal includes three elements. We call these the *downward diagonals*. The elements in each of these diagonals are multiplied together and their products are then added. We get

$$(8)(1)(7) + (5)(4)(6) + (9)(2)(3)$$
$$= \quad 56 \quad + \quad 120 \quad + \quad 54 \quad = 230$$

Next, starting with the three elements, 6, 3, and 7, in the bottom row, we have three diagonals extending *upward to the right*, shown by broken arrows. We call these the *upward diagonals*. The elements in each of these diagonals are multiplied together and their products are all *subtracted* from the products of the downward diagonals. For the upward diagonals we have the products:

$$(6)(1)(9); \quad (3)(4)(8); \quad (7)(2)(5)$$

The expansion of the determinant, in which the addition of the downward products and the subtraction of the upward products are indicated, can be shown as follows:

$$(8)(1)(7) + (5)(4)(6) + (9)(2)(3) - (6)(1)(9) - (3)(4)(8) - (7)(2)(5)$$
$$= \quad 56 \quad + \quad 120 \quad + \quad 54 \quad - \quad 54 \quad - \quad 96 \quad - \quad 70 \quad = 10$$

In evaluating a third-order determinant, we need not rewrite the first two columns if we simply imagine them in place and then select the elements correctly according to the directions indicated by the arrows. Remember, each diagonal multiplication must involve *three* elements.

The elements of a determinant are often shown with subscripts. Then the expansion of a third-order determinant is shown in the following way:

$$\begin{vmatrix} a_1 & b_1 & c_1 \\ a_2 & b_2 & c_2 \\ a_3 & b_3 & c_3 \end{vmatrix} = a_1b_2c_3 + b_1c_2a_3 + c_1a_2b_3 - a_3b_2c_1 - b_3c_2a_1 - c_3a_2b_1$$

The solution of three equations by determinants follows the same general plan as that used for two equations. The solution for each of x, y, and z, will be the quotient of two determinants, the denominator in each case being formed by taking the coefficients of x, y, and z as they appear in the equations, in proper order. In each case, the numerator will be the same as the denominator *except* that one column will be replaced by the constant terms.

Example 3. Solve by determinants:
$$4x + 3y - z = 7$$
$$3x + 5y + z = 6$$
$$5x + 2y - 2z = 9$$

Solution. For each unknown, the denominator will be the *determinant of the system* formed by taking the coefficients as shown here:

$$\begin{vmatrix} 4 & 3 & -1 \\ 3 & 5 & 1 \\ 5 & 2 & -2 \end{vmatrix}$$

Now we make each numerator determinant exactly the same as the denominator with the following exception. In the numerator for the x-solution, we replace the x-coefficients with the constant terms, 7, 6, and 9. In the numerator for the y-solution, we replace the y-coefficients with the constant terms. We follow the same plan in solving for z. Then we have the forms:

$$x = \frac{\begin{vmatrix} 7 & 3 & -1 \\ 6 & 5 & 1 \\ 9 & 2 & -2 \end{vmatrix}}{\begin{vmatrix} 4 & 3 & -1 \\ 3 & 5 & 1 \\ 5 & 2 & -2 \end{vmatrix}} \qquad y = \frac{\begin{vmatrix} 4 & 7 & -1 \\ 3 & 6 & 1 \\ 5 & 9 & -2 \end{vmatrix}}{\begin{vmatrix} 4 & 3 & -1 \\ 3 & 5 & 1 \\ 5 & 2 & -2 \end{vmatrix}} \qquad z = \frac{\begin{vmatrix} 4 & 3 & 7 \\ 3 & 5 & 6 \\ 5 & 2 & 9 \end{vmatrix}}{\begin{vmatrix} 4 & 3 & -1 \\ 3 & 5 & 1 \\ 5 & 2 & -2 \end{vmatrix}}$$

Expanding the numerator and denominator for the value of x, we get

$$x = \frac{-70 + 27 - 12 + 45 - 14 + 36}{-40 + 15 - 6 + 25 - 8 + 18} = \frac{12}{4} = 3$$

Note that the denominator is the same for all the unknowns. Then, instead of writing the denominator determinant for each, its value, 4, can be written down at once for each of the other unknowns. Expanding the determinants, we find the values,

$$y = -1; z = 2$$

Exercise 16.8

Solve by determinants Nos. 1–10 in Exercise 16.4.

Note. Determinants of the fourth and higher orders can be used to solve equations of more than three unknowns. However, their expansion is much more complicated than that of third-order determinants. If you wish to learn the method, you will find it explained in almost any book on college algebra.

17
Graphing

17.1 INTRODUCTION

A day seldom goes by that we do not see a graph of some kind. A graph is a pictorial representation of certain factual data. We see graphs in newspapers, in magazines, in books, and in almost every technical article. We see graphs of temperature changes, business losses and gains, and economic trends. Many important facts in electrical engineering are represented by graphs of some kind. We have graphs of current, voltage, and power, of magnetic circuits, and of what goes on in a vacuum tube.

The advantage of a graph is that it shows important facts at a glance. Looking at a business graph, we can tell quickly the high points and the periods of rapid·gains and losses. In electrical engineering a graph shows instantly the relation between current and power. Many ideas in mathematics are more easily understood when they are interpreted graphically. Some equations can be solved only by means of graphs. For these reasons graphs are extremely important in the study of mathematics and science.

17.2 THE RECTANGULAR COORDINATE SYSTEM FOR THE LOCATION OF POINTS

In most cities at least part of the street system is laid out so that some streets have an east-west direction and others have a north-south direction. Imagine a city laid out with two main streets perpendicular to each other and all other streets parallel to one or the other of these two main streets.

We have one main street extending east and west, which we might call street X and another main street extending north and south, which we might call street Y (Fig. 17.1). All points in the city can be located with reference to these two perpendicular streets. All distances are measured from the two main streets.

If we wish to direct someone to a particular house in the city, we might say, starting at the point of intersection of the main streets, "Go five blocks east and seven blocks north " This location is indicated by point A in Fig. 17.1.

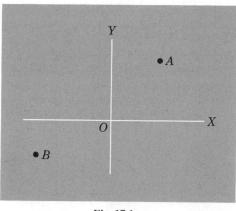

Fig. 17.1

To another we might say, "Go eight blocks west and three blocks south." This location is shown by point *B* in the figure.

If we wish to locate a point in a plane, we use a system like that of our perpendicular streets. We set up two perpendicular lines for reference lines (Fig. 17.2), which correspond to the two main streets. Each of the reference lines is called an *axis*. We call the horizontal line the *x*-axis and the vertical line the *y*-axis. The point of intersection is called the *origin*, denoted by *O*.

By means of this arrangement, we can tell the location of any point with reference to the two axes. This system of locating points is called the *rectangular coordinate system*. The two axes divide the entire plane into four quarters called *quadrants*. The quadrants are numbered, usually with Roman

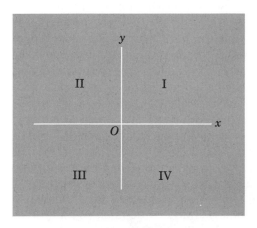

Fig. 17.2

numerals, I, II, III, IV, starting in the upper right-hand quadrant and going around in a counterclockwise direction. To tell the location of a point, we measure its distance from each axis.

Suppose a point is located 8 units to the right of the y-axis and 5 units upward from the x-axis (Fig. 17.3). Then we can say that these two numbers, 8 and 5, *taken in that order*, will definitely tell the location of the point. We call the numbers 8 and 5 the *coordinates* of the point. They are like a house number in a city.

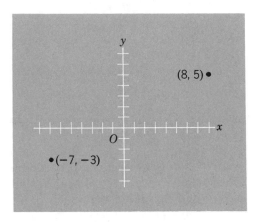

Fig. 17.3

The distance of the point in the x-direction is called the *abscissa* of the point. The distance in the y-direction is called the *ordinate* of the point. Note that the abscissa of a point is actually measured from the y-axis and the ordinate of the point is measured from the x-axis. Be careful *not* to call the x-axis the abscissa and the y-axis the ordinate. The abscissa and the ordinate are *distances*, not the lines of reference. For the point shown in Fig. 17.3, the abscissa is 8; the ordinate is 5.

In a city we speak of distances east or west and north or south. In the rectangular coordinate system distances to the right are called positive (+); distances to the left are called negative (−); distances upward are called positive; and distances downward are called negative.

If we wish to indicate a point 7 units to the left of the y-axis, we say that the abscissa, or x-distance, is −7. If the point is located 3 units downward from the x-axis, we say that the ordinate, or y-distance, is −3. The two numbers −7 and −3 are the coordinates of the point. The coordinates are enclosed in parentheses and separated by a comma: thus (−7, −3). The abscissa of the point is always written first. With this understanding, the set of numbers (−7, −3) will definitely determine one and only one point

(Fig. 17.3). Since the two numbers must be taken in the proper order, they are called an *ordered pair*.

The following points are shown on the graph in Fig. 17.4: $A(8,2)$, $B(2,8)$, $C(6,0)$, $D(0,6)$, $E(-5,7)$, $F(-7,0)$, $G(-6,-5)$, $H(0,-4)$, $I(3,-6)$, $J(9,-1)$.

The location of points on a graph is most conveniently done on "rectangular coordinate" graph paper. On this kind of paper, lines are evenly spaced horizontally and vertically.

To locate points on a graph, we first draw two axes, x and y, at right angles so that the origin is approximately in the center of the portion of the paper

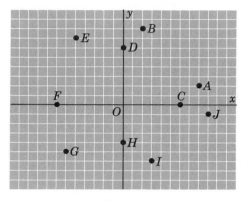

Fig. 17.4

to be used for the graph. The horizontal axis is labeled x, the vertical axis is labeled y. The exact position of the axes can be varied to suit each particular problem. In measuring the distances indicated by the coordinates of a point, the units may be of any convenient length, depending on the size of the paper and on the size of the numbers used. In most cases the units should have the same length on both axes.

The coordinates of each point are often written near the point on the graph. For practice, several points may be located on the same graph. To *plot* points means to locate the points on the graph.

Note. Notice especially that the rectangular system of coordinates and the plotting of points is *geometric*. It involves *geometry*. It has nothing to do with algebra.

Exercise 17.1

1. Plot these points on one graph: $A(7,3)$, $B(1,6)$, $C(0,3)$, $D(-8,2)$, $E(-5,-2)$, $F(0,0)$, $G(3,-5)$, $H(0,-7)$, $I(6,-6)$, $J(9,0)$.

2. Plot the following points on a graph and then connect the points in the order in which they are given with straight line segments: $A(8,0)$, $B(0,8)$, $C(-8,0)$, $D(0,-8)$, $A(8,0)$, $E(4,0)$, $F(0,4)$, $G(-4,0)$, $H(0,-4)$, $E(4,0)$.

Plot the points in each of the following sets on a graph and then connect the points in order by straight line segments to form polygons. Use a different portion of the graph paper for each set.

3. $A(8,7)$, $B(-5,3)$, $C(2,-6)$

4. $A(7,1)$, $B(-2,8)$, $C(4,-3)$

5. $A(3,0)$, $B(-3,7)$, $C(-8,-5)$

6. $A(-2,8)$, $B(-6,0)$, $C(7,-4)$

7. $A(5,-1)$, $B(0,4)$, $C(-6,-5)$, $D(0,-1)$

8. $A(7,5)$, $B(-3,2)$, $C(-6,-5)$, $D(4,-2)$

9. $A(9,-2)$, $B(-3,6)$, $C(-3,-1)$, $D(0,-3)$

10. $A(8,0)$, $B(2,6)$, $C(-5,0)$, $D(0,-7)$, $E(6,-5)$

11. $A(5,6)$, $B(-7,0)$, $C(6,-2)$, $D(-3,7)$, $E(-1,-6)$, $A(5,6)$

12. $A(12,-3)$, $B(9,-1)$, $C(3,3)$, $D(0,5)$, $E(-3,7)$

13. $A(9,9)$, $B(5,6)$, $C(1,3)$, $D(-3,0)$, $E(-7,-3)$, $F(-11,-6)$

14. $A(12,8)$, $B(0,4)$, $C(-3,2)$, $D(-4,0)$, $E(-3,-2)$, $F(0,-4)$, $G(12,-8)$

(Connect the points in Exercise 14 by a smooth continuous *curve*, instead of by straight line segments.)

15. Connect the following points by a smooth curve: $A(5,0)$, $B(4,3)$, $C(3,4)$, $D(0,5)$, $E(-3,4)$, $F(-4,3)$, $G(-5,0)$, $H(-4,-3)$, $I(-3,-4)$, $J(0,-5)$, $K(3,-4)$, $L(4,-3)$, $A(5,0)$.

17.3 GRAPHING AN EQUATION

Let us leave the problem of graphing for a moment and consider instead an algebraic equation, such as $x + y = 11$. A graph is a *geometric* concept, whereas an equation is *algebraic*.

We have seen that an equation containing x and y may have many *solution sets* or pairs of numbers that make the equation true. For example, the equation $x + y = 11$ is satisfied by the pair of numbers $x = 8$ and $y = 3$. We can find many other solution sets, some of which are shown in the table at the right. Any one of these pairs of values will satisfy this equation.

x	y
8	3
10	1
2	9
-2	13
0	11
11	0

Note especially that a pair of numbers satisfying the equation, such as $x = 8$ and $y = 3$, involves algebra. Finding a solution set for an equation is an algebraic process. It has nothing to do with geometry.

Now, here is one of the amazing stories in mathematics. For more than a thousand years the people of some nations had gone on happily finding numbers that would satisfy equations. They were chiefly interested in algebra. They had little or no interest in geometry. On the other hand, in other nations, many people were completely devoted to geometry. They cared little about algebra. They studied diagrams and geometric figures of all kinds and showed the location of points on a line and in a plane.

The algebraists were interested in finding numbers that would satisfy equations. The geometers were interested in points, lines, and planes. Yet, no one, for more than a thousand years, ever thought of connecting geometry and algebra.

Then along came Rene Descartes, born in 1596. While he was still a young man in his "teens," a brilliant idea flashed into his mind—an idea that marks one of the major advances in mathematics. This was his idea: if the numbers $x = 8$ and $y = 3$ satisfy the equation $x + y = 11$, let us call this pair of numbers the coordinates of a point on the rectangular system. In other words, we take a pair of numbers from an algebraic equation and then use this pair to represent a point in geometry.

The idea was revolutionary, and Descartes probably realized he was on the trail of something great. The amazing thing about the idea is that no one had thought of it before. Descartes spent many years developing the idea, which he later called *analytic geometry*. The result was a uniting of algebra and geometry into one of the most powerful tools in mathematical and scientific study.

Let us follow through on the equation $x + y = 11$. We have seen that several pairs of numbers satisfy the equation, and we call each pair of numbers the coordinates of a point. The result is several points; in fact, as many as we wish to find.

Here is Descartes' amazing discovery: if the points for this equation are connected by lines, the result is a straight line! If we find other pairs of numbers that satisfy the equation, each pair represents a point on the line (Fig. 17.5).

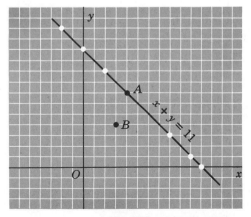

Fig. 17.5

There are two things we should note here:

1. We have written down six pairs of numbers in tabular form that satisfy the equation. No matter how many pairs we might find for the equation, every pair would represent a point on the line.

2. On the other hand, if we take any other point on the line, such as point *A*, and then find its coordinates from the graph, this pair of numbers will satisfy the equation. The coordinates of point *B* will not satisfy the equation because the point does not lie on the line.

Therefore, the straight line (a geometric figure) shown in Fig. 17.5 is the graph or picture of the algebraic equation $x + y = 11$. Moreover, an equation such as $x + y = 11$ is called a *linear* equation because its graph is a straight line.

To summarize:

1. If we find any pair of numbers that satisfies the equation, this pair will be the coordinates of a point on the line.

2. If we take any point on the line and find its coordinates, this pair of numbers will satisfy the equation.

We have seen that the graph of the equation $x + y = 11$ is a straight line. If we graph any equation containing only first-degree terms, the result will be a straight line.

A *first-degree term* is any term that contains only one variable raised to the first power. A *second-degree term* is a term that is the product of two variables, either the same or different. For instance, the terms x^2, $5y^2$, and $7xy$ are second-degree terms, since each term contains a variable multiplied by a variable.

A *first-degree equation* is an equation containing only first-degree terms, such as $3x + 2y = 12$.

A *second-degree equation* is an equation containing terms of the second degree, but no higher, such as the following:

$$x^2 + y^2 = 25 \qquad y = x^2 - 3x - 4 \qquad xy = 12$$
$$x^2 - 3xy + 4y^2 - 5x - 3y + 7 = 0$$

A *third-degree equation* is one that contains at least one term of the third degree but no higher, such as the following:

$$y = x^3 \qquad x^3 + y^3 + xy - 4x = 0 \qquad x^2y + 5xy - 7x + 4y = 20$$

The following statement can be shown to be true: *The graph of every first-degree equation is a straight line.*

In finding values and constructing the graph for a linear equation, we should keep several facts in mind:

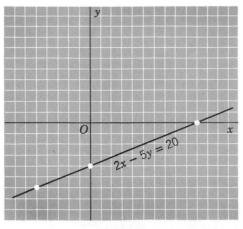

Fig. 17.6

1. Since we know the graph is a straight line, it would be sufficient to find only two points because two points determine a straight line. However, one or two extra points should be plotted as a check on the accuracy of the work.

2. If only two points are used, they should not be too close together. If the two points are some distance apart, the straight line can usually be drawn more accurately.

3. The easiest points to find are those at which the line cuts the x- and the y-axis. These points are easily found by setting each variable equal to zero and solving for the other. First, we set $x = 0$ and solve for y; then we set $y = 0$ and solve for x. However, in some equations, such as in $3x = 2y$, we get $y = 0$ at the same time that $x = 0$. Therefore, we need at least one other point.

4. The straight line should be drawn *through* the points and should not end at any of the points plotted. It should always be understood that the line is infinite in extent and is not limited by the size of the graph or the paper.

Example. Graph the equation $2x - 5y = 20$.

Solution. First find the zero values. If $x = 0$, then $y = -4$. If $y = 0$, $x = 10$. Then other points may be found. For instance, if $x = -5$, $y = -6$. To find any pair of points, take any convenient value for one variable and then compute the value of the other variable. Some values may be fractional. The graph is shown in Fig. 17.6.

Exercise 17.2

Graph the following linear equations. The same graph paper may be used for three or four different equations.

1. $x + 2y = 6$	**2.** $2x - y = 8$	**3.** $2x + 3y = 12$
4. $3x - 2y = 18$	**5.** $4x - 5y = 40$	**6.** $2x + y = 9$
7. $x - 3y = 10$	**8.** $3x + 2y = 15$	**9.** $2x - 5y = 20$
10. $5x - 3y = 20$	**11.** $4x - 7y = 28$	**12.** $3x - 5y = 0$
13. $4x + 3y = 23$	**14.** $3x + 7y = 17$	**15.** $5x - 3y = 16$
16. $7x - 4y = 18$	**17.** $6x + 5y = 20$	**18.** $4x = 3y$
19. $2y = 5x$	**20.** $4x + 2y = 15$	**21.** $x - 3y = 7$
22. $5x - 7y = 21$	**23.** $6x + y = 12$	**24.** $x + 10y = 15$
25. $3x - 8y = 9$	**26.** $5x + 2y = 1$	**27.** $2x - 7y = 5$
28. $3x - 5y = 0$	**29.** $8x + 3y = 4$	**30.** $9x + 7y = 2$

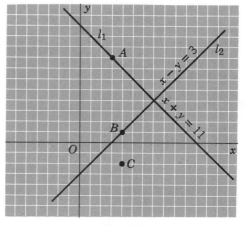

Fig. 17.7

17.4 SOLVING SYSTEMS OF EQUATIONS BY GRAPH

Graphing can be used to solve a system of equations. We have seen that the graph of the equation $x + y = 11$ is a straight line (Fig. 17.5). Let us graph the equation $x - y = 3$ on the same graph. We find several pairs of numbers that satisfy the equation. Some of the pairs are shown in the table at the right. Next, we assume that the two numbers in each ordered pair are the coordinates of a point. We plot the points on the graph and connect them with a line. Again we find that the graph is a straight line (Fig. 17.7).

x	y
10	7
8	5
4	1
0	-3
-2	-5

Figure 17.7 shows the lines for both of the equations:

$$x + y = 11 \qquad \text{and} \qquad x - y = 3$$

In the figure the line l_1 is the graph of the equation $x + y = 11$ and the line l_2 is the graph of the equation $x - y = 3$.

Since point A lies on line$_1$, its coordinates satisfy the equation $x + y = 11$.

Since point B lies on line$_2$, its coordinates satisfy the equation $x - y = 3$. Point C does not lie on either line, and therefore its coordinates will not satisfy either equation.

Only one point has coordinates that will satisfy both equations. That is the point where the two lines intersect. From the graph it appears to be the point whose coordinates are approximately as follows: $x = 7$ and $y = 4$. If we check these values in the equations, we shall find that they satisfy both equations.

These equations, of course, could have been solved by algebraic methods. However, there is sometimes an advantage in the graphical method.

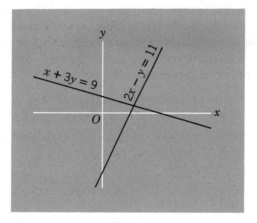

Fig. 17.8

In solving a system of equations, our objective is to find a pair of numbers that will satisfy both equations. To do so by graphing, we draw the graph of each equation. Each graph is a straight line. We know that the straight lines can intersect at only one point, the point that lies on both lines. Therefore, its coordinates must be the pair of values for x and y that satisfy both equations. We illustrate the method by examples.

Example 1. Solve this system of equations by graphing:

$$x + 3y = 9 \qquad 2x - y = 11$$

Solution. We first find pairs of numbers that satisfy each equation. The table of values may be arranged in horizontal form:

$x + 3y = 9$				$2x - y = 11$			
if $x = 0$	9	6	3	if $x =$ 0	$5\frac{1}{2}$	4	2
then $y = 3$	0	1	2	then $y = -11$	0	-3	-7

The graph is shown in Fig. 17.8.

The point of intersection appears to be approximately (6,1). If we check these values in the equations, we find that the values satisfy both equations.

In this example the coordinates of the point of intersection are rather easily determined. However, in many cases it is not easy to read the exact coordinates from the graph. This is especially true when the values are fractions.

If the graphs are made carefully, it is possible to determine fairly accurately the coordinates of the point of intersection even when fractions are involved. However, it should always be remembered that any *answers read from a graph must be assumed to be only approximate*. Therefore, such values may not check exactly when substituted in the equations. The solution of a set of linear equations can be checked by solving by some algebraic method, such as addition, subtraction, substitution, or comparison. If the answers obtained by graphing are the same or nearly the same as those obtained by algebraic methods, then the solution can be considered correct.

Example 2.   Solve the set of equations: $3x + 2y = 12$
$$4x - 5y = 20$$

Solution.   First, we find pairs of numbers that satisfy each equation:

$3x + 2y = 12$					$4x - 5y = 20$			
if $x = 0$	4	6	-4		if $x =$ 0	5	$7\frac{1}{2}$	-5
then $y = 6$	0	-3	12		then $y = -4$	0	2	-8

The graph is shown in Fig. 17.9.

The only pair of values for x and y that will satisfy both equations is the pair for the point of intersection. From the graph, the abscissa of the point appears to be approximately $4\frac{1}{3}$ and the ordinate approximately $-\frac{1}{2}$. Therefore, we have the solution $x = 4\frac{1}{3}$ and $y = -\frac{1}{2}$.

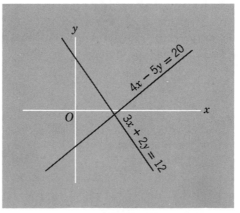

Fig. 17.9

If the equations are solved by algebraic methods, the answers are found to be exactly

$$x = 4\tfrac{8}{23} \qquad y = -\tfrac{12}{23}.$$

If the example calls for a graphical solution, the correct answer is the approximate solution, since it is almost impossible to read a value such as $4\tfrac{8}{23}$ on a graph. However, those answers may be estimated in tenths of a unit.

Exercise 17.3

Solve the following systems graphically:

1. $x + 2y = 10$
   $3x - y = 9$

2. $3x - 5y = 25$
   $4x + 3y = 14$

3. $5x - 2y = 13$
   $3x + 5y = 14$

4. $x - 2y = -4$
   $4x + 3y = 17$

5. $4x - 3y = -9$
   $3x + 2y = -11$

6. $2x + 5y = 20$
   $3x - 2y = 18$

7. $2x + y = -10$
   $x - 3y = -19$

8. $2x + 3y = -5$
   $4x - 5y = 23$

9. $2x + 5y = 24$
   $3x - 2y = -21$

10. $3x - 5y = 30$
    $2x + y = 10$

11. $5x - 6y = 30$
    $3x + y = 12$

12. $2x - 5y = -20$
    $5x + 4y = 2$

13. $4x - 5y = 16$
    $7x - 3y = 5$

14. $4x + 5y = 1$
    $5x + 7y = -1$

15. $6x + 5y = 8$
    $7x + 6y = 10$

16. $5x - 2y = 0$
    $3x + 5y = 0$

17. $4x + 5y = -14$
    $8x - 7y = -28$

18. $3x - 5y = 25$
    $5x - 7y = 35$

19. $4x - 5y = -20$
    $3x + 4y = 0$

20. $5x - 6y = 30$
    $6x - 5y = 15$

21. $8x - 3y = 24$
    $7x - 2y = 14$

Quiz on Chapters 16–17. Form A.

1. Solve this system by addition or subtraction:
$$\begin{cases} 4x - 7y = 6 \\ 5x - 3y = 2 \end{cases}$$

2. Solve by substitution:
$$\begin{cases} 8x - 3y = 13 \\ 5x - y = 3 \end{cases}$$

3. Solve by comparison:
$$\begin{cases} 4x + 3y = 2 \\ 5x - 2y = -6 \end{cases}$$

4. Solve by determinants:
$$\begin{cases} 8x - 5y = 3 \\ 5x - 4y = 6 \end{cases}$$

5. Sketch the graph of the two equations at the right and estimate the coordinates of the point where the lines intersect:
$$\begin{cases} 3x + 2y = 15 \\ 4x - 7y = 28 \end{cases}$$

6. Expand this determinant:
$$\begin{vmatrix} 3 & -1 & -2 \\ 2 & 2 & 3 \\ 3 & -1 & -4 \end{vmatrix}$$

7. Solve the system of three equations at the right by any method:

$$\begin{cases} 5x + 4y + z = 6 \\ 3x + 3y - 2z = 5 \\ 2x - y - z = 9 \end{cases}$$

Solve the following problems by the use of two or more unknowns:

8. A collection of 47 coins consisting of dimes and quarters is worth $7.35. How many coins of each kind are in the collection?

9. A man has $6500 invested, part of it at 4% and the remainder at 7%. If his total annual income is $329, how much has he invested at each rate?

10. How much of a 15% solution and how much of a 50% solution of alcohol should be mixed to form 80 gallons of a solution that is to test 25%?

Quiz on Chapters 16–17. Form B

1. Solve this system by addition or subtraction:

$$\begin{cases} 9x - 4y = 3 \\ 4x - 3y = 7 \end{cases}$$

2. Solve by substitution:

$$\begin{cases} 7x - 3y = 12 \\ 4x - y = 2 \end{cases}$$

3. Solve by comparison:

$$\begin{cases} 3x - 4y = 2 \\ 4x + 5y = -7 \end{cases}$$

4. Solve by determinants:

$$\begin{cases} 5x - 4y = 8 \\ 7x - 3y = 2 \end{cases}$$

5. Sketch the graph of the two equations at the right and estimate the coordinates of the point where the lines intersect:

$$\begin{cases} 3x + 2y = 9 \\ 4x - 5y = 20 \end{cases}$$

6. Expand this determinant:

$$\begin{vmatrix} 2 & 1 & 3 \\ 3 & -2 & -2 \\ 4 & -3 & -1 \end{vmatrix}$$

7. Solve the system of three equations at the right by any method:

$$5x + 6y - z = 6$$
$$4x + 5y - 2z = 7$$
$$3x - y + z = 5$$

Solve the following problems by the use of two or more unknowns:

8. A collection of 59 coins consisting of nickels and quarters is worth $6.35. How many coins of each kind are in the collection?

9. A man had $7200 invested, part of it at 3% and the remainder at 7%. If his income from the two investments is the same, how much has he invested at each rate?

10. How much of a 12% solution and how much of a 40% solution of alcohol should be mixed to form 60 gallons of a solution that is to test 25%?

18
Exponents, Powers, and Roots

18.1 MULTIPLICATION

In Chapter 10 we learned the meaning of an exponent. We also noted the rules to be observed in operations involving exponents. It is necessary at this time to review these rules carefully.

Let us see, again, what happens when we multiply quantities expressed as powers by the use of exponents. Suppose we have the example

$$(x^3)(x^5) =$$

We know that

$$x^3 \text{ means } x \cdot x \cdot x$$

and

$$x^5 \text{ means } x \cdot x \cdot x \cdot x \cdot x$$

Therefore,

$$(x^3)(x^5) \text{ means } (x \cdot x \cdot x)(x \cdot x \cdot x \cdot x \cdot x)$$

Since multiplication can be done in any order,

$$(x^3)(x^5) \text{ means } x \cdot x \cdot x \cdot x \cdot x \cdot x \cdot x \cdot x \qquad \text{or} \qquad x^8$$

that is,

$$(x^3)(x^5) = x^8$$

This example is an illustration of the rule for exponents in multiplication.

Rule 1. *In multiplying quantities expressed with exponents, we add exponents of the same base.*

This rule may be stated as a formula :

$$x^m \cdot x^n = x^{m+n}$$

Note carefully that the rule says, "When we *multiply quantities*, we *add exponents*." In the example

$$(x^3)(x^5) = x^8$$

we are not multiplying the exponents 3 and 5. Instead, we are multiplying the *quantity* x^3 by the *quantity* x^5.

To show that the rule holds true for positive integral exponents, we take the formula $(x^m) \cdot (x^n)$ and analyze its meaning:

$$x^m = x \cdot x \cdots \text{to } m \text{ factors}$$
$$x^n = x \cdot x \cdots \text{to } n \text{ factors}$$

Therefore, $(x^m)(x^n) = (x \cdot x \cdots \text{to } m \text{ factors})(x \cdot x \cdots \text{to } n \text{ factors})$
$$= x \cdot x \cdot x \cdots \text{to } m + n \text{ factors}$$
$$= x^{m+n}$$

It can be shown that the rule holds true also for all types of exponents, such as negative, zero, fractional, and literal. If no exponent is expressed, the exponent is understood to be 1. The rule can be extended to cover the product of several factors expressed as powers on the same base:

$$10^5 \cdot 10^3 \cdot 10 = 10^9$$
$$x^6 \cdot x^4 \cdot x^0 \cdot x^{-7} = x^3$$
$$x^n \cdot x^c \cdot x = x^{n+c+1}$$

The rule may be illustrated with an example involving only arithmetic numbers. Consider the example $(5^2)(5^4)$. By Rule 1, the product is $(5^2)(5^4) = 5^{2+4} = 5^6$. Note that the base does not change.

Now if we expand each power before multiplying, we get the same product. The problem $(5^2)(5^4)$ becomes $(25)(625) = 3125$. The product 3125 can be expressed as 5^6.

In the multiplication $(5^2)(5^4) = 5^6$ we are *not* multiplying the exponents 2 and 4. Instead, we are multiplying the *quantity* 5^2 by the *quantity* 5^4.

Exponents on different bases cannot be added. For instance, in multiplying $(x^2) \cdot (y^4)$, we *cannot* add the exponents. The product can only be *expressed* as $x^2 y^4$.

In an example involving only arithmetic numbers each factor can first be expanded and the results multiplied: thus

$$(3^2)(5^4) = (9)(625) = 5625$$

18.2   DIVISION

Division is the inverse of multiplication. Therefore, we can state the rule for division as the inverse of the rule for multiplication.

Rule 2.   *When we divide two quantities expressed as powers of the same base, we subtract the exponent in the divisor from the exponent in the dividend.*

The rule may be stated as a formula:

$$x^m \div x^n = x^{m-n}$$

Let us see why this rule holds true for an example such as

$$x^7 \div x^4$$

If we write the division as a fraction and then factor each quantity, we have

$$\frac{x^7}{x^4} = \frac{x \cdot x \cdot x \cdot x \cdot x \cdot x \cdot x}{x \cdot x \cdot x \cdot x} = x^3$$

The numerator and the denominator can be divided by x four times, leaving three x's in the numerator to be multiplied together.

Note carefully that the rule says, "When we *divide two quantities*, we *subtract exponents*." In the example shown, we are *not* dividing the exponents 7 and 4. Instead we are *dividing* the *quantity* x^7 by the *quantity* x^4.

To show that the rule holds true for positive integral exponents, we take the formula and analyze its meaning:

$$x^m \div x^n = x^{m-n}$$

$$\frac{x^m}{x^n} = \frac{x \cdot x \cdot x \cdots \text{to } m \text{ factors}}{x \cdot x \cdot x \cdots \text{to } n \text{ factors}} = x \cdot x \cdot x \cdots \text{to } (m-n) \text{ factors}$$

$$= x^{m-n}$$

Assuming that there are not more factors in the denominator than in the numerator, then the factor x can be divided into numerator and denominator n times, leaving only $(m-n)$ factors in the numerator.

It can be shown that the rule holds true also for all types of exponents, such as negative, zero, fractional, and literal. Thus

$$10^8 \div 10^2 = 10^6 \qquad\qquad x^n \div x = x^{n-1}$$
$$x^6 \div x^{-3} = x^9 \qquad\qquad x^{\frac{3}{4}} \div x^{\frac{1}{3}} = x^{\frac{5}{12}}$$
$$x^4 \div x^0 = x^{4-0} = x^4$$

The rule for division may be illustrated with an example involving only arithmetic numbers. Consider the example $3^6 \div 3^2$. By Rule 2, the quotient is $3^6 \div 3^2 = 3^{6-2} = 3^4$. Note that the base does not change.

Now if we expand each power before dividing, we get the same quotient. The problem $3^6 \div 3^2$ becomes $729 \div 9 = 81$. The quotient, 81, can be expressed as 3^4.

In the division $3^6 \div 3^2$ we are *not* dividing the exponents 6 and 2. Instead, we are dividing the *quantity* 3^6 by the *quantity* 3^2.

Exponents on different bases cannot be subtracted. For instance, in the example $x^6 \div y^2$ we *cannot* subtract the exponents. The quotient can only be expressed as $x^6 \div y^2$ or x^6/y^2.

In an example involving only arithmetic numbers the dividend and the divisor can first be expanded. Then the division itself can be performed: thus

$$4^5 \div 3^2 = 1024 \div 9 = 113\tfrac{7}{9}$$

18.3 POWER OF A POWER

The example $(x^4)^3$ may be called a power of a power; that is, the third power of the fourth power of x. We can simplify this expression if we recall the meaning of parentheses. Any algebraic expression enclosed in a set of parentheses is to be considered as a single quantity. Therefore, the expression $(x^4)^3$ means that the quantity x^4 is to be used three times as a factor: $(x^4) \cdot (x^4) \cdot (x^4)$. Now we apply the rule for multiplication:

$$(x^4)(x^4)(x^4) = x^{4+4+4} = x^{12}$$

Therefore, the expression $(x^4)^3$ can be simplified to x^{12}. The new exponent is the product of the two exponents 3 and 4.

Notice the difference between these two expressions and the result of each:

$$(x^3)(x^4) = x^{3+4} = x^7$$

but

$$(x^3)^4 = x^{(3)(4)} = x^{12}$$

In fact, whenever we have a power of a power, the result is equal to the base with an exponent equal to the *product of the powers*.

Rule 3. *In finding a power of a power, we multiply the exponents to get the new exponent on the same base.*

Note that the base remains the same. The rule may be stated as a formula:

$$(x^m)^n = x^{mn}$$

To prove the formula for positive integral exponents, we analyze its meaning.

$$(x^m)^n = x^m \cdot x^m \cdot x^m \cdots \text{to } n \text{ factors}$$
$$= x^{m+m+m \ldots \text{to } n \text{ terms}}$$
$$= x^{mn}$$

The rule holds true for all kinds of exponents. The following examples show its applications:

$$(x^5)^3 = x^{15} \qquad (n^{-\frac{2}{3}})^{\frac{5}{6}} = n^{-\frac{5}{9}}$$
$$(n^6)^{\frac{1}{2}} = n^3 \qquad (x^6)^0 = x^0$$

$$(x^{-3})^4 = x^{-12} \qquad (x^{3.14})^2 = x^{6.28}$$
$$(x^{-2})^{-3} = x^{+6} \qquad [(3^2)^2]^2 = 3^8$$
$$(x^{\frac{2}{3}})^{\frac{4}{5}} = x^{\frac{3}{5}} \qquad (10^{20})^2 = 10^{40}$$

The rule may be illustrated with an example involving only arithmetic numbers. Consider the example $(3^2)^4$. By Rule 3,

$$(3^2)^4 = 3^{2 \cdot 4} = 3^8$$

Now, if we first expand the quantity within parentheses, we get the same answer.

$$(3^2)^4 = (9)^4 = 6561$$

The number 6561 is the same as 3^8.

In the case of continued powers we multiply the several exponents together. As an example,

$$[(2^2)^3]^5 = 2^{(2)(3)(5)} = 2^{30}$$

18.4 POWER OF A PRODUCT

In the expression $(xy)^3$ the exponent 3 indicates that the entire quantity xy within the parentheses is to be raised to the third power; that is, $(xy)^3$ means $(xy)(xy)(xy)$. If we write the expression as separate prime factors, we have

$$(xy)^3 = x \cdot y \cdot x \cdot y \cdot x \cdot y$$
$$= x \cdot x \cdot x \cdot y \cdot y \cdot y$$
$$= x^3 y^3$$

This example is an illustration of the rule for the power of a product of several factors.

Rule 4. *The power of a product of several factors is equivalent to the product of the same power of each of the separate factors.*

The rule may be stated as a formula:

$$(xyz)^n = x^n y^n z^n$$

It may be illustrated with an example involving arithmetic numbers: $(3 \cdot 5)^4$. By Rule 4, $(3 \cdot 5)^4 = 3^4 \cdot 5^4 = (81) \cdot (625) = 50625$.

If we expand the quantity within the parentheses, we get the same answer: $(3 \cdot 5)^4 = (15)^4 = 50625$.

Simplifying an expression often involves several rules in the same problem.

Example 1. Simplify $(5x^2yz^4)^3$.

Solution. The expression, first of all, is a power of a product. The exponent 3 is placed on each of the factors within the parentheses: thus

$$5^3(x^2)^3 y^3 (z^4)^3$$

Now we have examples of a power of a power. In such cases the exponents are multiplied together. The expression becomes

$$125x^6y^3z^{12}$$

Example 2.   Simplify $(3x^{-4}y^5z^{-8})^{-\frac{1}{2}}$.

  Solution. $3^{-\frac{1}{2}}x^2y^{-\frac{5}{2}}z^4$.

If we have the product of several factors, each with separate powers, we must remember that *an exponent applies only to the factor on which it is placed.* For instance, in the expression xy^2 the exponent 2 applies only to the y.
Notice the difference in these values. If $x = 3$ and $y = 5$, then

$$xy^2 = 75, \text{ that is, } 3 \cdot 25 = 75,$$

but

$$(xy)^2 = 225, \text{ that is, } (15)^2 = 225$$

We must be especially careful when negative signs are involved. If $x = 7$, then

$$(-x)^2 = (-7)^2 = +49$$

but

$$-x^2 = -7^2 = -49$$

Also

$$-3^2 = -9 \qquad -(3)^2 = -9$$
$$(-3)^2 = +9 \qquad -(3^2) = -9$$

18.5 POWER OF A FRACTION

In the power of a fraction, such as $(\frac{3}{5})^4$, the expression within the parentheses is to be treated as a single quantity. The exponent 4 applies to the entire fraction; that is,

$$\left(\frac{3}{5}\right)^4 \text{ means } \frac{3}{5} \cdot \frac{3}{5} \cdot \frac{3}{5} \cdot \frac{3}{5}$$

If we now apply the rule for multiplying fractions, we get

$$\frac{3}{5} \cdot \frac{3}{5} \cdot \frac{3}{5} \cdot \frac{3}{5} = \frac{3 \cdot 3 \cdot 3 \cdot 3}{5 \cdot 5 \cdot 5 \cdot 5}$$

The product may be indicated as

$$\frac{3^4}{5^4}$$

In more general terms

$$\left(\frac{x}{y}\right)^3 = \frac{x}{y} \cdot \frac{x}{y} \cdot \frac{x}{y} = \frac{x \cdot x \cdot x}{y \cdot y \cdot y} = \frac{x^3}{y^3}$$

For the power of a fraction we have this rule.

Rule 5. *An exponent placed on a fraction as a quantity indicates that both numerator and denominator are to be raised to the indicated power.*

The rule may be stated as a formula:

$$\left(\frac{x}{y}\right)^n = \frac{x^n}{y^n}$$

Example 1. Simplify $\left(\frac{4x^2 y^4}{5z^5}\right)^3$.

Solution. By the fraction rule, the exponent 3 applies to numerator and denominator. Therefore, we have

$$\left(\frac{4x^2 y^4}{5z^5}\right)^3 = \frac{(4x^2 y^4)^3}{(5z^5)^3}$$

Since the numerator and denominator consist of several factors, the exponent 3 applies to each factor by Rule 4, the product rule. Therefore, we get

$$\frac{(4)^3 (x^2)^3 (y^4)^3}{(5)^3 (z^5)^3}$$

Now, we have powers of other powers. Therefore, we apply Rule 3 for the power of a power and get

$$\frac{64x^6 y^{12}}{125z^{15}}$$

The rules can be applied in a single step.

Example 2. Simplify $\left(\frac{2x^3 y^0 z^{\frac{1}{2}}}{3a^{-4} b^{-2} c^0}\right)^4$.

Solution. Applying several rules at once, we get

$$\left(\frac{2x^3 y^0 z^{\frac{1}{2}}}{3a^{-4} b^{-2} c^0}\right)^4 = \frac{16x^{12} y^0 z^2}{81a^{-16} b^{-8} c^0}$$

Exercise 18.1

Multiply as indicated:

1. $(-7)^3$
2. $(-3)^4$
3. $(\frac{4}{5})^3$
4. $-(-2)^5$
5. $-(-8)^2$
6. $(-\frac{1}{3})^2$

7. $(-0.1)^4$ **8.** $-(0.01)^4$ **9.** $-(-1.01)^3$
10. $(x^6)(x^3)$ **11.** $(y^5)(y)$ **12.** $(a^6)(a^{-2})$
13. $(n^{-3})(n^{-5})$ **14.** $(b)(b^{-4})$ **15.** $(y^2)(y^{-7})$
16. $(x^{3n})(x^{2n})$ **17.** $(b^{4n})(b^3)$ **18.** $(x^a)(x^a)$
19. $(x^{1.3})(x^{2.5})$ **20.** $(x^{\frac{2}{3}})(x^{\frac{4}{5}})$ **21.** $(x^{\frac{2}{3}})(x^{-\frac{1}{2}})$
22. $(x^5)(x^0)$ **23.** $(10^4)(10^3)$ **24.** $(2^{3n})(2)$
25. $(x^n)(x^a)(x)$ **26.** $(y^{5n})(y^t)(y)$ **27.** $(x^2)(x^8)(x^{-3})(x)$
28. $(y^{3.2})(y^{2.1})(y^{-1.3})$ **29.** $(10^6)(10^{-2})(10^0)(10)$ **30.** $(10^{4.153})(10^{1.572})$
31. $(10^{-5})(10^{0.68276})$ **32.** $(y^{3a+2})(y^{2a-5})$ **33.** $(x^{2n-3})(x^{n+3})$
34. $(2)(2^x)(2^5)(2^y)$ **35.** $(10^{2.13})(10^{-1.32})$ **36.** $(3^2)(3^4)(2^3)$

Divide as indicated:

37. $x^8 \div x^2$ **38.** $y^{12} \div y^3$ **39.** $x^2 \div x^{-5}$
40. $n^{-3} \div n^{-7}$ **41.** $x^n \div x$ **42.** $x^5 \div x$
43. $y^5 \div y^0$ **44.** $x^5 \div x^5$ **45.** $n^{25} \div n^5$
46. $x^{3n} \div x^n$ **47.** $y^{6n} \div y^{2n}$ **48.** $x^{4.8} \div x^{1.2}$
49. $z^{5.4} \div z^{2.7}$ **50.** $y \div y^{4.326}$ **51.** $(10^{2.8}) \div (10^{1.53})$
52. $(10^{1.423}) \div (10^{3.817})$ **53.** $(10^{2.45}) \div (10^{-1.62})$ **54.** $(x^{3n-1}) \div (x^{n+4})$
55. $(y^{2m+5}) \div (y^{-m-3})$ **56.** $(x^{a2}) \div (x^a)$ **57.** $(4^5) \div (3^2)$

Find the power as indicated:

58. $(x^5)^4$ **59.** $(-y^3)^5$ **60.** $(n^0)^3$ **61.** $(m^6)^2$
62. $(x^8)^{-\frac{3}{4}}$ **63.** $(x^4)^0$ **64.** $(10^4)^{-3}$ **65.** $(y^{-3})^{-5}$
66. $(x^{-5})^{\frac{1}{5}}$ **67.** $(a^{-6})^{-\frac{2}{3}}$ **68.** $(2^{2x})^x$ **69.** $(5^{3n})^3$
70. $(2^{-3})^{-6}$ **71.** $(x^{\frac{1}{2}})^{10}$ **72.** $(x^{-4})^{-\frac{1}{2}}$ **73.** $(10^{3.156})^2$
74. $(10^{-1.47})^3$ **75.** $(10^{-4})^{1.5}$ **76.** $(10^{-2.7})^{-1.2}$ **77.** $(10^{3.56})^{\frac{1}{2}}$

Simplify each of the following expressions:

78. $(x^2y^3)^4$ **79.** $(-5x^3y^{-1})^4$ **80.** $-(x^3y^4)^4$
81. $(-a^3b^5)^3$ **82.** $(-x^2y^{-3})^3$ **83.** $(3r^2s^{-2}t)^5$
84. $(3x^3)^3$ **85.** $(4n^4)^4$ **86.** $(-5^2a^5)^5$
87. $-(a^0b^3)^4$ **88.** $(3x^2y^{-3})^{-1}$ **89.** $(6a^{-3}b^4c^{-1})^2$
90. $(-2x^3y^2z)^6$ **91.** $(5a^{-3}b^4c^{-1})^3$ **92.** $-(7a^{-3}b^{-1}c^0)^{-2}$
93. $(5n^2)^2(3n^3)^{-4}(4a^4)^2$ **94.** $(-x^3)^4(-2x^3)(-x^2)^3$ **95.** $(5x^5)^2(3x^{-3})(-x^4)^{-2}$
96. $(-x^2)^3(-4y^3)(-x^3y)^4$ **97.** $(4x^4)^2(-x^{-3})^2(x^{-1})$ **98.** $(2x^{-3})^2(-x^2)^2(x^{-2})^3$
99. $(-x^{y2}y^{y3})^6$ **100.** $(a^{\frac{2}{3}}b^{\frac{3}{4}}c^{-\frac{1}{2}})^6$ **101.** $(3^{-1}x^{-\frac{1}{2}}y^{\frac{3}{4}}z^{\frac{1}{4}})^{-6}$
102. $-(-3x^{-\frac{1}{2}}y^{-6})^4$ **103.** $-(-4a^{-\frac{1}{8}}b^{\frac{1}{4}})^3$ **104.** $(x^{\frac{1}{4}}y^{-6}z^{-1})^{-\frac{1}{2}}$

105. $\left(\dfrac{4x^2}{5y^3}\right)^4$ **106.** $\left(\dfrac{5n^2}{7m^4}\right)^3$ **107.** $\left(\dfrac{3a^{-2}}{4b^5}\right)^3$

108. $\left(\dfrac{2n^{\frac{1}{2}}}{y^{\frac{4}{3}}}\right)^6$ **109.** $\left(\dfrac{x^2y^3}{a^4b^{-1}}\right)^4$ **110.** $\left(\dfrac{x^{-\frac{1}{3}}}{y^{-\frac{1}{2}}}\right)^6$

111. $\left(\dfrac{x^4}{y^5}\right)^{\frac{1}{2}}$ **112.** $\left(\dfrac{3x^2y^3}{4a^{\frac{3}{2}}}\right)^2$ **113.** $\left(\dfrac{2x^{-2}y^3}{3a^4b^{-1}}\right)^5$

114. $\left(\dfrac{x^0y^4z^2}{a^6b^8c^4}\right)^{\frac{1}{2}}$ **115.** $\left(\dfrac{x^6y^3z^2t}{ab^2c^3}\right)^4$ **116.** $\left(\dfrac{x^{-4}y^{-3}z^0}{x^0y^0z^{-3}}\right)^{-2}$

18.6 ZERO EXPONENT

In mathematics it often happens that we get a zero exponent, as in the terms x^0, $5x^0$, 7^0, and 10^0. Such expressions must be given some logical meaning.

Whenever an unusual expression forces itself into mathematics, we try to give it some reasonable and logical interpretation. At first sight some expressions appear to be illogical and meaningless. It was the same with negative numbers and with irrational numbers. We have mentioned the fact that when negative numbers forced themselves into mathematics people discarded them as "fictitious."

Now, when we try to explain the meaning of a zero exponent, as we explain other exponents, we run into trouble.

We have said that when we write the expression 5^3 the exponent 3 means that three 5's are to be multiplied together. In other words,

$$5^3 \text{ means } (5)(5)(5) \qquad 5^1 \text{ means } (5)$$
$$5^2 \text{ means } (5)(5) \qquad 5^0 \text{ means } \underline{\quad ? \quad}$$

An exponent, such as 3, means that we write down three 5's and multiply them together. The same meaning is given to other positive integral exponents. But how are we going to write down *no* 5's and multiply them together? If we try to explain that the zero (0) tells how many 5's to use as factors, the idea does not make sense. We might be inclined to say that the entire quantity is equal to zero. But we shall see that this is not correct.

The fact is that we cannot interpret a zero exponent in the same way we interpret other exponents. Yet we must give it some meaning. We *cannot* get at a correct meaning by the direct approach used with other exponents. We must get at the meaning in a roundabout way.

As a student, you should realize that in mathematics we do not deliberately set out to produce riddles or enigmas or concepts that are confusing. However, whenever a confusing or unusual idea forces itself into mathematics, such as a negative number or a zero exponent, the new idea must be given some logical interpretation. To get some meaning into the expression x^0, let us see how it comes about.

Suppose we have the division problem

$$x^5 \div x^5$$

Now, we know that the rule for division involving terms with exponents on the same base is shown by the formula $x^m \div x^n = x^{m-n}$; that is, when we divide quantities expressed as powers on the same base we subtract the exponents. Let us do the same with $x^5 \div x^5$. We get

$$x^5 \div x^5 = x^{5-5} = x^0$$

Whether we like it or not, the division results in x^0.

Now let us see what happens if we write the problem in a different form. The division can be written as a fraction:

$$\frac{x^5}{x^5}$$

This fraction reduces to 1. We know that any number divided by itself is 1. In whatever way we express the division, we get 1 for a quotient. Yet, when we use the rule for exponents in division of quantities, we get $x^5 \div x^5 = x^0$. Therefore, we must conclude that the two answers are equal to each other and

$$x^0 \text{ must be equal to } 1$$

Whatever example we use as an illustration, the answer always turns out to be 1. This means that if we have a zero exponent on any base (except 0) the *entire quantity* is equal to 1. Examples:

$$(3x)^0 = 1 \qquad (4x^2y^3)^0 = 1 \qquad (a^2 - 3ab - 5b^2)^0 = 1$$

However,

$$3x^0 = 3(1) = 3$$

Concerning a zero exponent, we have the following rule:

Rule 6.   *Any quantity (except 0) expressed with a zero exponent is equal to 1.*

This meaning of a zero exponent is consistent with the rule for exponents in multiplication. For instance

$$x^6 \cdot x^0 = x^{6+0} = x^6$$

By the rule in multiplication, the exponent in the product is $6 + 0 = 6$. If we remember that $x^0 = 1$, we see that $x^6 \cdot x^0 = x^6 \cdot 1 = x^6$.

18.7   NEGATIVE EXPONENT

In mathematics we sometimes get an expression with a negative exponent, such as 5^{-2}. Just as in the case of a zero exponent, a negative exponent must have some particular meaning. If we try to explain the meaning of a negative exponent as we explain the meaning of positive integral exponents, we again run into difficulty.

We have seen that the exponent 3 means that the base is to be used three times as a factor, as in $5^3 = (5)(5)(5)$. In the case of 5^0 we have seen that we cannot write down *no* 5's to represent 5^0. It is equally impossible to try to write out the meaning of 5^{-3} by writing down *minus* three 5's. We cannot write down a *negative* number of 5's, such as 3 less than *no* 5's.

Yet when an expression such as 5^{-3} does occur in mathematical computation, it must be given some logical meaning. Just as with a zero exponent, we can get some interpretation of its meaning by noting how a negative exponent comes about.

In the division of quantities expressed with exponents on the same base we have the rule that the exponents are subtracted; that is,

$$x^7 \div x^3 = x^4$$

By observing this rule carefully, we sometimes get negative exponents:

$$x^2 \div x^5 = x^{2-5} = x^{-3}$$

Now, if we write the division as a fraction and reduce, we get

$$\frac{x^2}{x^5} = \frac{x \cdot x}{x \cdot x \cdot x \cdot x \cdot x} = \frac{1}{x^3}$$

Therefore, we must conclude that

$$x^{-3} = \frac{1}{x^3}$$

This example is an illustration of the following rule:

Rule 7. *Any quantity with a negative exponent may be written as the reciprocal of the quantity with a positive exponent.*

The rule may be restated:

Any factor in the numerator of a fraction may be transferred to the denominator provided the sign of its exponent is changed; any factor in the denominator may be transferred to the numerator provided the sign of its exponent is changed.

Warning. Separate terms of polynomial numerators or denominators may *not* be shifted in this fashion. The rule says *factor*, not term.

As an example of the use of Rule 7, consider the following expression:

Example 1. $\dfrac{a^{-1}b^2}{x^3y^{-4}}$

In this expression the factor a^{-1} may be transferred to the denominator and the factor y^{-4} may be transferred to the numerator provided the signs of the exponents in these factors are changed: thus

$$\frac{a^{-1}b^2}{x^3y^{-4}} = \frac{b^2y^4}{ax^3}$$

The expression may also be written in a form in which the denominator is 1 by transferring all the terms to the numerator: thus

$$\frac{a^{-1}b^2}{x^3y^{-4}} = \frac{a^{-1}b^2x^{-3}y^4}{1} = a^{-1}b^2x^{-3}y^4$$

Example 2. Note especially the difference between the following two examples:

$$(A)\ \frac{a}{b^{-2}c^{-2}} \qquad (B)\ \frac{a}{b^{-2}+c^{-2}}$$

In Example A the two quantities, b^{-2} and c^{-2}, in the denominators are factors. Therefore, they can be transferred to the numerator if the signs of their exponents are changed. However, notice the difference in Example B, in which the denominator consists of two separate *terms*. These terms cannot be moved to the numerator because the denominator is an indicated *sum*. Example A can be changed to ab^2c^2. However, Example B is simplified as follows:

$$\frac{a}{b^{-2}+c^{-2}} = \frac{a}{\dfrac{1}{b^2}+\dfrac{1}{c^2}} = \frac{a}{\dfrac{c^2+b^2}{b^2c^2}} = \frac{ab^2c^2}{c^2+b^2}$$

A somewhat simpler method of simplifying Example B is to multiply the numerator and the denominator of the original fraction by the quantity b^2c^2. We get the simplified form in one step:

$$\frac{b^2c^2)}{b^2c^2)} \cdot \frac{a}{b^{-2}+c^{-2}} = \frac{ab^2c^2}{c^2+b^2}$$

Exercise 18.2

Simplify each of the following expressions as much as possible.

1. 3^0
2. $-x^0$
3. $(5y)^0$
4. $5x^0$
5. -3^0
6. $-(5x)^0$
7. $(8x^2y^3)^0$
8. $3(x+4)^0$
9. $(3x+4)^0$
10. $-(y^2-4)^0$
11. $8(x^2y^3)^0$
12. $-7^0x^0y^0$
13. $-3a^0b^0$
14. $-(-4x)^0$
15. $(4)(3^0)(x^0)$
16. $(-4)^0(-2)^0(-n)^0$
17. $-(3y^2+2x)^0$
18. $-6(x^2-5^0)^0$

19. $\dfrac{5x^0}{10y^0}$
20. $\dfrac{12n^0}{-3n^0}$
21. $\dfrac{-5x^0}{(-5x)^0}$

22. $\dfrac{8y^0}{-2(3x)^0}$
23. $\dfrac{(8x^0)(5y^0)}{4(2xy)^0}$
24. $\dfrac{3x^0+5n^0}{2y^0}$

25. $\dfrac{m^0+5n^0}{3-(3x)^0}$
26. $\dfrac{3n^0+5y^0}{(3n)^0+(5y^0)}$
27. $\dfrac{(6x)^0-9x^0}{4x^0-(7x)^0}$

28. $\dfrac{(5x)^0+15n^0-4y^0}{7a^0+(7b)^0}$
29. 7^{3x^0}
30. $(4x^2-5x+3)^0$

Express each of the following without negative exponents:

31. x^{-4}

34. $a^{-3}b^4c^{-2}$

37. $h^{-2}k^{-3}x^4$

40. $\dfrac{1}{5x^{-2}y}$

43. $\dfrac{x^{-4}y^3z}{-ab^{-1}c^2}$

46. $\dfrac{5^{-2}a^{-3}b^0}{-3^2x^{-1}y}$

49. $\dfrac{a-b}{a^{-1}-b^{-1}}$

52. $\dfrac{a^{-3}-b^{-3}}{a^{-1}-b^{-1}}$

55. $\dfrac{x^{-3}-y^{-3}}{x^{-4}-y^{-4}}$

32. $x^{-5}y^{-3}$

35. $a^5b^{-4}c^{-1}d$

38. $2^{-1}a^2b^{-5}c^3$

41. $\dfrac{1}{-3^2ab^3c^{-1}}$

44. $\dfrac{5x^{-3}y^2z^{-1}}{2ab^{-4}c^3}$

47. $\dfrac{1}{-3ab^4x^3}$

50. $\dfrac{x^{-2}-y^{-2}}{x^{-1}y^{-1}}$

53. $\dfrac{a^{-2}-b^{-2}}{a^{-3}+b^{-3}}$

56. $\dfrac{x^{-2}-y^{-2}}{x^{-4}-y^{-4}}$

33. $-x^{-3}y^2z^{-1}$

36. $m^{-4}x^{-1}y^2z^3$

39. $5^{-2}x^{-1}y^3z^{-4}$

42. $\dfrac{-3^{-2}x^{-3}y^{-1}}{4^{-1}a^{-2}b}$

45. $\dfrac{3^{-1}x^3y^{-4}z}{2^{-2}a^2b^3c^{-1}}$

48. $\dfrac{1}{a^{-1}-b^{-1}}$

51. $\dfrac{x^{-2}-y^{-2}}{x^{-1}+y^{-1}}$

54. $\dfrac{x^{-4}-y^{-4}}{x^{-1}+y^{-1}}$

57. $\dfrac{x^{-6}-y^{-6}}{x^{-2}-y^{-2}}$

58–66. Write each of the expressions, Nos. 40–48, with no expressed denominator; that is, with a denominator of $+1$ understood.

Evaluate each of the following expressions:

67. 5^{-3}

70. $(-0.1)^{-4}$

73. $5^{-2}-2^{-3}$

76. $50^{-1}+40^{-1}+30^{-1}$

79. $\dfrac{1}{4^{-2}+2^{-3}}$

82. $\dfrac{3^{-2}-5^{-2}}{3^{-1}+5^{-1}}$

68. $9^{-0.5}$

71. $(4^{-3})(6^2)$

74. $(5^{-2})(0.4)^{-1}$

77. $2^{-3}+3^{-2}-6^{-1}$

80. $\dfrac{1}{3^{-2}+5^0}$

83. $\dfrac{4^{-1}+3^{-1}}{4^{-3}+3^{-3}}$

69. $(1.5)^{-2}$

72. $4^{-2}+3^{-2}$

75. $(3^{-1})(4^{-2})(6^0)$

78. $(4^{-2}+2^{-3})^{-2}$

81. $\dfrac{3^{-2}+2^0}{2^{-3}+3^0}$

84. $\dfrac{5^{-2}-4^{-2}}{5^{-2}4^{-2}}$

Find the numerical value of each of the following expressions if $a = 3$, $b = 2$, and $x = -2$:

85. a^2

89. x^2

93. $(ax)^2$

97. $(-x)^2$

101. $-x^4$

105. $-abx^2$

109. $-abx^3$

113. $\dfrac{3a^0x^2}{10a^3x^0}$

86. $-a^2$

90. $-x^2$

94. $-(ax)^2$

98. x^3

102. $(-x)^4$

106. a^2bx^3

110. $a^{-2}x^{-1}$

114. $\dfrac{4a^2x}{9a^0b^{-1}}$

87. $(-a)^2$

91. ax^2

95. $-(ab)^2$

99. $(ax)^3$

103. bx^3

107. $-a^2bx$

111. $a^{-1}+b^{-1}$

115. $\dfrac{ax^3b}{a^{-1}x^0b^{-1}}$

88. $-(a)^2$

92. $-ax^2$

96. $(-ab)^2$

100. x^4

104. $(abx)^2$

108. $-(ax)^2b$

112. $(ax)^{-1}+b$

116. $\dfrac{1}{a^{-1}+b^{-1}}$

18.8 ROOTS OF NUMBERS

Before explaining a fractional exponent, we must mention briefly the meaning of a root of a number. A *root* of a given number is a number that can be raised to a specified power to produce the given number. For instance since 5 raised to the second power is 25, then 5 is a root of 25. Since 3 raised to the fourth power is 81, then 3 is a root of 81. The indicated root of a number is called a *radical*. Operations with radicals are fully explained in Chapter 19.

A root of a number may be defined as one of its equal factors. The *square root* of a number is one of the *two* equal factors of the number. For example the square root of 169 is 13 because 169 is equal to the product of the two factors, 13 and 13. The square root of 400 is 20 because $400 = (20)(20)$.

The *cube root* of a number is one of the *three* equal factors of the number. The cube root of 512 is 8 simply because $512 = (8)(8)(8)$. The *fourth root* of a number is one of the *four* equal factors of the number. Since $81 = (3)(3)(3)(3)$, then the fourth root of 81 is 3.

The symbol for a root is the *radical sign* ($\sqrt{}$). This symbol indicates that a root is to be found. The number under the radical sign is the number of which the root is to be found and is called the *radicand*. The particular root to be found is indicated by a small number placed in the notch of the radical sign. This number is called the *index* of the root. (It is sometimes called the *index of the radical*.) Thus, the expression

$$\sqrt[3]{64}$$

means that the cube root of 64 is to be found. The entire expression is called a *radical*. In this example the radicand is 64 and the index is 3. The cube root of 64 is 4 because 4 is one of the three equal factors of 64. Therefore, we can say

$$\sqrt[3]{64} = 4$$

For the square root of a number, the index "2" is usually omitted because this root is found most frequently. If the index of the root is not shown, then the square root is meant. Thus

$$\sqrt{81} = 9$$

The following examples are illustrations of roots of numbers:

$$\sqrt{361} = 19 \qquad \sqrt[5]{32} = 2 \qquad \sqrt{9x^2} = 3x$$
$$\sqrt[3]{125} = 5 \qquad \sqrt[4]{10,000} = 10 \qquad \sqrt[3]{8x^6} = 2x^2$$

8.9 FRACTIONAL EXPONENTS

Whether we like it or not, we sometimes get a fractional exponent such as $5^{\frac{1}{2}}$. When this happens, the expression must be given some meaning. First, we must remember that the expression does *not* mean $\frac{1}{2}$ of 5, which is $2\frac{1}{2}$. If we take $\frac{1}{2}$ of 5, then the "$\frac{1}{2}$" is a factor, not a power. Our problem here is to determine the meaning of the expression in which the "$\frac{1}{2}$" is the exponent of a power, as in $5^{\frac{1}{2}}$.

If we try to explain the meaning by saying that an exponent shows the number of times the base is used as a factor, then the expression has no meaning. We have seen that we cannot write zero 5's or a negative number of 5's to be multiplied together. Neither can we write a fractional number of 5's to be multiplied. Again, we must get at the meaning of a fractional exponent in another way. Let us see what meaning can be given to this kind of exponent. Consider the following example. Since

$$(17)(17) = 289$$

then

$$17 = \sqrt{289}$$

That is, if two equal factors are multiplied to form a product, one of these factors is the square root of the product. Now, we recall that when we multiply powers of the same base we add the exponents. Then

$$(x^{\frac{1}{2}})(x^{\frac{1}{2}}) = x^{\frac{1}{2}+\frac{1}{2}} = x$$

Here we have two equal factors whose product is x. One of the factors, $x^{\frac{1}{2}}$, must be the square root of x; that is,

$$x^{\frac{1}{2}} = \sqrt{x}$$

Therefore, we can say that *the fractional exponent, $\frac{1}{2}$, means the same as the square root of the base*. Here are two examples:

$$64^{\frac{1}{2}} = \sqrt{64} = 8 \qquad 5^{\frac{1}{2}} = \sqrt{5} = 2.236 \text{ (approx.)}$$

For the exponent $\frac{1}{3}$ we can get a meaning in the same way. Since

$$(7)(7)(7) = 343$$

then

$$7 = \sqrt[3]{343}$$

That is, if three equal factors are multiplied to form a product, one of these factors is the cube root of the product. By the rule for the multiplication of powers of the same base, we have

$$(x^{\frac{1}{3}})(x^{\frac{1}{3}})(x^{\frac{1}{3}}) = x^{\frac{1}{3}+\frac{1}{3}+\frac{1}{3}} = x$$

Here we have three equal factors whose product is x. One of the factors, $x^{\frac{1}{3}}$, must be the cube root of x; that is,

$$x^{\frac{1}{3}} = \sqrt[3]{x}$$

Therefore, we can say that *the fractional exponent* $\frac{1}{3}$ *means the same as the cube root of the base.* The fractional exponents, $\frac{1}{4}$, $\frac{1}{5}$, etc., have similar meanings. Here are some examples showing the meaning of such exponents.

$$8^{\frac{1}{3}} = \sqrt[3]{8} = 2 \qquad\qquad 64^{\frac{1}{3}} = \sqrt[3]{64} = 4$$
$$16^{\frac{1}{4}} = \sqrt[4]{16} = 2 \qquad (100,000)^{\frac{1}{5}} = \sqrt[5]{100,000} = 10$$

Finally, let us consider the meaning of the exponent $\frac{2}{3}$, in which the numerator is different from 1. The meaning of such an exponent can be explained in the same way as in the previous examples. By the rule for the multiplication of powers of the same base, we have

$$(x^{\frac{2}{3}})(x^{\frac{2}{3}})x^{\frac{2}{3}}) = x^{\frac{6}{3}} = x^2$$

Here, again, we have three equal factors whose product is x^2. Therefore, one of the factors, $x^{\frac{2}{3}}$, must be the cube root of x^2, that is,

$$x^{\frac{2}{3}} = \sqrt[3]{x^2}$$

This final example is an illustration of the general rule for the meaning of fractional exponents:

Rule 8. *In a fractional exponent, such as p/r, the numerator, p, of the exponent, indicates a power, and the denominator, r, indicates a root.*

The rule may be stated as a formula.

$$N^{p/r} = \sqrt[r]{N^p}$$

That is, a number, N, raised to the p/r power is equal to the rth root of the pth power of N.

Example 1. Find the value of $8^{\frac{2}{3}}$.

The expression $8^{\frac{2}{3}}$ means the cube root of 8^2, or $\sqrt[3]{64}$, which is 4. The expression can also be simplified as the square of the cube root of 8; that is, we can first find the cube root of 8, which is 2. This value can be squared. The result, 4, is the same as in the first method.

In an example of this kind either process may be performed first. We may start out with the power or the root. If the value is rational, then the root should always be found first.

Example 2. Find the value of $125^{\frac{2}{3}}$.

The expression $125^{\frac{2}{3}}$ is the same as $(125^{\frac{1}{3}})^2$ or $(125^2)^{\frac{1}{3}}$, that is, we may first find the cube root of 125 and then square this value; or we may first square 125 and then find the cube root of 125^2.

If we find the root first, we have

$$125^{\frac{1}{3}} = \sqrt[3]{125} = 5$$

Then we square 5 and get

$$5^2 = 25$$

If we find the power first, we have

$$125^2 = 15,625$$

Then we find the cube root and get

$$(15,625)^{\frac{1}{3}} = \sqrt[3]{15,625} = 25$$

The answer is the same in both cases. However, the procedure is often simpler when the root is found first.

Example 3. Find the value of $7^{\frac{3}{2}}$.

In this example, if we first find the square root of 7, we get the approximate value 2.646. This number must be raised to the third power. In this instance it is easier to find the third power first and then find the square root of the result. Thus

$$7^3 = 343$$

then

$$\sqrt{343} = 18.52 \text{ (approx.)}$$

Exercise 18.3

Express the following with fractional exponents:

1. $\sqrt{a}$ **2.** $\sqrt{ab}$ **3.** $\sqrt{29}$

4. $\sqrt[3]{343}$ **5.** $\sqrt{x^2 + y^2}$ **6.** $\sqrt[4]{x^3 + y^2}$

7. $\sqrt[5]{x^3 + 5}$ **8.** $\sqrt[3]{(x^2 y^2)}$ **9.** $\sqrt{(x^3 - 8)^3}$

10. $\sqrt{a^2 - b^2}$ **11.** $\sqrt{x^2 - a^2}$ **12.** $\sqrt[4]{x^3 y z^2}$

Evaluate each of the following expressions:

13. $16^{\frac{1}{2}}$ **14.** $81^{\frac{3}{4}}$ **15.** $27^{\frac{2}{3}}$

16. $16^{\frac{3}{4}}$ **17.** $32^{\frac{1}{5}}$ **18.** $(4/9)^{\frac{1}{2}}$

19. $(25/49)^{\frac{1}{2}}$ **20.** $(9/25)^{\frac{3}{2}}$ **21.** $(-8)^{\frac{1}{3}}$

22. $(.01)^{\frac{1}{2}}$ **23.** $8^{\frac{2}{3}}$ **24.** $4^{\frac{3}{2}}$

25. $9^{\frac{3}{2}}$ **26.** $32^{\frac{3}{5}}$ **27.** $16^{-\frac{1}{4}}$

28. $125^{-\frac{2}{3}}$ **29.** $64^{-\frac{1}{2}}$ **30.** $(-32)^{\frac{3}{5}}$

31. $-(32)^{\frac{4}{5}}$ **32.** $(512)^{\frac{2}{3}}$ **33.** $(4^2)(3^2)^{\frac{1}{2}}$

34. $(4^2 + 3^2)^{\frac{1}{2}}$ **35.** $(3^2 + 4^2)^{-\frac{1}{2}}$ **36.** $(5^2 + 12^2)^{\frac{1}{2}}$
37. $(6^2 + 8^2)^{\frac{1}{2}}$ **38.** $(15^2 + 8^2)^{\frac{1}{2}}$ **39.** $(3^3 - 2)^{\frac{1}{2}}$
40. $(11^2 + 4)^{\frac{3}{2}}$ **41.** $4(25)^{\frac{3}{2}}(4)^{\frac{3}{2}}$ **42.** $(12^2 + 16^2)^{\frac{3}{2}}$

Exercise 18.4 (Review)

Simplify the following expressions:

1. $x^0 =$ **2.** $3x^0 =$ **3.** $(25)^{\frac{1}{2}} =$
4. $8^{\frac{1}{3}} =$ **5.** $9^{-\frac{1}{2}} =$ **6.** $7^{-2} =$
7. $9^{\frac{3}{2}} =$ **8.** $5^2 x^0 =$ **9.** $-5^2 =$
10. $9^0 x^0 =$ **11.** $(3x^2 y)^0 =$ **12.** $6^0 \cdot 6^2 =$
13. $3 \cdot 2^3 \cdot 5^0$ **14.** $(7^2)(x^0)(y^0)$ **15.** $(5x^3 y^2)^0$
16. $4(x^2 + 3^2)^0$ **17.** $x^n \div x^{3n}$ **18.** $x^n \div x$
19. $2^n \cdot 2$ **20.** $h \cdot h^{2n-3}$ **21.** $x^{2n} \cdot y^{3n}$
22. $(a^2)^{-3}$ **23.** $(x^5)^{-\frac{2}{5}}$ **24.** $8^{-\frac{4}{3}}$

25. $\dfrac{1}{3x^0}$ **26.** $\dfrac{5x^0 y^0}{2^3 4^0 6^0}$ **27.** $\left(\dfrac{-2x^2}{3a^0}\right)^3$

28. $\left(\dfrac{6^0 x^3 y^{-2}}{3x^2 y^{-2}}\right)^2$ **29.** $\dfrac{(8^{\frac{1}{3}})^6}{9^{\frac{1}{2}}}$ **30.** $\dfrac{(125)^{\frac{2}{3}}}{10^2}$

31. $\dfrac{(32)^{\frac{2}{5}}}{8^0}$ **32.** $\dfrac{(64)^{\frac{2}{3}}}{(9 + 16)^{\frac{1}{2}}}$

Simplify and write without negative exponents:

33. y^{-2} **34.** $3x^{-4}$
35. $(3x)^{-4}$ **36.** $4^{-1} x^2 y^{-1}$
37. $3^2 x^{-3} y^4$ **38.** $5(2^{-1})(x^2)$

39. $\dfrac{3xa^{-2} b^3}{2^{-1} x^{-3} a}$ **40.** $\dfrac{2^{-3} a^{-2} x^{-1}}{5^2 a^{-2} y^3 x^4}$

41. $\dfrac{5^{-2} abc^{-1}}{3^{-4} x^{-2} y^3 z^{-1}}$ **42.** $\left(\dfrac{(-2x^{\frac{1}{2}})y^{-3} z^{-1}}{3^{-1} x^2 y^4 z^{-\frac{1}{3}}}\right)^3$

43. $\left(\dfrac{(3)^0 (a^{-2})(b^{-\frac{1}{3}})(c^{\frac{1}{2}})}{2^{-1} x^2 (y^{\frac{1}{2}}) z^{-3}}\right)^{-3}$ **44.** $\left(\dfrac{(4)x^2 y^3 (z^{\frac{3}{4}})}{(9^{\frac{1}{2}}) a^4 b^5 (c^{\frac{3}{4}})}\right)^{\frac{1}{2}}$

18.10   SCIENTIFIC NOTATION

In scientific work we often use numbers that are very large or very small. If such numbers are written in the usual way, they are sometimes awkward to use in computation. For instance, the number of electrons in one coulomb is approximately 6,280,000,000,000,000,000. The wavelength of yellow light is approximately 0.000023 inch. Such numbers are often written in a form called *scientific notation.*

A number is expressed in scientific notation in the following manner. Consider the number 93,200,000. In order to express this number in scientific notation, we first place the decimal point just to the right of the first significant digit. The first significant digit in a number is the first number that is not zero, starting at the left. In the number 93,200,000 the first significant digit is 9. Therefore, the decimal point is placed between the 9 and the 3: thus
$$9.32$$

This position is called the *standard position* of the decimal point.

Now this number, 9.32, is multiplied by a power of 10 that will make the value equal to the original value. The correct power of 10 to be used is determined by counting the number of places *from standard position* to the decimal point in the original number. In the number 93,200,000 the decimal point is understood to be at the right of the number, since it is a whole number. From the standard position, between 9 and 3, we count seven places to the *right* to the decimal point in the original number.

$$9\,3,2\,0\,0,0\,0\,0.$$
$$\uparrow$$
standard
position

The power of 10 to be used in this example is therefore 7. Written in scientific notation,
$$93,200,000 = (9.32)(10^7)$$

In order to see that the value of the original number is not changed, let us perform the multiplication $(9.32)(10^7)$. The expression means $(9.32)(10000000)$. Multiplying, we get 93,200,000.00. The value of the original number has not been changed.

In the case of a decimal fraction the number can be written in a similar manner. However, the power of 10 will be negative. For instance, consider the number 0.00000327. The first significant digit in this number is 3. Therefore, the standard position of the decimal point is between the 3 and the 2; thus
$$3.27$$

Now we count the number of places from the standard position to the decimal point in the original number. Notice that, in counting, we move to the *left* instead of the right. The decimal point is six places to the left from standard position

$$0.00000327$$
$$\uparrow$$
standard
position

Therefore, we multiply the number 3.27 by 10^{-6}. Writing the number in scientific notation, we have

$$0.00000327 = (3.27)(10^{-6})$$

In order to see that the value of the original number is not changed, let us perform the multiplication $(3.27)(10^{-6})$. The expression means

$$(3.27)\frac{1}{10^6} = \frac{3.27}{1000000}$$

To simplify the result, we multiply both numerator and denominator by 100. The result is

$$\frac{327}{100000000}$$

which is equal to 0.00000327.

The advantage of scientific notation is most evident in connection with extremely large or extremely small numbers. However, any number, no matter what its size may be, can be written in this form.

The number 25 can be written $(2.5)(10^1)$ or simply $(2.5)(10)$.

The number 7.2 can be written $(7.2)(10^0)$, which is $(7.2)(1)$.

The number 0.38 can be written $(3.8)(10^{-1})$.

When a slide rule is used for computation, it is especially desirable to express all numbers in scientific notation. Another advantage, aside from its advantage in any form of computation, is that extremely large or extremely small numbers may be more easily compared when written in this form. For example, it is difficult at first glance to tell which of the following numbers is the larger:

$$870000000000000000 \quad \text{or} \quad 63000000000000000000$$

However, if these numbers are written in scientific notation, the larger one can be identified at a glance:

$$870000000000000000 = (8.7)(10^{17})$$
$$63000000000000000000 = (6.3)(10^{19})$$

The following examples show numbers written in scientific notation:

$$5423000000 = (5.423)(10^9)$$
$$165.4 = (1.654)(10^2)$$
$$0.00000007328 = (7.328)(10^{-8})$$
$$1000000000000000 = (1)(10^{15}) = 10^{15}$$
$$0.000000000000000000000001 = (1)(10^{-24}) = 10^{-24}$$
$$0.000000000006 = (6.)(10^{-12})$$

Scientific notation is convenient for stating the relations between metric measurements. For example,

1 meter = 10 decimeters,	then	1 decimeter = 10^{-1} meter
1 meter = 10^2 centimeters,		1 centimeter = 10^{-2} meter
1 meter = 10^3 millimeters,		1 millimeter = 10^{-3} meter
1 meter = 10^6 microns,		1 micron = 10^{-6} meter
1 meter = 10^9 millimicrons,		1 millimicron = 10^{-9} meter
1 meter = 10^{12} micromicrons,		1 micromicron = 10^{-12} meter

For larger units we have the following:

1 dekameter = 10 meters,	1 meter = 10^{-1} dekameter
1 hectometer = 10^2 meters,	1 meter = 10^{-2} hectometer
1 kilometer = 10^3 meters,	1 meter = 10^{-3} kilometer
1 kilometer = 10^6 millimeters,	1 millimeter = 10^{-6} kilometer

Note. One *micron* is the name given to one-millionth of a meter. One-billionth of a meter is called a *nanometer*. One-trillionth of a meter is called a *picometer*. Then we have

1 meter = 10^9 nanometers	and	1 nanometer = 10^{-9} meter
1 meter = 10^{12} picometers	and	1 picometer = 10^{-12} meter

Exercise 18.5

Write the number in each of the following examples in scientific notation:

1. The sun is about 93,000,000 miles from the earth.
2. Light travels about 186,200 miles per second.
3. The wavelength of red light is approximately 0.00063 millimeter.
4. The length of a wave of yellow light is about 0.0000228 inch.
5. One angstrom unit is a measurement equal to one ten-millionth of a millimeter.
6. An atom weighs about 0.0000000000000000000000166 gram.
7. An atom is approximately 0.000000005 inch in diameter.
8. A certain radio station broadcasts at a frequency of 1260000 cycles per second.

9. The population of the United States in 1960 was about 180,000,000.
10. For the construction of Hoover Dam, about 4,400,000 cubic yards of material were required.
11. The capacity of Lake Mead formed by Hoover Dam is 9,720,000,000,000 gallons.
12. Light travels about 5,872,000,000,000 miles in 1 year.

19
Radicals

19.1 SQUARE ROOTS

In much work in algebra, as in arithmetic, we are faced with problems involving radicals, chiefly square roots. In our work in arithmetic we have already found the square roots of arithmetic numbers. For instance, if a square floor has an area of 169 square feet, the length of one side is found by taking the square root of 169, which is 13. We have usually written the problem

$$\sqrt{169} = 13$$

To consider a problem in geometry, suppose the two legs of a right triangle are 21 and 28 inches long, respectively. The hypotenuse is found by means of the Pythagorean rule. This involves finding the square root of a number. We find

$$28^2 + 21^2 = 1225$$

Then we find that

$$\sqrt{1225} = 35$$

In some actual problems, such as those given here, we do not consider negative values. It would be meaningless to say the side of a square is -13 feet or that the hypotenuse is -35 inches long. We cannot measure the length of a line in *negative* inches.

Yet, as we proceed in the study of mathematics, we find that negative numbers force themselves more and more into the solution of problems. We have seen that negative numbers often appear as the roots of simple equations, such as

$$5 - 3x = 17$$

Solving,

$$x = -4$$

Negative numbers also appear as the square roots of numbers. In order to be able to work with square roots correctly, it is necessary to understand exactly what is meant by the square root of any number.

By the *square root* of any number, we mean one of the two equal *factors* of that number. If two *equal* factors are multiplied to produce another number, then one of the two equal factors is called the *square root* of that number; that is, in testing the square root of any number, we multiply the square root by *itself*. For instance, the square root of 1225 is 35 simply because 35 can be multiplied by *itself* to make 1225. (35)(35) = 1225.

Now, if we multiply the number -35 by *itself*, we get $+1225$; that is, $(-35)(-35) = +1225$. Therefore, we must say that the square root of 1225 can also be -35. The test for the square root of any number is whether the square root can be multiplied by *itself* to produce the given number.

Consider a few further examples. If 17 times 17 is 289, then 17 is the square root of 289. Moreover, since -17 can be multiplied by *itself* to produce $+289$, then -17 is also a square root of 289. If 863 can be multiplied by itself to produce 744,769, then 863 is the *square root* of 744,769. If 3 could be multiplied by *itself* to produce exactly 12, then 3 would be the square root of 12. That is simply the definition of square root.

Every number has two square roots, one positive and the other negative. The root indicated by the positive radical is called the *principal square root*. The two square roots of 9 are $+3$ and -3.

$$(+3)(+3) = +9$$

$$(-3)(-3) = +9$$

The principal square root of 9 is $+3$.

When we use the symbol $\sqrt{}$ to indicate a root, we must be careful to use it correctly. The symbol means the *principal root*. If you will read the symbol as "the principal root," you will avoid many errors. The statement $\sqrt{25} = +5$ can be read, "the principal square root of 25 is $+5$." If we wish to indicate both square roots by use of the symbol, we must write $\pm\sqrt{25} = \pm 5$.

This statement is correct: $\sqrt{25} = +5$ (correct)

This is *not* correct: $\sqrt{25} = \pm 5$ (wrong)

For instance, $\sqrt{25} + 8 = 13$

19.2 ANY ROOT OF A NUMBER

If we wish to indicate the multiplication of three 7's, $(7 \cdot 7 \cdot 7)$, we can show it by the exponent 3: thus

$$7^3$$

The expression is read "7 cubed" or "7 raised to the third power." The third power of 7 is 343.

Now, suppose we have the number 343 given, and we wish to find a number that can be used three times as a factor to produce 343. Our problem is to find the *cube root* of the number 343. By cube root of a given number, we mean one of the *three equal* factors that can be multiplied to form the given number as a product. The problem may be indicated thus:

$$\sqrt[3]{343}$$

In this problem we use the same radical sign ($\sqrt{}$). The small 3, placed in the notch of the radical sign, is called the *index* (plural: indices) of the root. It indicates the root to be found; thus

$$\sqrt[3]{343} = 7$$

The square root of a number is indicated by the index 2. However, the square root is used so often that the index is usually omitted.

In the problem $\sqrt[3]{343}$ the number 343, under the radical sign, is called the *radicand*. The radicand is the number of which a particular root is to be found. The *radical* is the entire expression indicating a root.

In the expression $\sqrt[3]{64}$ the radicand is 64; the index of the root is 3. The expression means that the cube root of 64 is to be found; that is, we are to find some number that can be used as a factor three times to produce 64. The cube root of 64 is 4 because $4 \cdot 4 \cdot 4 = 64$; that is,

$$\sqrt[3]{64} = 4$$

We have said that the principal root is the positive value of the radical. In some cases the principal root may actually be negative. Suppose we have the problem

$$\sqrt[3]{-64}$$

The radical is understood to be preceded by a plus sign (+), since no sign is shown before it. In this case the principal cube root of -64 is -4, since $(-4)(-4)(-4) = -64$. In fact, the principal odd root of a negative number is negative. The principal odd root of a positive number is positive.

The following additional examples show principal roots of some numbers:

$$\sqrt[4]{16} = 2 \qquad \text{because} \qquad 2^4 = 16$$
$$\sqrt[4]{81} = 3 \qquad \text{because} \qquad 3^4 = 81$$
$$\sqrt[5]{-32} = -2 \qquad \text{because} \qquad (-2)^5 = -32$$
$$\sqrt[7]{-1} = -1 \qquad \text{because} \qquad (-1)^7 = -1$$

$$\sqrt{\frac{1}{4}} = \frac{1}{2} \qquad \text{because} \qquad \left(\frac{1}{2}\right)\left(\frac{1}{2}\right) = \frac{1}{4}$$

$$\sqrt[5]{243} = +3 \qquad \text{because} \qquad (+3)^5 = +243$$

$$\sqrt[6]{64} = 2 \qquad \text{because} \qquad 2^6 = 64$$

$$\sqrt[3]{-8} = -2 \qquad \text{because} \qquad (-2)^3 = -8$$

In algebra we use the radical sign with the same meaning as in arithmetic, as shown in the following examples:

$$\sqrt{x^2} = +x \qquad \text{because} \qquad x \cdot x = x^2$$

$$\sqrt{x^6} = +x^3 \qquad \text{because} \qquad (x^3)(x^3) = x^6$$

$$\sqrt[3]{x^{12}} = +x^4 \qquad \text{because} \qquad (x^4)(x^4)(x^4) = x^{12}$$

$$\sqrt{x^2 - 6x + 9} = (x - 3) \quad \text{because} \qquad (x - 3)(x - 3) = x^2 - 6x + 9$$

$$\sqrt[5]{x^{10}} = x^2 \qquad \text{because} \qquad (x^2)(x^2)(x^2)(x^2)(x^2) = x^{10}$$

From the foregoing examples we can formulate the following rule:

Rule.   *To find an indicated root of a given power expressed with exponents, divide the exponents by the indicated root. This rule holds true for all types of exponents.*

The rule may be stated as a formula:

$$\sqrt[r]{x^n} = x^{n/r}$$

that is, the rth root of the nth power of x is equal to x raised to a power which is n/r.

The following examples show how this rule is applied:

$$\sqrt[3]{10^6} = 10^{\frac{6}{3}} = 10^2 \qquad \sqrt[3]{x^5} = x^{\frac{5}{3}}$$

$$\sqrt[4]{10^{3.532}} = 10^{0.883} \qquad \sqrt[2]{x^7} = x^{\frac{7}{2}}$$

$$\sqrt{169x^2} = 13x \qquad \text{because} \qquad (13x)^2 = 169x^2$$

$$\sqrt[3]{-64x^6} = -4x^2 \qquad \text{because} \qquad (-4x^2)^3 = -64x^6$$

$$\sqrt[2]{25x^4y^6} = 5x^2y^3 \qquad \text{because} \qquad (5x^2y^3)^2 = 25x^4y^6$$

$$\sqrt[6]{64a^6b^{12}} = 2ab^2 \qquad \text{because} \qquad (2ab^2)^6 = 64a^6b^{12}$$

$$\sqrt[3]{125x^{12}} = 5x^4 \qquad \text{because} \qquad (5x^4)^3 = 125x^{12}$$

In algebra we should remember also that any expression has two square roots, one positive, the other negative. If no sign ($+$ or $-$) is shown before the radical sign, then the principal root is meant. For instance, the square roots of x^2 are $+x$ and $-x$. However,

$$\sqrt{x^2} = +x$$

Exercise 19.1

Find the indicated root in each radical.

1. $\sqrt{x^8}$

2. $\sqrt{10^4}$

3. $\sqrt{10^{5.6}}$

4. $\sqrt{10^{3.472}}$

5. $\sqrt{4^6}$

6. $\sqrt{10^{16}}$

7. $\sqrt{16x^6}$

8. $\sqrt[3]{125x^6}$

9. $\sqrt[3]{-64x^9}$

10. $\sqrt[4]{16x^8}$

11. $\sqrt[3]{8x^6}$

12. $\sqrt{16x^{16}}$

13. $\sqrt{9x^{20}}$

14. $\sqrt[3]{27n^{12}}$

15. $-\sqrt[3]{-125a^3}$

16. $\sqrt{\dfrac{4}{9}}$

17. $\sqrt{\dfrac{25}{49}}$

18. $\sqrt{\dfrac{100}{121}}$

19. $\sqrt{\dfrac{1}{16}}$

20. $\sqrt[5]{-32a^{30}}$

21. $\sqrt[6]{64x^6}$

22. $\sqrt{(x-4)^2}$

23. $\sqrt[3]{(x+y)^3}$

24. $-\sqrt[5]{1024x^{10}}$

25. $\sqrt[3]{n^4}$

26. $-\sqrt[5]{-243x^5y^5}$

27. $-\sqrt{81x^6y^8z^2}$

28. $\sqrt{121n^4t^3s^2}$

29. $\sqrt{x^2-4x+4}$

30. $\sqrt{4n^2+12n+9}$

19.3 IRRATIONAL NUMBERS

Such numbers as $\sqrt{2}$, $\sqrt{3}$, $\sqrt{5}$, and π, are called *irrational* numbers to distinguish them from rational numbers. A *rational* number is defined as a number that can be expressed as the quotient of two integers. In other words, a rational number can be written as a common fraction with numerator and denominator as whole numbers, either positive or negative.

1. All common fractions are rational.

   $\frac{3}{4}$ is the quotient of $3 \div 4$

   $\frac{15}{37}$ represents one integer divided by another: $15 \div 37$

2. All whole numbers are rational.

   3 means $\frac{3}{1}$

   -5 means $\frac{-5}{1}$ 483 means $\frac{483}{1}$

3. All decimal fractions are rational.

$$0.3 \quad \text{can be written } \tfrac{3}{10}$$
$$5.8 \quad \text{can be written } \tfrac{58}{10}$$
$$17.65 \text{ can be written } \tfrac{1765}{100}$$

The number $\sqrt{2}$ is irrational because the exact square root of 2 cannot be expressed as any common fraction. The same is true of the numbers $\sqrt{3}$, $\sqrt{5}$, $\sqrt{6}$ and many others. There are other irrational numbers besides some square roots. The number π, for instance, is irrational. It never comes out even as a decimal or a common fraction.

We often use rational numbers as approximations. We have said the number $\sqrt{2}$ is irrational. It is only approximately equal to 1.414. However, the number 1.414 is itself rational because it can be written $\tfrac{1414}{1000}$. The number π is irrational. It is only approximately equal to 3.14159. The number 3.14159, however, is itself rational because it can be written $\tfrac{314159}{100000}$.

Let us consider a little more carefully the irrational number, the square root of 2. Suppose we wish to know the *exact* square root of 2. It is close to 1.414. However, if we multiply 1.414 by *itself*, we get 1.999396, which is less than 2. If we multiply the number 1.4142 by itself, we still get a number slightly less than 2. The square root of 2 is irrational and will never come out even as a common fraction or as a decimal no matter how far we carry out the decimal part. We cannot write the square root of 2 as we write other numbers, such as whole numbers, fractions, or decimals. It is some elusive thing that we cannot get hold of. Yet we can write the square root of 2 as a *symbol*:

$$\sqrt{2}$$

Now, if we say that this symbol is going to represent the *exact square root* of 2, then we must conclude that this number, or symbol, multiplied by itself must equal 2. In other words,

$$(\sqrt{2})\,(\sqrt{2}) = 2$$

It could not be otherwise if we adhere to the definition of square root.

Remember, by definition, the square root of any given quantity means some other quantity that can be multiplied by itself to produce the given quantity; that is,

(the square root of the quantity)(the square root of the quantity) =
                                                    the quantity.

By use of symbols, this statement becomes

$$\sqrt{\text{quantity}} \cdot \sqrt{\text{quantity}} = \text{quantity}$$

Here are some other examples that show the meaning of square root:

$$(\sqrt{361})(\sqrt{361}) = 361 \qquad (\sqrt{41.2})(\sqrt{41.2}) = 41.2$$
$$(\sqrt{3})(\sqrt{3}) = 3 \qquad (\sqrt{x})(\sqrt{x}) = x$$
$$(\sqrt{\text{book}})(\sqrt{\text{book}}) = \text{book} \qquad (\sqrt{\text{you}})(\sqrt{\text{you}}) = \text{you}$$
$$(\sqrt{\text{chair}})(\sqrt{\text{chair}}) = \text{chair} \qquad (\sqrt{\text{me}})(\sqrt{\text{me}}) = \text{me}$$

Of course, the last four examples have no meaning in the ordinary sense of square roots. Yet they should help to show the meaning of the expression *square root*.

19.4 SIMPLIFYING RADICALS

Whenever a radicand represents a perfect power of some number of which the indicated root may be found, then the root should be stated as a rational number. For instance, the expression $\sqrt{36}$ should always be stated as 6. The following expression should be simplified as shown:

$$\sqrt[3]{125x^6} = 5x^2$$

However, it often happens that we have irrational numbers, $\sqrt{2}$, $5 \cdot \sqrt{3}$, and so on. Such irrational numbers are often changed to approximate rational decimal values.

$$\sqrt{2} = 1.414 \text{ (approx.)}$$
$$5 \cdot \sqrt{3} = 5(1.732) = 8.660 \text{ (approx.)}$$

It is possible to combine a rational and an irrational number. The result is another irrational number, as shown by the following examples:

$$7 + \sqrt{5} = 7 + 2.236 \text{ (approx.)} = 9.236 \text{ (approx.)}$$
$$2 - \sqrt{10} = 2 - 3.162 \text{ (approx.)} = -1.162 \text{ (approx.)}$$

In many instances a radical can be *simplified* to facilitate computation. *There are two immediate goals in simplifying radicals:*

1. *The radicand should be made as small as possible.*
2. *The radicand should not contain a fraction.*

To make a radicand as small as possible, we proceed as follows:

1. First we separate the radicand into two factors so that one factor is a perfect square or other power indicated by the index of the root. A perfect power is a number whose root, as indicated by the index, is rational.

2. Then we separate the radical into the product of two radicals.

3. Finally, we take the root of the perfect power and place this quantity as a coefficient of the second radical.

Example 1. Simplify the radical $\sqrt{18}$.

$$\sqrt{18} = \sqrt{(9)(2)} = \sqrt{9} \cdot \sqrt{2} = 3 \cdot \sqrt{2}$$

Let us see whether we have a right to separate a radical into the product of two separate radicals by factoring the radicand.

$$\text{Is } \sqrt{36} \overset{?}{=} \sqrt{9 \cdot 4} \overset{?}{=} \sqrt{9} \cdot \sqrt{4} \overset{?}{=} 3 \cdot 2 \overset{?}{=} 6? \quad \text{Yes.}$$

$$\text{Is } \sqrt{400} \overset{?}{=} \sqrt{16 \cdot 25} \overset{?}{=} \sqrt{16} \cdot \sqrt{25} \overset{?}{=} 4 \cdot 5 \overset{?}{=} 20? \quad \text{Yes.}$$

In the two examples shown, the answers are correct. Remember, however, that two examples do not necessarily establish a rule. Yet the following principle happens to be true:

A radicand may be factored and the radical may be written as the product of two radicals.

Example 2. $\sqrt{75} \qquad = \sqrt{25 \cdot 3} = \sqrt{25} \cdot \sqrt{3} = 5\sqrt{3}$

Example 3. $\sqrt{54} \qquad = \sqrt{9 \cdot 6} = 3\sqrt{6}$

Example 4. $7\sqrt{20} \qquad = 7\sqrt{4 \cdot 5} = 7\sqrt{4} \cdot \sqrt{5} = 14\sqrt{5}$

Example 5. $\sqrt{\dfrac{5}{9}} \qquad = \sqrt{\dfrac{1}{9} \cdot 5} = \dfrac{1}{3}\sqrt{5}$

Example 6. $5\sqrt[3]{32} \qquad = 5\sqrt[3]{8 \cdot 4} = 5 \cdot 2\sqrt[3]{4} = 10\sqrt[3]{4}$

Example 7. $\sqrt{12x^3y} \qquad = \sqrt{(4x^2)(3xy)} = 2x\sqrt{3xy}$

Example 8. $\sqrt{80x^3y^8z^7} = \sqrt{(16x^2y^8z^6)(5xz)} = 4xy^4z^3\sqrt{5xz}$

If a radicand is a fraction, it should be changed into a whole number. In this case the first step is to multiply the numerator and the denominator of the fraction by some number that will make the denominator a perfect power, as indicated by the root. Then the radical may be written as the product of two radicals, one of which is rational.

Example 9. Simplify the radical $\sqrt{\dfrac{2}{3}}$.

The first step in this example is to multiply the numerator and the denominator by 3. Then the denominator becomes a perfect square.

$$\sqrt{\frac{2}{3}} = \sqrt{\frac{2 \cdot 3}{3 \cdot 3}} = \sqrt{\frac{6}{9}} = \sqrt{\frac{1}{9} \cdot 6} = \frac{1}{3}\sqrt{6}$$

Example 10. Simplify $7\sqrt{\frac{5}{8}}$.

$$7\sqrt{\frac{5}{8}} = 7\sqrt{\frac{5 \cdot 2}{8 \cdot 2}} = 7\sqrt{\frac{10}{16}} = 7\sqrt{\frac{1}{16} \cdot 10} = \frac{7}{4}\sqrt{10}$$

Warning. You should be very careful about removing quantities from under a radical sign. In the following statements can you tell which equal signs are wrong? (Some equal signs are correct.)

$$\sqrt{13} = \sqrt{9 + 4} = \sqrt{9} + \sqrt{4} = 3 + 2 = 5 \qquad \text{(wrong)}$$
$$\sqrt{x^2 + y^2} = \sqrt{x^2} + \sqrt{y^2} = x + y \qquad \text{(wrong)}$$
$$\sqrt{24} = \sqrt{49 - 25} = \sqrt{49} - \sqrt{25} = 7 - 5 = 2 \qquad \text{(wrong)}$$
$$\sqrt{x^2 - y^2} = \sqrt{x^2} - \sqrt{y^2} = x - y \qquad \text{(wrong)}$$
$$\sqrt{25} = \sqrt{16 + 9} = \sqrt{4^2 + 3^2} = \sqrt{4^2} + \sqrt{3^2} = 4 + 3 = 7 \quad \text{(wrong)}$$
$$\sqrt{9} = \sqrt{25 - 16} = \sqrt{25} - \sqrt{16} = 5 - 4 = 1 \qquad \text{(wrong)}$$

You cannot take the root of a separate term of a polynomial radicand and place the root on the outside of the radical sign. Roots may be taken *only of factors*, not of separate terms of a radicand.

Exercise 19.2

Simplify each of the following expressions, if possible:

1. $\sqrt{48}$ 2. $\sqrt{75}$ 3. $\sqrt{147}$

4. $\sqrt{18x^3}$ 5. $\sqrt{25x^5}$ 6. $\sqrt{27x^7}$

7. $\sqrt[3]{16x^4}$ 8. $\sqrt{3/4}$ 9. $\sqrt{3/8}$

10. $\sqrt{\dfrac{5}{32}}$ 11. $\sqrt{\dfrac{4}{27}}$ 12. $\sqrt{\dfrac{9}{x}}$

13. $\sqrt{\dfrac{7a}{x^3}}$ 14. $\sqrt{4x^4}$ 15. $\sqrt{8x^8}$

16. $\sqrt{9x^9}$ **17.** $\sqrt[5]{64x^6}$ **18.** $\sqrt{128x^4}$

19. $\sqrt{256x^7}$ **20.** $\sqrt{12x^3y^6}$ **21.** $\sqrt{x^4(x+1)}$

22. $\sqrt{x^5 + x^2}$ **23.** $\sqrt{a^2x^3 - a^2x}$ **24.** $\sqrt{24x^6 - 4x^4}$

25. $\sqrt{x^2 + y^2}$ **26.** $\sqrt{96x^8y^6}$ **27.** $\sqrt{500x^4y^5z^8}$

28. $\sqrt{a^2 - b^2}$ **29.** $\sqrt{72x^2 - 36x^3}$ **30.** $\sqrt{36 \cdot 25 \cdot 6 \cdot 16}$

19.5 ADDITION AND SUBTRACTION OF RADICALS

Only *like* or *similar radicals* can be added or subtracted. Like radicals are those that have the same *radicand* and the same indicated *root*:

$$\sqrt{7} \qquad 3\sqrt{7} \qquad 15\sqrt{7} \qquad -8\sqrt{7}$$
$$4\sqrt[3]{5xy} \qquad -2\sqrt[3]{5xy} \qquad 7\sqrt[3]{5xy} \qquad -\sqrt[3]{5xy}$$

The coefficient of a radical is the number appearing as a factor outside the entire radical. If a radical has no expressed coefficient, the coefficient is understood to be 1.

Like radicals are added or subtracted by adding or subtracting their coefficients, just as in algebraic terms.

$$5\sqrt{2} + 7\sqrt{2} - 3\sqrt{2} = 9\sqrt{2}$$
$$7\sqrt[3]{4} - 2\sqrt[3]{4} + 9\sqrt[3]{4} = 14\sqrt[3]{4}$$

Sometimes unlike radicals may be transformed into like radicals and the results combined.

Example 1. Simplify $\sqrt{3} - 5\sqrt{2} - 5\sqrt{3} + \sqrt{2} + 6\sqrt{3} + 8$.

Combining like radicals, we get

$$2\sqrt{3} - 4\sqrt{2} + 8$$

Thus, the approximate rational value may be more easily found. The $\sqrt{3}$ equals approximately 1.732 and the $\sqrt{2}$ equals approximately 1.414. The approximate value of the expression is

$$2\sqrt{3} - 4\sqrt{2} + 8$$
$$= 2(1.732) - 4(1.414) + 8$$
$$= 3.464 - 5.656 + 8$$
$$= 5.808 \text{ (approx.)}$$

Example 2. Simplify and combine

$$5\sqrt{2} + \sqrt{12} + 6\sqrt{32} - 7\sqrt{18} - 8\sqrt{3} + \sqrt{\tfrac{1}{8}} =$$

If the radicals are simplified by reducing the radicands, the expression becomes

$$5\sqrt{2} + 2\sqrt{3} + 24\sqrt{2} - 21\sqrt{2} - 8\sqrt{3} + \tfrac{1}{4}\sqrt{2} = 8\tfrac{1}{4}\sqrt{2} - 6\sqrt{3}$$

The approximate value is found as follows:

$$
\begin{aligned}
&8\tfrac{1}{4}\sqrt{2} - 6\sqrt{3} \\
&= \tfrac{33}{4}(1.414) - 6(1.732) \\
&= 11.666 - 10.392 \\
&= 1.274 \text{ (approx.)}
\end{aligned}
$$

Exercise 19.3

Simplify the radicals in each of the following examples, and combine as much as possible. Finally, find the approximate value of each example.

1. $7\sqrt{5} + 3\sqrt{5} + 2\sqrt{5} - 4\sqrt{5} + \sqrt{5} + 3$

2. $5\sqrt{3} - 4\sqrt{3} + 7\sqrt{3} - \sqrt{3} - \sqrt{4} + \sqrt{2}$

3. $3\sqrt{32} - 5\sqrt{18} + 2\sqrt{50} + 3\sqrt{\dfrac{1}{8}} - \sqrt{8} - 2\sqrt{9}$

4. $5\sqrt{12} - 2\sqrt{27} + \sqrt{75} - 3\sqrt{18} + \sqrt{72}$

5. $3\sqrt{200} + 2\sqrt{45} - 6\sqrt{8} - 3\sqrt{20} + \sqrt{180}$

6. $2\sqrt{300} + 5\sqrt{28} - 4\sqrt{108} + \sqrt{288} - 4$

7. $\sqrt{500} + \sqrt{100} + \sqrt{600} + \sqrt{400} + \sqrt{900}$

8. $2\sqrt{125} - 3\sqrt{27} + 4\sqrt{243} - 5\sqrt{192} + \sqrt{9}$

9. $\sqrt{800} - \sqrt{80} + \sqrt{8} - \sqrt{45} + \sqrt{288} + \sqrt{450}$

10. $3\sqrt{40} + 5\sqrt{90} - \sqrt{250} + 2\sqrt{1000} + \sqrt{10000}$

11. $3\sqrt{12} + 2\sqrt{18} + 4\sqrt{20} + 5\sqrt{24} + \sqrt{28} + \sqrt{4}$

12. $\sqrt{147} - 2\sqrt{75} + 5\sqrt{48} - 3\sqrt{27} - \sqrt{\dfrac{1}{3}} + \sqrt{108}$

13. $2\sqrt{24} + \sqrt{96} - 3\sqrt{54} + \sqrt{\dfrac{1}{6}} - \sqrt{\dfrac{2}{3}} - 2\sqrt{16}$

14. $\sqrt{40} + 2\sqrt{90} - 4\sqrt{\dfrac{2}{5}} - 3\sqrt{\dfrac{5}{2}} + \sqrt{1000} + \sqrt{\dfrac{5}{32}}$

15. $4\sqrt{45} - 3\sqrt{20} - 4\sqrt{\dfrac{1}{5}} + 5\sqrt{80} - 3\sqrt{\dfrac{4}{5}} + \sqrt{180}$

16. $\sqrt{12} + \sqrt{16} + \sqrt{72} - \sqrt{98} + \sqrt{300} - \sqrt{\dfrac{3}{16}}$

17. $\sqrt{28} - \sqrt{63} + \sqrt{\dfrac{4}{7}} - \sqrt{7} + \sqrt{5} + \sqrt{3} + 1$

18. $\sqrt[3]{16} + \sqrt[3]{54} + \sqrt[3]{128} - \sqrt[3]{2} - \sqrt[3]{343}$

19. $\sqrt{5} + \sqrt[3]{5} + \sqrt[4]{5} + 5$

20. $(18)^{\frac{1}{2}} + (125)^{\frac{1}{3}} + (72)^{\frac{1}{2}} + (64)^{\frac{1}{3}}$

19.6 MULTIPLICATION OF RADICALS

In the multiplication of radicals there are several things we must consider. Let us look again at the definitions of the numbers used in connection with radicals. Consider the radical

$$-4\sqrt[2]{15}$$

In this radical expression the *index* of the root is 2. The index is the number that shows what root is to be found. The *radicand* is the number of which root is to be found. In this example the radicand is 15. The radical has the *coefficient* -4, which means that the value of the radical is to be multiplied by -4.

If two or more radicals are to be multiplied together, they must have the same index. If two radicals do not have the same index, their product can simply be indicated or they may be reduced to the same index. We shall consider, first, the case in which the indices are equal.

If two or more radicals have the same index, they can be multiplied together. The radicands need not be the same.

For the multiplication of radicals with the same index, we have the following steps:

1. The sign of the product will follow from the rule for the multiplication of signed numbers. This applies to the signs of the coefficients.
2. Multiply the coefficients for the coefficient in the product.
3. Multiply the radicands for the radicand in the product.
4. Simplify the resulting radical if possible.

Note. One other point should be mentioned here. For the multiplication of radicals, all rules *except one* for multiplying signed numbers hold true. The usual rule for the multiplication of signed numbers when both are negative may be stated symbolically, $(-)(-) = +$. However, if two radicals have negative radicands, these two negative radicands *cannot* be written as a positive product for the radicand of the new radical. For instance, $\sqrt{-9} \cdot \sqrt{-4}$ is not equal to $\sqrt{(-9)(-4)} = \sqrt{+36}$. The radicand of the product is *not* positive. *Neither is it negative.* In this chapter we do not include examples of this kind. The multiplication of such numbers is fully explained in Chapter 21.

Example 1. Multiply $(-7\sqrt{3})(-2\sqrt{5})$.
For the sign of the product, we have $(-)(-) = +$.
For the coefficient of the product, we have $(7)(2) = 14$.
For the radicand in the product, we have $(3)(5) = 15$.
The complete answer is $+14\sqrt{15}$.
The entire product may, of course, be expressed approximately by finding the approximate square root of 15, which is 3.873. Then we have

$$14(3.873) = 54.222$$

Example 2. Multiply $(+4\sqrt{7})(-5\sqrt{3})(-2\sqrt{5})$.
For the sign of the product, we have $(+)(-)(-) = +$.
For the coefficient, we have $(4)(5)(2) = 40$.
For the product of the radicands, we have $(7)(3)(5) = 105$.
For the entire product of the radicals, we have $+40\sqrt{105}$.
The answer cannot be reduced. It can, of course, be expressed as an approximate number, since $\sqrt{105}$ is approximately 10.247.

$$40\sqrt{105} = 40(10.247) = 409.88 \text{ (approx.)}$$

Example 3. Multiply $(5\sqrt{3})(-7\sqrt{3})$.
In this example notice that the radicands are equal. Whenever the two radicands are equal, they should not be multiplied together to form a product under the radical sign. In this example we do not multiply $3 \cdot 3 = 9$. Instead, the product of the radicals should be stated at once: $(\sqrt{3})(\sqrt{3}) = 3$; that is, we recall that the square root of a number multiplied by the square root of the number equals the number itself. Thus

$$(\sqrt{x})(\sqrt{x}) = x.$$

If we multiply the radicands and then find the square root of the product, the method is not only longer but it can easily lead to errors. The answer to Example 3 is

$$(5\sqrt{3})(-7\sqrt{3}) = (-35)(3) = -105$$

Example 4. Multiply: $(+\sqrt{2})(\sqrt{8})$.
In most instances, if an irrational number is multiplied by another irrational number, the product is also irrational. However, it sometimes happens that the product of two irrational numbers is rational. In Example 4 each of the radicals is irrational. Yet when they are multiplied, the product is rational.

$$(\sqrt{2})(\sqrt{8}) = \sqrt{16} = 4, \qquad \text{a rational number.}$$

19.7 MULTIPLICATION OF POLYNOMIALS CONTAINING RADICALS

In the multiplication of polynomials involving radicals, we follow the same general procedure that we use in the multiplication of polynomials involving literal numbers.

Consider the following example.

Example 1. Multiply $2\sqrt{3}(4\sqrt{3} + 2\sqrt{5} - 3\sqrt{7})$.

This example is similar in form to an example containing rational literal numbers:

$$2x(4x + 2y - 3z)$$

In multiplying a polynomial by a monomial, we multiply each term of the polynomial by the monomial. Thus $2x(4x + 2y - 3z) = 8x^2 + 4xy - 6xz$.

In a similar way we find the product in the example containing radicals.

For the first term, we have $(2\sqrt{3})(4\sqrt{3}) = (8)(3) = 24$.

For the second term, we have $(2\sqrt{3})(2\sqrt{5}) = 4\sqrt{15}$.

For the third term, we have $(2\sqrt{3})(-3\sqrt{7}) = -6\sqrt{21}$.

The complete product is $24 + 4\sqrt{15} - 6\sqrt{21}$.

In the multiplication of two polynomials involving radicals, we follow the same general procedure as in the usual multiplication of polynomials involving rational literal terms.

Example 1. Multiply $(5\sqrt{3} - 4\sqrt{2})(7\sqrt{3} + 3\sqrt{2})$.

This expression is similar in form to the expression

$$(5x - 4y)(7x + 3y)$$

Of course, in this example, the product can be found as a special product. However, let us show all the steps by writing one binomial below the other and taking note of each separate step in the multiplication.

$$
\begin{array}{r}
5x - 4y \\
7x + 3y \\
\hline
35x^2 - 28xy \\
+ 15xy - 12y^2 \\
\hline
35x^2 - 13xy - 12y^2
\end{array}
$$

Now we do the same for the binomials containing radicals. Note especially the multiplications,

$$\sqrt{3} \cdot \sqrt{3} = 3 \qquad \text{and} \qquad \sqrt{2} \cdot \sqrt{2} = 2$$

$$
\begin{array}{r}
5\sqrt{3} - 4\sqrt{2} \\
7\sqrt{3} + 3\sqrt{2} \\
\hline
35 \cdot 3 - 28\sqrt{6} \\
+ 15\sqrt{6} - 12 \cdot 2 \\
\hline
105 - 13\sqrt{6} - 24
\end{array}
$$

The product in this case can be simplified to $81 - 13\sqrt{6}$.

Therefore, we see that

$$(5\sqrt{3} - 4\sqrt{2})(7\sqrt{3} + 3\sqrt{2}) = 81 - 13\sqrt{6}$$

We can easily see the advantage of this kind of simplification if we wish to compute the approximate rational value of the expression. To find the value from the original expression involves much work. The $\sqrt{3}$ is approximately equal to 1.732, and the $\sqrt{2}$ equals approximately 1.414. Substituting these values in the binomials, we get

$$[5(1.732) - 4(1.414)][7(1.732) + 3(1.414)]$$
$$= (8.660 - 5.656)(12.124 + 4.242)$$
$$= (3.004)(16.366) = 49.163 \text{ (rounded off)}$$

Instead, if the answer, $81 - 13\sqrt{6}$, is used to find the approximate rational value, the work is much less. The $\sqrt{6}$ is approximately equal to 2.449. Therefore, the answer can be stated as

$$81 - 13\sqrt{6} = 81 - 13(2.449)$$
$$= 81 - 31.837 = 49.163 \text{ (approx.)}$$

The approximate values do not always check in the last digit for both methods, since the values used are only approximate.

If radicals do not have the same index, their product can only be indicated. For instance, the product of $\sqrt[2]{5}$ and $\sqrt[3]{4}$ can only be indicated in some way such as $(\sqrt[2]{5})(\sqrt[3]{4})$.

Of course, the approximate product may be found by multiplying the approximate values of the given radicals.

The product may also be simplified by reducing the radicals to the same order by the following steps:

1. *Change the radicals to exponential form.*
2. *Reduce the fractional exponents so that they have the same denominator.*
3. *Change back to the radical form.*
4. *Multiply the radicands.*

Example 3. Multiply $(\sqrt{5})(\sqrt[3]{4})$.

Solution. Here we first change each radical so that they have the same index. This is done by writing each radical in exponential form and then changing the fractional exponents to fractions with the same denominators.

$$\sqrt{5} = 5^{\frac{1}{2}} = 5^{\frac{3}{6}} = \sqrt[6]{5^3} = \sqrt[6]{125}$$

$$\sqrt[3]{4} = 4^{\frac{1}{3}} = 4^{\frac{2}{6}} = \sqrt[6]{4^2} = \sqrt[6]{16}$$

Now we can multiply the radicals, since they have the same index. We get

$$(\sqrt[6]{125})(\sqrt[6]{16}) = \sqrt[6]{2000}$$

In many, if not most, problems that we encounter in scientific work involving multiplication of radicals the radicals are of the same order; that is, they have the same index. Then the multiplication is rather easy.

Exercise 19.4

Multiply and find approximate decimal values:

1. $(3\sqrt{2})(4\sqrt{5})$
2. $(-4\sqrt{3})(5\sqrt{2})$
3. $(-5\sqrt{2})(-3\sqrt{2})$
4. $(-3\sqrt{7})(8\sqrt{7})(\sqrt{2})$
5. $(9\sqrt{8})(4\sqrt{2})$
6. $(5\sqrt{10})(4\sqrt{13})(\sqrt{2})$
7. $(4\sqrt{5})(3\sqrt{5})(2\sqrt{5})$
8. $(-2\sqrt{3})(4\sqrt{3})(-5\sqrt{3})$
9. $(\sqrt{42})(\sqrt{42})(\sqrt{42})$
10. $(3\sqrt{6})(-2\sqrt{6})(-\sqrt{6})$
11. $(5\sqrt{6})(2\sqrt{3})(\sqrt{2})$
12. $(3\sqrt{7})(5\sqrt{14})(2\sqrt{3})$
13. $3\sqrt{2}(5\sqrt{3} - 4\sqrt{5} - 5\sqrt{2})$
14. $-4\sqrt{3}(2\sqrt{5} - 3\sqrt{3} + 7\sqrt{6})$
15. $5\sqrt{5}(\sqrt{3} - \sqrt{5} + 4\sqrt{15})$
16. $(\sqrt{3} + 2\sqrt{5})(2\sqrt{3} - 7\sqrt{5})$
17. $(3\sqrt{2} - 5\sqrt{7})(4\sqrt{2} + 2\sqrt{7})$
18. $(2\sqrt{5} - 3\sqrt{2})(2\sqrt{5} + 3\sqrt{2})$
19. $(3\sqrt{2} + \sqrt{5})(\sqrt{3} - 4)$
20. $(4\sqrt{3} - 3\sqrt{5})(5\sqrt{2} + 4\sqrt{7})$
21. $(4\sqrt{3} - 2\sqrt{7})^2$
22. $(2\sqrt{5} + \sqrt{2})^2$
23. $(\sqrt{7} - 3)^2$
24. $(3\sqrt{2} - 5)^2$

19.8 DIVISION OF RADICALS

If, in the division of radicals, having the same indices, we have a monomial radical as a divisor and *if the radicand of the divisor can be divided evenly into the radicand of the dividend*, then the division is easily done.

Example 1. Divide as indicated: $3\sqrt{55} \div 7\sqrt{5}$.

In this example, we write the coefficient as $\frac{3}{7}$, which is the same as $3 \div 7$. Dividing the radicands, we get 11 for the radicand of the quotient. The rules for the sign of a quotient must be observed just as in the division of algebraic terms involving literal numbers. The answer to Example 1 is $\frac{3}{7}\sqrt{11}$.

If, in the division of radicals, *the divisor contains a radical*, the division involves one main objective: when the division is indicated as a fraction, *eliminate any radical in the denominator*.

Suppose we have fractions such as the following:

$$\frac{3}{\sqrt{2}} \qquad \frac{2\sqrt{5}}{5\sqrt{3}} \qquad \frac{5\sqrt{3}}{3 + \sqrt{5}}$$

You will notice that all the denominators are irrational. If we wish to compute the value of each fraction (that is, find the approximate decimal value), we might find the approximate values of the denominators. Then we should have to use long division. The divisors would be long decimal fractions. Instead, there is an easier way.

Our main objective is to eliminate any radical in a denominator. To do this, we multiply the numerator and the denominator of the fraction by *some quantity* that will make the denominator *rational.* In other words, we *rationalize* the denominator.

Take a simple example. Suppose we have the fraction

$$\frac{1}{\sqrt{2}}$$

If we wish to work out the *numerical value* of the fraction as it stands, we have the following problem in *very long* division:

$$\frac{1}{1.4142} \qquad \text{or} \qquad 1.4142\overline{)1}.$$

There is a better way to find the numerical value of this fraction.

Instead of doing the long division, suppose we take the fraction as it stands:

$$\frac{1}{\sqrt{2}}$$

Now, *multiply the numerator and the denominator* of the fraction by the quantity $\sqrt{2}$. Then we get

$$\frac{1}{\sqrt{2}} = \frac{1 \cdot \sqrt{2}}{\sqrt{2} \cdot \sqrt{2}} = \frac{\sqrt{2}}{2} = \frac{1.4142}{2} = \,?$$

The result is *easy division.*

In the example just given you will note that we first made the denominator *rational.* Then the division is much easier. The answer is the same in both methods.

If the denominator is a *binomial,* the *multiplying factor* will have to be the *conjugate form* of the denominator. *The conjugate form* of a binomial is the same binomial, *except that the middle sign is changed.* So the numerator and the denominator are *both* multiplied by the *conjugate form of the denominator.* The conjugate form of $4 - \sqrt{5}$ is $4 + \sqrt{5}$.

Example 2. Simplify $\dfrac{3}{4 - \sqrt{5}}$.

We multiply numerator and denominator by the rationalizing factor, $4 + \sqrt{5}$.

$$\frac{3(4 + \sqrt{5})}{(4 - \sqrt{5})(4 + \sqrt{5})} = \frac{3(4 + \sqrt{5})}{16 - 5} = \frac{3(4 + \sqrt{5})}{11}$$

The decimal value of the fraction is approximately 1.701. This value can be computed much more easily from the final form than from the original fraction. The final form involves easy division.

Exercise 19.5

Rationalize the denominator in each of the following fractions:

1. $\dfrac{12}{5\sqrt{2}}$ **2.** $\dfrac{5}{3\sqrt{5}}$ **3.** $\dfrac{1}{\sqrt{3}}$

4. $\dfrac{2}{3\sqrt{5}}$ **5.** $\dfrac{3}{\sqrt{13}}$ **6.** $\dfrac{\sqrt{3}}{\sqrt{2}}$

7. $\dfrac{2\sqrt{5}}{5\sqrt{3}}$ **8.** $\dfrac{\sqrt{2}}{4\sqrt{5}}$ **9.** $\dfrac{2}{\sqrt{7}}$

10. $\dfrac{5}{\sqrt{34}}$ **11.** $\dfrac{3}{3 - \sqrt{5}}$ **12.** $\dfrac{\sqrt{2}}{4 + \sqrt{5}}$

13. $\dfrac{8}{2 - \sqrt{3}}$ **14.** $\dfrac{6}{\sqrt{5} + \sqrt{2}}$ **15.** $\dfrac{\sqrt{3}}{2\sqrt{3} - \sqrt{5}}$

16. $\dfrac{2\sqrt{3}}{5 - 2\sqrt{3}}$ **17.** $\dfrac{3 - \sqrt{3}}{3 + \sqrt{3}}$ **18.** $\dfrac{3 + \sqrt{2}}{\sqrt{5} + \sqrt{2}}$

19. $\dfrac{2 + \sqrt{3}}{2 - \sqrt{3}}$ **20.** $\dfrac{\sqrt{3} + \sqrt{5}}{4\sqrt{3} - 2\sqrt{5}}$ **21.** $\dfrac{2 + \sqrt{3}}{3\sqrt{3} - \sqrt{5} + 2}$

22. $\dfrac{4 - \sqrt{2}}{2\sqrt{2} + 2}$ **23.** $\dfrac{\sqrt{6} - 1}{\sqrt{2} + \sqrt{3}}$ **24.** $\dfrac{2\sqrt{5} + 3}{\sqrt{5} - 6}$

25. $\dfrac{2\sqrt{3} - \sqrt{5}}{\sqrt{15} - 2}$ **26.** $\dfrac{1}{4\sqrt{2} - 3\sqrt{3}}$ **27.** $\dfrac{-3\sqrt{2} + 5\sqrt{10}}{\sqrt{2} - 3\sqrt{10}}$

28. $\dfrac{4\sqrt{3} - 5\sqrt{6}}{2\sqrt{3} + \sqrt{6}}$ **29.** $\dfrac{3\sqrt{6} - 2\sqrt{2}}{3\sqrt{2} - 5\sqrt{6}}$ **30.** $\dfrac{3\sqrt{5} - \sqrt{10}}{\sqrt{5} + 2\sqrt{10}}$

Exercise 19.6

Simplify the following radicals:

1. $4\sqrt{48}$ **2.** $3\sqrt{75}$ **3.** $5\sqrt{32}$

4. $2\sqrt{8}$ **5.** $4\sqrt{147}$ **6.** $\sqrt{125}$

7. $3\sqrt{27}$ **8.** $\sqrt{200}$ **9.** $-3\sqrt{800}$

10. $5\sqrt{288}$ **11.** $-2\sqrt{300}$ **12.** $\sqrt{\frac{1}{2}}$

13. $36\sqrt{\frac{2}{3}}$ **14.** $\sqrt{\frac{3}{4}}$ **15.** $4\sqrt{\frac{3}{8}}$

16. $3\sqrt{\frac{5}{32}}$ **17.** $6\sqrt{\frac{5}{8}}$ **18.** $-3\sqrt{\frac{4}{7}}$

19. $-2\sqrt{\frac{3}{5}}$ **20.** $\sqrt{\frac{2}{11}}$ **21.** $\sqrt{a^3}$

22. $3\sqrt{a^5 b^2}$ **23.** $5\sqrt{4\cdot 9}$ **24.** $\sqrt{4+9}$

25. $\sqrt{25+49}$ **26.** $\sqrt{25\cdot 49}$ **27.** $\sqrt{81-64}$

28. $\sqrt{18a^3 b^7 c^6}$ **29.** $\sqrt{9x^3 y^2 z}$ **30.** $4\sqrt{32a^3 b^8 c^9}$

31. $\sqrt{x^4 - x^2}$ **32.** $\sqrt{a^2 + b^2}$ **33.** $\sqrt{a^2 + 2ab + b^2}$

Combine the following radicals. Only like radicals can be added or subtracted. Find decimal value:

34. $3\sqrt{2} + 5\sqrt{72} + \sqrt{200} - 3\sqrt{128} + 4\sqrt{3} - \sqrt{3} =$

35. $5\sqrt{3} + 7\sqrt{2} + 4\sqrt{2} + \sqrt{5} - \sqrt{3} + 3\sqrt{5} + 7 - \sqrt{2} =$

36. $\sqrt{20} + 2\sqrt{3} + \sqrt{180} - \sqrt{40} + \sqrt{50} - \sqrt{12} + \frac{1}{3}\sqrt{3} - \frac{2}{3}\sqrt{2} =$

37. $\sqrt{75} - \sqrt{2} + \sqrt{\frac{3}{32}} - \sqrt{48} + \sqrt{\frac{1}{2}} + \sqrt{\frac{1}{3}} + \sqrt{\frac{3}{8}} + \frac{1}{5}\sqrt{5} =$

38. $2\sqrt{12} + 5\sqrt{32} + 2\sqrt{18} + 4\sqrt{45} + \sqrt{\frac{2}{5}} - \sqrt{\frac{1}{2}} - \sqrt{\frac{2}{3}} =$

39. $(-1 + \sqrt{3})^3$ **40.** $(\sqrt{5} - 3 + \sqrt{2})(\sqrt{5} - 3 - \sqrt{2})$

41. $(2 - 2\sqrt{5})^3$ **42.** $(\sqrt{7} + \sqrt{3} - \sqrt{5})(\sqrt{7} - \sqrt{3} + \sqrt{5})$

43. $(\sqrt{3} - \sqrt{2})^4$ **44.** $(3\sqrt{3} + 2\sqrt{2})(2\sqrt{3} - 3\sqrt{2})(6 + 5\sqrt{6})$

45. Divide $(3\sqrt{2} - 2\sqrt{3})$ by $(3\sqrt{2} + 2\sqrt{3})$.

46. Find the reciprocal of $(3 + \sqrt{5})$.

47. Find the reciprocal of $(2\sqrt{3} - 5)$.

48. Find the reciprocal of $(5 - \sqrt{3} - \sqrt{2})$.

20

Quadratic Equations

20.1 DEFINITION

A *quadratic* equation is an equation containing the second power of an unknown such as x^2, but no higher power. An example of a quadratic equation is $x^2 - 5x + 6 = 0$.

In order to understand better the meaning of a quadratic equation, let us first take a look at some other equations that are not quadratics.

An equation containing only the first power of x or any unknown is called a *linear* equation.

Linear equation: $\quad 3x + 7 = 24$

An equation containing a term in the second power of the unknown, but no higher power, is called a *quadratic* equation.

Quadratic equations: $\quad 3x^2 - 5x + 2 = 0$
$$5x^2 = 2x - 7$$

An equation containing the third power of the unknown, but no higher power, is called a *cubic* equation.

Cubic equations: $\quad x^3 + 5x^2 - 7x + 4 = 0$
$$2y^3 - 4y^2 + 5 = 0$$

An equation containing the fourth power of the unknown, but no higher power, is called a *quartic* equation.

Quartic equations: $\quad x^4 + 3x^3 - 5x^2 + 2x - 8 = 0$
$$3n^4 + 5n^2 - 4n = 0$$

Equations above the second degree are often named simply after the highest degree term.

Third degree equation: $\quad x^3 + 5x^2 - 7x + 4 = 0$
Fourth degree equation: $\quad y^4 - 7y^3 + 3y = 0$
Fifth degree equation: $\quad n^5 - 6n^2 + 4n + 9 = 0$

A *root* of any equation is *any* number that satisfies the equation. The real test of any root is to see whether it makes the equation true. We shall find that a quadratic equation has two roots, a cubic has three roots, and a quartic has four roots. In general, the number of roots of any equation is equal to the degree of the equation.

In this book we do not solve any equation above the quadratic unless they are very easy. We mention others only occasionally. Our concern here is with quadratic equations.

The general form of a quadratic equation is

$$ax^2 + bx + c = 0$$

This means

1. The x^2 term will have some coefficient we call a.
2. The x term will have some coefficient we call b.
3. The constant term, which we call c, is the term or part that does not contain x in any form.

One or both of the coefficients, b and c, may be zero. Here are some examples of quadratic equations:

$$3x^2 + 5x + 2 = 0 \qquad 4x^2 = 5x \qquad 2x^2 + 7 = 0$$
$$6x^2 = 7x + 4 \qquad 3x^2 = 0 \qquad 7x^2 + 3x = 0$$

If $b = 0$, the equation contains no term in x. Then the equation is called a *pure quadratic*. For example, $3x^2 - 5 = 0$ is a pure quadratic equation.

If the equation contains both the x^2 term and the x term, it is called a *complete quadratic*. Here are two complete quadratics:

$$x^2 = 5x + 6 \qquad \text{and} \qquad 3x^2 - 7x = 0$$

A *root* of a quadratic equation is any number that satisfies the equation. Consider the following quadratic equation:

$$x^2 - 5x + 6 = 0$$

Let us try to find the roots by trial and error.

Does $x = 1$?	Does $1^2 - 5(1) + 6 = 0$?	No
Does $x = 2$?	Does $2^2 - 5(2) + 6 = 0$?	Yes. "2" is a root.
Does $x = 3$?	Does $3^2 - 5(3) + 6 = 0$?	Yes. "3" is a root.
Does $x = 4$?	Does $4^2 - 5(4) + 6 = 0$?	No.

We find that the equation has two roots, 2 and 3. We usually call the roots r_1 and r_2.

The two roots of a quadratic equation are sometimes called a *solution set*. The set of numbers is often enclosed in braces: $\{2, 3\}$. The solution set is then the set of numbers, $\{2, 3\}$, which may also be written as the set $\{3, 2\}$. Notice that this set of numbers does *not* mean an ordered pair. The numbers in this case may be written in any order in the set. The result and meaning is *not* the same as the solution we get in solving a system of equations, in which we get one particular value for x and a particular value for y. In that case, we have seen that we enclose the numbers in parentheses and call the numbers an ordered pair because they must be taken in a certain order to show the values of x and y, respectively. However, in the case of the equation $x^2 - 5x + 6 = 0$ the solution set is the set $\{2, 3\}$, in which the numbers may be shown in any order. The set simply means that either of the two numbers will satisfy the equation. Remember:

(1) We use braces to denote a *set* of numbers, such as the set $\{7, 3\}$, in which we simply mean that the two numbers, 7 and 3, are members of the set, and therefore the order is unimportant.

(2) We use parentheses to denote an *ordered pair* of numbers, as $(7, 3)$, in which the two numbers must be taken in that order, for example, to show the x and y coordinates of a point.

To *solve* an equation means to find the roots. In the foregoing equation we found the roots by trial and error. We need a more systematic method. There are at least four methods for solving quadratic equations. These will now be explained.

20.2 SOLVING A PURE QUADRATIC EQUATION

The method of solving pure quadratics has an approach similar to that for solving linear equations. In general, we may use the following steps:

1. *Isolate the term containing x^2, transposing if necessary.*

2. *If x^2 has a coefficient other than "1", divide both sides of the equation by the coefficient.*

3. *Take the square roots of both sides of the equation.*

We illustrate the procedure with examples.

Example 1. Solve the pure quadratic $\qquad 3x^2 - 75 = 0$

Solution. Transposing the constant term, $\qquad 3x^2 = 75$

Dividing both sides by 3, $\qquad\qquad\qquad x^2 = 25$

Taking the square root of both
sides of the equation,
$$x = \begin{cases} +5 \\ -5 \end{cases}$$

The answer is often written $\qquad\qquad x = \pm 5$
or as the solution set $\{5, -5\}$.

Note. Actually, it should be understood that the square roots of the left side of the equation are $+x$ and $-x$, just as the square roots of the right side are $+5$ and -5. This would lead to the following condition:

$$\left.\begin{array}{r}+x \\ -x\end{array}\right\} = \left\{\begin{array}{r}+5 \\ -5\end{array}\right.$$

The foregoing statement really means four equations:

$$+x = +5$$
$$+x = -5$$
$$-x = +5$$
$$-x = -5$$

However, we notice that the first and the fourth equations have the same meaning and the second and the third equations have the same meaning. For this reason, in actual work the "$+$" and "$-$" are omitted before the x on one side of the equation.

Example 2. Solve the pure quadratic $\qquad 4x^2 - 7 = 0$

Solution. Transposing the constant term, $\qquad 4x^2 = 7$
Dividing both sides by 4, $\qquad x^2 = \frac{7}{4}$
Taking the square root of both sides of
the equation, $\qquad x = \dfrac{\pm\sqrt{7}}{2}$

In this example the roots are irrational. In decimal form they may be stated approximately:

$$r_1 = \frac{+2.646}{2} = +1.323 \qquad r_2 = \frac{-2.646}{2} = -1.323$$

Example 3. Solve the pure quadratic $\qquad 2x^2 + 24 = 0$

Solution. Transposing the constant term, $\qquad 2x^2 = -24$
Dividing both sides by 2, $\qquad x^2 = -12$
Taking the square root of both sides of
the equation, $\qquad x = \pm\sqrt{-12}$

At this point we simply mention the fact that the square roots of negative numbers are called *imaginary numbers*. Imaginary numbers are more fully discussed in Chapter 21. All we do at this point is to say that in equations such as Example 3 the roots are *imaginary*.

Exercise 20.1

Solve the following pure quadratic equations by the foregoing method:

1. $x^2 - 9 = 0$ 2. $25 - x^2 = 0$ 3. $4x^2 - 25 = 0$
4. $9n^2 - 49 = 0$ 5. $x^2 - 5 = 0$ 6. $3y^2 - 6 = 0$

7. $2t^2 - 7 = 0$ **8.** $4x^2 - 3 = 0$ **9.** $x^2 + 13 = 0$

10. $18y^2 - 5 = 0$ **11.** $9x^2 - 1 = 0$ **12.** $r^2 - 32 = 0$

13. $R^2 - 10^6 = 0$ **14.** $x^2 + 9 = 0$ **15.** $2x^2 + 5 = 0$

16. $n^2 + 23 = 0$ **17.** $16 - 9h^2 = 0$ **18.** $x^2 - a^2 = 0$

19. $8y^2 - 3 = 0$ **20.** $3x^2 + 7 = 0$ **21.** $S - 16t^2 = 0$
                                                                             (solve for t)

22. $A - \pi r^2 = 0$ **23.** $V = \pi r^2 h$ **24.** $V = \frac{1}{3}\pi r^2 h$

     (solve for r)   (solve for r)   (solve for r)

25. $F = \dfrac{Kab}{d^2}$ **26.** $K = \dfrac{Mv^2}{2}$ **27.** $F = \dfrac{Mv^2}{r}$

     (solve for d)   (solve for v)   (solve for v)

20.3 SOLVING A QUADRATIC EQUATION BY FACTORING

A quadratic equation may sometimes be solved by *factoring*. Consider the equation $x^2 - 5x + 6 = 0$. Factoring the left side, we get

$$(x - 2)(x - 3) = 0$$

Before we finish the solution of this equation by factoring, consider what is implied in the statement

$$(x - 2)(x - 3) = 0$$

Here we have two factors whose product is zero (0). Let us see what this implies.

Now, we know that if we multiply two or more factors and if one of the factors is zero then the product must be zero, regardless of the other factors. Examples:

$$(4) \cdot (0) = 0 \qquad (0) \cdot (5) = 0 \qquad (6) \cdot (0) \cdot (3) = 0$$

$$(2847) \cdot (5963) \cdot (791) \cdot (0) \cdot (645) = 0$$

Moreover, we know that if the product of two or more factors is zero, one of the factors *must* be zero. It is impossible to multiply numbers together and get zero for a product unless *one* of the numbers is zero. Examples:

If $a \cdot b = 0$, then either a or b *must* be zero (0).

If $x \cdot y \cdot z = 0$, then x, y, or z must be zero.

If $a \cdot b \cdot c \cdot d \cdot e = 0$, then at least *one* of the factors must be zero. They need not all be zero.

Suppose we have the following equation:

$$(x - 4)(x - 2)(x + 3)(x)(x - 1) = 0$$

Here we have five factors whose product is equal to zero. Therefore, we know that at least *one* of the factors must be equal to zero. The equation will be true if *any* one of the factors is equal to zero. Therefore, we may set each one of the factors equal to zero and solve the resulting equation.

If the first factor, $x - 4$, is equal to 0, then $x = 4$. The number 4 is a root of the equation because if 4 is put in place of x in the equation the statement is true. Does $(4 - 4)(4 - 2)(4 + 3)(4)(4 - 1) = 0$? Yes.

You will note that all of the factors do not have to be equal to zero at the same time.

The equation $(x - 4)(x - 2)(x + 3)(x)(x - 1) = 0$ has five roots. They are found by setting each factor equal to zero and solving the resulting equations. The work usually takes the following form:

if $x - 4 = 0$	if $x - 2 = 0$	if $x + 3 = 0$
then $x = 4$;	then $x = 2$;	then $x = -3$;
if $x = 0$	if $x - 1 = 0$	
then $x = 0$;	then $x = 1$	

The foregoing equation has five roots: 4, 2, -3, 0 and 1. Any one of these roots will make the equation true. The roots are usually called

$$r_1 \qquad r_2 \qquad r_3 \qquad r_4 \qquad \text{and} \qquad r_5$$

Now let us go back to the equation $x^2 - 5x + 6 = 0$
Factoring the left side, $(x - 2)(x - 3) = 0$

We set each factor equal to zero and solve:

if $x - 2 = 0$	if $x - 3 = 0$
then $x = 2$, r_1	then $x = 3$, r_2

It is immaterial which root is called r_1 and which r_2.

The entire procedure of solving a quadratic equation by factoring depends on having *zero* as the product of two factors; that is, one side of the equation must be zero. If the product of two factors is not zero, we know nothing about either factor. For instance, consider the equation

$$x^2 - 5x + 6 = 12.$$

It is possible to factor the left side: $(x - 2)(x - 3) = 12$.

We cannot solve the equation in this form because we know nothing about either factor. If the product were zero, we would be certain that one of the factors would be zero. This problem may possibly be solved if we transpose the 12, so that one side of the equation becomes zero.

$$x^2 - 5x + 6 = 12$$

Transposing, we get $\qquad x^2 - 5x + 6 - 12 = 0$

or $\qquad\qquad\qquad\qquad x^2 - 5x - 6 = 0$

Factoring the left side, $\qquad (x - 6)(x + 1) = 0$

$$\text{if} \quad x - 6 = 0 \qquad\qquad \text{if} \quad x + 1 = 0$$
$$\text{then} \quad x = 6, \quad r_1 \qquad\qquad \text{then} \quad x = -1, \quad r_2$$

Although factoring can sometimes be used to solve quadratics, it cannot be used when an expression cannot be factored. For this reason, this method is not very useful in most practical problems involving quadratics.

To show how quadratic equations may be solved by factoring, we shall work out several examples.

Example 1.   Solve by factoring: $3x^2 + 7x + 2 = 0$

Solution.   Factoring, $(3x + 1)(x + 2) = 0$
Set each factor equal to zero and solve:

$$\text{if } 3x + 1 = 0 \qquad\qquad \text{if } x + 2 = 0$$
$$\text{then} \quad x = -\tfrac{1}{3}, \; r_1 \qquad\qquad \text{then} \quad x = -2, \; r_2$$

Example 2.   Solve by factoring: $4x^2 = 5x + 6$

Solution.   Transposing, $4x^2 - 5x - 6 = 0$
Factoring, $(4x + 3)(x - 2) = 0$
Set each factor equal to zero and solve:

$$\text{if } 4x + 3 = 0 \qquad\qquad \text{if } x - 2 = 0$$
$$\text{then} \quad x = -\tfrac{3}{4}, \; r_1 \qquad\qquad \text{then} \quad x = 2, \; r_2$$

Example 3.   Solve by factoring: $3x^2 = 5x$

Solution.   Transposing, $3x^2 - 5x = 0$
Factoring, $x(3x - 5) = 0$
Set each factor equal to zero and solve:

$$\text{if} \quad x = 0 \qquad\qquad \text{if } 3x - 5 = 0$$
$$\text{then} \quad x = 0, \; r_1 \qquad\qquad \text{then} \quad x = \frac{5}{3}, \; r_2$$

Note.   In solving the equation $3x^2 = 5x$, we must be careful to solve for both roots. A common error is to divide both sides of the equation by x. If this is done, we get the new equation $3x = 5$, from which we get $x = \tfrac{5}{3}$. By dividing both sides of the equation by x, we lose one root, $x = 0$. A quadratic equation has *two* roots.

Example 4.   Solve by factoring: $x^2 - 8x + 16 = 0$

Solution.   Factoring, $(x - 4)(x - 4) = 0$

Set each factor equal to zero and solve:

$$\text{if } x - 4 = 0 \qquad\qquad \text{if } x - 4 = 0$$
$$\text{then} \quad x = 4, \; r_1 \qquad\qquad \text{then} \quad x = 4, \; r_2$$

In this equation, we note that the two roots are equal. The roots are $+4$ and $+4$. We might be inclined to say that the equation has only one root. It is true that the only number we need to use for a check is 4. However, we have said that every quadratic equation has two roots. For this reason, it is better to think of the equation in Example 4 as having two roots, but both are the same. Such an equation is sometimes said to have a *double root*.

Example 5. Even a pure quadratic may be solved by factoring.
Solve by factoring: $x^2 - 9 = 0$

Solution. Factoring, $(x - 3)(x + 3) = 0$
By setting each factor equal to zero, we get $x = 3$ and $x = -3$.

Exercise 20.2

Solve the following by factoring, if possible:

1. $x^2 - x - 6 = 0$	**2.** $y^2 + 7y = -12$	**3.** $n^2 + 6 = 5n$
4. $r^2 = 4r + 12$	**5.** $x^2 = 8x + 84$	**6.** $42 = x + x^2$
7. $6x^2 - 5x = 6$	**8.** $12y^2 - 12 = 7y$	**9.** $x^2 - 16 = 0$
10. $x^2 = 25$	**11.** $4R^2 = 49$	**12.** $3x^2 + 7x = 0$
13. $5N^2 = 2N$	**14.** $4x^2 + 9 = 12x$	**15.** $9x^2 = 100$
16. $9n^2 + 1 = 6n$	**17.** $3x^2 + x = 2$	**18.** $n + 5 = 6n^2$
19. $5x + 6 = 2x^2$	**20.** $e^2 + 9 = 6e$	**21.** $5p + 4 = 6p^2$
22. $7k = 4k^2$	**23.** $x^2 - 2x = 3$	**24.** $15y^2 = 3y$

20.4 SOLVING A QUADRATIC EQUATION BY COMPLETING A SQUARE

We illustrate this method by an example.

Example 1. Solve by completing a square: $x^2 - 6x - 7 = 0$.
Solution. The first step is to see that the coefficient of x^2 is 1.
Transpose the constant term, -7: $\qquad x^2 - 6x = 7$.
Now we add a quantity to both sides of the equation that will make the left side a perfect square in x. In this case we add the number 9 to both sides of the equation and get $\qquad\qquad x^2 - 6x + 9 = 7 + 9$.
We write the left side as a square and combine the numbers
on the right: $\qquad\qquad\qquad (x - 3)^2 = 16$

Take the square root of both sides: $\qquad x - 3 = \begin{cases} +4 \\ -4 \end{cases}$

This is usually written $\qquad\qquad\qquad x - 3 = \pm 4$
Solve for x: $\qquad\qquad\qquad x = 3 + 4 \qquad$ and $\qquad x = 3 - 4$
$\qquad\qquad\qquad\qquad\qquad\qquad\qquad x = 7 \qquad\qquad\qquad\qquad x = -1$

Of course, the foregoing equation could have been solved more easily by factoring.

The method of solving a quadratic equation by completing a square can be used for all types of quadratics, even when factoring is not possible. However, the method is a rather long, complicated process. For this reason it is not often used in practical work. In much work in advanced mathematics, however, the technique of completing a square is a useful device. Its chief use for our purpose here is in deriving a general formula for solving all quadratics. For this reason we shall work out a few examples by this method.

For the method of solving a quadratic by completing a square, we have this general procedure:

1. *See that the coefficient of x^2 is 1. If it is some other number than 1, divide both sides by the coefficient of x^2.*

2. *Transpose the constant term to the right side of the equation.*

3. *Add some quantity to both sides that will make the left side a perfect square. The quantity to be added will always be the square of one half of the coefficient of x.*

4. *Write the left side as a square and at the same time combine the terms on the right side.*

5. *Take the square root of both sides, using both signs ($+$ and $-$) on the right side.*

6. *Solve the resulting equation for x.*

Example 2.   Solve by completing a square: $3x^2 + 7x + 2 = 0$

Solution.   Divide both sides of the equation by 3: $x^2 + \dfrac{7}{3}x + \dfrac{2}{3} = 0$

Transpose $\frac{2}{3}$ to the right side: $x^2 + \dfrac{7}{3}x = -\dfrac{2}{3}$

Add the square of $\frac{1}{2}$ of $\frac{7}{3}$ to both sides; in this case $\frac{49}{36}$: $x^2 + \dfrac{7}{3}x + \dfrac{49}{36} = -\dfrac{2}{3} + \dfrac{49}{36}$

Write the left side as a square, and combine the terms on the right: $\left(x + \dfrac{7}{6}\right)^2 = \dfrac{25}{36}$

Take the square root of both sides: $x + \dfrac{7}{6} = \pm\dfrac{5}{6}$

Solve for x: $x = -\dfrac{7}{6} \pm \dfrac{5}{6} = -\dfrac{1}{3}$ and -2.

Example 3.   Solve by completing a square: $x^2 - x - 5 = 0$

Solution.   Transpose the -5 to the right side: $x^2 - x = 5$

Add the square of $\frac{1}{2}$ of the coefficient of x to both sides: $x^2 - x + \dfrac{1}{4} = 5 + \dfrac{1}{4}$

Write the left side as a square: $\left(x - \dfrac{1}{2}\right)^2 = \dfrac{21}{4}$

Take the square root of both sides: $x - \dfrac{1}{2} = \dfrac{\pm\sqrt{21}}{2}$

Solve for x:

$$x = \frac{1 \pm \sqrt{21}}{2}$$

Note that the roots of this equation are irrational. In decimal form they may be stated approximately:

$$r_1 = 2.7913 \qquad r_2 = -1.7913$$

Example 4. Solve by completing a square: $\qquad 5x^2 - 2x + 3 = 0$

Solution. Divide both sides of the equation by 5: $\qquad x^2 - \frac{2}{5}x + \frac{3}{5} = 0$

Transpose $\frac{3}{5}$: $\qquad x^2 - \frac{2}{5}x = -\frac{3}{5}$

Add $(\frac{1}{5})^2$ to both sides: $\qquad x^2 - \frac{2}{5}x + \frac{1}{25} = -\frac{3}{5} + \frac{1}{25}$

Write the left side as a square: $\qquad \left(x - \frac{1}{5}\right)^2 = \frac{-14}{25}$

Take the square root of both sides: $\qquad x - \frac{1}{5} = \frac{\pm\sqrt{-14}}{5}$

Solve for x: $\qquad x = \frac{1 \pm \sqrt{-14}}{5}$

Note that the foregoing equation has *imaginary* roots.

Exercise 20.3

Solve by completing a square:

1. $x^2 - 8x - 9 = 0$
2. $3x^2 - 10x + 3 = 0$
3. $2y^2 - 5y - 3 = 0$
4. $4c^2 + 3c - 1 = 0$
5. $5I^2 - 18I + 9 = 0$
6. $t^2 + 7t + 12 = 0$
7. $2n^2 + 6n + 1 = 0$
8. $4x^2 + 3x - 2 = 0$
9. $2x^2 - 4x + 5 = 0$
10. $x^2 - 6x + 9 = 0$
11. $3x^2 + 5x = 0$
12. $4x^2 - 9 = 0$
13. $7x^2 - 3x = 0$
14. $x^2 - 4x + 12 = 0$
15. $x^2 + 5x - 3 = 0$
16. $4E^2 - 5E - 6 = 0$
17. $6x^2 + 5x - 6 = 0$
18. $3x^2 - 2x + 1 = 0$
19. $7y^2 - 4y + 3 = 0$
20. $8x^2 + 14x - 15 = 0$

20.5 SOLVING A QUADRATIC EQUATION BY FORMULA

In any quadratic equation, for example, $3x^2 + 7x + 2 = 0$, the roots are determined by the constants 3, 7, and 2. If these numbers are placed into the proper formula, the roots will be obtained. Here is the formula:

$$x = \frac{-b \pm \sqrt{b^2 - 4ac}}{2a}$$

In the quadratic formula a represents the coefficient of x^2; b represents the coefficient of x; c represents the constant term.

In the quadratic equation $3x^2 + 7x + 2 = 0$

$$a = 3 \qquad b = 7 \qquad c = 2$$

In order to identify properly the three constants, a, b, and c, in any quadratic equation, all the terms must be on one side of the equation and a zero (0) on the other side.

If the a, b, and c are placed properly in the formula, the result will be the roots of the equation. Let us see where the formula comes from.

The formula is derived by starting with the general quadratic equation $ax^2 + bx + c = 0$. We solve this general equation by completing a square in x.

We start with $\qquad\qquad ax^2 + bx + c = 0$

Divide through by a: $\qquad\qquad x^2 + \frac{b}{a}x + \frac{c}{a} = 0$

Transpose: $\qquad\qquad x^2 + \frac{b}{a}x = -\frac{c}{a}$

Add $\left(\dfrac{b}{2a}\right)^2$ to both sides: $\qquad x^2 + \frac{b}{a}x + \frac{b^2}{4a^2} = -\frac{c}{a} + \frac{b^2}{4a^2}$

Write the left side as a square: $\qquad \left(x + \frac{b}{2a}\right)^2 = \frac{b^2 - 4ac}{4a^2}$

Take the square root of both sides $\qquad x + \frac{b}{2a} = \frac{\pm\sqrt{b^2 - 4ac}}{2a}$

Solve for x: $\qquad\qquad x = \frac{-b \pm \sqrt{b^2 - 4ac}}{2a}$

This is the famous quadratic formula. If the numbers represented by the constants a, b, and c are placed properly in the formula, the roots are easily computed. It is important that we identify these constants correctly, especially with regard to sign. The equation should always be written so that the a is positive.

The quadratic formula can be used for *all* types of quadratic equations. For this reason it is the most useful method for solving quadratics. The formula should be thoroughly memorized. To illustrate its use, we solve several examples.

Example 1. Solve by formula: $3x^2 + 7x + 2 = 0$.

Solution. In this example $a = 3$, $b = 7$, $c = 2$. One of the best ways to memorize the formula is to write it down for each of the first few problems.

$$x = \frac{-b \pm \sqrt{b^2 - 4ac}}{2a}$$

Inserting the constants, $x = \dfrac{-7 \pm \sqrt{49 - (4)(3)(2)}}{6}$

$$= \frac{-7 \pm \sqrt{49 - 24}}{6}$$

$$= \frac{-7 \pm \sqrt{25}}{6}$$

$$= \frac{-7 \pm 5}{6}$$

$$x = \frac{-2}{6} = -\frac{1}{3}, \ r_1 \qquad x = \frac{-12}{6} = -2, \ r_2$$

Example 2. Solve by formula: $\qquad 4x^2 = 5x + 6$

Solution. Rewrite the equation: $\quad 4x^2 - 5x - 6 = 0$
In this equation, $\qquad\qquad\qquad a = 4 \qquad b = -5 \qquad c = -6$

Inserting the constants, $\qquad x = \dfrac{+5 \pm \sqrt{25 - (4)(4)(-6)}}{8}$

$$= \frac{+5 \pm \sqrt{25 + 96}}{8}$$

For one root, $\qquad x = \dfrac{+5 + 11}{8} = \dfrac{16}{8} = +2$

For the other root, $\qquad x = \dfrac{+5 - 11}{8} = \dfrac{-6}{8} = -\dfrac{3}{4}$

Example 3. Solve by formula: $\qquad x^2 - 6x + 9 = 0$

Solution. Inserting the constants, $\qquad x = \dfrac{+6 \pm \sqrt{36 - 36}}{2}$

$$x = \frac{+6 \pm 0}{2} = \begin{cases} +3 \\ +3 \end{cases}$$

In this equation we note that the roots are equal. This will always be the case when the quantity under the radical sign is equal to zero (0). In such an equation, although we get only one distinct value for x, we should remember that there are two roots but that they are equal.

Example 4.   Solve by formula: $x^2 - 6x + 4 = 0$

Solution.   Inserting the constants, $x = \dfrac{+6 \pm \sqrt{36 - 16}}{2}$

$$= \dfrac{+6 \pm \sqrt{20}}{2}$$

In this example we note that the roots are irrational. However, the radical may be simplified and the roots reduced to simpler terms.

$$x = \dfrac{+6 \pm 2\sqrt{5}}{2} = +3 \pm \sqrt{5} \quad \text{or} \quad x = \begin{cases} 5.236 \text{ (approx.)} \\ 0.764 \text{ (approx.)} \end{cases}$$

Example 5.   Solve by formula: $3x^2 + 5x + 4 = 0$

Solution.   Inserting the constants, $x = \dfrac{-5 \pm \sqrt{25 - 48}}{6}$

$$= \dfrac{-5 \pm \sqrt{-23}}{6}$$

At this point we simply state that the roots are imaginary, since we have the square root of a negative number.

Example 6.   Solve by formula: $3x^2 - 5x = 0$

Solution.   Inserting the constants, $x = \dfrac{+5 \pm \sqrt{25 - (4)(3)(0)}}{6}$

In this equation, $c = 0$. $x = \dfrac{+5 \pm \sqrt{25 - 0}}{6} = \dfrac{+5 \pm 5}{6}$

In this equation one root is zero. $x = \dfrac{+5}{3} \quad \text{and} \quad x = 0$

Exercise 20.4

Solve the exercises in Section 20.3 by formula. Solve the following quadratic equations by any method that seems most convenient.

1. $x^2 - 6x + 4 = 0$ 2. $5y^2 + 7y + 2 = 0$
3. $2n^2 = 3n + 5$ 4. $9x^2 + 12x + 1 = 0$
5. $4h^2 + 4 = 9h$ 6. $4r^2 + 9 = 12r$

7. $3y + 7 = 4y^2$

8. $2 = x + 3x^2$

9. $3y^2 - 2y + 6 = 0$

10. $0 = 4b^2 + 7b + 3$

11. $t^2 - t + \frac{1}{4} = 0$

12. $3 - 2x = 6x^2$

13. $7a^2 - 4a - 3 = 0$

14. $3t^2 + 2t + 1 = 0$

15. $4c^2 = 7c + 2$

16. $9E^2 + 24E + 16 = 0$

17. $5x^2 = 2x + 2$

18. $4Z^2 - Z - 2 = 0$

19. $0 = k^2 + 6k + 3$

20. $x^2 + 2x - 1 = 0$

21. $2n^2 - 5n = 3$

22. $5x^2 + 2x + 1 = 0$

23. $E^2 + E = 3$

24. $3x^2 + 2x = 0$

25. $4x = 5x^2 - 1$

26. $2R^2 + 8R + 1 = 0$

27. $4x^2 = 5x + 6$

28. $3I^2 = 4I + 3$

29. $2x^2 - 8 = 0$

30. $E^2 - 7E - 8 = 0$

31. $2h^2 + 7 = 15h$

32. $4I^2 + 12I + 9 = 0$

33. $\dfrac{4}{x+3} + 2 - \dfrac{3}{x-3} = 0$

34. $\dfrac{4}{x-2} + 3 - \dfrac{3}{x+3} = 0$

35. $\dfrac{x}{x-2} - \dfrac{3x}{x+1} - 1 = 0$

36. $\dfrac{2}{x-1} + \dfrac{8}{x+3} - 5 = 0$

Exercise 20.5

1. Divide 20 into two parts whose product is 84.

2. Divide 11 into two parts whose product is $29\frac{3}{4}$.

3. The sum of a number and its square is 72. Find the number.

4. Find two consecutive odd numbers whose product is 143.

5. The sum of the squares of two consecutive even numbers is 340. What are the numbers?

6. The reciprocal of a fraction is $\frac{16}{15}$ more than the fraction. What is the fraction itself?

7. A rectangle whose length is 4 in. more than its width has an area of 45 sq in. Find the width and the length of the rectangle.

8. Two square fields have a combined area of 5625 sq rd. The side of one field is 15 rd longer than the side of the other square. Find the length of a side of each square.

9. A lawn is 120 ft long and 90 ft wide. After a strip of uniform width has been mowed around the two sides and the two ends, half the total area has been mowed. Find the width and the length of the remainder.

10. A rectangular lawn is 4 ft longer than it is wide. It is surrounded by a sidewalk of uniform width. The walk contains 32 sq ft more than the lawn itself. Find the size of the lawn if the walk is 4 ft wide.

11. A rectangular flower garden whose width is 7 ft less than its length is surrounded by a walk 3 ft wide. The total area of the walk and the garden is twice the area of the garden alone. Find the dimensions of the garden.

12. A man makes a regular trip of 180 miles by car at a regular average speed. One day, because of bad weather, his average speed was reduced by 9 mph. As a result, his trip took 1 hr longer. What was his usual speed?

13. A man made a trip of 360 miles. On the return trip his average speed was reduced by 15 mph, and, as a result, the return trip required 4 hr longer. Find his average speed each way.

14. A bus driver on a regular trip of 72 miles found that on one particular run his speed was reduced by 12 mph. As a result he was $\frac{1}{2}$ hr late. What was his regular speed?

15. A bus driver on a scheduled trip of 312 miles found that he had to reduce his average speed by 9 mph. As a result, the trip took $1\frac{1}{2}$ hr longer than the usual time. What was his usual speed?

16. A particular rifle bullet is fired directly upward from the ground. Its distance from the ground is given by the formula $s = 1200t - 16t^2$, in which s represents the distance (in feet) and t represents the time (in seconds). How long will it take the bullet to reach a height of 5600 ft?

17. An iron bar of uniform cross-sectional area weighs 180 lb. If the length is increased 3 ft by rolling, the weight per foot is 2 lb less. Find the length of the original bar.

18. A number of people chartered a bus for a trip for $270, the expense to be shared equally. At the last moment six of the people were unable to go, and, as a result, the share of each of those who went on the trip was increased by $1.50. How many people went on the trip?

19. A square, 3 in. on a side, is cut out of each corner of a square sheet of aluminum, and the sides are then turned up to form a rectangular container. If the volume of the container is 192 cu in., what was the size of the original sheet of aluminum?

20. A rectangular sheet of metal has a length 6 in. longer than the width. A 4-in. square is cut out of each corner and the edges are turned up to form a rectangular container. If the volume of the container is 640 cu in., find the dimensions of the original sheet of metal.

Quiz on Chapters 18–20. Form A.

1. Simplify the expressions:

   (a) $\dfrac{(3x)^0 - 9x^0}{6x^0 - (8x)^0}$

   (b) $\dfrac{x^{-3} + y^{-3}}{x^{-2} - y^{-2}}$

2. Simplify these expressions:

   (a) $9^{\frac{3}{2}} - 8^{-\frac{2}{3}} + 16^{\frac{1}{4}} - 3(5)^0$

   (b) $\sqrt{16 + 9 + 144}$

3. Simplify:

   (a) $5\sqrt{48} - 2\sqrt{147} + 4\sqrt{180} + \sqrt{16}$

   (b) $\sqrt{\dfrac{3}{8}} + \sqrt{\dfrac{3}{50}} - \sqrt{\dfrac{5}{32}}$

4. Divide as indicated:

   (a) $(\sqrt{5}) \div (3 - \sqrt{5})$

   (b) $(5\sqrt{3} - 2\sqrt{6}) \div (2\sqrt{3} + \sqrt{6})$

5. Solve the following as pure quadratics:

   (a) $16x^2 - 25 = 0$

   (b) $8x^2 - 3 = 0$

   (c) $x^2 + 16 = 0$

6. Solve the following by factoring:

(a) $x^2 = 13x + 48$ (b) $5x + 2 = 3x^2$ (c) $3x^2 = 7x$ (d) $9x^2 = 49$

7. Solve by completing the square:

(a) $x^2 = 8x + 9$ (b) $2x^2 + 3 = 7x$

8. Solve by formula:

(a) $4x + 3 = 3x^2$ (b) $109 = 12x - 4x^2$ (c) $9x^2 + 4 = 12x$

Quiz on Chapters 18–20. Form B.

1. Simplify the expressions:

(a) $\dfrac{8x^0 - (5x)^0}{(6x)^0 - 4x^0}$ (b) $\dfrac{c^{-2} - d^{-2}}{c^{-3} - d^{-3}}$

2. Simplify these expressions:

(a) $4^{3/2} - 16^{-3/4} + 27^{1/3} - 2(7)^0$ (b) $\sqrt{81 + 4 + 36}$

3. Simplify:

(a) $4\sqrt{45} - 3\sqrt{80} + 2\sqrt{192} - \sqrt{36}$ (b) $\sqrt{\dfrac{5}{18}} + \sqrt{\dfrac{5}{8}} - \sqrt{\dfrac{5}{27}}$

4. Divide as indicated:

(a) $(\sqrt{3}) \div (5 + \sqrt{3})$ (b) $(3\sqrt{6} - 4\sqrt{2}) \div (\sqrt{6} - 2\sqrt{2})$

5. Solve the following as pure quadratics:

(a) $4x^2 - 49 = 0$ (b) $18x^2 - 5 = 0$ (c) $x^2 + 9 = 0$

6. Solve the following by factoring:

(a) $x^2 = 60 - 17x$ (b) $2 = 5x^2 + 3x$ (c) $7x^2 = -3x$ (d) $4x^2 = 25$

7. Solve by completing the square:

(a) $x^2 + 9 = 10x$ (b) $5x = 2 - 3x^2$

8. Solve by formula:

(a) $5x^2 = 4x + 2$ (b) $117 = 6x - 2x^2$ (c) $20x = 4x^2 + 25$

21
Imaginary and Complex Numbers

21.1 IMAGINARY NUMBERS

In this chapter we study a new kind of number, called an *imaginary* number. This number is entirely different from any kind we have used up to this time. Imaginary numbers come about through the solution of some quadratic and higher degree equations. They are very useful in the study of electricity, especially in the theory of alternating currents. Let us see, then, what is meant by an imaginary number and how it comes about.

In much work in mathematics it often happens that we are faced with finding the square root of -9, -25, or of some other negative number. Suppose we have the equation

$$x^2 + 9 = 0$$

Transposing, we get $\qquad x^2 = -9$

To solve the equation, we must find a value for x. Taking the square root of both sides, we see that x must be equal to $\pm\sqrt{-9}$. In other words, x must be equal to some number such that this number squared (that is, the number multiplied by itself) will equal -9.

Now, we know that the square root of -9 is neither $+3$ nor -3. If we multiply $+3$ by itself, we get $+9$. If we multiply -3 by itself, we also get $+9$. Whenever we square any positive or negative number we always get a positive number as the product. If we are to have the square root of -9, we must have some number that can be multiplied by *itself* to produce -9. This is the meaning of square root. At first thought this may seem impossible, yet the problem may not be so difficult as it first appears.

In solving an equation, if we get some answer such as $\sqrt{-9}$, our first question may be: "What does it mean?" The first thing to do is to recognize that the square root of a negative number must be a new kind of number different from those we have already studied. In order to get a better understanding of its meaning, let us first recall exactly what we mean by the square root of any number.

You will recall that the $\sqrt{2}$, $\sqrt{3}$, etc., *cannot* be expressed as exact decimals or as exact common fractions. Such numbers are called irrational numbers.

Although we cannot express the exact square root of 2 as a decimal, we can write it as a symbol: $\sqrt{2}$.

Now, we have seen that the square root of a -9 is neither $+3$ nor -3. We know that we *cannot* express the square root of -9 as we express the square root of 25, for example. Yet, we must also know that if we were able to find the *exact* square root of -9 and then multiply it by *itself*, we must get -9 as the product. This must be so, simply from the definition of square root.

Although we cannot express the square root of -9 as an ordinary number, we can write it as a symbol:

$$\sqrt{-9}$$

If we use the symbol $\sqrt{-9}$ as the exact square root of -9, then this symbol multiplied by itself must equal -9, that is,

$$(\sqrt{-9})(\sqrt{-9}) = -9$$

In this multiplication, if we were to say that the answer is anything but -9, then we would not have had the exact square root of -9 to begin with.

The symbol $\sqrt{-9}$ is called an imaginary number. *The square root of any negative number is called an imaginary number.* This is not a good name for such numbers. Here the word *imaginary* does not mean what we ordinarily mean by that word. Anything imaginary is usually understood to be something we can only imagine. These numbers were *called* imaginary at a time when people did not fully understand them.

However, we can do much more than merely imagine such numbers. We can actually write the square root of -9: thus $\sqrt{-9}$. We can actually see the number. Moreover, we can compute with it. We can add, subtract, multiply, and divide such numbers. Therefore, they cannot be something that exists only in our imagination. Still, they are called imaginary numbers. All other numbers are called *real numbers*.

The terms "real numbers" and "imaginary numbers," are probably misleading, since we can really work with all of them. Some people have proposed calling the square roots of negative numbers by some other name than imaginary, but such proposals have not been generally accepted. Therefore, at the present time we have these definitions:

1. The even roots of negative numbers are called *imaginary numbers*.
2. All other numbers are called *real numbers*.

Examples.

Imaginary numbers: $\sqrt{-4}$, $\sqrt{-7}$, $-\sqrt{-16}$, $\sqrt{-3/5}$, $-\sqrt{-20}$.

Real numbers: 3, -5, $2/3$, $-\sqrt{7}$, π, $-\pi$, $-3/7$, -4.37.

Imaginary numbers are always confusing to a student when he is faced
with them for the first time. You may wonder, "What good are such numbers
anyway?" It is true, we cannot count with imaginary numbers, but neither
can we count with negative numbers. We cannot measure the length of a
room with imaginary numbers, but neither can we do so with negative
numbers. You will recall that people once called negative numbers "fictitious"
and discarded them as having no meaning. Yet negative numbers kept
forcing themselves into the solution of equations, and now they have very
important meanings. It has been the same with imaginary numbers. Although
imaginary numbers may at first be confusing, they have a very important use
in engineering and other mathematics and should therefore be understood.

21.2 SIMPLIFYING IMAGINARY NUMBERS

When we come to imaginary numbers, the first problem we face is to devise
methods and rules for working with them. The first thing we must do is to
simplify the form of the number.

Imaginary numbers can be simplified in a way that is similar to the
method of simplifying radicals. We have seen that a radical, such as $\sqrt{32}$,
can be simplified thus:

$$\sqrt{32} = \sqrt{16 \cdot 2} = \sqrt{16} \cdot \sqrt{2} = 4\sqrt{2}$$

Imaginary numbers may be simplified in a similar manner. The radicand
is factored so that one of its *factors* is (-1). The remaining factor is simplified
as any ordinary radical. The following examples show how this is done:

$$\sqrt{-9} \ \ = \sqrt{9(-1)} \ \ = \sqrt{9} \cdot \sqrt{-1} \ \ = 3\sqrt{-1} \quad \text{or 3 of these:} \sqrt{-1}$$

$$\sqrt{-25} \ = \sqrt{25(-1)} \ = \sqrt{25} \cdot \sqrt{-1} \ = 5\sqrt{-1} \quad \text{or 5 of these:} \sqrt{-1}$$

$$\sqrt{-64} \ = \sqrt{64(-1)} \ = \sqrt{64} \cdot \sqrt{-1} \ = 8\sqrt{-1} \quad \text{or 8 of these:} \sqrt{-1}$$

$$\sqrt{-121} = \sqrt{121(-1)} = \sqrt{121} \cdot \sqrt{-1} = 11\sqrt{-1}$$

$$\sqrt{-32} \ = \sqrt{32(-1)} \ = \sqrt{32} \cdot \sqrt{-1} \ = \sqrt{32}\sqrt{-1} = 4\sqrt{2} \cdot \sqrt{-1}$$

21.3 THE IMAGINARY UNIT

You will notice that in each of the foregoing examples the $\sqrt{-1}$ can be
isolated as a factor. This factor, $\sqrt{-1}$, is a sort of measuring *unit* for determining what might be called the amount of an imaginary number. It is called
the *imaginary unit*; that is,

$$\sqrt{-9} \quad \text{is 3 of these units} \qquad \text{or} \qquad 3\sqrt{-1}$$

$$\sqrt{-25} \text{ is 5 of these units} \quad \text{or} \quad 5\sqrt{-1}$$

$$\sqrt{-64} \text{ is 8 of these units} \quad \text{or} \quad 8\sqrt{-1}$$

Let us say, then, that

$$\sqrt{-1} = (i)\text{maginary unit}$$

This definition is often shortened to read $\sqrt{-1} = i$. In this case the i is used because it is the initial letter of the word *imaginary*. Then we can say

$$\sqrt{-9} = 3i; \quad \sqrt{-64} = 8i$$

$$\sqrt{-25} = 5i; \quad \sqrt{-169} = 13i$$

Remember, we do not get rid of the radical simply by calling it i. The letter i is used only for convenience to represent the number $\sqrt{-1}$. In electrical engineering the number $\sqrt{-1}$ is usually represented by the letter j, since it is common practice to let the letter i represent current. In this chapter we shall use both forms so that the student may become familiar with both.

One important fact to keep in mind is that such numbers as $\sqrt{-9}$ and $\sqrt{-25}$ are actual numbers. We may at first be inclined to feel that these numbers do not exist, since we cannot express them by the use of our common number expressions, such as whole numbers, fractions, and decimals. However, we do call them numbers because we can perform arithmetic operations with them. They can be added, subtracted, multiplied, and divided.

21.4   ADDITION AND SUBTRACTION OF IMAGINARY NUMBERS

Imaginary numbers may be added. First, we simplify all of them so that each one shows the imaginary unit $\sqrt{-1}$, or i. Then the numbers are added by adding the coefficients of i in the same way as similar algebraic terms are added.

Example 1.   Add
$$\sqrt{-9} + \sqrt{-25} + \sqrt{-49}$$
$$= 3\sqrt{-1} + 5\sqrt{-1} + 7\sqrt{-1}$$
$$= 3i + 5i + 7i$$
$$= 15i$$

Imaginary numbers may also be subtracted. Again, we simplify each imaginary number so that it shows the imaginary unit i. Then we subtract the numbers by subtracting the coefficients, just as we do with similar algebraic terms.

Example 2.   Subtract $\sqrt{-81} - \sqrt{-16}$
$$= 9\sqrt{-1} - 4\sqrt{-1}$$
$$= 9i - 4i$$
$$= 5i$$

Example 3.   Combine into one term $\sqrt{-4} + \sqrt{-36} - \sqrt{-144} + \sqrt{-1}$
$$= 2\sqrt{-1} + 6\sqrt{-1} - 12\sqrt{-1} + \sqrt{-1}$$
$$= 2i + 6i - 12i + i$$
$$= -3i$$

21.5   MULTIPLICATION OF IMAGINARY NUMBERS

Imaginary numbers may be multiplied together; they may also be multiplied by real numbers. However, in multiplication, we must remember that

$$\sqrt{-1} \cdot \sqrt{-1} = -1 \qquad i^2 = -1$$
$$i \cdot i = -1 \qquad j^2 = -1$$

Example 1.   Multiply $(9i)(5i)$.

In this example we multiply the two coefficients, 9 and 5, just as we would if we were multiplying $(9x)(5x)$. The coefficient in the answer is 45. Next, we multiply $(i)(i)$, which is equal to i^2. The product is $45i^2$. However, at this point, we remember that $i^2 = -1$. Therefore,

$$(9i)(5i) = 45i^2 = 45(-1) = -45$$

In fact, in our multiplication of imaginary numbers, whenever we get i^2, we should immediately call it -1.

Example 2.   Multiply $(-4)(7j)(3j)(2j)$.

The product of the coefficients is -168. In multiplying $(j)(j)(j)$, we first multiply the first two factors: $(j)(j) = -1$. This answer, -1, is then multiplied by the third factor: $(-1)(j) = -j$. Therefore,

$$(-4)(7j)(3j)(2j) = (-168)(-j) = +168j$$

Example 3.   Multiply $(\sqrt{-4})(\sqrt{-9})$.

In this example we first express each factor in terms of i.

The expression $\qquad\qquad (\sqrt{-4})(\sqrt{-9})$
becomes $\qquad\qquad (2i)(3i) = 6i^2 = 6(-1) = -6$

An example of this kind can easily lead to error in multiplication. For example, the following method is *incorrect*:

$$(\sqrt{-4})(\sqrt{-9}) = \sqrt{(-4)(-9)} = \sqrt{+36} = +6 \qquad \text{(wrong)}$$

The answer is wrong because the two negative radicands cannot be written as the product for the radicand of a single radical. The rule for signs in multiplication does *not* hold true for the multiplication of two separate radicands *when both radicands are negative.**

Note. Division of imaginary numbers is explained in connection with complex numbers.

Exercise 21.1

Simplify each of the following and express each in terms of i (or j):

1. $\sqrt{-4}$ **2.** $\sqrt{-25}$ **3.** $\sqrt{-49}$ **4.** $\sqrt{-100}$

5. $\sqrt{-169}$ **6.** $\sqrt{-400}$ **7.** $\sqrt{-16x^2}$ **8.** $\sqrt{-36b^2}$

9. $\sqrt{-64y^6}$ **10.** $\sqrt{-81a^4c^8}$ **11.** $\sqrt{-8}$ **12.** $\sqrt{-75}$

13. $\sqrt{-27}$ **14.** $\sqrt{-45x^3}$ **15.** $\sqrt{-\frac{1}{4}}$ **16.** $\sqrt{-9/16}$

17. $\sqrt{-3/8}$ **18.** $\sqrt{-7/32}$ **19.** $\sqrt{-50n^3r^5}$ **20.** $\sqrt{-5a/8x}$

Combine each of the following sets of imaginary numbers into a single term containing i (or j):

21. $\sqrt{-16} + \sqrt{-25} + \sqrt{-1}$ **22.** $\sqrt{-36} + \sqrt{-49} - \sqrt{-9}$

23. $\sqrt{-144} + \sqrt{-81} - \sqrt{-64}$ **24.** $\sqrt{-121} + \sqrt{-100} - \sqrt{-169}$

25. $3\sqrt{-4} + 5\sqrt{-9} - 2\sqrt{-25} - \sqrt{-1}$

26. $4\sqrt{-16} - 5\sqrt{-1} + 6\sqrt{-49} - 3\sqrt{-900}$

Multiply as indicated: (simplify answers):

27. $\sqrt{-25} \cdot \sqrt{-4}$ **28.** $\sqrt{-2} \cdot \sqrt{-32}$ **29.** $\sqrt{-5} \cdot \sqrt{-5}$

30. $(-3\sqrt{-4})(\sqrt{-49})$ **31.** $(-4\sqrt{-2})(-5\sqrt{-2})$ **32.** $\sqrt{-16} \cdot \sqrt{-9}$

* Imaginary numbers are usually considered neither positive nor negative, since they cannot be compared in size with real numbers. We cannot say that $8i$ is more or less than the real number 8. To try to compare $8i$ with the number 8 to see which is the larger is like trying to compare the two quantities 8 hours and 8 apples to see which is the greater. We might even go one step further and try to see which is larger, 8 inches or the number 8.

However, imaginary numbers do have positive and negative signs before them, as we have seen. Whether or not we call them positive and negative, a number such as $-5i$ has a direction and value opposite to that of the number $+5i$. We may choose to place the number $+5i$ in a *positive* direction on a scale and then call it a *positive imaginary number*. Then the number $-5i$ may be said to be an imaginary number in a *negative* direction and, therefore, *a negative imaginary number*. The terms *positive real number* and *negative real number* refer to *real* number directions; these directions have no reference to imaginary numbers. In the same way, we may say that the terms *positive imaginary number* and *negative imaginary number* refer only to imaginary numbers and have no reference to real numbers.

If we try to put ourselves in a world of only imaginary numbers, then we may speak of imaginary numbers in the same way we usually speak of real numbers. In this world of imaginary numbers we may choose to call one direction positive and the opposite direction negative. Then we may say the imaginary number $8i$ is greater than the imaginary number $5i$. However, there is no way to compare the size of an imaginary number with the size of a real number.

33. $\sqrt{-4} \cdot \sqrt{-81}$ **34.** $(5i)(4i)$ **35.** $(-3i)(-7i)$

36. $(-8j)(+3j)$ **37.** $(\sqrt{-7})^2$ **38.** $(4j)(-9j)$

39. $(j)(j)(j)$ **40.** i^4 **41.** i^5

42. i^8 **43.** j^{-4} **44.** i^{-2}

45. $(\sqrt{-4})^3$ **46.** j^{-1} **47.** i^{14}

21.6 COMPLEX NUMBERS

A complex number is a number that is partly real and partly imaginary. Such a number appears in the solution of some equations.

Suppose we solve the quadratic equation $x^2 - 4x + 13 = 0$. By using the quadratic formula, we find the two roots of the equation:

$$x^2 - 4x + 13 = 0$$

$$x = \frac{4 \pm \sqrt{16 - 52}}{2}$$

$$x = \frac{4 \pm \sqrt{-36}}{2}$$

$$x = \frac{4 \pm 6i}{2} = 2 \pm 3i$$

The roots are $2 + 3i$ and $2 - 3i$.

We must remember that the entire expression, $2 + 3i$, is to be considered as one number. It is one of the roots. The number $2 + 3i$, consists of two parts, one real and the other imaginary. The "2" is the real part; "3i" is the imaginary part. The entire number, $2 + 3i$, is called a *complex number*.

A complex number is defined as a number consisting of two parts, one real and the other imaginary. It has the form $a + bi$. By this expression, we mean that a represents the real part, and bi represents the imaginary part. The real part is separated from the imaginary part by a plus or minus sign. The coefficient b itself is real. The real part should always be written first, the imaginary part second.

If the letter j is used instead of i for $\sqrt{-1}$, as is usually done in electrical engineering, then the general form of a complex number is $a + bj$. The j factor is often written before its coefficient: thus $3 + 7i$ is often written $3 + j7$; $-5 + 4.32i$, is often written $-5 + j4.32$.

In the general complex number, $a + bi$, the real part a and the coefficient b may have any values. If the real part a is equal to zero, then the number is entirely imaginary and is called a *pure imaginary*. If b is equal to zero, then the number is entirely *real*. The complex number $0 + 5i$ is a pure imaginary number. The number $6 + 0i$ is a real number. Any number that is entirely real may be written as a complex number. For example, the number 6 may be written $6 + 0i$.

We often get complex numbers as roots of quadratic and higher degree equations. Here are some examples of complex numbers:

$3 + 4i$	$5 - 2i$	$-6 + 9j$	$8 - 3j$	$4 + j$	$\frac{3}{4} - \frac{2}{3}i$
$-9 - 5j$	$7 + 0i$	$-1 - j5.31$	$-7i$	$\frac{1}{2} - \frac{1}{2}i$	$\sqrt{3} - j\sqrt{5}$

21.7 CONJUGATE COMPLEX NUMBERS

Conjugate complex numbers are defined as any two complex numbers that differ only in the sign of the imaginary part, such as the two numbers $3 + 4i$ and $3 - 4i$. Each of the numbers is called the conjugate of the other. In two conjugate complex numbers the real parts are identically the same. The imaginary parts are exactly alike, except that they have opposite signs.

Exercise 21.2

Solve the following quadratic equations by formula. Notice that the two roots of each equation are conjugate complex numbers.

1. $x^2 - 6x + 13 = 0$	**2.** $y^2 - 10y + 34 = 0$	**3.** $2n^2 + n + 1 = 0$
4. $c^2 - 8c + 20 = 0$	**5.** $n^2 - 4n + 9 = 0$	**6.** $p^2 - 2p + 2 = 0$
7. $x^2 + 6x + 10 = 0$	**8.** $5r^2 + 2r + 1 = 0$	**9.** $v^2 + 4v + 16 = 0$
10. $t^2 - 2t + 3 = 0$	**11.** $q^2 - 5q + 52 = 0$	**12.** $3x^2 + x + 2 = 0$
13. $2h^2 - 8h + 5 = 0$	**14.** $t^2 + 12t + 100 = 0$	**15.** $x^2 - 20x + 500 = 0$
16. $2I^2 + 4I + 3 = 0$	**17.** $x^2 + 32 = 0$	**18.** $y^2 + 64 = 0$
19. $8n^2 + 3 = 0$	**20.** $7x^2 + 2 = 4x$	**21.** $5R^2 + 2 = 6R$
22. $9x^2 + 10 = 6x$	**23.** $10y = 13 + 2y^2$	**24.** $9z^2 + 29 = 12z$

21.8 ADDITION AND SUBTRACTION OF COMPLEX NUMBERS

The two parts of a complex number cannot be combined as we combine real numbers. We have seen that a rational number may be combined with an irrational number, if both are real. For instance, if we solve the quadratic equation $x^2 - 4x + 1 = 0$, we get the following roots:

$$x = 2 + \sqrt{3} \quad \text{and} \quad x = 2 - \sqrt{3}$$

In the first answer, $2 + \sqrt{3}$, the two parts can be combined to become a new irrational number approximately equal to 3.732. The number $2 - \sqrt{3}$ becomes approximately equal to 0.268. The two parts of such numbers can be combined because both parts are real. However, in the case of a complex number, such as $2 + 3i$, the two parts are entirely different kinds of numbers. To attempt to combine the real number 2 and the imaginary number $3i$ is like trying to combine 2 pounds and 3 hours. The only way to add a real number to an imaginary number is to indicate the sum such as $2 + 3i$.

Two complex numbers are added by adding separately their real parts and their imaginary parts. The same is true with regard to subtraction. The addition or the subtraction of two complex numbers, such as $3 - 4i$ and $-6 + 3i$, is similar to the addition or subtraction, respectively, of two binomials, such as $3 - 4x$ and $-6 + 3x$. The following examples show addition and subtraction of complex numbers.

Example 1.

Addition	Subtraction
$3 - 4i$	$3 - 4i$
$-6 + 3i$	$-6 + 3i$
$-3 - i$	$9 - 7i$

Example 2.

Addition	Subtraction
$-4.37 - j5.21$	$-4.37 - j5.21$
$-6.14 + j2.48$	$-6.14 + j2.48$
$-10.51 - j2.73$	$+1.77 - j7.69$

Example 3. Horizontal addition and subtraction: combine the following complex numbers:

$$(3 - 2i) + (-5 + 6i) - (4 + i) - (2 - 7i)$$

Removing parentheses, $3 - 2i - 5 + 6i - 4 - i - 2 + 7i$

Combining, $-8 + 10i$

21.9 MULTIPLICATION OF COMPLEX NUMBERS

In multiplication involving imaginary numbers, the letter i (or j) is treated first as any other literal number, such as x. The multiplication of complex numbers is analogous to the multiplication of any two binomials; that is, the problem $(3 - 4i)(-2 - 5i)$ is analogous to the problem of multiplying the two binomials $(3 - 4x)$ and $(-2 - 5x)$. However, as soon as the expression i^2 appears, it should be immediately stated in its equivalent form, -1.

Example 1. Multiply $(3 - 4i)(-2 - 5i)$.

$$\begin{aligned}
(3 - 4i)(-2 - 5i) &= -6 - 7i + 20i^2 \\
&= -6 - 7i + 20(-1) \\
&= -6 - 7i - 20 \\
&= -26 - 7i
\end{aligned}$$

Example 2. Multiply $(-7 + 2j)(3 - j)$.

$$\begin{aligned}
(-7 + 2j)(3 - j) &= -21 + 13j - 2j^2 \\
&= -21 + 13j - 2(-1) \\
&= -21 + 13j + 2 \\
&= -19 + 13j
\end{aligned}$$

If the multiplier is only a real number or a pure imaginary, the multiplication is similar to the multiplication of a polynomial by a monomial.

Example 3. Multiplication: $\quad -3(5 - 4i) = -15 + 12i$

Example 4. Multiplication: $\quad -2i(-3 - 7i) = +6i + 14i^2 = -14 + 6i$

Exercise 21.3

Combine the following as indicated:

1. $(3 + 2i) + (5 - 3i)$ 2. $(4 - 3j) - (3 - 2j)$
3. $(2 - 3i) + (-4 - 5i)$ 4. $(5 + 7i) - (-2 - 3i) + (-3 - i)$
5. $(-5 + 2j) - (3 + 4j) - (-6 + 0j)$ 6. $(2 + 3i) + (0 - 5i) - (5 - 2i)$

Add the following sets of complex numbers:

7.	$3 + 2i$	$-4 + 4j$	$-5 - 6i$	$2 - 5j$	$5 - 3i$
	$\underline{4 - 4i}$	$\underline{7 - 3j}$	$\underline{-2 - 3i}$	$\underline{-3 + 4j}$	$\underline{5 + 3i}$
8.	$-3 - j$	$7 + 4i$	$8 - j3$	$4 - 5i$	$-1 - j6$
	$\underline{-3 + j}$	$\underline{-7 + 0i}$	$\underline{2 + j4}$	$\underline{1 + 3i}$	$\underline{4 - j5}$
9.	$4 + 3i$	$-5 + 4j$	$-3 - 2i$	$-2 + j7$	$7 - 9j$
	$-7 + 2i$	$3 - 5j$	$-1 + 5i$	$-8 + j4$	$8 + 4j$
	$5 - i$	$-7 - 3j$	$2 - 4i$	$-1 - j3$	$-9 - 7j$
	$\underline{-6 - 6i}$	$\underline{6 + 2j}$	$\underline{-5 + i}$	$\underline{9 + j5}$	$\underline{-1 + j}$

In each set of complex numbers in Examples 7 and 8, subtract the bottom complex number from the top one.

Multiply the following complex numbers as indicated. Write each product in a simplified form with the real part written first.

10. $2i(4 - 3i)$ 11. $-5i(3 + 2i)$ 12. $-4j(-2 + 5j)$
13. $3j(-5 - 7j)$ 14. $3i(-8 + 3i)$ 15. $(3 + 2i)(4 - i)$
16. $(2 - 5j)(2 - 5j)$ 17. $(4 + 5i)(4 - 5i)$ 18. $(-5 + i)(-1 + 2i)$
19. $(-6 - 5i)(3 + 2i)$ 20. $(3 + 4i)(3 - 4i)$ 21. $(-5 - 2i)(-5 + 2i)$
22. $(-3 + i)(3 + i)$ 23. $(4 + 3j)(4 + 3j)$ 24. $(-3 + 2i)(4 - i)$
25. $(5 - 7i)^2$ 26. $(-3 + 5j)^2$ 27. $(-1 - \sqrt{3i})^3$

To each of the following complex numbers, add its conjugate:

28. $5 + 2i$ 29. $-7 - 3j$ 30. $-4 + 5j$ 31. $3 - 7j$
32. $-8 + j$ 33. $6 - 6i$ 34. $9 + 0i$ 35. $0 - 4j$

36–43. From each complex number in Exercises 28–35 subtract its conjugate.
44–51. Multiply each complex number in Exercises 28–35 by its conjugate.

21.10 DIVISION OF COMPLEX NUMBERS

When we add, subtract, or multiply complex numbers, we get an answer that is another complex number. The answer can always be reduced or combined in such a way that it contains only two parts, real and imaginary.

Examples.   Add $(-3 + 7i) + (5 - 6i) = 2 + i$
Subtract $(-3 + 7i) - (5 - 6i) = -8 + 13i$
Multiply $(-3 + 7i)(5 - 6i) = -15 + 53i - 42i^2 = 27 + 53i$

Notice that the answer in each case is still a complex number consisting of two parts, real and imaginary. It takes the form $a + bi$. Of course, in some examples a or b or both may be zero.

In *division* our objective is the same: *to reduce the answer, or quotient, to a complex number that contains the two parts, real and imaginary, in such a way that they can be separated by a plus or minus sign.*

If we have a problem in division such that the divisor is a real number, the problem is very simple. We merely divide each part of the complex number by the divisor. For instance, suppose we have the problem

$$\frac{12 - 20i}{4}$$

Here we divide each part of the numerator by 4 and get the answer $3 - 5i$. The procedure is similar to the division of a polynomial by a monomial.

Of course, the numbers a and b may be fractions.

Example 1.   Divide $\dfrac{-3 + 8i}{-7} = +\dfrac{3}{7} - \dfrac{8}{7}i$.

Notice that the real part is separated from the imaginary part.

In the division of complex numbers, the chief difficulty occurs when the divisor, or denominator of a fraction, is an imaginary or a complex number; that is, when i appears in the denominator. When this happens, our main objective is to *eliminate any imaginary appearing in the denominator*. The purpose is to make it possible to state the quotient in the general form of all complex numbers, $a + bi$, in which the real part is separated from the imaginary part by a plus or minus sign. The procedure is shown by examples.

Example 2.   Divide $(-2 + 5i) \div (3 - 2i)$.
First we write the division as a fraction:

$$\frac{-2 + 5i}{3 - 2i}$$

This fraction, in its present form, cannot be written so that the real part is separated from the imaginary part. Our first objective is to eliminate the imaginary from the denominator.

In order to make the denominator a real number, we multiply the numerator and the denominator of the fraction by the *conjugate form of the denominator*, that is, by $3 + 2i$.

$$\frac{(-2 + 5i)(3 + 2i)}{(3 - 2i)(3 + 2i)} = \frac{-6 + 11i + 10i^2}{9 - 4i^2} = \frac{-16 + 11i}{13}$$

The answer can now be written in two parts: $\quad -\dfrac{16}{13} + \dfrac{11}{13}i$

We can now recognize the general form of the complex number, in which the real part, a, is equal to $-\frac{16}{13}$, and b, or coefficient of i, is equal to $+\frac{11}{13}$.

Whenever a complex number appears as the denominator of a fraction, the denominator can be transformed into a real number by multiplying it by the conjugate form of complex number. For the division of complex numbers, we have this rule:

Rule. *Multiply the numerator and denominator by the conjugate form of the denominator. Then expand both numerator and denominator. Since the denominator will be real, the entire answer should then be written in a form in which the real part is separated from the imaginary part by a plus or minus sign.*

Note. If the denominator is a pure imaginary, the multiplier may simply be i.

Example 3. Divide $\dfrac{6}{2 - 3i}$.

Multiply numerator and denominator by the conjugate form of the *denominator*. In this example we multiply both by $2 + 3i$.

$$\frac{6(2 + 3i)}{(2 - 3i)(2 + 3i)} = \frac{6(2 + 3i)}{4 - 9i^2} = \frac{6(2 + 3i)}{4 + 9} = \frac{12 + 18i}{13}$$

The answer may now be written in the form

$$\frac{12}{13} + \frac{18}{13}i$$

21.11 EQUAL COMPLEX NUMBERS

In the complex number $5 + 3i$ we have seen that the imaginary part $3i$ is a completely different kind of number from the real part 5. The number might be said to resemble the expression 5 hours + 3 pounds. Therefore, the two parts cannot be combined into a single term.

For this reason, if two complex numbers are said to be equal, the two real parts must be equal to each other and the imaginary parts must be equal to each other. As an illustration, suppose we have the statement:

$$x \text{ hours} + y \text{ pounds} = 5 \text{ hours} + 3 \text{ pounds}$$

The only possible way that the left side of the equation can be equal to the right side is on the condition that x hours are equal to 5 hours and y pounds are equal to 3 pounds. In other words, $x = 5$ and $y = 3$.

Suppose we have an equation which states that two complex numbers are equal:

$$a + bi = c + di$$

We know then that a must be equal to c and b must be equal to d.

Exercise 21.4

In each exercise No. 1–10, (a) add the two complex numbers; (b) subtract the second complex number from the first; (c) multiply the two complex numbers.

1. $5 + 2i$ and $1 + 3i$
2. $-5 + 4i$ and $2 + 5i$
3. $3 + 2j$ and $-5 + 3j$
4. $-4 - 3j$ and $-2 + 7j$
5. $5 - 2j$ and $3 + 5j$
6. $-4 + i$ and $4 - i$
7. $5 - 4j$ and $5 - 4j$
8. $-1 + 3j$ and $2 + 4j$
9. $-3 - 5j$ and $-2 - 3j$
10. $6 + 7j$ and $4 - 2j$

Multiply the following (11–20):

11. $(3 - 5i)^2$
12. $(2 + 3j)^3$
13. $(7 - j)(7 + j)$
14. $(1 + j)^2$
15. $(3 + 4i)(3 - 4i)$
16. $i(5 + 2i)$
17. i (answer for No. 16)
18. i (answer for No. 17)
19. i (answer for No. 18)
20. i (answer for No. 19)
21. In Nos. 1–10 divide the first complex number by the second. Write answer in the form $a + bi$.

Divide the following (22–25):

22. $\dfrac{3}{5 - 2i}$
23. $\dfrac{4j}{3 - 5j}$
24. $\dfrac{5}{-3 + 2j}$
25. $\dfrac{5}{4j}$

26. Simplify i^n, where n ranges from 1 to 20.
27. Find reciprocals of (a) $3 + 2j$; (b) $5 - j$; (c) $-3 - 5j$; (d) $-2 + 4j$.
28. If $3 + 5i = 4x + 3yi$, find x and y.
29. Show that the sum of two conjugate complex numbers is a real number.
30. Show that the difference between two conjugate complex numbers is a pure imaginary.
31. Show that the product of any two conjugate complex numbers is real.

21.12 GRAPHING OF IMAGINARY AND COMPLEX NUMBERS

Imaginary and complex numbers had been studied for a long time before any attempt was made to represent them on a number scale. Since early times, real numbers had been represented on a horizontal line. The first numbers to be shown in this way were probably the positive integers. This was probably done in prehistoric times soon after the beginning of counting.

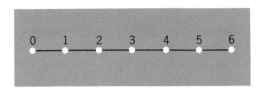

Fig. 21.1

To represent the positive integers on a horizontal line, we begin at a point we call zero (0) (Fig. 21.1).

To show the points representing the integers, we start at 0 and then mark off equal distances to the right for each of the integers, 1, 2, 3, 4, and so on. We can say that each of these points represents an integer, or number.

Later, fractions and irrational numbers were shown on the same line. When negative numbers were to be shown on this line, they were laid off in a direction opposite to that used for positive numbers (Fig. 21.2).

On this line we can represent all of the real numbers: positive, negative, fractional, and irrational numbers.

When imaginary numbers first forced themselves upon the scene, there was no way to represent them on the common number line. Then, in 1797, Caspar Wessel, a Norwegian surveyor, demonstrated before a mathematical meeting in Europe how imaginary and complex numbers might be shown on a graph together with real numbers. His method was to represent imaginary numbers on another straight line drawn perpendicular to the line of real numbers. The arrangement was similar to the rectangular coordinate system consisting of the x-axis and the y-axis.

In the representation of real numbers and imaginary numbers, the horizontal axis is called the axis of *real* numbers. The vertical axis is the axis of *imaginaries*. Real numbers and pure imaginary numbers can be represented on these two axes as shown in Fig. 21.3.

The graphing of imaginary and complex numbers on a pair of perpendicular axes in the same plane proved to be one of the most valuable inventions in mathematics. However, although the demonstration was made before 1800,

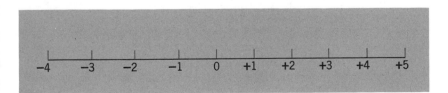

Fig. 21.2

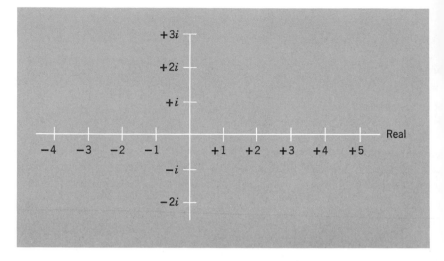

Fig. 21.3

almost one hundred years passed before the importance of it was fully realized. Then it was discovered that the graphing of complex numbers was a most useful idea in the study of electricity involving alternating currents.

Complex numbers that are partly real and partly imaginary, such as the number $5 + 2i$, can be represented as a point on the graph. The real part is laid off in the direction of the axis of reals, that is, to the right or left of zero. The imaginary part is laid off in the direction of the axis of imaginaries,

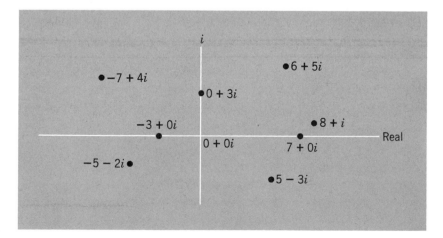

Fig. 21.4

that is, upward or downward. To locate the point representing the number 5 + 2*i*, we count off five units to the *right of zero*. We then count two units in the *upward* direction.

In terms of the *x*- and *y*-axes coordinate system, the point representing 5 + 2*i* would be indicated by the notation (5, 2). You will remember that we call the *x*-distance the abscissa of the point and the *y*-distance the ordinate of the point. The point is designated by the two coordinates, 5 and 2, written within parentheses and separated by a comma. However, when this point represents a complex number, we indicate the sum of the two parts, 5 and 2*i*, and we do not enclose the complex number by parentheses.

On the graph in Fig. 21.4 are shown several complex numbers.

21.13 ADDITION OF COMPLEX NUMBERS BY GRAPHING

Complex numbers can be added graphically. The method is different from algebraic addition, but the result, the sum of the numbers, must be the same. Graphical addition is explained by an example.

Example. Add graphically 5 + 2*i* and 1 + 3*i*.

Solution. The first step is to show each number as a point on the graph for complex numbers (Fig. 21.5).

Next, we draw a line to each point from the point 0 + 0*i*. The point 0 + 0*i* is the point of intersection of the two axes, real and imaginary, and corresponds to the origin in the *x*- and *y*-coordinate system. The two lines drawn are often called *vectors*.

On the two vectors we complete a parallelogram, using the vectors as two adjacent sides of the parallelogram (Fig. 21.6). The point at which the two other sides intersect represents the sum of the two complex numbers.

The sum of the two numbers can be further shown by drawing another vector from the point 0 + 0*i* to the point representing the sum.

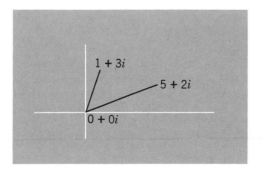

Fig. 21.5

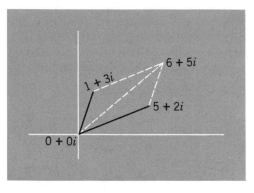

Fig. 21.6

The sum of the two numbers can be read directly from the graph as a complex number. In order to determine the real part and the imaginary part, we estimate the distance in the direction of reals and the distance in the direction of imaginaries. If the construction is done carefully, the sum can be estimated fairly accurately.

The sum of the two numbers, as indicated by graphical addition, can, of course, be checked by algebraic addition.

In the graphical addition of two complex numbers the necessary parallelogram can be constructed by different methods. One method makes use of the definition of a parallelogram: *a parallelogram is a quadrilateral whose opposite sides are parallel.* The two vectors representing the given complex numbers are drawn first. Let us assume that the two complex numbers are represented by the points *A* and *B* (Fig. 21.7) and that the two vectors, *OA* and *OB*, have been drawn. Then, through *A*, we draw a line parallel to *OB*, and, through *B*, we draw a line parallel to *OA*. These two lines intersect at

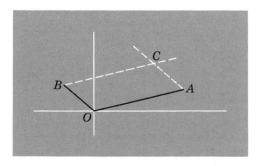

Fig. 21.7

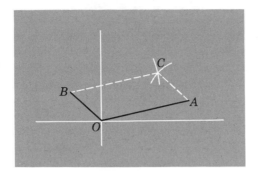

Fig. 21.8

point *C*. Point *C* represents the sum of the two numbers *A* and *B*. The parallels may be drawn by making equal angles with a horizontal line.

In another method, by use of a compass, we draw two intersecting arcs. For one arc we use *A* as a center and the vector *OB* as a radius. For the other arc we use *B* as a center and the vector *OA* as a radius. The point of intersection of the arcs is point *C*, which represents the sum of the two numbers *A* and *B*. If this point is connected with each of the points *A* and *B*, a parallelogram is formed. This method makes use of the theorem that *a quadrilateral is a parallelogram if its opposite sides are equal* (Fig. 21.8).

If three complex numbers are to be added graphically, two of them are added first. The sum is then treated as a new single complex number, and this number is added to the third. Several complex numbers can be added in the same way.

21.14 SUBTRACTION OF COMPLEX NUMBERS BY GRAPH

Graphical subtraction follows the rule for algebraic subtraction of numbers. You will recall that when we wish to subtract two numbers in algebra we do not really subtract at all. Instead, we change the sign of the subtrahend, and then proceed as in algebraic addition. We do the same in graphical subtraction; that is, we change the sign of the subtrahend and then add.

Example. To subtract $6 + 3i$ change to $6 + 3i$
               $5 - 2i$ add $-5 + 2i$
                                            $1 + 5i$

In algebraic subtraction we change the sign of the complex number to be subtracted. We do the same in graphical subtraction. In the foregoing example we first change the complex number $5 - 2i$ to its negative $-5 + 2i$. Then we add the two numbers $6 + 3i$ and $-5 + 2i$ graphically.

21.15 MULTIPLICATION AND DIVISION OF COMPLEX NUMBERS BY GRAPH

Graphical multiplication and division of complex numbers, although possible, is not practical. If we wish to represent a product graphically, the best procedure is to multiply the numbers algebraically, and then locate the point that represents the product. If we wish to represent a quotient on the graph, we divide the complex numbers algebraically and then locate on the graph the point that represents the quotient.

21.16 OPERATOR-j OR j-OPERATOR

In electrical work, as we have mentioned, the imaginary unit $\sqrt{-1}$ is represented by the letter j rather than by i, since the letter i is used to represent electric current. Whatever is said with reference to the j-operator also holds true if we use i to represent $\sqrt{-1}$.

Suppose we represent a pure imaginary or a complex number by a point on the graph. Then, multiplying that number by the multiplier j has the effect of rotating the number through 90° on the graph. (Counterclockwise rotation is called *positive* rotation.)

Suppose we begin with the real number 5. If we multiply 5 by j, we get a product of $5j$ (sometimes written $j5$). The rotation of 90° is shown in Fig. 21.9 by the curved arrow from 5 to $5j$. Now, if we multiply the product $5j$ by j, the number $5j$ rotates through another 90° and becomes $5j^2$, $5(-1)$, or -5. We have thus multiplied the original number 5 by j^2, or -1.

If we multiply this product, -5, again by j, we get $-5j$. The result is another 90° rotation. A fourth multiplication by j becomes $j(-5j) = -5j^2$ $= +5$. The result is still another 90° rotation.

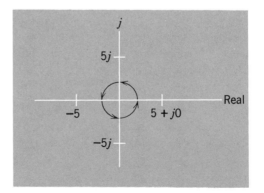

Fig. 21.9

The number 5 has now made one complete rotation of 360°, since it has been multiplied by j four times, which is j^4 or $+1$. A similar change takes place if we start with any real number, positive or negative.

Each time a number is multiplied by j the number is rotated through 90°. For this reason we refer to the multiplier j as "operator-j" or the "j-operator." (The same may be said with regard to the letter i, if that letter is used to represent $\sqrt{-1}$.)

In the same way we can show that multiplying any number by j^2 is the same as multiplying by the operator -1 and has the effect of rotating the number through an angle of 180°. This is a simple explanation of the fact that the product of two negative numbers is a positive number:

$$(-1)(-5) = +5, \text{ that is, } (j^2)(-5) = +5$$

In the foregoing example we began with the real number 5. The result after each multiplication by the j-operator was either another real number or a pure imaginary. Now, if we show a complex number on the graph and multiply the number by the j-operator several times, we still get a rotation of 90° for each multiplication by j.

Suppose we start with the number $5 + 2j$ (Fig. 21.10). If we multiply this number by the j-operator once, we get the first product, $-2 + 5j$.

$$j(5 + 2j) = 5j + 2j^2 = 5j + 2(-1) = -2 + 5j$$

The original number $5 + 2j$ has been rotated through 90° to the position $-2 + 5j$.

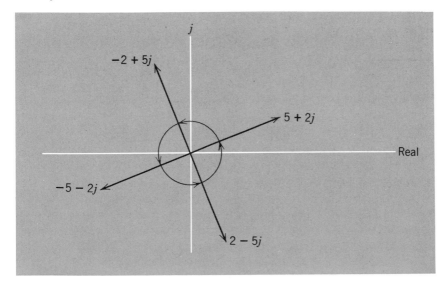

Fig. 21.10

If this product, $-2 + 5j$, is then multiplied by j, the product is $-5 - 2j$. Now we have multiplied the original number $5 + 2j$ by j^2, or -1, and the rotation is another 90°, or a total rotation of 180°.

$$j^2(5 + 2j) = -1(5 + 2j) = -5 - 2j$$

Another multiplication by j makes a product of $2 - 5j$, and the result is another rotation of 90°. A fourth multiplication by j makes a product of $5 + 2j$. The number is back at its original position because it has been multiplied by j^4, or $+1$, and it has been rotated through 360°.

Exercise 21.5

Add the following graphically:

1.	$5 + 2i$	2.	$6 + 2i$	3.	$-5 + 4i$	4.	$-6 + 5j$
	$2 + 4i$		$-2 + 4i$		$1 + 3i$		$-7 - 2j$

5.	$4 + i$	6.	$-5 - 4i$	7.	$-3 + 3j$	8.	$-5 + 3j$
	$5 - 7i$		$1 - 3i$		$-3 + 5j$		$7 - 2j$

9.	$3 + 4j$	10.	$-5 + 2j$	11.	$7 + 3j$	12.	$5 + 3j$
	$-7 - 3j$		$2 - 6j$		$-4 - 6j$		$5 - 3j$

13.	$3 + 5i$	14.	$-5 + j$	15.	$5 + 2i$	16.	$-9 - 8i$
	$-3 + 5i$		$-5 - j$		$-6 - i$		$-8 + 7i$

17.	$-6 + 3i$	18.	$-1 - 5j$	19.	$2 - 5i$	20.	$4 + 3i$
	$4 + 2i$		$4 - 3j$		$-3 - 2i$		$2 + 5i$
	$-5 - 4i$		$-4 + 2j$		$-7 + 4i$		$-5 + i$

21–32. In the first twelve of the foregoing examples, subtract the bottom complex number from the top number graphically.

Graph the following complex numbers and then find the point that represents their product (33–38):

33. $(3 + 2i)(1 + 4i)$ **34.** $(4 + 2j)(1 + 5j)$ **35.** $(1 - 5j)(-2 + j)$
36. $(-2 - 4i)(3 - 2i)$ **37.** $(3 + i)(3 + 4i)$ **38.** $(1 + 4j)(-2 + j)$
39. Graph the number $1 + 4j$.
40. Multiply this number by j and show the product on the graph.
41. Multiply the result in (40) by j again and show the product.
42. Multiply by j again and show the product on the graph.
43. Multiply by j a fourth time and show the product on the graph.
44. Graph the number $5 - 3j$. Then multiply by j^2 and show the result on the graph.

22
Roots of Equations

22.1 ROOTS OF A QUADRATIC EQUATION

We have seen that every quadratic equation has two roots. Of course, in some equations, the two roots are equal. In that case we might call the root a *double root*. An example is the equation

$$x^2 - 6x + 9 = 0$$

The roots of this equation are 3 and 3, or the double root 3.

We have found that some quadratic equations have imaginary roots, as distinguished from real roots. In some equations the roots are rational and in others they are irrational. In the equation

$$3x^2 - 7x + 2 = 0$$

the roots are $\frac{1}{3}$ and 2, which are real and rational. In the equation

$$x^2 - 4x + 13 = 0$$

the roots are $2 + 3i$ and $2 - 3i$, which are imaginary.

It is possible to tell something about the roots of a quadratic equation without knowing the roots themselves. By studying the equation, we can tell, without solving it, whether the roots are real or imaginary, whether they are rational, and whether they are equal. There is sometimes an advantage in knowing something about the roots even before solving the equation.

We shall work out several equations by formula to illustrate the different kinds of roots. Note especially the quantity $b^2 - 4ac$ under the radical sign. This quantity is called the *discriminant* because it enables us to discriminate between the different kinds of roots.

Example 1. First, consider the equation

$$3x^2 - 7x + 2 = 0$$

Solution. Let us solve this equation by the quadratic formula:

$$x = \frac{-b \pm \sqrt{b^2 - 4ac}}{2a}$$

Substituting numerical values, we get

$$x = \frac{7 \pm \sqrt{49 - 24}}{6} = \frac{7 \pm \sqrt{25}}{6}$$

At this point in the solution we see that the discriminant, 25 (that is, the quantity under the radical sign), is a perfect square. Therefore, in the final solution the radical sign will disappear and we know at once that the roots are *rational*. Continuing the solution,

$$x = \frac{7 \pm 5}{2} = \begin{cases} \dfrac{7 + 5}{6} = 2, & r_1 \\[2mm] \dfrac{7 - 5}{6} = \dfrac{1}{3}, & r_2 \end{cases}$$

As we expected, the roots are *rational*. They are also *real*.

Example 2. Consider a second example:

$$x^2 - 6x + 7 = 0$$

Solution. Substituting numerical values in the quadratic formula, we have

$$x = \frac{6 \pm \sqrt{36 - 28}}{2} = \frac{6 \pm \sqrt{8}}{2}$$

At this point in the solution we see that the discriminant, 8, although positive, is not a perfect square. Therefore, in the final solution the radical sign will *not* disappear and we know at once that the roots are *irrational*.

Continuing the solution,

$$x = \frac{6 \pm 2\sqrt{2}}{2} = \begin{cases} 3 + \sqrt{2} \\ 3 - \sqrt{2} \end{cases}$$

As we expected, the roots are *irrational*. They are also *real*.

Example 3. Consider a third example:

$$x^2 - 4x + 13 = 0$$

Solution. Substituting numerical values in the quadratic formula, we get

$$x = \frac{4 \pm \sqrt{16 - 52}}{2} = \frac{4 \pm \sqrt{-36}}{2}$$

At this point in the solution we see that the discriminant is negative, -36. Therefore, in the final solution a negative will appear under the radical sign and we know at once that the roots are *imaginary*. Continuing the solution,

$$x = \frac{4 \pm 6i}{2} = \begin{cases} 2 + 3i \\ 2 - 3i \end{cases}$$

The roots are *imaginary*, as we expected. We do not use the terms *rational* or *irrational* with reference to imaginary numbers.

Example 4. Consider the equation,

$$4x^2 - 12x + 9 = 0$$

Solution. Substituting numerical values in the quadratic formula, we get

$$x = \frac{12 \pm \sqrt{144 - 144}}{8} = \frac{12 \pm \sqrt{0}}{8}$$

At this point in the solution we see that the discriminant is zero (0). Now, if zero is added to, or subtracted from, the 12, the result is the same. Therefore, we know the roots are *equal*. This can happen only if the discriminant is *zero*.

Continuing the solution,

$$x = \frac{12}{8}; \quad x = \frac{3}{2} \quad \text{and} \quad \frac{3}{2}, \quad \text{a double root}$$

The two roots are *equal*, as we expected. They are also *real* and *rational*.

To summarize:

1. If the discriminant, $b^2 - 4ac$, is *negative*, the roots are *imaginary*; in all other cases the roots are real.
2. If the discriminant is *zero*, the roots are *equal*; in all other cases the roots are unequal.
3. If the discriminant is *zero* or a *positive perfect square*, the roots are *rational*; otherwise real roots are irrational.

Remember, the only condition that produces *imaginary roots* is a *negative discriminant*. The only condition that produces *equal roots* is a *zero discriminant*.

Exercise 22.1

Solve the following equations by the quadratic formula and notice the relation between the discriminant and the kinds of roots in each:

1. $3x^2 + 8x + 5 = 0$	**2.** $x^2 - 4x + 5 = 0$
3. $9x^2 - 6x + 1 = 0$	**4.** $3x^2 - 5x + 1 = 0$
5. $5x^2 - 2x - 4 = 0$	**6.** $x^2 + 3x + 7 = 0$
7. $4x^2 - 20x + 25 = 0$	**8.** $x^2 - 2x + 4 = 0$
9. $x^2 - 10x + 16 = 0$	**10.** $6x^2 - 7x - 6 = 0$
11. $2x^2 - 3x + 2 = 0$	**12.** $12x^2 - x - 6 = 0$

22.2   THE SIGNIFICANCE OF THE DISCRIMINANT

The discriminant has an important bearing on the appearance of the graph of a function. By the term *function of x*, we mean any expression containing x whose value can be determined if the value of x is known. In the function $x^2 - 3x - 4$, if the value of x is 5, then the value of the function is 6.

To graph the function $x^2 - 3x - 4$, we set it equal to y: thus $x^2 - 3x - 4 = y$. Now we graph this equation in x and y on the x- and y-coordinate system. If the function is of the second degree, as in $x^2 - 3x - 4$, the graph is a *parabola*. Moreover, if the term containing x^2 is positive, the parabola opens *upward*.

The points at which the curve cuts the x-axis are the values for which y is equal to zero. Therefore, such points will represent solutions of the equation $x^2 - 3x - 4 = 0$. The roots of this equation are $x = -1$ and $x = 4$. When any function of x is set equal to zero, the roots of the resulting equation are called the *zeros* of the function. The roots -1 and 4 are the zeros of the function $x^2 - 3x - 4$. They indicate that the graph of the function intersects the x-axis in two real and distinct points.

If the two roots of a quadratic equation are equal, such as in the equation $x^2 - 6x + 9 = 0$, then the graph of the equation is tangent to the x-axis at a *double point*. Such a condition will always exist when the discriminant of the equation equals zero. If the roots of a quadratic are imaginary, as in the equation $x^2 - 4x + 13 = 0$, then the graph does not touch the x-axis at any real point. This condition will always exist when the discriminant is negative. In the equation $x^2 - 4x + 13 = 0$ the discriminant is -36 and the roots are the complex numbers $2 + 3i$ and $2 - 3i$.

One value of the discriminant is its use in pointing out the presence or absence of imaginary roots in an equation. In practical problems it sometimes happens that imaginary roots can be discarded. Under such conditions, if we can determine by the discriminant that the roots of the equation are imaginary, we need not solve the equation, since it has no "practical" significance.

However, it should never be assumed that all imaginary roots must be discarded. In connection with electric circuits, for example, an imaginary or complex root of an equation is just as significant as a real root. It has often been said that "imaginary" volts are just as dangerous as "real" volts. An imaginary or complex root of an equation involving impedance to current flow simply indicates that the circuit contains some impedance besides pure resistance.

In the following equations compute the value of the discriminant and then tell the nature of the roots without solving the equations.

Example 1. $4x^2 - 5x - 6 = 0$.

The discriminant is given by the expression $b^2 - 4ac$.

In this equation $a = 4$, $b = -5$, $c = -6$.

Substituting numerical values, we find that the discriminant is

$$25 - 4 \cdot 4(-6) = +121$$

The discriminant, $+121$, is not negative. Therefore, the roots are not imaginary, but *real*. The discriminant is not zero. Therefore, the roots are *unequal*. The discriminant is a perfect square. Therefore, the roots are *rational*, In summary, the roots are *real*, *unequal*, and *rational*.

Remember, the discriminant does *not* show the roots themselves. It shows only some characteristics of the roots. If we wish to find the roots, we must solve the equation. As a check, the student should solve some of these examples for the roots themselves.

Example 2. $9x^2 + 42x + 49 = 0$.

In this equation $a = +9$, $b = +42$, $c = +49$.

Substituting numerical values in the expression $b^2 - 4ac$, we find that the discriminant is

$$(42)^2 - 4(9)(49) = 1764 - 1764 = 0$$

The discriminant 0 indicates that the roots of the equation are *real*, *equal*, and *rational*.

Example 3. $3x^2 - 4x + 5 = 0$.

In this equation $a = +3$, $b = -4$, $c = +5$.

Substituting numerical values in the expression $b^2 - 4ac$, we find that the discriminant is

$$(-4)^2 - 4(3)(5) = 16 - 60 = -44$$

The negative discriminant, -44, shows that the roots are *imaginary*. Imaginary roots of quadratic equations are always unequal. The only condition that produces equal roots is a zero discriminant.

Example 4. $2x^2 - x - 5 = 0$.

In this equation $a = +2$, $b = -1$, $c = -5$.

Substituting numerical values, we find that the discriminant is

$$(-1)^2 - 4(2)(-5) = 1 + 40 = +41$$

The positive discriminant, $+41$, shows that the roots are *real*. They are also *unequal*. However, they are *irrational*, since 41 is not a perfect square.

Example 5. $x^2 - 8x + 25 = 0$.

In this equation $a = +1$, $b = -8$, $c = +25$.

Substituting numerical values, we find that the discriminant is

$$(-8)^2 - 4(1)(25) = 64 - 100 = -36$$

The negative discriminant indicates the roots are *imaginary* and *unequal*.

Exercise 22.2

Compute the value of the discriminant in each of the following equations and, from the value thus obtained, describe the roots of the equation. Also describe briefly the graph of each equation when the zero is replaced by y.

1. $x^2 + 5x + 4 = 0$
2. $5x^2 - 2x - 3 = 0$
3. $x^2 - 4x + 8 = 0$
4. $x^2 - 10x + 25 = 0$
5. $x^2 + 6x + 34 = 0$
6. $2x^2 - 3x - 5 = 0$
7. $x^2 + 25 = 0$
8. $2x^2 - 2x + 5 = 0$
9. $4x^2 - 20x + 25 = 0$
10. $x^2 + 6x - 4 = 0$
11. $x^2 + 4x + 6 = 0$
12. $4x^2 + 9 = 0$
13. $2x^2 - x = 4$
14. $x^2 + 6 = 3x$
15. $2x^2 + 4x - 3 = 0$
16. $x^2 - 8x + 1 = 0$
17. $3x^2 = 8 + 5x$
18. $x^2 = 3x + 7$
19. $5x^2 + 4x + 4 = 0$
20. $2x^2 + 5 = 4x$
21. $5x^2 = 2$
22. $x^2 = 3x + 5$
23. $x^2 - 3x = 4$
24. $3x^2 + 5x + 4 = 0$
25. $x^2 + 3 = 8x$
26. $3x^2 = 4x$
27. $x^2 + 4x + 25 = 0$
28. $x^2 - 2x + 7 = 0$
29. $2x^2 - 4x - 1 = 0$
30. $x^2 - x = 0$

22.3   WRITING AN EQUATION THAT SHALL HAVE EQUAL ROOTS

In some problems we may find it desirable to establish a specific condition so that the roots of a quadratic equation will be equal. Suppose we have a quadratic equation containing an undetermined constant such as k in the following example:

Example 1. $3x^2 + 5x + k = 0$.

Solution.   Now, we may wish to determine the proper value of k so that the two roots of the equation will be equal. We recall that the only condition that will produce equal roots is a *zero discriminant*. Therefore, we first set up the form of the discriminant $b^2 - 4ac$. In the foregoing example $a = +3, b = +5, c = k$.

The discriminant is

$$25 - 4(3)(k)$$

If the roots are to be equal, the discriminant must equal zero. So we simply make the statement that

$$25 - 4(3)(k) = 0$$

or

$$25 - 12k = 0$$

Solving for k, $k = +\dfrac{25}{12}$

If $\frac{25}{12}$ is substituted for k in the given equation, the resulting equation should have equal roots. Let us see if this is so.

Substituting $\frac{25}{12}$ for k, we get

$$3x^2 + 5x + \frac{25}{12} = 0$$

This equation can now be solved by factoring or by formula.

Multiplying both sides of the equation by 12,

$$36x^2 + 60x + 25 = 0$$

Factoring,
$$(6x + 5)(6x + 5) = 0$$

Solving,
$$x = \begin{cases} -\dfrac{5}{6} \\[2mm] -\dfrac{5}{6} \end{cases}$$

The roots are equal, as we intended they should be.

Example 2. In the equation

$$3kx^2 - 2x^2 + 5x - kx + 4 = 0$$

determine the value of the constant k so that the roots of the equation will be equal.

Solution. In this equation $a = 3k - 2$, $b = 5 - k$, $c = +4$. Therefore, the discriminant is

$$(5 - k)^2 - (4)(4)(3k - 2)$$

If the roots of the equation are to be equal, the discriminant must equal zero. So we simply state that

$$(5 - k)^2 - (4)(4)(3k - 2) = 0$$

or

$$(5 - k)^2 - 16(3k - 2) = 0$$

Expanding,
$$25 - 10k + k^2 - 48k + 32 = 0$$

Solving for k,
$$k = 1$$
$$k = 57$$

Now, if either 1 or 57 is substituted for k in the given equation, the resulting equation should have equal roots. Let us see if this is so.

First, substituting 1 for k, we get

$$3x^2 - 2x^2 + 5x - x + 4 = 0$$

Combining,
$$x^2 + 4x + 4 = 0$$

Solving for x,
$$x = \begin{cases} -2 \\ -2 \end{cases}$$

The roots are equal, as we intended they should be.
Now, we try $k = 57$. Substituting 57 for k, we get

$$171x^2 - 2x^2 + 5x - 57x + 4 = 0$$

Combining, $$169x^2 - 52x + 4 = 0$$
Factoring, $$(13x - 2)(13x - 2) = 0$$

Solving, $$r_1 = \frac{2}{13} \qquad r_2 = \frac{2}{13}$$

In this case, also, the roots are equal, as we intended them to be.

Exercise 22.3

In each of the following equations, find the value of k or m that will make the two roots of the equation equal:

1. $x^2 - 6x + k = 0$ **2.** $x^2 + 3x - k = 0$
3. $mx^2 - x - 2 = 0$ **4.** $3mx^2 + 4x + 1 = 0$
5. $2kx^2 - 3x + 4 = 0$ **6.** $x^2 - 3mx + 4 = 0$
7. $9x^2 + 5x + kx + 1 = 0$ **8.** $2mx^2 - 3x + 2m = 0$
9. $x^2 - 3mx - 1 = 0$ **10.** $3x^2 + 3kx + k + 1 = 0$

11. Suppose we wish to write the following equation, choosing a value for k that will make the roots of the equation real, rational, but unequal:

$$x^2 - 2x + k = 0$$

We write the discriminant and set it equal to some perfect square, such as 36. Now, find the value of k that will make the discriminant equal to 36 so that the roots will be unequal but rational.

12. In the following equation, find some value of k that will make the roots of the equation imaginary:

$$x^2 - 4x + k = 0$$

22.4 FORMING AN EQUATION FROM GIVEN ROOTS

It is occasionally desirable to write an equation so that it will have certain specified roots. For instance, we may wish to write an equation having the roots 3 and 5. To see how this is done, let us look carefully at the following example of a quadratic equation:

$$x^2 - 10x + 24 = 0$$

We solve the equation by the factoring method.

Factoring, $$(x - 4)(x - 6) = 0$$
Solving, $$x = 4 \quad \text{and} \quad x = 6$$
that is, $$r_1 = 4 \quad \text{and} \quad r_2 = 6$$

The two roots are 4 and 6. Now, notice that in the factored form of the equation we have

$$(x - 4)(x - 6) = 0$$

We see that each factor consists of

x minus a root

If we indicate the two roots by r_1 and r_2, the factored form of the equation is

$$(x - r_1)(x - r_2) = 0$$

Let us consider the cubic equation

$$x^3 - 3x^2 - 10x + 24 = 0$$

This equation can be solved by factoring. The quantity on the left side of the equation can be factored into three factors: thus

$$(x - 2)(x - 4)(x + 3) = 0$$

Now we set each factor equal to zero and solve. We find that the roots are 2, 4, and -3. Note that in the factored form of the equation, each factor consists of the quantity

x minus a root

If we call the roots $2 = r_1$, $4 = r_2$, $-3 = r_3$, then the equation consists of

$$(x - r_1)(x - r_2)(x - r_3) = 0$$

For this reason, if the roots of any quadratic equation are denoted by r_1 and r_2, then the equation can be formed by writing the two factors $(x - r_1)(x - r_2)$ and setting the product equal to zero:

$$(x - r_1)(x - r_2) = 0$$

The same procedure can be followed in writing an equation of any degree if the roots are known. For instance, if the roots of a quartic equation are denoted by r_1, r_2, r_3, and r_4, the equation is

$$(x - r_1)(x - r_2)(x - r_3)(x - r_4) = 0$$

Example 1. Write the quadratic equation that has the roots 7 and -4.

Solution.
$$(x - 7)(x + 4) = 0$$
Expanding,
$$x^2 - 3x - 28 = 0$$

Example 2. Write the quadratic equation that has the roots $-\frac{2}{3}$ and $+\frac{1}{4}$.

Solution.
$$\left(x + \frac{2}{3}\right)\left(x - \frac{1}{4}\right) = 0$$

The equation can be expanded as it stands, or the fractions can first be eliminated in the following manner:

Multiply both sides of the equation by 3 and by 4. The multiplier 3 will eliminate the denominator 3; the multiplier 4 will eliminate the denominator 4. The right side will still be zero. The result is

$$(3x + 2)(4x - 1) = 0$$

Expanding, $$12x^2 + 5x - 2 = 0$$

Example 3.   Write the equation that has the roots

$$\frac{-3 + 5i}{2} \quad \text{and} \quad \frac{-3 - 5i}{2}$$

Solution. $$\left(x - \frac{-3 + 5i}{2}\right)\left(x - \frac{-3 - 5i}{2}\right) = 0$$

Multiplying both sides of the equation by (2)(2).

$$(2x + 3 - 5i)(2x + 3 + 5i) = 0$$

Expanding, $$4x^2 + 12x + 9 - 25i^2 = 0$$

Combining, $$4x^2 + 12x + 34 = 0$$

or

$$2x^2 + 6x + 17 = 0$$

The resulting equation can be checked by solving.

Example 4.   Write the cubic equation that has the roots 2, −3, −3.

Solution. $$(x - 2)(x + 3)(x + 3) = 0$$

Expanding, $$x^3 + 4x^2 - 3x - 18 = 0$$

Exercise 22.4

Write equations having the following sets of roots:

1. 3, −5   **2.** $-\dfrac{1}{2}, \dfrac{3}{4}$ **3.** $\dfrac{1}{3}, -\dfrac{2}{3}$

4. $2 \pm \sqrt{3}$ **5.** $2 \pm 3j$ **6.** $-1 \pm \dfrac{\sqrt{3}}{2}$

7. $1 \pm \dfrac{2i}{3}$ **8.** $-2 \pm \dfrac{\sqrt{5}}{3}$ **9.** $2 \pm \dfrac{i\sqrt{2}}{2}$

10. 5, 5   **11.** −3, 0   **12.** $\pm 2j\sqrt{3}$

13. Write the cubic equation having the roots 2, −3, 1.

14. Write the cubic equation having the roots −2, +3, −3.

15. Write the quartic equation having the roots 2, 3, −1, $-\frac{1}{2}$.

16. Express the equation having the five roots 2, 2, 0, $1 \pm 2j$.

22.5 ROOTS OF SIMPLE HIGHER DEGREE EQUATIONS

If an equation of any degree can be factored into linear and/or quadratic factors, then the roots can easily be found. Factoring a higher degree equation is often a somewhat difficult matter. It can sometimes be done by the "trial and error" method.

Example 1. Solve $x^3 - 3x^2 - 10x + 24 = 0$.

Solution. Suppose we try $x = 1$ to see if 1 is a root of the equation. Substituting 1 for x in the equation, we ask

$$\text{does } 1 - 3 - 10 + 24 = 0? \text{ No.}$$

Therefore, 1 is not a root. Now we try 2. Substituting 2 for x in the equation, we ask

$$\text{does } 8 - 12 - 20 + 24 = 0? \text{ Yes.}$$

Therefore, 2 is a root of the equation.

Since 2 is a root of the equation, we know $x - 2$ must be a factor of the expression $x^3 - 3x^2 - 10x + 24$. If we divide the expression by the factor $x - 2$, we get another factor, $x^2 - x - 12$. This factor can be further split up into two factors, $(x - 4)(x + 3)$. Therefore, the equation $x^3 - 3x^2 - 10x + 24 = 0$ can be written

$$(x - 2)(x - 4)(x + 3) = 0$$

Now, the three roots may be found by setting each factor equal to zero:

if $x - 2 = 0$	if $x - 4 = 0$	if $x + 3 = 0$
then $x = 2$	then $x = 4$	then $x = -3$

To check each root, it is substituted for x in the original equation.

Some higher degree equations contain quadratic factors that cannot be separated into linear factors. In such equations the roots may be found by setting each quadratic factor equal to zero and solving by formula.

Example 2. Solve $x^3 - 3x^2 - 16x + 6 = 0$.

Solution. After trying several small numbers as roots of the equation, we eventually discover that the value $x = -3$ will satisfy the equation. Dividing the expression $x^3 - 3x^2 - 16x + 6$ by $x + 3$, we get a quotient of $x^2 - 6x + 2$. The equation $x^3 - 3x^2 - 16x + 6 = 0$ can be written $(x + 3)(x^2 - 6x + 2) = 0$.

Now, if we set each factor equal to zero, we shall get the roots. If $x + 3 = 0$, then $x = -3$. For the second factor, $x^2 - 6x + 2 = 0$, we use the quadratic formula.

$$x = \frac{6 \pm \sqrt{36 - 8}}{2} = \frac{6 \pm \sqrt{28}}{2} = \frac{6 \pm 2\sqrt{7}}{2} = 3 \pm \sqrt{7}$$

Therefore, the roots are -3, $3 + \sqrt{7}$, and $3 - \sqrt{7}$.

Solving equations above the second degree can sometimes be done by "trial and error" as we did in Example 2. However, the technique of *synthetic division* can often be used to detect linear factors. If the equation can be reduced by synthetic division to a quadratic, then if the remaining quadratic is not factorable, it can be solved by the quadratic formula. This was done in Example 2. For a review of synthetic division, see Chapter 10. Its use is shown in the following example.

Example 3.   Solve the equation $x^4 - 2x^3 - 7x^2 + 8x + 12 = 0$.

Solution.   If we had the roots of this equation, then we could write it

$$(x - r_1)(x - r_2)(x - r_3)(x - r_4) = 0$$

Now, if any number r is a root of the equation, then $(x - r)$ is a factor of the expression. Then, dividing the polynomial by $(x - r)$ should give us a remainder of zero. To see if 1 is a root, we divide by $(x - 1)$. In synthetic division form, we have

$$
\begin{array}{r|rrrrr}
1 & 1 & -2 & -7 & 8 & 12 \\
  &   & 1 & -1 & -8 & 0 \\
\hline
  & 1 & -1 & -8 & 0 & 12
\end{array}
$$

Note that the remainder is 12. Since the remainder is not zero, then $(x - 1)$ is not a factor of the expression, and 1 is not a root of the equation.

To see whether (-1) is a root, we divide by $[x - (-1)]$, or $(x + 1)$. We have

$$
\begin{array}{r|rrrrr}
-1 & 1 & -2 & -7 & 8 & 12 \\
   &   & -1 & +3 & +4 & -12 \\
\hline
   & 1 & -3 & -4 & 12 & 0
\end{array}
$$

Since the remainder is zero, then $(x + 1)$ is a factor of the polynomial, and (-1) is a root of the equation. Then one factor is $(x + 1)$ and the other factor is the quotient. Then the original equation can be written:

$$(x + 1)(x^3 - 3x^2 - 4x + 12) = 0$$

Now we set the second factor equal to zero and get the reduced equation,

$$x^3 - 3x^2 - 4x + 12 = 0$$

To find another root of the equation, we attempt to factor this expression, again by synthetic division. Let us try the factor $(x - 2)$:

$$
\begin{array}{r|rrrr}
2 & 1 & -3 & -4 & 12 \\
  &   & 2 & -2 & -12 \\
\hline
  & 1 & -1 & -6 & 0
\end{array}
$$

Since the remainder is zero, then $(x - 2)$ is a factor of the expression and therefore 2 is a root of the equation. Now we can write the second quotient as a further reduced equation:

$$x^2 - x - 6 = 0$$

Factoring, $$(x + 2)(x - 3) = 0$$
Solving for x, $$x = -2 \quad \text{and} \quad +3$$

If we wish to see the entire original equation written in factored form we can write

$$(x + 1)(x - 2)(x + 2)(x - 3) = 0$$

Now we recognize all the roots: $x = -1, +2, -2, +3$. Note again, as we have stated, in the factored form of the equation, each factor consists of $x - (a\ root)$.

It might be pointed out that if the algebraic sum of all of the coefficients in the equation is equal to zero, then 1 is a root of the equation. This is equivalent to setting 1 for x in the equation.

If an equation cannot be reduced to a quadratic by factoring (so that the remaining reduced equation is a cubic or higher degree), then the equation can be solved only by complicated formulas. Moreover, such formulas can be used only for cubics or quartics. There are no formulas for solving equations of a degree higher than the fourth unless the polynomial can be factored. Fortunately, most equations encountered in practical work can be solved by the methods we have discussed.

Exercise 22.5

Solve the following equations.

1. $x^3 - x^2 - 4x + 4 = 0$
2. $x^3 - 6x^2 + 11x - 6 = 0$
3. $x^3 + 5x^2 - 14x = 0$
4. $x^3 + 2x^2 - 5x - 6 = 0$
5. $x^3 + 5x^2 - 5x - 1 = 0$
6. $x^3 + x^2 + 3x - 5 = 0$
7. $x^3 - 8 = 0$ (factor)
8. $x^3 + 125 = 0$ (factor)
9. $x^4 - 1 = 0$
10. $x^4 - 5x^2 + 4 = 0$
11. $x^3 - 3x^2 - 4x + 12 = 0$
12. $x^3 + 4x^2 + x = 6$
13. $x^4 - 4x^3 + x^2 + 6x = 0$
14. $x^4 - x^3 - 11x^2 + 9x + 18 = 0$
15. $3x^4 - 13x^3 - 8x^2 + 52x = 16$
16. $2x^4 - 8x^3 + 19x^2 - 5x = 34$
17. $3x^4 - 11x^3 + 9x^2 + 5x = 6$
18. $3x^4 - 5x^3 - 9x^2 + 20x = 12$
19. $x^5 + x^4 - 7x^3 - x^2 + 6x = 0$
20. $x^5 - 7x^4 + 8x^3 + 28x^2 = 48x$
21. $x^4 - 6x^3 + 5x^2 + 24x - 36 = 0$
22. $x^4 - 15x^2 + 10x + 24 = 0$
23. $2x^4 - 5x^2 - 15x - 18 = 0$
24. $x^5 - 13x^3 + 36x = 0$

23

Systems of Equations Involving Quadratics

23.1 REVIEW OF GRAPHS OF LINEAR EQUATIONS

In Chapter 17 we solved systems of equations such as the following by graphing:

$$2x - 3y = 12$$
$$5x + 4y = 7$$

In solving the system we are looking for a pair of numbers for x and y, respectively, that will make both equations true. The two equations are of the first degree in x and y. If we graph the equations, we get two straight lines (Fig. 23.1). Since the graph of each equation is a straight line, the equations are called *linear equations*.

Now we know that any ordered pair of numbers that will satisfy both equations must represent a point that lies on both lines. From the graph we see that there is only one such point, since two straight lines can intersect in only one point. Since the lines have only one point in common, there is only one pair of numbers that will satisfy both equations. That pair consists of the coordinates of the point of intersection.

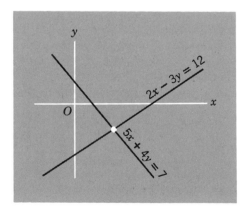

Fig. 23.1

If the two equations are graphed carefully, the coordinates of the inter-section point can be read directly from the graph. The graphic method of solving equations has many advantages, but the greatest difficulty is in read-ing the exact coordinates of a point, especially when fractions are involved. In many instances we can only estimate the values. The values on the graph in Fig. 23.1 appear to be approximately $(3, -2)$.

If we solve the system by some algebraic method, such as addition or sub-traction, we get the exact values of x and y. They are the pair $(3, -2)$. Although these are the same values as we obtained by graphical solution, we must remember that values read from a graph may be only approximate.

Note especially the meaning of the following two statements:

(1) *When we solve a system of equations graphically, the coordinates of the point or points of intersection will satisfy both equations.*

(2) *When we solve the system of equations by some algebraic method, the values we get for x and y, as ordered pairs, will be the coordinates of the point or points of intersection.*

23.2 GRAPHS OF HIGHER DEGREE EQUATIONS

Suppose we have a system of equations consisting of at least one quadratic equation, such as the following:

$$2x - y = 5$$
$$x^2 + y^2 = 25$$

Our problem now is to find a pair of numbers for x and y, respectively, that will satisfy both equations.

If we consider the graph of each equation, we can get some idea of the number of solutions. The graph of the first equation is a straight line, as we have seen. For the second equation, if we get pairs of values that satisfy the equation, we shall find that the graph is not a straight line but a *curve*. (In analytic geometry every graph, even a straight line, is often called a *curve*. However, here we restrict the use of the word *curve* to its ordinary meaning; that is, a line that continuously changes direction, such as a circle.) We shall find that the graph of the second equation is indeed a circle. Then, for the points of intersection of the two graphs, a straight line and a curve, we should expect two possible solutions.

In graphing equations of the second, third, and higher degree, we run into some difficulties not encountered in graphing linear equations. If the graph is a curve, then it is necessary to take some points very close together in order to determine as accurately as possible the shape of the curve where it changes direction sharply. In most cases the general shape of the curve can be determined by a careful study of its behavior as the variables change. We shall show the equations of a few common curves.

23.3 THE CIRCLE

To graph the equation $x^2 + y^2 = 25$, we find several pairs of values for x and y that satisfy the equation. Some of the pairs of values are shown in the following horizontal table:

If $x =$	0	± 3	± 4	± 5	± 2
$y =$	± 5	± 4	± 3	0	$\pm\sqrt{21}$

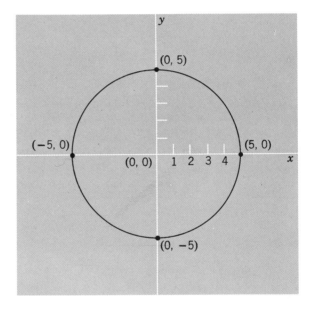

Fig. 23.2

Remember, the notation $(\pm 3, \pm 4)$ represents four points: $(3,4)$; $(3,-4)$; $(-3,4)$; $(-3,-4)$. Now we take the pairs of values as the coordinates of points and plot the points on a graph. When the points are connected with a smooth curve, the result is a circle (Fig. 23.2). Yet we must also be sure that all intermediate points arising from intermediate values of x and y would also lie on the same circle.

Now let us graph the two equations in Section 23.2. If we draw the graph of the linear equation and the graph of the quadratic equation on the same graph, we note that there are two points of intersection (Fig. 23.3). These points appear to be approximately (4,3) and (0, −5). Each of these two points lies on the straight line and the circle. Therefore, we can conclude that each set of values will satisfy both equations. Yet the values as read from the graph may be only approximate.

Let us see now under what general conditions the graph of an equation is a circle. We have seen that the graph of the equation, $x^2 + y^2 = 25$, is a circle with its center at the origin (0,0) and with radius equal to 5. If we graph the following equations, we also get a circle for each with the center at the point (0,0):

$$x^2 + y^2 = 16 \qquad x^2 + y^2 = 4$$
$$x^2 + y^2 = 9 \qquad x^2 + y^2 = 1$$

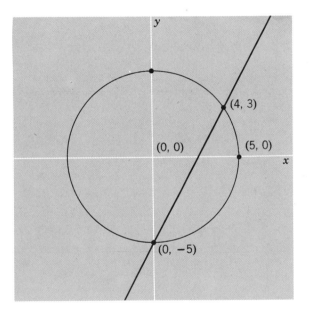

Fig. 23.3

The four circles are shown in Fig. 23.4. The radius of each circle is equal to the square root of the number on the right. In fact, any circle with its center at (0,0) has the *standard* form

$$x^2 + y^2 = r^2$$

Note that both the terms x^2 and y^2 have the coefficient 1. The right side of the equation, r^2, represents the square of the radius.

To see that this equation holds true whatever the values of x and y, let us take the general circle with center at (0,0) and any given radius r (Fig. 23.5).

Now let us take any general point on the circle, (x,y). Then, by the Pythagorean rule, it follows that

$$x^2 + y^2 = r^2$$

As an example, consider the equation $x^2 + y^2 = 40$. This represents the standard form of a circle with its center at $(0,0)$. The square of the radius is equal to 40. Therefore, the radius is equal to the $\sqrt{40}$, which is approximately 6.325. With this information, the circle can be drawn with a compass.

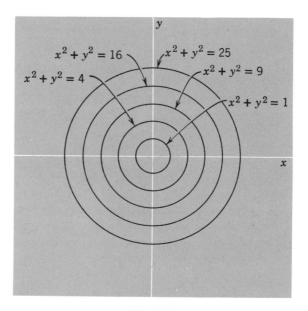

Fig. 23.4

If the terms x^2 and y^2 have the same constant coefficient, even though it is other than 1, the equation can be put into standard form. For example, suppose we have the equation

$$3x^2 + 3y^2 = 49$$

Dividing both sides by 3, $x^2 + y^2 = 49/3$. Then the circle has a radius equal to

$$\sqrt{\frac{49}{3}} = \frac{7}{\sqrt{3}} = \frac{7\sqrt{3}}{3} = 4.041 \text{ (approx.)}$$

Of course, if $r^2 = 0$, then $r = 0$, and we have a circle with a center but no radius. This situation, $x^2 + y^2 = 0$, is sometimes called a *point circle*. As another exception, if r^2 is negative, then r is imaginary, and we have what is sometimes called an *imaginary circle*.

In general, the equation of a circle may be written in the form

$$Ax^2 + By^2 = C$$

This is the general form of the equation of a circle provided that the coefficients A and B are equal, and that C has the same sign as A and B.

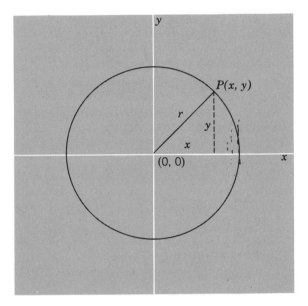

Fig. 23.5

If a circle is at some other position so that its center is no longer at the origin $(0,0)$, we say the circle is *translated*. Suppose the circle has been moved to some new position so that its center is at the point (h, k). Then, knowing the radius, we can first write, as though it were in standard position,

$$x^2 + y^2 = r^2$$

Now we put $(x - h)$ for x, and $(y - k)$ for y, and get the standard form for a circle out of standard position:

$$(x - h)^2 + (y - k)^2 = r^2$$

Example 1. Find the equation of the circle whose center is at the point $(6, -2)$ and whose radius is equal to 5 units.

Solution. If the center were at the origin, the equation would be

$$x^2 + y^2 = 25$$

Since the center is at the point $(6, -2)$, then we see that $h = 6$, and $k = -2$. Then we have the equation

$$(x - 6)^2 + (y + 2)^2 = 25$$

Simplifying this equation, we get,

$$x^2 + y^2 - 12x + 4y + 15 = 0$$

Now suppose, on the other hand, we have the equation of a translated circle and wish to find its radius and center. We try to put the equation into standard form so as to identify the center and the radius. To do so we complete the squares in x and y, and then write the result showing the squares of binomials.

Example 2. Find the center and the radius of the circle

$$x^2 + y^2 - 6x - 8y - 24 = 0$$

Solution. We arrange terms and transpose the constant to the right side. We first write

$$x^2 - 6x + y^2 - 8y = 24$$

Now we add enough to both sides of the equation to complete the squares in x and y. Adding 9 and 16 to both sides, we have

$$x^2 - 6x + 9 + y^2 - 8y + 16 = 24 + 9 + 16$$

The result can be written in the standard form

$$(x - 3)^2 + (y - 4)^2 = 49$$

Comparing this result with the standard form, we see that $h = 3$, $k = 4$, and $r^2 = 49$. Then the center of the circle is at the point $(3,4)$ and the radius is 7.

23.4 ALGEBRAIC SOLUTION OF A LINEAR AND A QUADRATIC EQUATION

A system of two equations in which one equation is linear and the other is a quadratic can always be solved algebraically by the method of *substitution*. We follow these steps:

(1) *Solve the linear equation for one letter.*
(2) *Substitute the new expression in the quadratic.*
(3) *Solve the resulting quadratic.*
(4) *Find the corresponding values of the other variable* by use of the *linear* equation. Do not use the quadratic to find the value of the second variable.

Now let us solve the system mentioned in Section 23.2.

Example 3. Solve the system

$$2x - y = 5$$
$$x^2 + y^2 = 25$$

Solution. Solving the linear equation for y, $y = 2x - 5$.
Substituting in the quadratic, $x^2 + (2x - 5)^2 = 25$
Expanding and simplifying, $5x^2 - 20x = 0$
Solving for x, $x = 0$ and $x = 4$

Now we use the *linear* equation to find the corresponding values of y. When $x = 0$, then $y = -5$; when $x = 4$, then $y = 3$. Then the two solutions are $(0, -5)$ and $(4,3)$, representing the two points of intersection.

Example 4. Find the points of intersection of the curves of the equations

$$x^2 + y^2 = 25 \quad \text{and} \quad 4x - 3y = 25$$

Solution. Solving the linear equation for y, $y = \dfrac{4x - 25}{3}$

Substituting in the quadratic, $x^2 + \left(\dfrac{4x - 25}{3}\right)^2 = 25$

Expanding, $x^2 + \dfrac{16x^2 - 200x + 25}{9} = 25$

Multiplying by 9, $9x^2 + 16x^2 - 200x + 625 = 225$
or $25x^2 - 200x + 400 = 0$
Dividing by 25, $x^2 - 8x + 16 = 0$

Solving the equation for x, we get $x = 4$, and $x = 4$, a *double root*. We use the linear equation to find the corresponding values of y. We also get a double value for y. When $x = 4$, $y = -3$. Then the point $(4, -3)$ represents the *double point* of intersection of the graphs.

If we sketch the graph of the two equations, we can see immediately the significance of the double root and the two equal values (Fig. 23.6). The figure shows that the line is tangent to the circle. However, we can say that the line intersects the circle in two points, but that the two points coincide.

Example 5. Solve algebraically $2x^2 + 2y^2 = 25$ and $2x - y = 10$. Sketch the graphs of each and explain the result.

Solution. Solving the linear equation, $y = 2x - 10$.
Substituting in the quadratic, $2x^2 + 2(2x - 10)^2 = 25$
Expanding, $2x^2 + 2(4x^2 - 40x + 100) = 25$
Simplifying, $10x^2 - 80x + 175 = 0$
Dividing by 5, $2x^2 - 16x + 35 = 0$

Solving by formula, we get $x = \dfrac{8 \pm \sqrt{6i}}{2}$

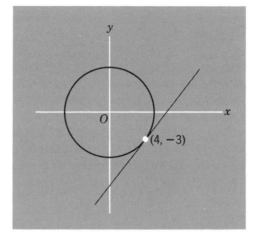

Fig. 23.6

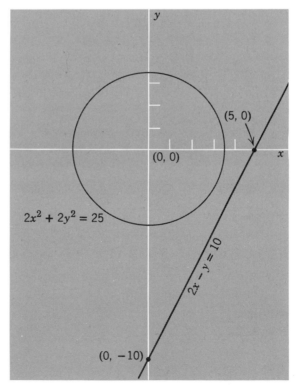

Fig. 23.7

Now we use the linear equation to find the values of y.

When $x = \dfrac{8 + \sqrt{6}i}{2}$, then $y = 2\left[\dfrac{8 + \sqrt{6}i}{2}\right] - 10 = -2 + \sqrt{6}i$

When $x = \dfrac{8 - \sqrt{6}i}{2}$, then $y = 2\left[\dfrac{8 - \sqrt{6}i}{2}\right] - 10 = -2 - \sqrt{6}i$

Note that the x values are two conjugate complex numbers. The y values are also two conjugate complex numbers.

If we graph the two equations, we can see at once the meaning of the imaginary values for the solutions. The straight line does not intersect or touch the circle in any real point (Fig. 23.7). Yet here again we might say that "the graphs intersect in two points but the points are imaginary."

The foregoing method of substitution can be used in solving a system of equations when one equation is linear and the other is a quadratic. The substitution method can also be used sometimes in the case of a system of two quadratics and in systems including higher degree equations.

23.5 THE PARABOLA

Another second-degree curve is a *parabola*. This is the type of curve we get when we graph the following equation:

$$y = x^2 - 3x - 4$$

In this equation we have one variable, x, raised to the second power, and the other variable only to the first power. In such an equation, it is usually best to assign values first to the variable that is squared, in this case, x. Then we compute the corresponding values of y.

The values should be taken rather closely together. Let us take x-values from $x = -3$ to $x = 6$, by integral values. We have the following pairs:

If $x =$	-3	-2	-1	0	1	2	3	4	5	6
then $y =$	14	6	0	-4	-6	-6	-4	0	6	14

At this point we note that if we take values less than -3 or greater than 6, then the value of y will continue to increase at a faster rate.

The points represented by the pairs of values are plotted and then connected by a smooth curve without any sharp corners (Fig. 23.8). Note especially the shape of the curve along the portion of the curve from $(1, -6)$ to $(2, -6)$. At the left of $x = -3$, and to the right of $x = 6$, the curve will continue to rise. This curve is called a *parabola*. Notice that the curve is symmetrical with respect to a vertical line through the lowest point which is the point (1.5, −6.25). The graph of an equation will always be a parabola when *one variable* (letter) is raised to the *second power* and the *other variable* is raised only to the *first power*.

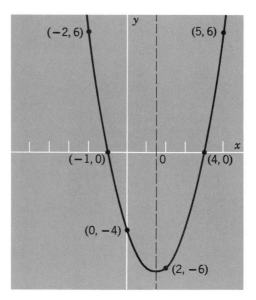

Fig. 23.8

Example 6. As another example of a parabola, let us graph the equation $y^2 = 8x$.

Solution. In this example, we first assign values to y, since y is raised to the second power. Then we compute the corresponding values of x. Negative as well as positive values should be considered. We may have the following pairs of values:

If $y =$	1	2	3	4	5	6	7	8	−1	−3...
then $x =$	$\frac{1}{8}$	$\frac{1}{2}$	$\frac{9}{8}$	2	$\frac{25}{8}$	$\frac{9}{2}$	$\frac{49}{8}$	8	(same as for positive values)	

Note that in this particular example, we get the same values for x whether y is positive or negative. The graph is shown in Fig. 23.9.

A parabola is symmetrical with respect to a straight line called the *principal axis*. The principal axis divides the parabola into two halves such that one half is a reflection of the other half. The *vertex* of the parabola is the point of greatest curvature; that is, where the curve changes direction most sharply. In the graph of the equation $y^2 = 8x$, the vertex is at the origin (0,0), and the principal axis is along the x-axis.

In general, we might recognize the following forms of the equations of parabolas. Suppose K represents some positive constant, then:

(1) If we have $y^2 = Kx$, the parabola opens to the right.
(2) If we have $y^2 = -Kx$, the parabola opens to the left.
(3) If we have $x^2 = Ky$, the parabola opens upward.
(4) If we have $x^2 = -Ky$, the parabola opens downward.

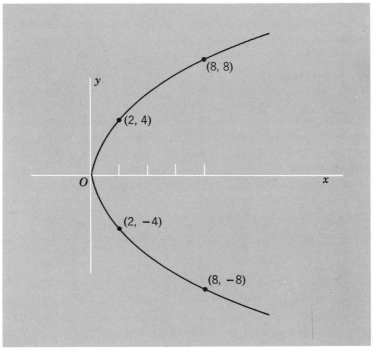

Fig. 23.9

All the foregoing equations represent parabolas with the vertex at the origin (0,0), and the principal axis along the x-axis or the y-axis.

We have seen that if an equation contains one variable raised to the second power and the other variable only to the first power, then the graph is a parabola. Now, if the equation contains also a first-degree term of the squared variable, then the general shape of the parabola is not affected, such as in the equation

$$y^2 = 8x - 4y$$

The parabola is simply translated to a new position with reference to the coordinate axes. The same is true if the equation also contains a constant term, as in the equation

$$x^2 - 4x - 6y + 8 = 0$$

Example 7.   Solve the system algebraically: $x + 4 = 2y$ and $x^2 = 4y$.

Solution.   Solving the linear equation for x, $x = 2y - 4$
Substituting in the quadratic, $(2y - 4)^2 = 4y$
Expanding, $4y^2 - 16y + 16 = 4y$
Simplifying, $4y^2 - 20y + 16 = 0$
or $y^2 - 5y + 4 = 0$
Solving for y, $y = 1$ and $y = 4$

Now we make use of the linear equation to find corresponding values of x: when $y = 1$, then $x = -2$; when $y = 4$, then $x = 4$. The points of intersection of the graphs of the two equations are $(-2,1)$ and $(4,4)$. The solutions might also have been found by first solving the linear equation for y. The student should sketch the two graphs and verify the points of intersection.

23.6   THE ELLIPSE

We have seen that the following equation represents a circle:

$$x^2 + y^2 = 36$$

Now if the coefficients of x^2 and y^2 are different, then the graph is an ellipse, as in the equation

$$4x^2 + 9y^2 = 36$$

The ellipse might be thought of as a flattened circle. The longest diameter is called the *major axis*, and the shortest diameter is called the *minor axis*.

Taking the same general equation, $Ax^2 + By^2 = C$, let us suppose the three constants, A, B, and C, are all positive. Then, if $A = B$, the graph is a circle. If $A \neq B$, the graph is an ellipse.

To graph an ellipse, we set *each* variable equal to zero and then solve for the value of the *other*. In doing so, we get two values, one positive, the other negative. The four points thus found will give a good idea of the shape of the ellipse.

Example 8.   Graph the ellipse $4x^2 + 9y^2 = 36$.

Solution.   This is an ellipse with its center at the origin. If we set each letter equal to zero and then solve for the other, we get the following four points: if $x = 0$, $y = \pm 2$; if $y = 0$, $x = \pm 3$. The four points are $(3,0)$; $(-3,0)$; $(0,2)$; $(0,-2)$. These four points are a good guide in sketching the curve. The curve has in general the shape of an oval. Of course, a more accurate figure can be drawn by locating more points whose co-ordinates satisfy the equation. However, with some practice, it is possible to get a good approximation to the true shape by using these four points (Fig. 23.10).

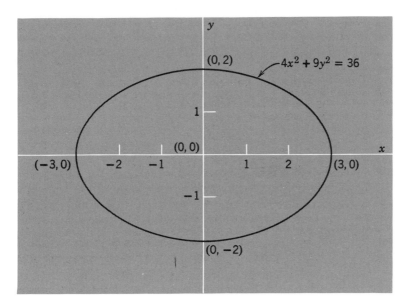

Fig. 23.10

23.7 THE HYPERBOLA

There is one other type of second degree curve called a *hyperbola*. We shall see that this curve has two branches that do not touch each other. Another characteristic is that the curve approaches but never touches two fixed straight lines, called *asymptotes*. An asymptote is a fixed straight line approached by a curve. Many types of higher-degree curves have asymptotes. The hyperbola has two asymptotes.

Let us graph the equation

$$4x^2 - 9y^2 = 36$$

We cannot take values of x that make y imaginary. In fact, if x lies between -3 and $+3$, then y becomes imaginary. For example, if $x = 0$, then $y^2 = -4$, and y is imaginary. We may use the following pairs of approximate values to sketch the graph:

If $x =$	± 3	± 4	± 5	± 6	± 7	± 8	± 9	± 10
then $y =$	0	± 1.76	± 2.67	± 3.46	± 4.22	± 4.94	± 5.66	± 6.36

When we plot the points and connect them by a smooth curve, we get the hyperbola (Fig. 23.11). The curve has two branches that do not touch each other. There can be no part of the curve for values of x between -3 and $+3$.

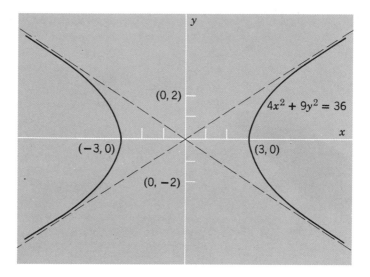

Fig. 23.11

Note that the curve approaches but does not touch the two diagonal lines shown in the figure. These lines are the asymptotes.

This hyperbola opens toward the right and left. If the signs of x^2 and y^2 are reversed, the hyperbola would open upward and downward, provided that we keep the right side of the equation positive.

Let us again consider the following general equation

$$Ax^2 + By^2 = C$$

For an ellipse we have said that A, B, and C must all be positive. Now, if A and C are positive and B is negative, then the graph is a hyperbola. An example is the equation $2x^2 = 5y^2 = 20$. If A is negative and B and C are positive, then the hyperbola opens upward and downward. If we have an equation in which C is negative, we multiply through the equation by -1 to determine correctly the signs of A and B. For example, the equation $3x^2 - 5y^2 = -60$, is changed to $-3x^2 + 5y^2 = 60$. Then we see that the hyperbola opens upward and downward. In summary, if A and B are opposite in sign and $C \neq 0$, the figure is a hyperbola.

Another form of the equation of a hyperbola is one such as

$$xy = 6$$

In any equation of the form $xy = C$, the x-axis and the y-axis are asymptotes. If C is positive, the branches of the hyperbola lie in the first and third quadrants. If C is negative, they lie in the second and fourth quadrants. Then the figure is called a *equilateral hyperbola* because the asymptotes are perpendicular to each other.

23.8 ALGEBRAIC SOLUTION OF SYSTEMS CONTAINING TWO QUADRATICS

We have seen that the method of substitution can be used to solve a system containing one linear and one quadratic equation. The method can also be used sometimes when both equations are quadratics. However, sometimes other methods must be used. Some systems can be solved by addition or subtraction.

Example 1. Solve the system:
$$x^2 + y^2 + 6x - 7 = 0 \quad (1)$$
$$x^2 + y^2 = 25 \quad (2)$$

Solution. The graph of each equation is a circle (Fig. 23.12).

Rearranging terms in (1), $x^2 + y^2 + 6x = 7$

Subtracting Equation (2), $\underline{x^2 + y^2 \quad\quad = 25}$

we get $6x = -18$

Solving for x, $x = -3$

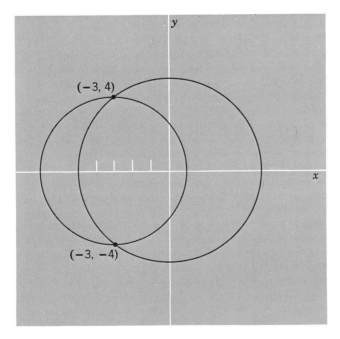

Fig. 23.12

Here we have only one value for x. To find the corresponding value of y, we substitute $x = -3$ in either of the quadratics. Using Equation (2), we get $9 + y^2 = 25$
Solving, $y^2 = 16$ and $y = \pm 4$
Then we have solutions of the system representing the points of intersection:

$$(-3,4) \quad \text{and} \quad (-3,-4)$$

Note that two circles can intersect in only two points.

Example 2.   Solve the system $y = 2x^2 - 3x - 2$ and $y = 5 + x - x^2$.

Solution.   The system can easily be solved by comparison. Since both equations are already solved for y, we equate the two expressions for y:

$$2x^2 - 3x - 2 = 5 + x - x^2$$

or

$$3x^2 - 4x - 7 = 0$$

Solving for x, we get two values, $x = 7/3$ and $x = -1$.

Now we substitute the values for x into either of the two given equations to find the corresponding values of y.

When $x = 7/3, y = 17/9$; when $x = -1, y = 3$.

The two solutions are then the ordered pairs $(7/3, 17/9)$ and $(-1, 3)$.

These two equations represent two parabolas, the first opening upward and the second downward. The two algebraic solutions represent the real points of intersection of the graphs. The student should sketch the graphs and confirm the algebraic solution. Note that the foregoing system could have been solved by subtraction.

In solving a system of two quadratics, we often get four answers because two curves often intersect in four points. When the curves are sketched, the points of intersection can be identified, unless some of the solutions are imaginary. In some instances we get a double point when two curves are tangent to each other.

Exercise 23.1

Solve the following sets of simultaneous equations by any method. Sketch the graphs for each set.

1. $x^2 = 4y$
   $x + 2y = 4$

2. $y^2 = 16x + 25$
   $2x - y = 1$

3. $y = x^2 - 4x - 5$
   $2x + y = -6$

4. $x^2 + y^2 = 20$
   $2x + y = 10$

5. $y = x^2 - 3x - 4$
   $2y = x - 4$

6. $x^2 = 2y + 3$
   $2x - 3y = 1$

7. $x^2 - y^2 = 9$
   $x - 2y = 3$

8. $xy = 6$
   $2x + 3y = 12$

9. $x^2 + y^2 = 16$
$x - y = 6$

10. $xy = 6$
$2x + 3y = 6$

11. $y^2 - 4x - 6y + 5 = 0$
$x - y = -1$

12. $x^2 + y^2 + 2x - 24 = 0$
$2x - 3y = -8$

13. $x^2 + y^2 + 2x - 24 = 0$
$2x - 3y + 8 = 0$

14. $x^2 + y^2 = 25$
$9y^2 = 4x$

15. $x^2 + y^2 = 25$
$y^2 = 8x + 40$

16. $y^2 + 8x - 24 = 0$
$y^2 - 4x - 12 = 0$

17. $y^2 - 2x + 3 = 0$
$y^2 + 3x - 7 = 0$

18. $x^2 + 4y^2 = 20$
$x^2 - 6y = 0$

19. $xy = 3$
$x^2 - y^2 = 8$

20. $x^2 = 2y + 3$
$2x - 3y = 4$

21. $3x^2 + 2y^2 = 21$
$x - y = 2$

22. $4x^2 + 9y^2 = 36$
$x + 2y = 2$

23. $x^2 + y^2 = 25$
$y^2 = 2x - 14$

24. $x^2 + y^2 = 25$
$y^2 = 2x - 10$

25. $x^2 + y^2 = 25$
$y^2 = 3x - 3$

26. $x^2 + y^2 = 25$
$y^2 = 3x + 15$

27. $x^2 + y^2 = 25$
$y^2 = 3x + 21$

24

Equations Containing Radicals

24.1 INTRODUCTION

Expressions containing radicals, such as $\sqrt{x + 5}$ and $\sqrt{x^2 + 9}$, are called *irrational* expressions in x. The radical cannot be eliminated from these expressions until some numerical value is assigned to x. In the first expression $\sqrt{x + 5}$, if x has the value 11, then the expression is *rational* because it has the value $\sqrt{11 + 5}$, or $\sqrt{16}$, which is equal to 4, a rational number. In the second expression $\sqrt{x^2 + 9}$, if x has the value 4, then the expression is rational because it has the value $\sqrt{16 + 9}$, or $\sqrt{25}$, which is 5, a rational number. In such expressions, until a numerical value is assigned to the variable the radical does not disappear, and the expression is called *irrational* in x.

24.2 IRRATIONAL EQUATIONS

It sometimes happens that we are faced with the problem of solving an equation containing a radical, such as a square root, a cube root, or some other root, in which the variable x appears in the radicand. Such an equation is called an *irrational equation.*

If an irrational expression appears in an *equation,* the radical may be eliminated by certain algebraic processes. The equation then becomes rational in x, and it can usually be solved. The solving of such equations involves many of the same steps followed in the solving of simple equations. However, one additional step is always necessary; that is, both sides of the equation must be raised to a higher power. The method is illustrated by several examples.

Example. $\sqrt{x + 1} = 7$.

To solve an equation of this kind, we raise both sides of the equation to a power. The power must always be such that the radical disappears. In this equation, since the square root is indicated by the radical, we raise both sides to the second power; that is, we *square* both sides.

This operation is permissible because the axioms cover, in general, the following principle concerning equations:

370

Any operation may be performed on one side of an equation, provided the same thing is done to the other side.

Note especially that if we take the square root of a given quantity and then square the root we get back to the original quantity; that is,

$$(\sqrt{x + 1})^2 = x + 1$$

Now let us go back to the original equation:

$$\sqrt{x + 1} = 7$$

Squaring both sides, we get $\quad\quad x + 1 = 49$

Solving for x $\quad\quad\quad\quad\quad\quad\quad x = 48, \quad$ root

To check the root, 48, we substitute 48 for x in the original equation, and ask

does $\quad \sqrt{48 + 1} = 7$?

does $\quad\quad \sqrt{49} = 7$? Yes.

As soon as we see that one side of the equation is equal to the other side, we know the solution we have obtained for x is correct.

24.3 EXTRANEOUS ROOTS

In solving any equation by raising both sides to a higher power, the answer *must* be *checked* in the *original equation*. This is necessary because the raising of any quantity to a higher power may introduce new roots into the equation. In many such cases we get answers that do not satisfy the original equation.

Let us see why the squaring of both sides of an equation may introduce new roots. Suppose we have this equation:

$$x - 3 = 0$$

We know that there is only one answer; that is, there is only one root of this equation. The only value of x that will make this equation true is $x = 3$. However, suppose we transpose the 3.

Then $\quad\quad\quad\quad\quad\quad\quad\quad\quad\quad\quad\quad\quad\quad x = 3$

Now suppose we square both sides: $\quad\quad\quad\quad\quad x^2 = 9$

Transpose again: $\quad\quad\quad\quad\quad\quad\quad\quad\quad\quad x^2 - 9 = 0$

Solve by factoring: $\quad\quad\quad\quad\quad\quad (x - 3)(x + 3) = 0$

$$x = +3$$
$$x = -3$$

Every step in this example is entirely legitimate. After squaring both sides of the equation, we end up with a quadratic, which has the two roots, $x = +3$ and $x = -3$. Both roots satisfy the quadratic equation, which was derived by squaring; but only one of the roots is the correct one for the original equation. The only root that satisfies the original equation is $+3$.

You may wonder how it is possible to get an equation with two roots, yet one of these roots does not satisfy the original equation. The reason is that whenever an equation is raised to a higher degree, new roots may be introduced. Every equation has as many roots as the degree of the equation. Therefore, after an equation has been solved by squaring, all roots must be carefully checked in the *original* equation.

Any roots obtained in the *derived* equation that do not check in the *original* equation are called *extraneous roots*. Such answers should be discarded as being no solution of the original equation.

24.4 STEPS IN SOLVING EQUATIONS CONTAINING RADICALS

There are certain steps that should be followed in solving equations containing radicals. Let us summarize the steps.

1. *Isolate the radical by transposing.* If the equation contains two radicals, isolate the more complicated radical.

2. *Raise both sides of the equation to a power* that will eliminate one radical. If the square root is indicated, then square both sides. If the cube is indicated, then raise both sides to the third power. If other roots are indicated, raise both sides of the equation to a power equal to the index of the root.

3. *Simplify the resulting expression.* If another radical is still present, repeat the process for eliminating a radical.

4. *Solve for the variable x or other variable.*

5. *Check all roots for extraneous roots.*

Example 1. Solve $\sqrt{x + 4} + 7 = 2x$.

Solution. First, we isolate the radical by transposing,

$$\sqrt{x + 4} = 2x - 7$$

Now we square both sides of the equation. Remember, the right side of the equation is a binomial. The square of this binomial consists of three terms. The square of the left side is simply $x + 4$.

Squaring both sides, $x + 4 = 4x^2 - 28x + 49$
Transposing, $0 = 4x^2 - 29x + 45$
This is a quadratic equation and may be solved by factoring or by the formula.
Solving, $x = 5$ and $x = \frac{9}{4}$.

The equation has two roots and both must be checked in the original equation. To check the root 5, we ask

does $\sqrt{5 + 4} + 7 = 10$?
does $\sqrt{9} + 7 = 10$?
does $3 + 7 = 10$?   Yes.

Therefore, 5 is a root of the original equation.

To check the root $\frac{9}{4}$, we substitute $\frac{9}{4}$ for x and ask

$$\text{does} \quad \sqrt{\tfrac{9}{4}} + 4 + 7 = \tfrac{9}{2}?$$
$$\text{does} \quad \sqrt{\tfrac{25}{4}} + 7 = \tfrac{9}{2}?$$
$$\text{does} \quad \tfrac{5}{2} + 7 = \tfrac{9}{2}? \quad \text{No.}$$

As soon as we see that one side of the equation is not equal to the other side, we can say that the value $x = \frac{9}{4}$ is an *extraneous* root. Although it occurs as a root of the derived equation, it is not a root of the original equation and must be discarded.

Example 2.   Solve $(3x - 2)^{\frac{2}{3}} = 4$.

Solution.   First, we raise both sides of the equation to the third power.

$$(3x - 2)^2 = 64$$

Expanding the left side, $\qquad 9x^2 - 12x + 4 = 64$

Transposing and combining, $\quad 9x^2 - 12x - 60 = 0$

Solving, $\qquad\qquad\qquad\qquad x = -2 \quad \text{and} \quad x = \tfrac{10}{3}$

To check $x = -2$, we ask

$$\text{does} \quad (-6 - 2)^{\frac{2}{3}} = +4?$$
$$\text{does} \quad (-8)^{\frac{2}{3}} = +4?$$
$$\text{does} \quad (-2)^2 = +4? \quad \text{Yes.}$$

To check $x = \frac{10}{3}$, we ask

$$\text{does} \quad (3 \cdot \tfrac{10}{3} - 2)^{\frac{2}{3}} = +4?$$
$$\text{does} \quad (10 - 2)^{\frac{2}{3}} = +4?$$
$$\text{does} \quad (8)^{\frac{2}{3}} = +4?$$
$$\text{does} \quad (2)^2 = +4? \quad \text{Yes.}$$

Therefore, both roots check, and each one is a solution of the original equation.

Example 3.   Solve $\sqrt{3x - 5} + x = 1$.

Solution.   Transposing to isolate the radical,

$$\sqrt{3x - 5} = 1 - x$$

Squaring both sides, $\qquad\qquad 3x - 5 = 1 - 2x + x^2$

Transposing and combining, $\qquad 0 = x^2 - 5x + 6$

Solving, $\qquad\qquad\qquad\qquad x = +2 \quad \text{and} \quad x = +3$

To check $x = +2$, we substitute 2 for x in the original equation and ask

$$\text{does} \quad \sqrt{6 - 5} + 2 = 1?$$
$$\text{does} \quad \sqrt{1} + 2 = 1?$$
$$\text{does} \quad 1 + 2 = 1? \quad \text{No.}$$

Therefore, 2 is not a root of the original equation.

To check $x = 3$, we substitute 3 for x in the original equation and ask

$$\text{does} \quad \sqrt{9 - 5} + 3 = 1?$$
$$\text{does} \quad \sqrt{4} + 3 = 1?$$
$$\text{does} \quad 2 + 3 = 1? \quad \text{No.}$$

Therefore, 3 is not a root of the original equation. Both values of x obtained in the solution are extraneous roots, and the original equation has no solution.

Example 4. Solve $\sqrt{3x - 2} + \sqrt{x - 1} = 3$.

Solution.

Transposing,	$\sqrt{3x - 2} = 3 - \sqrt{x - 1}$
Squaring both sides,	$3x - 2 = 9 - 6\sqrt{x - 1} + x - 1$
Transposing,	$6\sqrt{x - 1} = 9 - 1 + 2 + x - 3x$
Combining,	$6\sqrt{x - 1} = 10 - 2x$
Dividing both sides by 2,	$3\sqrt{x - 1} = 5 - x$
Squaring both sides,	$9(x - 1) = 25 - 10x + x^2$
Removing parentheses,	$9x - 9 = 25 - 10x + x^2$
Transposing and combining,	$0 = x^2 - 19x + 34$
Solving,	$x = 2 \quad \text{and} \quad x = 17$

To check $x = 2$, we ask

$$\text{does} \quad \sqrt{6 - 2} + \sqrt{2 - 1} = 3?$$
$$\text{does} \quad \sqrt{4} + \sqrt{1} = 3?$$
$$\text{does} \quad 2 + 1 = 3? \quad \text{Yes.}$$

Therefore, 3 is a root of the original equation.
To check $x = 17$, we ask

$$\text{does} \quad \sqrt{51 - 2} + \sqrt{17 - 1} = 3?$$
$$\text{does} \quad \sqrt{49} + \sqrt{16} = 3?$$
$$\text{does} \quad 7 + 4 = 3? \quad \text{No.}$$

Therefore, 17 is an extraneous root. It is not a root of the original equation.

Exercise 24.1

Solve the following equations. Check all answers and indicate which answers, if any, are extraneous.

1. $\sqrt{x + 3} = 4$

2. $\sqrt{2x + 3} - x = 0$

3. $\sqrt{x - 2} = x - 4$

4. $5 - \sqrt{x + 7} = x$

5. $\sqrt{3x + 1} + 3 = x$

6. $\sqrt{3 - 2x} - 2x = 9$

7. $2x = \sqrt{13 + 2x} - 7$

8. $7 = \sqrt{5 - 2x} - 2x$

9. $\sqrt{10 + 2x} - 8 = 2x$

10. $\sqrt{3x - 2} - \sqrt{2x + 4} = 0$

11. $\sqrt{x} + \sqrt{6x + 1} = 3$

12. $\sqrt{6x + 1} - \sqrt{x} = 3$

13. $\sqrt{5x - 1} - x = 1$

14. $\sqrt{x} + \sqrt{5 - x} = 3$

15. $\sqrt{2x} + \sqrt{11 - x} = 5$

16. $\sqrt{5 - x} - \sqrt{x - 1} = 2$

17. $\sqrt{2x - 5} + \sqrt{x - 3} = 5$

18. $\sqrt{7x - 5} + \sqrt{x + 1} = 6$

19. $\sqrt{x} + \sqrt{2x + 1} = 5$

20. $2 = \sqrt{x} - \sqrt{5x - 4}$

21. $\sqrt{3 - 2x} + \sqrt{x - 1} = 1$

22. $(1 - 4x)^{\frac{1}{3}} + (2 - x)^{\frac{1}{3}} = 1$

23. $\sqrt[3]{x + 1} = 2$

24. $(x^2 - 6x)^{\frac{1}{3}} = 3$

25. $(x^2 - 2x - 7)^{\frac{1}{3}} = 2$

26. $x^{\frac{2}{3}} = 8$

27. $x^{\frac{2}{3}} = -27$

28. $x^{\frac{3}{3}} = -4$

29. $x^{\frac{3}{3}} = 64$

30. $\sqrt{5 - 2x} + \sqrt{3x - 1} = \sqrt{x}$

31. One leg of a right triangle is 7 in. longer than the other, and the hypotenuse is 6 in. less than the sum of the legs. Find the area of the triangle.

32. The area of a rectangle is 240 sq in. The diagonal is 2 in. longer than the longest side. Find the dimensions of the rectangle.

33. One leg of a right triangle is 5 in. longer than the other leg. The hypotenuse is 10 in. less than the sum of the two legs. Find the perimeter.

34. One number is 9 more than another. The cube root of the sum of the squares of the two numbers is equal to 5. What are the two numbers?

25

Ratio, Proportion, Variation

25.1 RATIO

Much work in mathematics is concerned with comparing quantities. We can compare two quantities in various ways. For instance, if we wish to compare 8 feet with 6 feet, we can use subtraction:

$$8 \text{ feet} - 6 \text{ feet} = 2 \text{ feet}$$

That is, we can say 8 feet is 2 feet more than 6 feet.

Whenever we say one quantity is a certain amount *greater* than, or *less* than, another, we are comparing the two by *subtraction*. When we say "John is 2 inches taller than James," we are comparing by *subtraction*.

We can also compare quantities by *division*. A *comparison by division* is called the *ratio* between the two quantities. When we compare two quantities, such as 12 pounds and 4 pounds, by division we find the *ratio* between the two. For instance, the ratio of 12 pounds to 4 pounds is 12 pounds ÷ 4 pounds, which is equal to 3. Here the "3" is a pure number; it has no denomination, such as inches, feet, yards, miles, pounds, hours, or any other name.

Note that when we compare quantities by subtraction the difference between the quantities has the same kind of denomination as the quantities themselves. Examples;

$$12 \text{ ft} - 9 \text{ ft} = 3 \text{ ft}$$
$$12 \text{ hr} - 9 \text{ hr} = 3 \text{ hr}$$
$$12 \text{ lb} - 9 \text{ lb} = 3 \text{ lb}$$

When we compare two quantities by division (that is, when we find the ratio between the two), the answer has no denomination:

$$12 \text{ ft} \div 9 \text{ ft} = \frac{4}{3} \qquad\qquad 12 \text{ lb} \div 9 \text{ lb} = \frac{4}{3}$$

$$12 \text{ hr} \div 9 \text{ hr} = \frac{4}{3} \qquad\qquad 20 \text{ lb} \div 4 \text{ lb} = 5$$

A ratio is often indicated by a colon. As an example, the ratio of 6 pounds to 10 pounds is written

$$6 \text{ lb} : 10 \text{ lb}$$

This is read "6 pounds *is to* 10 pounds." The colon represents the words "*is to*."

A ratio can also be written as a fraction:

$$6 \text{ ft} : 10 \text{ ft} = \frac{6 \text{ ft}}{10 \text{ ft}} = \frac{3}{5}$$

When the fraction is reduced, it becomes $\frac{3}{5}$. This number $\frac{3}{5}$ is a *pure number* without any denomination.

Examples.

$$\$15 : \$20 = \frac{\$15}{\$20} = \frac{3}{4}; \quad 14 \text{ in.} : 21 \text{ in.} = \frac{2}{3}$$

As you progress further and further in mathematics, you will discover that the concept of *ratio* becomes more and more important. For example, it is the basis for a study of calculus. The idea of *ratio* should therefore be thoroughly understood.

A ratio is a comparison of two like quantities by division.

When we wish to compare two quantities, these quantities must be of the same kind. We cannot compare, for instance, 12 pounds and 4 hours. Pounds and hours do not measure the same kind of quantity. However, two different units may be compared if they measure the same kind of quantity. We may compare 4 feet with 2 yards by first changing one so that both are expressed in the same units. The ratio of 4 feet to 6 feet (2 yards) is $\frac{2}{3}$; that is, 4 feet is two-thirds as much as 2 yards.

Exercise 25.1

Express the ratio indicated in each of the following examples, and reduce the ratio to its simplest form:

1. The ratio of $8 to $12.
2. The ratio of 16 in. to 20 in.
3. The ratio of 24 lb to 30 lb.
4. The ratio of 21 ft to 18 ft.
5. The ratio of 5 ft to 4 yd.
6. The ratio of 2 ft to 8 in.
7. The ratio of 32 lb to 2 lb.
8. The ratio of 1 in. to 1 cm.
9. The ratio of 1 ft to 1 mile.
10. The ratio of 1320 ft to $\frac{3}{4}$ mile.
11. One circle has a diameter of 12 in., and another circle has a diameter of 6 in. What is the ratio of the radius of the first circle to the radius of the second? What is the ratio of the circumferences? What is the ratio of their areas?

12. Similar triangles are triangles that have exactly the same shape but not necessarily the same size. In similar figures all corresponding sides have the same ratio. The same is true regarding any set of corresponding lines. A certain right triangle has its sides equal to 3, 4, and 5 in., respectively. A similar triangle has a hypotenuse of 10 in. What is the ratio between the short side of the small triangle to the short side of the large triangle?

13. One square has a side of 4 in. and a second square has a side of 12 in. What is the ratio of their perimeters, diagonals, and areas?

14. On a certain house plan $\frac{1}{4}$ in. represents 1 ft of actual length of the house. What is the ratio between the distance on the plan and the actual distance on the ground?

15. On a certain map one inch represents 10 miles. What is the ratio of the distances on the map to the actual distances on the earth?

25.2 PROPORTION

Suppose we have the following ratios:

$$6 \text{ ft} : 9 \text{ ft}$$
$$10 \text{ min} : 15 \text{ min}$$

We find that the ratio of each is $\frac{2}{3}$. We may then write an equation stating that the two ratios are equal:

$$6 \text{ ft} : 9 \text{ ft} = 10 \text{ min} : 15 \text{ min}$$

or, as ratios,
$$\frac{2}{3} = \frac{2}{3}$$

A statement of equality between two equal ratios is called a proportion.

Both ratios involved in a proportion may refer to the same denomination, as in the following example, in which both ratios refer to feet:

$$5 \text{ ft} : 15 \text{ ft} = 7 \text{ ft} : 21 \text{ ft}$$

However, the ratios may refer to different denominations as in the following:

$$6 \text{ ft} : 8 \text{ ft} = 15 \text{ lb} : 20 \text{ lb}$$

Since each ratio is equal to $\frac{3}{4}$, the two can be stated as a proportion.

You will notice that a proportion contains four terms, since the proportion consists of two ratios and each ratio has two terms. The foregoing proportions can be written as fractions:

$$\frac{5 \text{ ft}}{15 \text{ ft}} = \frac{7 \text{ ft}}{21 \text{ ft}} \qquad \frac{6 \text{ ft}}{8 \text{ ft}} = \frac{15 \text{ lb}}{20 \text{ lb}}$$

The four terms of a proportion are usually designated as *first term, second term, third term,* and *fourth term.* The first and fourth terms are called the *extremes* of the proportion; the second and third are called the *means.*

The fourth term is sometimes called the *fourth proportional* to the first three terms.

We have said that a proportion is an equation expressing an equality between two ratios. Therefore we may treat it in the same way as any other equation.

Consider the proportion

$$a : b = c : d$$

Writing it in fractional form, we have

$$\frac{a}{b} = \frac{c}{d}$$

If we multiply both sides of the equation by bd, we get

$$ad = bc$$

Notice that the term ad is the *product of the extremes* of the proportion and the term bc is the *product of the means*. From this general equation we may formulate the important *principle* of a proportion.

Principle. *In any proportion the product of the means equals the product of the extremes.*

This principle enables us to find any missing term of a proportion. For instance, suppose we have

$$5 : x = 8 : 17$$

The product of the means is $8x$. The product of the extremes is 85. Therefore, we can write the equation

$$8x = 85$$
Solving,
$$x = 10\tfrac{5}{8}$$

It is possible that the second term of a proportion will be the same as the third term. This is true in the following proportion:

$$2 : 6 = 6 : 18$$

If the second and third terms are the same, that quantity is called the *mean proportional between the other two terms*. In that case we have only three *different* quantities. The fourth term is then called the *third proportional* to the first and second terms. In the foregoing example 18 is the third proportional to 2 and 6, and 6 is the mean proportional between 2 and 18.

In the proportion

$$a : b = b : c$$

b is the mean proportional between a and c. Also $b^2 = ac$ and

$$b = \pm\sqrt{ac}$$

We can find the mean proportional between two numbers by use of the principle previously stated.

Example. Find the mean proportional between 2 and 32.

Solution.
We set up the proportion $2 : x = x : 32$
Then $x^2 = 64$
Solving for x, $x = \pm 8$

It will be noted that the mean proportional may be either $+8$ or -8.

To check the answer, we write $2 : (+8) = (+8) : 32$

Stated as fractions, $\dfrac{1}{4} = \dfrac{1}{4}$

Using -8, we have $2 : (-8) = (-8) : 32$

Stated as fractions, $-\dfrac{1}{4} = -\dfrac{1}{4}$

Exercise 25.2

Find the value of the unknown in each of the following proportions:

1. $7 : x = 4 : 16$ **2.** $5 : 8 = x : 32$
3. $x : 6 = 7 : 15$ **4.** $8 : 3.5 = 12 : y$
5. $4 : x = x : 64$ **6.** $x : 2 = 16 : x$
7. $14 : (3 + x) = 7 : 13$ **8.** $x : (x - 4) = (x + 4 : (x - 2)$
9. $(n + 2) : (n - 3) = (3n - 2) : (n + 3)$ **10.** $y : (y - 2) = (y + 2) : (y - 3)$
11. $5 : (k + 2) = 15 : (4k - 1)$ **12.** $480 : 592 = 12 : x$
13. $4.5 : 16 = 22.5 : n$ **14.** $1 : 7.5 = 3.5 : k$
15. Find the fourth proportional to the three numbers 2, 3, and 7.
16. Find the mean proportional between 4 and 12.
17. Find the mean proportional between 2 and 98.
18. What is the mean proportional between -2 and -18?
19. What is the mean proportional between -2 and $+32$? (Explain.)
20. What is the mean proportional between $\frac{1}{8}$ and 2?
21. A recipe calls for $1\frac{1}{2}$ cups of flour. The recipe is set up for serving ten people. How many cups of flour should be used for servings for four people?
22. A certain antifreeze mixture calls for $4\frac{1}{2}$ qt of antifreeze in 10 gal of water. How much should be used for a mixture for a car radiator that holds 18 qt of the solution?

23. According to Hooke's law, in any elastic body the distortion is proportional to the distorting force if kept within what is called the "elastic limit." If a force of 5 lb will stretch a spring $3\frac{1}{2}$ in., what force will stretch it 2 in.?

24. If 1 kg (2.2 lb) will stretch a certain spring $1\frac{7}{16}$ in., what force will be required to stretch it 1 ft at the same rate?

25.3 CONSTANTS AND VARIABLES

A *constant* is a number whose value is assumed to remain the same in any given problem. A *variable* is a number that may change or take on different values in a problem.

In the equation $3x + 5y = 30$, 3, 5, and 30 are constants; x and y are *variables*.

In the formula $V = \frac{4}{3}\pi r^3$ the constants are 4, 3, and π. The variables are V and r.

25.4 FUNCTION

It often happens that two variables are related in some way so that if one is known, the other can be found. Then we say that one variable is a *function* of the other. For instance, suppose we have the equation

$$y = 3x + 2$$

Now, if we know the value of x, we can determine the value of y and say "y is a function of the variable x."

The term *function* involves the idea of *dependence*. Whenever we find one variable dependent on another, we can say the first variable is a *function* of the second.

Many situations in everyday life involve the idea of dependence, even though it may not be possible to write an equation for the relation between the variables. For instance, consider the following:

1. Our weight depends on how much we eat.
2. Our school grades depend on how much we study.
3. Good crops depend on the amount of rainfall.

Sometimes one variable may depend on several other variables. Name *several variable factors* on which each of the following depends:

1. Success in school depends on . . . .
2. Success in athletics depends on . . . .
3. Whether it will rain tomorrow depends on . . . .
4. Success in marriage depends on . . . .

5. The cost of postage on a package depends on . . . .
6. The economic condition of a nation depends on . . . .

In many problems it is possible to express the relation between two variables in the form of an equation. For example, if a car travels at an average rate of 40 miles per hour, then the total distance traveled depends on the time of traveling. If we let d represent the total distance traveled and t represent the number of hours of traveling, we can express the relation between the two variables, d and t, by the equation $d = 40t$.

In an equation such as $y = 5x$ there is a definite mathematical relation between the two variables x and y. The equation indicates that, as the value of x changes, the value of y will always be five times as great as the value of x. For each value of y there is a corresponding value of x. Then we say y is a function of x.

25.5 VARIATION

If two variables are interdependent and one variable changes or varies, the other variable will also change; that is, a change in one variable will cause a change in the related variable. Then we say *one variable varies as the other*.

25.6 DIRECT VARIATION

A simple type of variation is one in which two variables increase or decrease at a uniform rate. As an example, suppose we drive a car at an average rate of 40 miles per hour. As the time changes, the distance traveled will also change. The two related variables are the *distance* and the *time*. If we represent the distance in miles by d and the time in hours by t, we can say that d varies with t. Moreover, the variation is at a uniform rate. The relation can be expressed by the equation $d = 40t$.

From the equation we see that, if t increases, d also increases. If t decreases, d also decreases. This example is an illustration of *direct variation*.

Another example is the equation

$$y = 3x$$

In this equation, if x increases, y also increases; if x decreases, y also decreases. The relation is easily seen if we list some corresponding values for x and y:

if $x =$	1	2	5	7	10
then $y =$	3	6	15	21	30

It will be seen that any two pairs of these numbers form a proportion:

$$2 : 6 = 7 : 21$$

Variation is sometimes indicated by the symbol $\propto$: thus

$$y \propto x$$

This statement is read, "*y* varies directly as *x*." This does *not* mean that *y* is equal to *x*. In each of the following equations we can say $y \propto x$:

$$y = 7x \qquad y = 10x \qquad y = 15x$$

To avoid using the difficult variation symbol ($\propto$), we write the equation with an arbitrary constant K :

$$y = Kx$$

You will notice that this equation does not say that *y* is equal to *x*. Instead, if *K* represents any constant, the equation means that *y varies directly as x*. The *K* is called the *constant of variation*. For *direct variation* we have the following definition:

One quantity varies directly as another quantity when the first is equal to a constant times the second.

In direct variation, if one variable increases, the other also increases; if one decreases, the other decreases.

Examples of direct variation.

1. The total cost of a certain number of articles varies directly as the price of each.
2. The number of miles traveled in five hours varies directly as the speed.
3. The amount of light in a room varies directly as the number of lamps.
4. The amount of current varies directly as the electromotive force.
5. The amount of work done varies directly as the number of workers.
6. The cost of any number of articles at a certain price varies directly as the number of articles.
7. The circumference of a circle varies directly as the radius.
8. The area of a circle varies directly as the *square* of the radius.

25.7 JOINT VARIATION

It often happens that one variable depends on two or more other variables. For instance, the area of a triangle depends on the *base* and the *altitude*. The formula for the area of a triangle is

$$A = \frac{1}{2}b \cdot h$$

In this equation, if b is doubled and h remains unchanged, the area is doubled. If h is tripled and b remains constant, then the area is tripled.

Now, if the base is doubled and the altitude is tripled, the area is multiplied by 6; that is, the area varies as the *product* of the base and the altitude.

If one variable, A, varies as the *product* of two variables, b and h, then we say A varies *jointly* as b and h. *Joint* variation always implies a *product* of two variables.

If Z varies jointly as x and y, then Z varies as the *product* of x and y. For the general variation statement in this case, we write

$$Z = Kxy$$

Note that the constant of variation, K, is included as a factor.

Exercise 25.3

By use of appropriate letters to represent quantities, express the indicated relation in each of the following statements as an equation of variation. Be sure to use a constant of variation in each equation.

1. The total cost, C, of a certain number of articles varies directly as the price, p, of each.
2. The number of miles traveled in 5 hr varies directly as the speed.
3. The amount of light in a room varies directly as the number of watts of power represented by the lamps.
4. The amount of electric current varies directly as the electromotive force, provided other factors remain constant.
5. The amount of work done on a construction job varies directly as the number of days worked.
6. The cost of a particular kind of beef roast varies as the weight.
7. The circumference of a circle varies directly as the radius.
8. The area of a circle varies directly as the square of the radius.
9. The amount of wages earned varies jointly as the number of days worked and the number of hours per day.
10. The interest paid on money borrowed varies jointly as the amount of money borrowed, the rate of interest, and the time for which it is borrowed.
11. The speed attained by a falling object varies directly as the time of falling. (The speed, however, reaches a limit after a certain time of falling.)
12. The distance a falling object has traversed varies as the square of the time of falling.
13. The weight of a cylinder of a particular material varies jointly as the height and square of the radius.
14. The cost of carpeting a floor varies jointly as the length and the width of the room and the cost per square yard for the carpet.
15. The weight of a sphere of a particular material varies as the cube of the radius.

25.8   INVERSE VARIATION

Suppose we must drive a distance of 120 miles. The time required to cover this distance will depend upon our speed. The two variables, time and speed, are related. However, they are related in such a way that *one decreases* as the *other increases*. The time required depends upon speed, but if the speed is *decreased*, the time required is *increased*. This is an example of *inverse variation*.

If we let r represent the rate of speed in miles per hour and t represent the time in hours, then we can relate the two variables by the equation

$$t = \frac{120}{r}$$

We can set up a table of corresponding values of r and t:

if $r =$	60	40	30	20	15
then $t =$	2	3	4	6	8

For instance, if our rate of speed is 60 miles per hour, it will require 2 hours to drive the 120-mile distance. As the *rate decreases*, the *time increases*. For *inverse variation* we have the following definition:

One quantity is said to vary inversely as another when the one variable is equal to a constant divided by the second variable.

Note that a constant is also involved in inverse variation. The general equation for inverse variation is

$$y = \frac{K}{x}$$

where K represents the *constant* of variation and x and y are the variables. In inverse variation, as *one variable increases, another decreases*.

In many situations we have a combination of joint variation and inverse variation. However, in writing the general variation statement, only one constant, K, is necessary, since the K represents any positive constant whatever.

Example.   Suppose we say that a variable F varies jointly as x and y and inversely as the square of Z. The general variation equation can be written

$$F = K\frac{x \cdot y}{Z^2}$$

The constant K can also be written with the numerator of the fraction.

Exercise 25.4

By use of appropriate letters to represent quantities, express the indicated relation-ship in each of the following statements as an equation of variation. Be sure to use a constant of variation in each equation.

1. The time, t, required for a certain trip varies inversely as the speed, r.
2. The number of days, d, required to erect a particular building varies inversely as the number of men, m, and the number of hours, h, per day.
3. The force of attraction between two opposite magnetic poles varies inversely as the square of the distance between them.
4. The amount of light that falls on this page varies inversely as the square of the distance of the page from the source of light, provided that the page is held at right angles to the direction of light.
5. The resistance to the flow of electricity in a conductor varies inversely as the square of the diameter of the wire.
6. The amount of water discharged from a pipe varies directly as the water pressure and inversely as the square of the radius of the pipe.
7. The volume of a gas under constant temperature varies inversely as the pressure.
8. To balance a teeter-board, if you weigh less you sit farther from the fulcrum (the balancing point). Is this an example of direct or inverse variation?
9. The lens setting in a camera varies inversely as the square root of the shutter speed.
10. The number of vibrations of a pendulum varies inversely as the square root of the length.

25.9   FINDING AND USING THE CONSTANT OF VARIATION

Suppose we know that a variable Z varies jointly as x and y. Suppose also we know that $Z = 12$ when $x = 5$ and $y = 7$. Then it is possible to find the constant of variation.

Our *first step* is to write the general variation equation:

$$Z = Kxy$$

This equation must include K, the constant of variation.

As a *second step*, we substitute the known values for x, y, and Z and solve for K:

$$12 = K \cdot 5 \cdot 7$$

This equation can now be solved for the value of K. We get

$$K = \frac{12}{35}$$

As a *third step*, the value of the constant K is inserted in the variation equation:

$$Z = \frac{12}{35}xy$$

The result is a formula that can be used to find an unknown value of Z.

As a *fourth step*, now that we have the formula for Z, suppose we wish to find Z when $x = 15$ and $y = 8$. The formula says

$$Z = \frac{12}{35}x \cdot y$$

Substituting the new values of x and y, we get

$$Z = \frac{12}{35}(15)(8) = 41\tfrac{1}{7}$$

There are *four* principal steps in solving a problem in variation.

1. *Set up the general variation equation including the constant of variation.* (The constant may be represented by K or some other letter. However, it should not be confused with a variable.)

2. *From known values of all the variables, find the value of K.*

3. *Insert the numerical value of K in the general variation equation. The result is a formula.*

4. *Use the formula to solve the new problem involving new values of the variables.*

Example 1. Suppose L varies directly as N and inversely as the square of d. If $L = 200$, when $N = 3$ and $d = 5$, find L when $N = 8$ and $d = 10$.

Solution. *Step 1.* The variation equation is

$$L = K\frac{N}{d^2}$$

Step 2. Supplying the given values and solving for K,

$$200 = K\frac{3}{25}; \quad K = \frac{5000}{3}$$

Step 3. Inserting the value of K in the general equation,

$$L = \frac{5000}{3} \cdot \frac{N}{d^2}$$

Step 4. Using the formula to find L for the new values of N and d,

$$L = \frac{5000}{3} \cdot \frac{8}{100} = \frac{400}{3} = 133\tfrac{1}{3}$$

Example 2. Suppose T varies jointly as x and the square of y and inversely as the square root of Z. If $T = 36$ when $x = 3$, $y = 8$, and $Z = 25$, find T when $x = 5$, $y = 6$, and $Z = 81$.

Solution. *Step 1.* The variation equation is

$$T = \frac{Kxy^2}{\sqrt{Z}}$$

Step 2. Supplying the given values and solving for K,

$$36 = \frac{K \cdot 3 \cdot 64}{\sqrt{25}} ; \quad K = \frac{15}{16}$$

Step 3. Inserting the value of K in the general equation,

$$T = \frac{15}{16} \cdot \frac{xy^2}{\sqrt{Z}}$$

Step 4. Using the formula to find T for the new values of the other variables,

$$T = \frac{15}{16} \cdot \frac{5 \cdot 36}{\sqrt{81}} ; \quad T = 18\tfrac{3}{4}$$

Exercise 25.5

Use appropriate letters for the quantities in each problem:

1. Suppose a variable, Z, varies directly as x and the square of y. If $Z = 12$, when $x = 25$ and $y = 15$, find Z when $x = 15$ and $y = 25$.

2. A variable, F, varies jointly as a and b and inversely as the square of r. If $F = 200$ when $a = 8$, $b = 6$, and $r = 40$, find F when $a = 15$, $b = 4$, and $r = 60$.

3. If Z varies directly as w and the square of x and inversely as the square root of t, find Z when $w = 20$, $x = 24$, and $t = 45$, if $Z = 5$ when $w = 15$, $x = 32$, and $t = 20$.

4. The amount of wages earned varies directly as the number of hours worked. If the amount earned in 24 hr is $62.40, find by means of a variation equation the amount earned in 78 hr.

5. The interest paid for money borrowed varies directly as the principal, P, and the time, t. If the interest is $168 when the principal is $800 and the time is $3\tfrac{1}{2}$ yr, find the interest on $500 for $4\tfrac{1}{2}$ yr at the same rate of interest.

6. The surface area, A, of a sphere varies as the square of the radius. If the area is 100π when the radius is 5, find the area when the radius is 10.

7. The weight of a sphere varies as the cube of the radius. If a sphere with a 3-in. radius weighs 100 lb, what is the weight of a sphere of the same material having a radius of 6 in.?

8. The time required to make a certain trip varies inversely as the speed. If the trip takes 7 hr at 45 mph, how long will it take at 56 mph?

9. The distance traversed by a falling object varies directly as the square of the time. If the distance is 256 ft at the end of 4 sec, find the distance fallen at the end of 5 sec. How far does the object fall in the fifth second?

10. If the distance traversed by a ball rolling down an inclined plane varies as the square of the time and if the distance is 36 in. when the time is 3 sec, find the distance traversed at the end of 6 sec. How far does it roll in the fifth second?

11. The weight of a cylinder of a certain material varies as the height and the square of the radius. If a cylinder with a radius of 4 in. and a height of 18 in. weighs 30 lb, what is the weight of a cylinder of the same material if it has a radius of 3 in. and a height of 36 in.?

12. The cost of carpeting a floor varies jointly as the length and the width of the floor. If the cost is $180 for a room 15 ft wide and 16 ft long, what will it cost to carpet a floor 18 ft wide and 23 ft long?

13. The volume of water under constant pressure delivered by a circular pipe varies approximately as the square of the diameter. If a $\frac{1}{2}$-in. pipe delivers 30 gal of water per minute, what amount will be delivered per minute by a 3-in. pipe?

14. The resistance to the flow of electricity in a wire varies directly as the length and inversely as the square of the diameter of the wire. If the resistance is 0.26 ohm when the diameter is 0.02 in. for a wire 10 ft long, what is the resistance of a wire of the same material 5 ft long and 0.01 in. in diameter?

15. The power in an electric circuit varies directly as the resistance and the square of the current. If the power is 15 watts when the current is 0.5 amp and the resistance is 60 ohms, find the constant of variation and then find the power when the current is 3 amp and the resistance is 45 ohms.

16. The number of vibrations of a musical string is inversely proportional to the length. If a violin string approximately $12\frac{3}{4}$ in. long with a particular tension has 430 vibrations per second (approximately the tone A), what must be the length of the same string for 510 vibrations per second?

17. The number of days required to erect a certain building varies inversely as the number of men working and the number of hours per day. If the building requires 45 days to complete when 80 men work for 8 hr per day, how long will be required if 60 men work for 9 hr a day?

18. The length of time required to fill a swimming pool varies inversely as the square of the diameter of the pipe through which the water enters the pool. If it takes 5 hr for a 6-in. pipe to fill the pool, how long will it take a 3-in. pipe?

19. The force of attraction between two magnetic poles of opposite polarity varies inversely as the square of the distance between them. If the force is 80 dynes when the distance is 4 cm, what is the force when the distance is 8 cm?

20. The intensity of illumination, L, varies inversely as the square of the distance from the source of light. If the amount of light falling on a page of this book is 100 units when the book is 6 ft from the light source, how many units will fall on the page if it is held 3 ft from the source of light?

21. A student reading a book said, "I shall move nearer the lamp so that I'll be just half as far from the light. Then I'll have twice as much light on the page." What was wrong with his statement?

22. The wind pressure on a wall varies directly as the area, A, of the wall and as the square of the speed, or velocity, of the wind. If the force on a wall 12 ft wide and 18 ft long is 120 lb when the velocity of the wind is 15 mph, what is the force on a wall 10 ft wide and 20 ft long when the velocity of the wind is 25 mph?

23. The lens setting of a camera varies inversely as the square root of the shutter speed. If the speed is $\frac{1}{50}$ sec for an opening of 11.2, what should the lens opening be for a shutter speed of $\frac{1}{100}$ sec?

Sample Quiz on Chapters 21–25.   Form A.

1. (a) Add graphically: $-5 + 2i$ and $1 - 5i$.

(b) Multiply the complex number, $1 + 4i$, by i four times successively and show the original number and each product on a graph.

2. (a) Divide as indicated: $(-2 + 3i) \div (-3 - 5i)$.

(b) Find the reciprocal of the complex number, $-2 - 5i$, and write the result as a complex number showing the real part separated from the imaginary part.

3. In each of the following quadratic equations, find the numerical value of the discriminant and tell what it shows about the nature of the roots:

(a) $4x^2 = 9x - 5$ (b) $10x = 2x^2 + 225$ (c) $25 = 30x - 9x^2$

4. In the following equation, find the value of k that will give the equation equal roots. Then check each value in the original equation and show that the roots of the equation are then equal by solving the resulting equation:

$$3x^2 - 3x + kx - 2k - 3 = 0$$

5. (a) Write the equation that has the roots: $-\frac{4}{3}$ and $\frac{2}{3}$.

(b) Write the equation that has the roots: $-3 + \sqrt{2}$ and $-3 - \sqrt{2}$.

6. Name each of the graphs for these equations, and then solve the two as a system for the point or points of intersection:

$$x^2 - 2x - 4y - 11 = 0 \quad \text{and} \quad x - 2y = 3$$

7. Solve the following equation containing radicals and check all roots and tell which roots, if any, are extraneous: $\sqrt{1 - 5x} - 2x = 10$.

8. A quantity T varies directly as x and the square root of y, and inversely as the sum of c and d. If $T = 4$, when $x = 20$, $y = 9$, $c = 5$, and $d = 3$, find T when $x = 12$, $y = 16$, $c = 4$, and $d = 2$. (Be sure to solve for the value of the constant of variation.)

Sample Quiz on Chapters 21–25.   Form B.

1. (a) Add graphically: $5 + i$ and $-4 - 3i$.

(b) Multiply the complex number, $5 + i$, by i four times in succession and show the original number and each product on a graph.

2. (a) Divide as indicated: $(5 - 2i) \div (-2 - 3i)$.

(b) Find the reciprocal of the complex number, $-5 + 3i$, and write the result as a complex number showing the real part separated from the imaginary part.

3. In each of the following quadratic equations, find the numerical value of the discriminant and tell what it shows about the nature of the roots:

(a) $4x = 4x^2 + 101$ (b) $4 = 7x - 3x^2$ (c) $9x^2 = 4x + 4$

4. In the following equation, find the value of k that will give the equation equal roots. Then check each value in the original equation and show that the roots of the equation are then equal by solving the resulting equation:

$$3x^2 - kx - 4x + 5 - k = 0$$

5. (a) Write the equation that has the roots: $\frac{2}{5}$ and $-\frac{3}{4}$.
   (b) Write the equation that has the roots: $-5 + 3i$ and $-5 - 3i$.

6. Name the graph of each of these equations, and then solve the two as a system for the point or points of intersection:

$$y^2 - 2y - 4x - 7 = 0 \quad \text{and} \quad 2x - y = -1$$

7. Solve the following equation containing a radical and check all roots and tell which roots, if any, are extraneous: $\sqrt{5 - 2x} - 3x = 9$.

8. A quantity Z varies directly as x and the square of y and inversely as the square root of t. If $Z = 10$ when $x = 8$, $y = 3$, and $t = 25$, then find Z when $x = 6$, $y = 4$, and $t = 9$.

Part III

GEOMETRY

26

Plane Figures

26.1 THE ELEMENTS OF GEOMETRY

Geometry deals with *form* and *size*. The form and size of geometric figures continually influence our living and thinking from day to day.

Every day in countless ways we are conscious of *form*. Whenever we use expressions such as the following, we are aware of geometric form: a round plate; a square box; a long pencil; an oval table; a rectangular rug; a straight path; a curved road; a crooked trail.

We are also conscious of *size*. Whenever we use the following expressions, we have a feeling of size and measurement: a big apple; a little child; a large man; a small box; a long, narrow room; a thin board; a thick rug.

Geometry is not concerned with qualities that are not measurable. Many such qualities make life beautiful and pleasant, but they do not enter in the study of geometry, although some geometric forms are considered more beautiful than others. Geometry is not concerned with the qualities indicated in the following expressions: a red apple; a blue bird; a fierce black bear; a soft rug; a tender steak; a sweet apple; a sour lemon; a good man; a happy woman. The qualities so expressed are an essential part of our lives, but geometry is concerned instead with only *form* and *size*.

The form and size of geometric figures are determined by *points*, *lines*, and *surfaces*. A point is an *undefined element* in geometry. A true geometric point has no size—no length, width, or thickness. It indicates position or location only. We usually make a dot of some kind to indicate the location of a point, but such a dot is not a true point because it has length, width, and thickness. You can get some idea of a true point if you think of the tip of a needle just at the place where you leave the needle.

A *line* has length only. It has neither width nor thickness. A line is another undefined element in geometry, although it is sometimes defined as *the path of a moving point*. Since the point has no size, the line has no width. We often indicate a line by drawing a mark with a pen or pencil. However, such a mark is not a true line because even the finest line has some width and some thickness.

In geometry the word *line* is understood to refer to unlimited extent; that is, it has no end. A limited portion of a line is called a *line segment*. In most

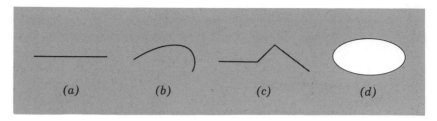

(a)   *(b)*   *(c)*   *(d)*

Fig. 26.1

problems we deal with line segments rather than lines of unlimited length. A line segment has a limited length. However, in much discussion in geometry the word *line* is used to refer to a line segment.

A line is often named by the letter l on the line. If more than one line is under discussion in a problem, the separate lines are indicated by subscripts, such as l_1, l_2, and so on. A line segment is often indicated by a single letter or sometimes by a letter at each end.

A *straight line* (Fig. 26.1a) is the path formed by a moving point that always moves in the same direction. A *curved line* (Fig. 26.1b) is a line no part of which is straight. A *broken line* (Fig. 26.1c) is a line consisting of straight line segments. A *closed* curve is one that encloses a definite amount of area (Fig. 26.1d).

A *surface* has two dimensions, *length* and *width*. It has no thickness. When

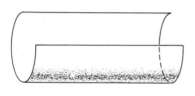

Fig. 26.2

we speak of any kind of surface, such as the surface of this paper, we are not concerned with the thickness of the paper. A surface is sometimes defined as the geometric figure generated by a moving line that does not move in its own direction. A surface may be *flat* or *curved*. Fig. 26.2 shows a curved surface.

A *plane* surface is a surface usually described as "flat." More technically, a plane surface is a surface such that if a straight line has any two of its separate and distinct points anywhere in the surface, then the entire line lies in the surface.

A *plane* figure in geometry means a figure that can be drawn on a flat surface. Such figures have no thickness, only length and width. For instance, if we think of a flat piece of paper as a plane, we can show on this flat surface several kinds of plane figures, such as a line, an angle, a triangle, a circle, a square, and many other shapes and sizes of plane figures (Fig. 26.3).

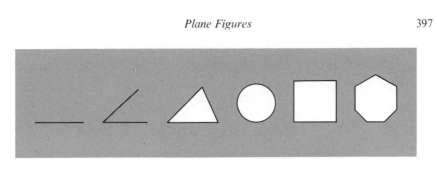

Fig. 26.3. Plane figures.

Plane geometry deals with figures on a plane surface; that is, with plane figures. *Solid geometry* is the study of figures that take up space; that is, geometric solids. Solid geometry is therefore sometimes called *space geometry*.

26.2 LINES: INTERSECTING AND PARALLEL

Two straight lines in the same plane are either parallel or intersecting lines. If the lines cross each other, they are called *intersecting* lines and they intersect at one point only (Fig. 26.4a). If two straight lines in the same plane do not intersect no matter how far they are extended, they are called *parallel* lines (Fig. 26.4b). According to this definition, two parallel lines never intersect.

In space, however, two lines can be nonparallel, yet not intersect. Such lines are called *skew* lines. Two telephone wires extending in different directions, one above the other, form skew lines.

26.3 ANGLE

The word *angle* is used so frequently in geometry that it is often represented by a small angle, $\angle$, as a symbol. (Plural: $\angle$s.)

An angle can be defined as the figure formed when two straight lines intersect. Actually, when two straight lines intersect, four angles are formed, such as the angles, 1, 2, 3, and 4 in Fig. 26.5. Two angles that have a common vertex and a common side between them are called *adjacent* angles, such as

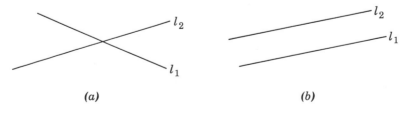

(a)   (b)

Fig. 26.4

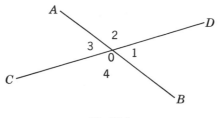

Fig. 26.5

$\angle$ 1 and $\angle$ 2. The following sets are also pairs of adjacent angles: $\angle$ 2 and $\angle$ 3; $\angle$ 3 and $\angle$ 4; $\angle$ 4 and $\angle$ 1. Opposite angles, such as angles 1 and 3, are called *vertical*.

An angle is sometimes defined as *the amount of opening between two straight lines that meet at a point*. Another definition that is especially useful in most engineering is the following: *an angle is the amount of turning or rotation of a line about a point on the line* from one position to a new position. In Fig. 26.5 we can say that the angle is the amount of rotation of the line *AB* about the point *O*, until the line reaches the new position, *CD*.

The two lines that form an angle are called the *sides* of the angle. The point where the two sides meet is called the *vertex* of the angle (plural: *vertices*). A small curved line is often drawn between the sides of the angle near the vertex, thus $\angle$.

Notice that an angle can be shown by two straight lines on a plane, or flat sheet of paper. It might be well to think of this kind of angle as a *plane* angle.

An angle is often named by placing a capital letter at the vertex, such as $\angle$ *B* (Fig. 26.6). It is sometimes named with three letters, usually capital letters, such as $\angle$ *ABC*. If three letters are used to name an angle, the vertex letter is mentioned second. The angle should be read in the same order as you would draw it without raising the pencil from the paper. An angle may also be named by a small letter inside the angle, such as $\angle x$. For naming

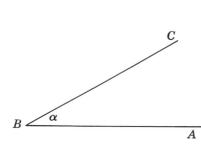

Fig. 26.6

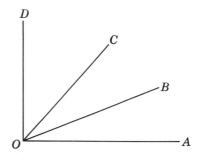

Fig. 26.7

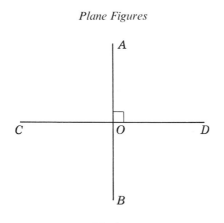

Fig. 26.8

angles with a single letter, we often use Greek letters, such as *alpha* (α), beta (β), *gamma* (γ), and so on. The Greek letters, theta (θ) and phi (ϕ), are also common names for angles.

If there is any danger of confusion as to which angle is meant, the angle should be named by using three letters. In Fig. 26.7 the meaning is not clear if we simply say angle *O*.

26.4 PERPENDICULAR LINES

If two intersecting lines form two equal adjacent angles, the lines are said to be *perpendicular* to each other, or mutually perpendicular. The symbol, $\perp$, is used for the word *perpendicular*. In Fig. 26.8, $AB \perp CD$. (This is read *AB is perpendicular to CD*.) Also, $CD \perp AB$.

If two straight lines are perpendicular to each other, the two adjacent angles are called *right* angles. A right angle is what we often call a square corner. In Fig. 26.8, since the lines are perpendicular to each other, angle *DOA* and angle *AOC* are right angles. The other two angles are also right angles. A right angle can be indicated by the symbol $\llcorner$.

26.5 KINDS OF ANGLES

As we have seen, if the two sides of an angle are perpendicular to each other, the angle formed is a right angle (Fig. 26.9*a*). An angle smaller than a right angle is called an *acute* angle (Fig. 26.9*b*). An angle greater than a right angle but less than the sum of two right angles is called an *obtuse* angle (Fig. 26.9*c*).

If two right angles are placed adjacent to each other, a straight line is formed by two of the sides. An angle formed as the sum of two right angles is called a *straight* angle (Fig. 26.9*d*). Actually, a straight angle forms a straight line.

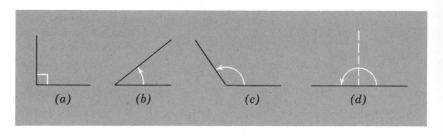

Fig. 26.9

Suppose you need a square corner, or right angle, and all you have is an irregular sheet of paper. You can easily form a right angle. Fold the paper once at any place. The fold represents a straight line. Now fold the paper again so that the straight line is folded over exactly along itself. The result is a square corner because the two adjacent angles are equal and together they form a straight line, or straight angle.

26.6 MEASUREMENT OF ANGLES

In order to measure the size of angles, the early Babylonians decided to divide a complete circle or one rotation into 360 parts. (They might just as well have divided it into 100 parts or 60 parts or some other number.) Each part they called one *degree*. This system of measuring angles is still in common use. The unit of measurement, one degree (written 1°), is therefore $\frac{1}{360}$ of a complete rotation (Fig. 26.10).

Since one rotation is called 360 degrees (360°), then one right angle is called 90 degrees (90°), and one straight angle is called 180°. An angle greater than 180° and less than 360° is called a *reflex* angle.

The size of an angle can be measured by an instrument called a *protractor*.

For very fine measurements (that is, for more accuracy) the degree is divided into 60 smaller parts or angles, called *minutes*. For extreme accuracy, such as that required in astronomy, the minute is divided into 60 parts called *seconds*. One *second* of rotation is a very small angle. In fact, an angle of one

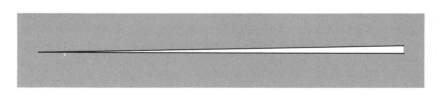

Fig. 26.10. An angle of approximately one degree.

second is so small that the distance between its sides is only about $\frac{3}{10}$ of an inch at a distance of a mile from the vertex.

Two angles whose sum is equal to a right angle, or 90°, are called *comple-mentary*. Two complementary angles need not be adjacent. An angle of 37° and an angle of 53° are complementary, since their sum is 90°. Two angles whose sum is equal to one straight angle, or 180°, are called *supplementary*. Two supplementary angles need not be adjacent. An angle of 49° and an angle of 131° are supplementary, since their sum is 180°.

Exercise 26.1

1. Draw two intersecting lines that are not perpendicular to each other. Measure the four angles formed. What can you conclude about a pair of vertical angles? What conclusion can you make concerning adjacent angles?
2. Draw two parallel lines approximately 2 inches apart. Now draw another line, called a transversal, intersecting the two parallel lines but not perpendicular to them. Measure the eight angles thus formed. What can you conclude about the eight angles formed? Mark each of four *equal* angles with the letter x and the other four angles with the letter y.
3. Show by a drawing that if a transversal is perpendicular to one of two parallel lines it is also perpendicular to the other.
4. Name five different examples of the use of parallel lines in everyday life. Which ones are necessary?
5. Name five examples of intersecting lines in everyday life. Why are they necessary?
6. Can you see ten different examples of right angles in your immediate surroundings as you look up from reading this page?
7. Name five examples of skew lines in everyday life. Why are they necessary?
8. Draw two complementary angles that are not adjacent.
9. Draw two supplementary angles that are not adjacent.
10. From a given point draw seven lines outward in different directions. Measure each of the seven angles formed and add them together. What do you conclude about the total numbers of degrees in all the angles around a point?

26.7 POLYGONS

A *polygon* may be defined as a *plane closed figure bounded by straight line segments*. If the figure is not closed it is not a polygon. A polygon therefore contains a definite amount of area on a flat surface. The boundary consists of any number of straight line segments. The line segments forming the boundary are called the *sides* of the polygon. The *perimeter* of the polygon is the sum of the sides or the distance around the polygon. The points at which the sides meet are called the *vertices* of the polygon.

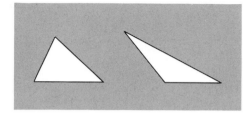

Fig. 26.11. Triangles.

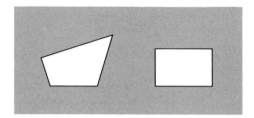

Fig. 26.12. Quadrilaterals.

Fig. 26.13. Pentagons.

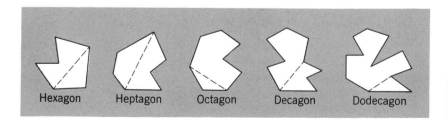

Fig. 26.14. Polygons showing one diagonal in each.

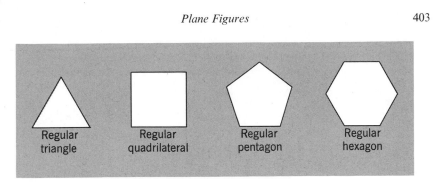

Fig. 26.15. Regular polygons.

Polygons are named according to the number of sides. If a closed figure is to be bounded by straight line segments, it must have at least three sides. A polygon of three sides is called a *triangle*. The prefix "tri" means three. Notice that the word triangle really means "three angles." Yet we define the triangle in terms of the sides instead of angles. Fig. 26.11 represents a triangle. Remember that in any polygon the sides must be *straight*. Perhaps no figure that is drawn is a perfect polygon.

A polygon of four sides is called a *quadrilateral* (Fig. 26.12). The prefix "quad" means four, and "lateral" refers to side. Therefore the word really means four sides. If a triangle were to be named after its three sides, it might be called a "trilateral." Moreover, a quadrilateral can also be named after the angles and called a "quadrangle."

A polygon of five sides is called a *pentagon*. The prefix "penta" means five, and "gon" is another name for angle. Fig. 26.13 shows pentagons.

A polygon of six sides is called a *hexagon*; a polygon of seven sides is called a *heptagon*; a polygon of eight sides, an *octagon*; a polygon of ten sides, a *decagon*; and one of twelve sides is called a *dodecagon* (Fig. 26.14).

A *diagonal* of a polygon is a straight line segment joining any two non-adjacent vertices. A *regular polygon* is one that has all angles equal and all sides equal. Fig. 26.15 shows some regular polygons.

26.8 TRIANGLES (SYMBOLS: △, ▲)

Triangles are named according to their sides. A triangle may have all three sides equal, two sides equal, or no two sides equal. A triangle having all three sides equal is called an *equilateral* triangle (Fig. 26.16a). It can be proved that if the three sides of a triangle are equal then all three angles are equal; that is, an equilateral triangle is also *equiangular*. This condition is not necessarily true for other polygons. A quadrilateral may have all its four sides equal, yet not have all its angles equal.

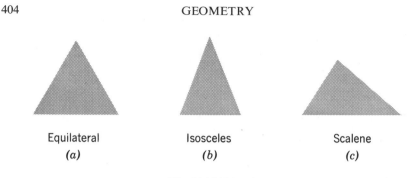

Equilateral   Isosceles   Scalene
(a)   *(b)*   *(c)*

Fig. 26.16. Triangles.

A triangle having two sides equal is called an *isosceles* triangle (Fig. 26.16*b*). *In an isosceles triangle it can be proved that the angles opposite the equal sides are also equal. Moreover, if a triangle has two equal angles, then the sides opposite are also equal to each other.* A triangle having no two sides equal is called a *scalene* triangle (Fig. 26.16*c*).

A triangle may have angles of various sizes. However, the following statement is true with regard to the angles of all triangles:

In any triangle the sum of the three angles is equal to 180° (two right angles, or one straight angle).

As an example, if one angle of a triangle is 47° and a second angle is 74°, then the third angle must be 59° because the sum of the three angles must be 180°.

Triangles are also named according to their angles. A triangle having one right angle is called a *right triangle* (Fig. 26.17*a, b*). Since a right triangle has one right angle, the other two angles must be acute angles. Moreover, the two acute angles are complementary; that is, their sum is 90°. The two sides forming the right angle are often called the *legs* of the right triangle. The side opposite the right angle is called the *hypotenuse*. If the two legs of a right triangle are equal in length, then the triangle is also isosceles (Fig. 26.17*b*).

A triangle having one obtuse angle is called an *obtusè* triangle (Fig. 26.17*c*). A triangle all of whose angles are acute is called an *acute* triangle (Fig. 26.17*d*).

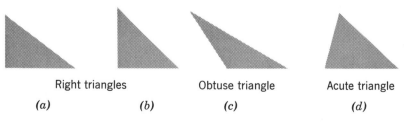

Right triangles   Obtuse triangle   Acute triangle
(a)   *(b)*   *(c)*   *(d)*

Fig. 26.17. Triangles.

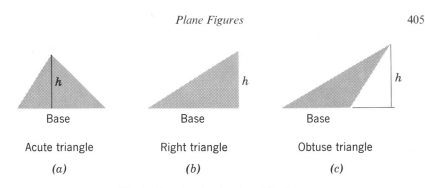

Fig. 26.18. Triangles showing altitudes.

Acute triangles and obtuse triangles are often called *oblique* to distinguish them from right triangles.

The *base* of a triangle is the side on which it is understood to rest. Any side of a triangle may be considered as the base. The *vertex of a triangle* is the vertex opposite the base. The *altitude* of a triangle is a straight line segment drawn from the vertex perpendicular to the base (Fig. 26.18). Since any side of a triangle may be considered as the base, a triangle has three altitudes. All three altitudes meet at the same point. An altitude is often indicated by the letter *h*.

If one leg of a right triangle is taken as the base, then the other leg is the altitude (Fig. 26.18*b*). In an obtuse triangle two of the altitudes fall outside the triangle and must be taken to the base extended (Fig. 26.18*c*).

A *median* of a triangle is a straight line segment drawn from a vertex to the mid-point of the opposite side (Fig. 26.19). A triangle has three medians, all of which meet at a point called the *centroid*. This point is an important one, since it is the *center of gravity*, or balancing point, of the triangle.

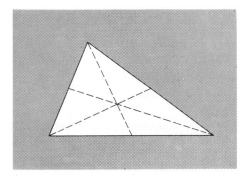

Fig. 26.19. Medians of a triangle.

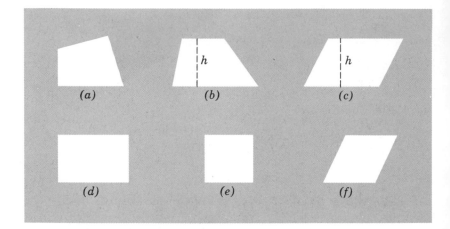

Fig. 26.20. Quadrilaterals.

26.9 QUADRILATERALS

A quadrilateral may have many different shapes. Some of these are shown in Fig. 26.20.

A quadrilateral having no pair of opposite sides parallel is called a *trapezium* (Fig. 26.20a).

A quadrilateral having one pair of opposite sides parallel is called a *trapezoid* (Fig. 26.20b). If the two nonparallel sides of a trapezoid are equal, the figure is called an *isosceles trapezoid.* The two parallel sides are called the *bases* of the trapezoid. The *altitude* of a trapezoid is the distance between the bases.

A quadrilateral having both pairs of opposite sides parallel is called a *parallelogram.* (Symbols: $\square$, $\boxed{s}$.) By this definition the figures (c), (d), (e), and (f) are parallelograms, since in each of these figures both pairs of opposite sides are parallel.

Now, if we focus our attention on the four parallelograms, we see that some of them have right angles. A parallelogram whose angles are right angles is called a *rectangle.* (Symbols: $\square$, $\boxed{s}$.) By this definition, both of the figures (d) and (e) are rectangles, since each one is a parallelogram with right angles.

If we go one step further and distinguish between the two rectangles, we notice one rectangle has all its sides equal. This figure (e) is a *square.* (Symbols: $\square$, $\boxed{s}$.) A square is defined as a rectangle having equal sides.

Notice that all rectangles are parallelograms and that they are also quadrilaterals. A square is a rectangle, a parallelogram, and a quadrilateral.

A *rhombus* is defined as a parallelogram having equal sides. By this definition, a square is also a rhombus. However, the word *rhombus* is usually restricted to mean an equilateral parallelogram that is *not* a square (Fig. 26.20*f*).

The following facts concerning quadrilaterals can be shown to be true. The student should make a drawing or sketch of a figure and try to understand clearly the meaning of each statement.

1. *The sum of all the interior angles of a quadrilateral is 360°.*
2. *Any two opposite sides of a parallelogram are equal.*
3. *If the opposite sides of a quadrilateral are equal, the figure is a parallelogram.*
4. *The opposite angles of any parallelogram are equal.*
5. *If the opposite angles of a quadrilateral are equal, the figure is a parallelogram.*
6. *The diagonals of any rectangle (including a square) are equal.*
7. *The diagonals of any rhombus (including a square) are perpendicular to each other.*

Exercise 26.2

1. Carefully draw a quadrilateral that has no two sides parallel. Measure the interior angle at each corner and find the total number of degrees in the four angles. How near is the result to 360°?
2. If you start at any point on one side of the quadrilateral and walk around the quadrilateral until you arrive at your starting point, through how many degrees will you turn?
3. Draw a hexagon, not necessarily a *regular* hexagon. Measure the interior angle at each corner and find the total number of degrees in the six angles of the hexagon. How near is the total to 720°? It can be proved that the six interior angles of a hexagon have a total of 720°.
4. If you start at any point on a side of a hexagon and *walk* around the figure until you arrive at your starting point, through how many degrees will you turn? Through how many degrees would you turn if the figure were a decagon?
5. How many diagonals can be drawn in (a) a square? (b) A pentagon? (c) A hexagon? (d) A triangle?
6. Draw a right triangle, an acute triangle, and an obtuse triangle, and measure the three angles in each triangle. Do your measurements confirm the statement that the sum of the three angles of any triangle is 180°?
7. Draw an obtuse triangle that is also scalene. Carefully draw the three altitudes. If the altitudes are extended, do they all intersect at the same point?
8. Draw an obtuse triangle that is also isosceles. Measure the angles opposite the two equal sides. Are these angles equal?

9. Why can a triangle not have more than one obtuse angle?

10. Draw a right triangle and show the three altitudes.

11. In a right triangle why must the two acute angles be complementary?

12. Draw two right triangles, one larger than the other, but with one acute angle in each triangle equal to 35°. Notice that the angles of one triangle are equal, respectively, to the angles of the other. Such figures that have the *same shape* are called *similar* figures.

13. Draw two acute triangles with the angles of each one equal, respectively, to 42°, 65°, and 73°. Are these triangles similar?

14. Draw a quadrilateral having sides equal to 2 in., 1 in., $1\frac{1}{2}$ in., and $2\frac{1}{4}$ in., respectively. Can you draw another quadrilateral having sides of the same length but of an entirely different shape?

15. Draw a triangle having its sides equal to 2 in., $2\frac{1}{4}$ in., and $1\frac{1}{2}$ in., respectively. Can you draw another triangle having sides of the same lengths as those mentioned in this problem but of an entirely different shape?

16. Draw a quadrilateral having two opposite sides each equal to 1 in. and the two other opposite sides each equal to $1\frac{1}{2}$ in. After this is done, try to determine whether the opposite sides are also parallel.

17. Draw a quadrilateral, making the opposite sides parallel without trying to make them equal. Now measure them and determine whether they are also equal.

18. Draw a rectangle and then draw the two diagonals. Are the diagonals equal to each other? Are they perpendicular to each other?

19. Draw a rectangle much longer than it is wide. Now draw one diagonal and try to determine whether the diagonal divides the right angle into two equal angles.

20. Draw a parallelogram that is not a rectangle. Now draw the diagonals. Are the diagonals equal to each other?

21. Draw the diagonals of a square and state several facts concerning them.

27
Measurement of Plane Figures

27.1 THE NEED FOR MEASURING

Geometry is concerned with measurement as well as with form. In the measurement of plane figures we are interested in two measurable quantities: the lengths of line segments and the areas of limited portions of surface. For example, we may need to find the length of a rectangle, the distance (which means length) around a circle, or the height of a triangle (which also is a measure of length). We might also want to know how much surface area is covered by a rectangle, a circle, a triangle, or some other plane figure.

27.2 MEASUREMENT: ITS IMPORTANCE

It has been said that man first became civilized when he started to measure things. Probably the first kinds of measurement were those of length. Now we live in a world created by measurement. All scientific ideas must be translated into measurement before they can become useful to man. Thousands of things must be measured. We want to know how long, how heavy, how fast, how much is this, how far is that? It is hard to realize what our lives would be like if it were not for measurement. Measurement is necessary, whether in the making of a cake or in the building of a satellite.

In order to measure any quantity, we must use a unit of measure. The unit is simply a small amount of the same kind of thing as the quantity measured. To measure length, we use some small unit of length, such as an inch or a foot. To measure weight, we use a unit of weight, such as an ounce or a pound. To measure area, we use a unit of area, such as a square inch or an acre. To measure volume, we use some small unit of volume, such as a cubic inch, a pint, or a gallon. To measure time, we use some unit of time, such as a minute, an hour, or a day. To measure angles, we use a small unit angle, such as a degree. To measure electric current, we use a small unit of current called the *ampere*. To measure electromotive force, we use a unit of electromotive force called the *volt*. To measure electrical resistance we use a small unit of resistance called the *ohm*.

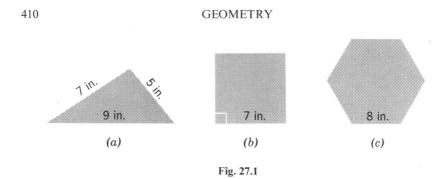

Fig. 27.1

The unit used for measuring anything must be of the *same kind* of thing. For example, we cannot measure length in pounds; we cannot measure angles in inches, or weight in minutes; and we cannot measure electric current in feet, inches, pounds, or minutes.

27.3 PERIMETER

The *perimeter* of a polygon is the distance around a polygon. The perimeter is found by adding the lengths of the sides. For instance, if the sides of a triangle are equal to 5 inches, 7 inches, and 9 inches, respectively, the perimeter is $5 + 7 + 9 = 21$ inches (Fig. 27.1*a*). If one side of a square is 7 inches, the perimeter of the square is 28 inches (Fig. 27.1*b*).

If any polygon is equilateral (that is, having equal sides), then the perimeter can easily be found by multiplication. If we know that one side of a regular hexagon is 8 inches, then the perimeter is 48 inches (Fig. 27.1*c*).

Notice that the perimeter of any polygon is expressed in *linear units*, since the perimeter is a *length*.

27.4 AREA

Measuring a given area is done by taking a small unit of area and laying off the unit area as many times as possible on the given area. For example, if we wish to measure the area of this page, we can take a coin, such as a nickel, and see how many times the area of the page contains the small unit of area covered by the coin. The trouble with a circular unit of area is that the units do not fit together. That is the reason we use a unit of area that is rectangular. Rectangular units fit together and fill the space around a point. The same is true with a triangular or hexagonal unit. However, a square unit, such as a square inch or a square foot, has another advantage, as we shall see presently.

27.5 THE RECTANGLE

Suppose we have a rectangle 6 inches long and 4 inches wide (Fig. 27.2). To find the area of a rectangle, we usually say multiply the length by the width, or

(6 inches)(4 inches) = 24 square inches

The answer is correct, but does it not seem strange that we can multiply *two lines* together and get an area? To see the problem more clearly, suppose we draw two line segments, one 6 inches long and the other 4 inches long (Fig. 27.3).

Now we see that the statement, "multiply the two lines or lengths, 6 inches and 4 inches, together" has no meaning. Yet we get the correct answer. If you will take a moment to analyze this problem carefully, you will probably understand much better all later problems in areas and volumes. Let us see why we get the correct answer to the problem.

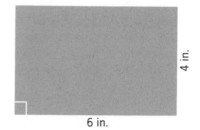

6 in.

4 in.

Fig. 27.2

Consider again the rectangle, 6 inches long and 4 inches wide. We cannot measure its area with a unit of linear measure such as an inch. To measure area we must use a unit of area. We shall use a unit that is 1 inch long and 1 inch wide. This unit is called a *square inch.*

6 in.   4 in.

Fig. 27.3

Now, starting in one corner of the rectangle, we lay off this unit of area as many times as possible along the side of the rectangle (Fig. 27.4). We know that we can lay off six units in one row because the unit is 1 inch long and there are 6 inches in the length of the rectangle.

After laying off one row of 6 units, we consider the number of rows. We see there will be 4 rows because each row is 1 inch wide and the width of the rectangle is 4 inches.

At this point we see that the total number of square inches in the rectangle can be found by multiplication:

(4)(6 sq in.) = 24 sq in.

The advantage of using a square unit of measure for area is that we can

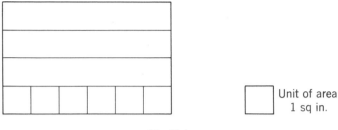

Unit of area
1 sq in.

Fig. 27.4

measure the length in *linear units* (inches), the width in *linear units* (inches), and then easily find the area by the following rule:

Rule. *Multiply the number of linear units in the length by the number of the same kind of linear units in the width. The result is the number of corresponding square units in the area.* Stated in short form the rule is

$$\text{area} = (\text{length})(\text{width})$$

If we let l represent the number of linear units in the length, let w represent the number of linear units in the width, and let A represent the number of corresponding square units in the area, we can write the rule as a formula:

$$A = lw$$

This formula can be used for all rectangles. For example, if a rectangle is 12.5 inches long and 7 inches wide, its area is 87.5 sq in. Note that the area is expressed in square units since the unit of area is a *square inch.*

The formula can also be used in reverse. For example, if a rectangle is 7 inches wide and has an area of 60 sq in., we can find the length by division: $60 \div 7 = 8\frac{4}{7}$. The answer will represent the number of linear units in the length. If we divide both sides of the formula by l, we get the formula for the width w:

$$w = \frac{A}{l}$$

If we divide both sides by w, we get the formula for the length l:

$$l = \frac{A}{w}$$

In all cases the length and width are measured in linear units, the area in square units.

The perimeter of a rectangle is equal to twice the length plus twice the width, or as a formula

$$P = 2l + 2w$$

The perimeter is of course expressed in *linear* units. Whenever we *add linear* units, we get an answer representing *linear* units. Whenever we *multiply linear* units by *linear* units, we get a product that represents an area in terms of the *square of the linear unit*.

27.6 THE SQUARE

A square is a special rectangle in which all sides are equal. The length is equal to the width (Fig. 27.5). If we represent one side of the square by the letter *s*, we have for the area

$$A = (s)(s) \qquad \text{or} \qquad A = s^2$$

Since all four sides are equal in length, we find the perimeter by taking 4 times the length of one side. Stated as a formula,

$$P = 4s$$

s

s

Fig. 27.5

27.7 THE PARALLELOGRAM

If we know the lengths of the four sides of a parallelogram, we cannot find the area from this information alone. For instance, if we have a parallelogram with sides of 12, 8, 12, and 8 inches, respectively (Fig. 27.6) we can find its perimeter but we cannot tell the area. In order to determine the area, we must know the altitude. The altitude is the perpendicular distance between two sides. Parallelograms may have the given sides as shown and yet may have different altitudes. One side of a parallelogram, such as the 12-inch side in the example, is called its *base* rather than its *length*.

If we assume that one triangle is cut off one end of the parallelogram and attached to the other end, the result is a rectangle having the same base and the same altitude as the parallelogram. It also has the same area. Therefore, the area of a parallelogram can be found by the formula

$$A = bh$$

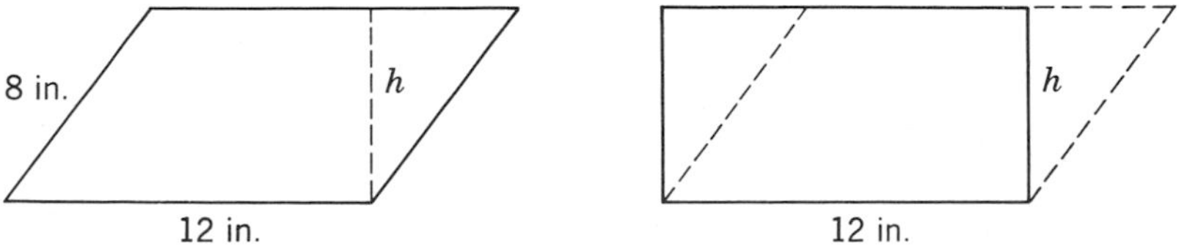

8 in.

h

12 in.

h

12 in.

Fig. 27.6

in which A represents the area, b represents the base, and h represents the altitude or height.

If the area and the base of a parallelogram are known, the altitude can be found by dividing the area by the base. If the area and the altitude are known, the base can be found by dividing the area by the altitude; that is,

$$h = A/b \qquad \text{and} \qquad b = A/h$$

If we know the altitude and the base of a parallelogram, we cannot find the perimeter from this information alone. Parallelograms may have the same bases and the same altitudes, yet have different perimeters.

27.8 THE TRIANGLE

Suppose we have the triangle ABC, with base, b, equal to 11 inches, and altitude, h, equal to 8 inches (Fig. 27.7a).

In order to formulate a rule for the area of the triangle, we first construct another congruent triangle adjacent to the given triangle but in an inverted position (Fig. 27.7b). We see at once that a parallelogram is formed. The parallelogram has the same base and the same altitude as the given triangle, $b = 11$, $h = 8$. We know that the area of a parallelogram is $(8)(11)$ or 88 square inches. For the parallelogram, we have the formula

$$A = bh$$

We also see that the area of the original triangle is exactly one-half the area of the parallelogram. Therefore, the area of the triangle is $(\frac{1}{2})(11)(8) = 44$. We can say that the area of any triangle is equal to one-half the product of the base and the altitude. This rule can be stated as a formula:

$$A = \tfrac{1}{2}bh \qquad \text{or} \qquad A = \frac{bh}{2}$$

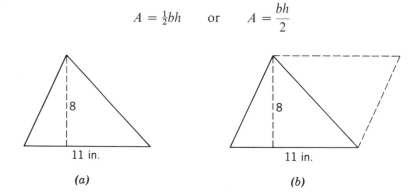

(a)   (b)

Fig. 27.7

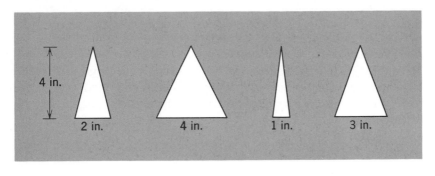

Fig. 27.8

In a right triangle either leg can be considered as the base and the other leg as the altitude. The area of a right triangle is therefore one-half the product of the two legs.

If we have several triangles, all with the same altitude, the total area may be found by computing the area of each separately, or the bases may first be added (Fig. 27.8). If we compute each of the areas separately, we have

$$4 + 8 + 2 + 6 = 20 \text{ sq in.}$$

If we first add all the bases and then consider the figure as one large triangle with an altitude of 4 inches and a base of 10 inches, we have

$$(\tfrac{1}{2})(10)(4) = 20 \text{ sq in.}$$

In general terms let us see why the foregoing process is valid. Suppose we have any number of triangles, all having the same altitude h, and various bases, $b_1, b_2, b_3, \ldots$. Adding the separate areas we have

$$\text{total area} = \tfrac{1}{2}b_1 h + \tfrac{1}{2}b_2 h + \tfrac{1}{2}b_3 h + \cdots$$

Factoring,

$$\text{total area} = \tfrac{1}{2}h(b_1 + b_2 + b_3 \cdots)$$

The result shows that the bases may first be added provided the altitude is the same for all the triangles.

The formula for the area of a triangle can also be used in reverse. For example, if we know the area and either the altitude or base, we can find the unknown dimension. The formula for the area can be solved for either h or b. Since

$$A = \frac{bh}{2}$$

then

$$h = \frac{2A}{b} \quad \text{and} \quad b = \frac{2A}{h}$$

To find the perimeter of a triangle, we must know the lengths of the three sides. Then the perimeter is found simply by adding the lengths of the sides. If we let p represent the perimeter, and a, b, and c represent the sides, respectively, then we have the formula: $p = a + b + c$. For example, if a triangle has sides equal to 7 inches, 9 inches, and 10 inches, respectively (Fig. 27.9), its perimeter is given by

$$p = 7 + 9 + 10 = 26 \text{ inches}$$

In the triangle in Fig. 27.9 since the three sides are 7, 9, and 10 inches, respectively, the shape and the size of the triangle are definitely determined. In other words, if the three sides of a triangle are given, then there is only *one shape and size* of the triangle. This is not true with respect to a quadrilateral or any other polygon. In fact, this principle forms the basis for the use of triangles in bracing. Triangular bracing produces rigidity in buildings, bridges, furniture, etc.

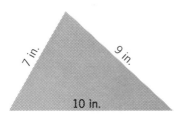

Fig. 27.9

Now, since the triangle in Fig. 27.9 has a definite shape and area, it should be possible to compute the area from the lengths of the three sides. The method was explained almost two thousand years ago by a mathematician named Hero (Heron). Hero showed that the area of a triangle can be computed from the three sides by the following formula. If we let a, b, and c, respectively, represent the three sides, and let s equal one-half the sum of the three sides, then the formula for the area is as follows:

$$A = \sqrt{s(s - a)(s - b)(s - c)}$$

For the foregoing triangle (Fig. 27.9) we have $a = 7$, $b = 9$, $c = 10$, $s = 13$. Therefore, in the triangle

$$A = \sqrt{13(13 - 7)(13 - 9)(13 - 10)}$$

$$= \sqrt{(13)(6)(4)(3)}$$

$$= \sqrt{936}$$

$$= 30.59 \text{ sq in. in area}$$

If we estimate the altitude of the triangle, we see that it appears to be approximately six units. Using this altitude, 6, the base, 10, and the formula, $A = \frac{1}{2}bh$, we get 30 square units as the area, which is approximately the value computed by the use of Hero's formula.

27.9 THE TRAPEZOID

A trapezoid is a quadrilateral with two sides parallel and the other two sides not parallel. Suppose we wish to find the area of a trapezoid having a bottom base B equal to 8 inches, a top base b equal to 5 inches, and the altitude h equal to 4 inches (Fig. 27.10*a*).

In order to formulate a rule for the area of a trapezoid, we first construct a congruent trapezoid adjacent to the given trapezoid but in an inverted position (Fig. 27.10*b*). A parallelogram is formed by the two trapezoids. The parallelogram has an altitude, h, the same as the given trapezoid. The base of the parallelogram is equal to the *sum* of the bases of the trapezoid, that is, $B + b$. Therefore, the area of the parallelogram is

$$h(B + b)$$

We see that the area of the original trapezoid is exactly one-half the area of the parallelogram and therefore is given by the formula

$$A = \frac{1}{2}h(B + b)$$

The area of the trapezoid is $(\frac{1}{2})(4)(8 + 5) = 26$.

The formula for the area of a trapezoid can be solved for h, B, or b, to get the corresponding formula for each of these dimensions. Since

$$A = \frac{1}{2}h(B + b)$$

then

$$h = \frac{2A}{B + b}; \qquad B = \frac{2A}{h} - b; \qquad b = \frac{2A}{h} - B$$

The perimeter of a trapezoid can be found only if the length of each side is known. The lengths of the nonparallel sides can be computed by means of trigonometry if certain angles are known.

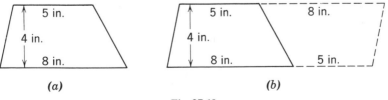

(a)   (b)

Fig. 27.10

27.10 OTHER POLYGONS

The areas of other polygons are usually computed by dividing the polygons into triangles, rectangles, or parallelograms. The area of each separate part is computed, and then these areas are added together for the total area of the polygon.

27.11 CONVERSION OF UNITS OF AREA

It is often desirable to change the size of units of area. Let us see how this is done. We use an example from our English system of measurements.

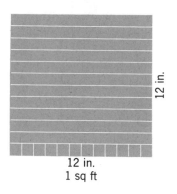

12 in.
1 sq ft

Fig. 27.11

Consider a square 1 foot long and 1 foot wide (Fig. 29.11). Such a square contains 1 square foot of area. The length of the square is 12 inches and the width is 12 inches. The formula for the area of a square is

$$A = s^2$$

Substituting numerical values, we have

$$\text{area (1 sq ft)} = 12^2 \text{ sq in.}$$

or

$$1 \text{ sq ft} = 144 \text{ sq in.}$$

The square of a linear unit is often indicated by the exponent 2 placed on the linear unit itself. For example,

$$1 \text{ sq ft} = 144 \text{ sq in.}$$

is often written

$$1 \text{ ft}^2 = 12^2 \text{ in.}^2 \quad \text{or} \quad 1 \text{ ft}^2 = 144 \text{ in.}^2$$

In the same way we can say,

since 1 yard = 3 feet,   1 sq yd = 3^2 sq ft;   or 1 yd^2 = 9 ft^2;
since 1 mile = 320 rods, 1 sq mi = 320^2 sq rd; or 1 mi^2 = 320^2 rd^2;
since 1 rd = 16.5 ft,   1 sq rd = $(16.5)^2$ sq ft; or 1 rd^2 = 272.25 ft^2.

Notice that when we multiply a *linear* measure, such as inches, by the same *linear* measure, we get *square units* or units of area.

The rule is easily remembered if we think of squaring both sides of an equation. For example, suppose we have the formula,

$$1 \text{ rd} = 5.5 \text{ yd}$$

Squaring both sides, $1 \text{ rd}^2 = (5.5)^2 \text{ yd}^2$

Note. It is well to remember that *one square foot of area* need not be square. A rectangle 6 inches wide and 2 feet long contains one square foot of area. In the same way, one square inch of area need not be a square. A triangle having a base of $\frac{1}{2}$ inch and an altitude of 4 inches contains 1 square inch of area. *A square inch of area may have any shape, even circular.*

The relation between units of area in the metric system and the English system can be stated in a similar manner. Since

$$1 \text{ in.} = 2.54 \text{ cm}$$

then

$$1 \text{ sq in.} = 6.4516 \text{ sq cm}$$

or

$$1 \text{ in.}^2 = (2.54)^2 \text{ cm}^2$$

To change square inches to square centimeters, multiply by $(2.54)^2$, or 6.45. To change square centimeters to square inches, divide by $(2.54)^2$, or 6.45.

Exercise 27.1

In each of the following, find the values indicated:

1. Rectangle: 16.3 in. long and 13.4 in. wide. Find the area and perimeter.
2. Triangle: altitude, 11.3 in., base, 17.3 in. Find the area.
3. Parallelogram: base, 23.4 cm, altitude, 7.6 cm. Find the area.
4. Trapezoid: bases, 12.3 and 18.5 cm, altitude 13.4 cm. Find the area.
5. Trapezoid: bases, 24.5 and 16.3 in., altitude, 9.2 in. Find the area.
6. Triangle: base, 35.0 cm, altitude, 26.3 cm. Find the area.
7. Triangle: sides, 7.3, 9.2, and 10.5 in., respectively. Find the area of the triangle by Hero's formula. Also find the perimeter.
8. Square: side, 25.3 cm. Find the area and perimeter.
9. Rectangle: area, 63.2 sq in., 5.8 in. wide. Find the length and perimeter.
10. Rectangle: area, 23.5 sq yd., length, 21.4 ft. Find the width and perimeter.
11. Triangle: area, 63.4 sq in., base, 17.6 in. Find the altitude.
12. Square: area, 5463 sq ft. Find one side and the perimeter.
13. Find the cost of a piece of plywood 4 ft wide, 8 ft long, at 11.2 cents per sq ft.
14. A baseball diamond is a square 90 ft between bases. What is the area of the diamond? What part of an acre does it contain? (One acre contains 160 sq rd.)
15. Find the cost of building a driveway 60 ft long and 12 ft wide at $2.10 per square yard.
16. Find the cost of paving 10 miles of road 32 ft wide at $2.40 per square yard.
17. A large rectangular hall has 1000 sq yd floor space. If one side measures 120 ft, what is its length?
18. A field is 68 rd long, 45 rd wide. How many acres does it contain?

19. A rectangular field contains 54 acres. If it is 120 rd long, how wide is it? Find its perimeter.

20. A garden is 99 ft long and 66 ft wide. What part of an acre does it contain?

21. A field in the shape of a trapezoid has bases of 48 and 34 rd, respectively. The distance between the bases is 72 rd. Find the area of the field in acres.

22. A rug $8\frac{1}{2}$ by 11 ft is laid in a room 12 by $13\frac{1}{2}$ ft. How many square feet are not covered?

23. Rectangle: 38 by 15 in. Find the size of an equivalent square and the difference in the perimeters.

24. A blackboard is 26 ft, 3 in. long, 3 ft, 4 in. high. How many square feet does it contain?

25. The end of a box has the shape of a trapezoid having bases of 40 and 28 in., respectively, and an altitude of 28 in. Find the area of the end of the box.

26. A wire 120 in. long is to be bent to form a rectangle. Find the area of each rectangle formed if the following values are taken for the width:

(a) 30 in.	(b) 24 in.	(c) 20 in.
(d) 15 in.	(e) 12 in.	(f) 10 in.
(g) 8 in.	(h) 6 in.	(i) 4 in.
(j) 2 in.	(k) 1 in.	(l) 0.5 in.

27. A rectangle contains 576 sq in. Find the perimeter of each of the rectangles formed if the following values are taken for the width:

(a) 24 in.	(b) 18 in.	(c) 16 in.
(d) 12 in.	(e) 9 in.	(f) 8 in.
(g) 6 in.	(h) 4 in.	(i) 3 in.
(j) 2 in.	(k) 1 in.	(l) 0.5 in.

28. A rectangular field bounded on one side by a river is to be fenced on the three remaining sides with a total length of 180 rods of fence. If the length is taken as the distance along the river and the width the distance outward from the river, find the area enclosed for each of the following widths:

(a) 10 rd	(b) 20 rd	(c) 30 rd
(d) 40 rd	(e) 45 rd	(f) 50 rd
(g) 60 rd	(h) 70 rd	(i) 80 rd

28
The Right Triangle

28.1 DEFINITION

A triangle having one right angle is called a *right* triangle. Since one angle is a right angle, the other two angles are acute angles.

We know that the sum of the three angles of any triangle is 180°. Since the right angle itself is equal to 90°, the sum of the two acute angles must be 180° − 90°, or 90°. Therefore, *the two acute angles of a right triangle are complementary.*

In a right triangle the side opposite the right angle is called the *hypotenuse.* The hypotenuse happens to be the longest side. The other two sides are sometimes called the *legs* of the right triangle. Since the legs are perpendicular to each other, if one is taken as the base of the triangle, then the other is the altitude.

28.2 THE PYTHAGOREAN RULE

A right triangle has the following important characteristic:

In every right triangle the square of the hypotenuse is equal to the sum of the squares of the legs.

This principle is known as the *Pythagorean rule.* It is one of the most useful rules in all mathematics. Let us see what it means.

Suppose we have the right triangle shown in Fig. 28.1. The two legs of the triangle measure 3 and 4 inches, respectively, and the hypotenuse is 5 inches long.

The sum of the two legs, 3 + 4, does not equal the hypotenuse. However, if we square each leg and the hypotenuse, we have

$$3^2 = 9$$
$$4^2 = 16$$
Adding the squares, $\qquad 5^2 = \overline{25}$

Notice that if the legs are squared and the squares are added, the sum 25 is the square of the hypotenuse.

421

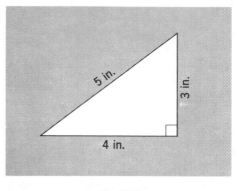

Fig. 28.1

The Pythagorean rule is named after Pythagoras, a Greek philosopher and mathematician who proved the truth of the principle about 500 B.C. The idea was known and used for specific examples long before that, but no one before Pythagoras had proved the rule to be true for all right triangles. Many people often use the rule in their work without realizing why it is true. The truth of the rule has been proved in many different ways.

As an example of a proof in mathematics, we shall show why the Pythagorean rule is true. It is often called the *Pythagorean Theorem*. The word *theorem* means a statement that is to be proved. In proving a theorem, we should first ask ourselves, "Is this true?" Then we proceed step by step and by careful reasoning to show that the statement must be true. We must give a reason for each statement we make. However, in the proof as given here, we shall have to make statements that are assumed to have been previously shown to be true.

One form of the proof of the Pythagorean Theorem makes use of a trapezoid. Suppose we have the right triangle ABC (Fig. 28.2), with sides a, b, and c, respectively, in which c is the hypotenuse. Now we wish to show that

$$a^2 + b^2 = c^2$$

To show that this is true, we first extend side CB to D, making BD equal to b. (Construction lines are shown as broken lines.) Next, we draw DE perpendicular to CD, making DE equal to a. Finally, we draw AE.

Now we can say CA is parallel to DE because they are both perpendicular to the line CD. Then $ACDE$ is a trapezoid, having bases of a and b, and an altitude of $(a + b)$. Then by the formula for the area of a trapezoid, we have

Area of $ACDE = \frac{1}{2}$ (altitude)(sum of bases)

or

Area $= \frac{1}{2}(a + b)(a + b) = \frac{1}{2}(a^2 + 2ab + b^2)$

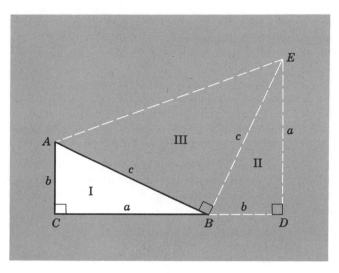

Fig. 28.2

Now we see that the trapezoid is made up of three triangles. Their areas are

$$A(\text{I}) = \tfrac{1}{2}ab; \qquad A(\text{II}) = \tfrac{1}{2}ab; \qquad A(\text{III}) = \tfrac{1}{2}c^2$$

Adding the three triangles, we get a total area: $A = \tfrac{1}{2}(ab + ab + c^2)$. Since this total area is equal to the area of the trapezoid, we have

$$\tfrac{1}{2}(a^2 + 2ab + b^2) = \tfrac{1}{2}(ab + ab + c^2) \qquad \text{or} \qquad a^2 + 2ab + b^2 = 2ab + c^2$$

Subtracting $2ab$ from both sides, we get

$$a^2 + b^2 = c^2$$

The result is exactly what we set out to prove to be true.

The value of the Pythagorean rule lies in the fact that it enables us to find the hypotenuse of a right triangle if the two legs are known. For example, if the legs a and b are 5 inches and 12 inches, respectively, then the hypotenuse can be computed by the formula

$$c^2 = a^2 + b^2$$

Substituting numerical values,

$$c^2 = 5^2 + 12^2; \qquad c^2 = 169; \qquad \text{then} \qquad c = 13$$

If the hypotenuse and a leg are known, we make use of one of the following forms of the Pythagorean rule, involving subtraction:

$$a^2 = c^2 - b^2 \qquad \text{or} \qquad b^2 = c^2 - a^2$$

In using the Pythagorean rule, we shall often find that the length of an unknown side is not rational. For example, if the hypotenuse is 9 inches and one leg is 6 inches, then for the other leg we get

$$9^2 - 6^2 = 81 - 36 = 45; \qquad \text{the other leg is} \qquad \sqrt{45} = 3\sqrt{5}$$

Example 1. A telephone pole is to be braced with a wire, one end of which is fastened to the pole 32 feet above the ground and the other end to a stake in the ground 43 feet from the foot of the pole. Assuming that the ground is level and the pole is perpendicular to the ground, how long a wire will be required if 4 feet extra are needed for fastening?

Solution. In this problem we see that a right triangle is formed by the pole, the ground, and the wire. The pole and the ground form the legs of the right triangle and the wire represents the hypotenuse. Therefore, we square the given numbers and then add the squares. We get

$$32^2 = 1024$$
$$43^2 = 1849$$

Adding the squares, $\qquad\qquad\qquad 2873$

The number 2873 represents the square of the hypotenuse. To find the hypotenuse, we take the square root of 2873:

$$\text{hypotenuse} = \sqrt{2873} = 53.6 \text{ ft (approx.)}$$

The answer is rounded off to three significant digits. Since 4 feet is needed for fastening, the length of wire required is 57.6 feet.

Example 2. One leg of a right triangle measures 23.5 in. and the hypotenuse is 31.4 in. Find the length of the other leg.

Solution. Since the hypotenuse, the longest side, is given, we square the two numbers and then find the difference between the squares. We get

$$31.4^2 = 985.96$$
$$23.5^2 = 552.25$$

Subtracting squares, $\qquad\qquad\qquad 433.71$

The number 433.71 represents the square of the unknown leg. To find the length of the leg, we take the square root of 433.71:

$$\sqrt{433.71} = 20.8 \text{ in. (rounded off)}$$

Therefore, the other leg is approximately 20.8 in. long.

28.3   THE ISOSCELES RIGHT TRIANGLE

We have defined an isosceles triangle as one having two sides equal. If a right triangle has its two legs equal, then the triangle is also isosceles. Fig. 28.3 shows an isosceles right triangle with each of the legs equal to 6 inches, denoted by a and b, respectively.

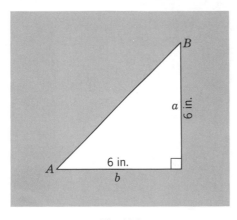

Fig. 28.3

In any isosceles triangle it can be proved that *the angles opposite the equal sides are also equal.* That is, if side a = side b, then we know that angle A is also equal to angle B.

In an isosceles right triangle the two acute angles are equal, and therefore each angle must be 45°. A right triangle of this particular shape is sometimes called a "45° right triangle."

Our problem here is to find the length of the hypotenuse. To find this length, we square the two legs, add the squares, and then find the square root of the sum. Adding the squares,

$$6^2 + 6^2 = 36 + 36 = 72$$

The number 72 represents the square of the hypotenuse. To find the hypotenuse, we take the square root of 72.

$$\sqrt{72} = \sqrt{(36)(2)} = 6\sqrt{2} \quad \text{or} \quad 6(1.414) = 8.484 \text{ in.}$$

An isosceles right triangle appears when we draw the diagonal of a square. Suppose we have the square $ABCD$ with diagonal d and each side s (Fig. 28.4). Then triangle BCD is an isosceles right triangle. Each leg of the triangle is a side of the square, and the hypotenuse is the diagonal. Then by the Pythagorean rule, we have

$$d^2 = s^2 + s^2 \quad \text{or} \quad d^2 = 2s^2$$

Then

$$d = \sqrt{2s^2} \quad \text{or} \quad d = s\sqrt{2}$$

Stated in words: *The diagonal of any square is equal to the length of a side multiplied by the square root of 2.*

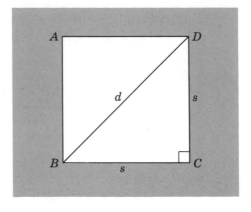

Fig. 28.4

28.4　THE 30°-60° RIGHT TRIANGLE

A special triangle that occurs often in engineering mathematics is a right triangle whose acute angles are 30° and 60°, respectively. A triangle of this particular shape is often called a "30°-60° right triangle" (Fig. 28.5), Such a triangle is the kind that Plato, a famous Greek philosopher, called the "most beautiful scalene right-angled triangle." A very important fact concerning such a triangle is the following:

In any 30°-60° right triangle, the hypotenuse is always twice as long as the shortest side.

By use of this fact, we can find all the sides of such a triangle, provided that we know one side.

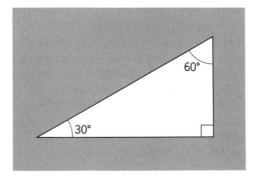

Fig. 28.5

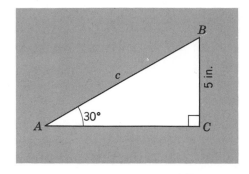

Fig. 28.6

Example. Suppose we have a 30°-60° right triangle, *ABC* (Fig. 28.6), with the shortest leg equal to 5 in. and angle *A* = 30°. By the foregoing rule, we know that the hypotenuse is twice the side *BC*, or 10 in. Since the hypotenuse is 10 in. and one leg is 5 in., we can find the other leg by the Pythagorean rule. Squaring both numbers, we have

$$10^2 = 100$$
$$5^2 = \underline{25}$$

Subtracting squares, $\qquad\qquad 75$

The difference, 75, represents the square of the unknown leg. Therefore, the leg is equal to the square root of 75:

$$\sqrt{75} = \sqrt{(25)(3)} = 5\sqrt{3}$$

28.5 THE EQUILATERAL TRIANGLE

An equilateral triangle is a triangle in which all three sides are equal. We have said that if two sides of a triangle are equal, then the angles opposite these sides are also equal. From this fact it follows that an equilateral triangle is also *equiangular*. Therefore, each angle in an equilateral triangle is 60° (Fig. 28.7).

With regard to the equilateral triangle, there are two problems with which we are often concerned. One is the altitude and the other is the area. We shall show how to obtain the formula for each.

Suppose we have an equilateral triangle *ABC* with a side equal to 8 inches (Fig. 28.7). We draw a straight line bisecting the angle *C* into two equal angles. The line meets the opposite side at point *D*. Since angle *C* is divided into two equal angles, each one of these is 30°.

In the figure triangle *DBC* is a 30°-60° right triangle. The hypotenuse of this right triangle is one side of the original equilateral triangle, which is 8 inches. Therefore, the short leg of the right triangle *DBC* is 4 inches.

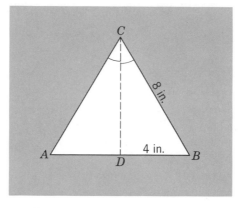

Fig. 28.7

Now, in order to find the altitude of the equilateral triangle, we use the Pythagorean rule. Squaring, we have

$$8^2 = 64$$
$$4^2 = 16$$

Subtracting squares, $\overline{48}$

The number 48 represents the square of the other leg, which, in this example, is the altitude of the equilateral triangle. Therefore, the altitude is equal to

$$\sqrt{48} = \sqrt{(16)(3)} = 4\sqrt{3}$$

By using a general equilateral triangle, ABC (Fig. 28.8), with one side represented by s, we can show that the altitude, h, of any equilateral triangle

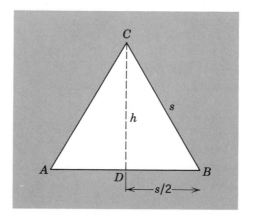

Fig. 28.8

is equal to one-half one side multiplied by the square root of 3. In the right triangle BCD, the hypotenuse is s, and one leg is $s/2$. Squaring these two sides and subtracting, we get

$$h^2 = s^2 - \left(\frac{s}{2}\right)^2 = s^2 - \frac{s^2}{4} = \frac{3s^2}{4}; \qquad h = \sqrt{\frac{3s^2}{4}}; \qquad h = \frac{s}{2}\sqrt{3}$$

To find the area of an equilateral triangle, we simply use the formula for the area of any triangle,

$$A = \tfrac{1}{2}hb$$

Notice that the base in the general equilateral triangle is equal to s, or one side. Since we have the altitude, $h = \tfrac{1}{2}s\sqrt{3}$, we use these values to get the formula for the area:

$$A = \tfrac{1}{2}hb$$

Substituting values,

$$A = \tfrac{1}{2}(\tfrac{1}{2}s\sqrt{3})(s)$$

or

$$A = \tfrac{1}{4}s^2\sqrt{3}$$

That is, the area of an equilateral triangle is one-fourth the square of a side multiplied by the square root of 3.

Exercise 28.1

In each of the following right triangles, find the required quantity:

1. Hypotenuse $= 17.2$ in., one leg $= 13.8$ in. Find the area and the perimeter.
2. One leg $= 24.3$ cm, the other leg $= 34.1$ cm. Find the area in square inches and the perimeter in inches.
3. The legs are 3.42 and 5.13 cm, respectively. Find the area and the perimeter.
4. Hypotenuse $= 26.9$ in., one leg $= 22.5$ in. Find the area in square centimeters and the perimeter in centimeters.
5. Hypotenuse $= 160$ ft, one leg $= 80$ ft. Find the area in square yards and the perimeter in yards.
6. How long a wire will be needed to brace a telephone pole if the wire is fastened to the pole 32 ft from the ground and to a stake in the ground 54 ft from the foot of the pole?
7. A TV broadcasting tower is braced with a cable 360 ft long. The cable is fastened in the ground at a point 270 ft from the tower. How far up on the tower is the cable fastened?

8. How long a diagonal brace is required for a gate 5 ft high and 16 ft long?

9. Two cars start at the same point, one traveling north at 45 mph and the other east at 34 mph. How far apart are they after 30 min?

10. A man rows his boat directly across a river at right angles to the current. The river is 800 ft wide. If he rows at 200 ft per min and the river flows at a rate of 150 ft per min, how fast does he travel and in what direction? How long will it take him to cross the river? How far does he travel?

11. A field is 60 rd long and 30 rd wide. A road extends diagonally from one corner to the opposite corner. How long is the road?

12. A ladder 32 ft long leans up against a wall. How high up on the wall does the ladder reach if the foot is placed 7.2 ft from the wall?

13. A ladder is 28 ft long. How far from the wall must the foot be placed in order that the ladder will just reach a window 26.4 ft from the ground.

14. The length of a rectangle is 42.3 cm. The diagonal is 53.4 cm. Find the area and perimeter of the rectangle.

15. Find the length of the diagonal of each of the following squares:

    (a) A side = 13.2 in.   (b) A side = 28.7 cm

    (c) A side = 3.52 m   (d) A side = 1000 m

    (e) A side = 4570 mm   (f) A side = 5280 ft

    (g) A side = 360 rd   (h) A side = 16.5 ft

    (i) A side = 5.5 yd   (j) The perimeter = 39 in.

    (k) The perimeter = 54.3 cm   (l) The perimeter = 13.2 mm

    (m) The perimeter = 1 ft

16. Find the area and perimeter of each of the following 30°-60° right triangles:

    (a) The shortest side = 7.4 in.   (b) The hypotenuse = 25.2 cm

    (c) The hypotenuse = 485 ft   (d) The shortest side = 3.57 mm

    (e) The hypotenuse = 6.73 in.   (f) The hypotenuse = 21.47 cm

17. Find the area of each of the following equilateral triangles:

    (a) A side = 18 in.   (b) A side = 13.4 cm

    (c) The perimeter = 42 in.   (d) The perimeter = 23.4 cm

    (e) A side = 72.4 ft

29
Circles

29.1 DEFINITIONS

The circle is one of the most common as well as the most useful of all geometric figures. It is used for its beauty in architecture and design. It has a practical and necessary use in the wheels of machinery in industry. In fact, the wheel, which is a circle, was one of the most important inventions in the history of civilization.

Although the circle is a very common geometric figure, it is not easy to define. We might say that the *circle is a plane closed curve such that every point on the curve is the same distance from a point within, called the center.* According to this definition, the circle is the curve itself (Fig. 29.1). For the word *circle* we use the symbols ⊙, Ⓢ.

The *circumference* of a *circle* is the length of the curve. If the curve itself is called the circumference, then the circle is taken to mean the space enclosed within the circumference.

A straight line segment, such as *AB*, with its ends on the circumference and passing through the center, is called a *diameter* of the circle. A straight line segment, such as *OC*, joining the center with any point on the circumference, is called a *radius* (plural, *radii*). From these definitions, we see that a diameter is equal in length to twice the radius. If *D* represents the number of

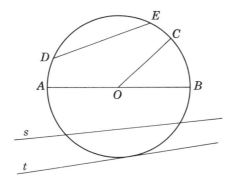

Fig. 29.1

units of length in the diameter and r represents the number of units of length in the radius, then we have the formulas

$$D = 2r \quad \text{and} \quad r = \frac{D}{2}$$

Since the definition of a circle states that all the points on the circumference are the same distance from the center, it follows that *all radii of a circle are equal*. Moreover, since all radii of a circle are equal, it follows that, if the center and the radius are known, a circle can be drawn by means of an instrument called a *compass*.

A *chord* is a straight line segment, such as *DE*, whose ends lie on the circumference. A chord has a limited length. The longest chord that can be drawn in a circle is a diameter. A *secant line* is a straight line that cuts through the circle in two points, such as line *s*. A chord is a portion of a secant line. A *tangent line* is a line that touches a circle in only one point, such as line *t*. It has an unlimited extent.

A *semicircle* is a half circle. A *semicircumference* is half a circumference. An *arc* is part of a circumference, such as arc *BC*. Any two points on a circumference divide the circumference into two arcs. If one arc is longer than the other, the longer arc is called the *major arc* and the other is called the *minor arc*. An arc can be named by the letters at the end of the arc. The symbol for the arc *BC* is $\overset{\frown}{BC}$. If a major arc is meant, it must be indicated by using three letters, such as $\overset{\frown}{BAC}$. The midpoint of an arc is a point that divides the arc into two equal arcs. However, an arc is also said to have a *center*. By the *center of an arc* we mean the center of the circle of which the arc is a part. For instance, the center of the arc *DE* is the point *O* (Fig. 29.1).

A *sector* of a circle is a portion of the area of the circle bounded by an arc and two radii (Fig. 29.2). A *segment* of a circle is a portion of the area bounded by an arc and a chord. *Concentric* circles are two or more circles that have the same center but different radii (Fig. 29.3).

An angle formed by two radii at the center of a circle cuts off, or *intercepts*, an arc on the circumference.

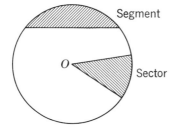

Fig. 29.2

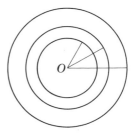

Fig. 29.3

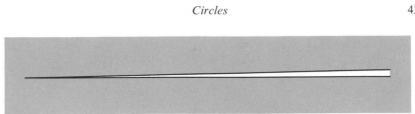

Fig. 29.4. An angle of approximately one angle degree.

We have said that an angle is sometimes defined as the amount of opening between two lines drawn from the same point. If the amount of opening is only $\frac{1}{360}$ of one complete rotation, we call the size of the angle one degree (1°). One degree is really a small angle. We can call this small angle *one angle degree* (Fig. 29.4).

An angle formed by two radii at the center of a circle cuts off, or intercepts, an arc on the circumference. An *arc degree* is the small arc cut off the circumference of a circle *by one angle degree at the center.* Therefore, one arc degree is $\frac{1}{360}$ of the entire circumference. In order to distinguish between one *angle degree* and one *arc degree*, try to think of *one angle degree* as a *small angle* and *one arc degree* as a very *small portion of the circumference* (Fig. 29.5).

An angle formed by two radii at the center of a circle is called a *central angle.* In Fig. 29.6 angle *AOB* is a central angle. If a central angle contains 10 *angle degrees*, then it cuts off an arc of 10 *arc degrees* on the circumference. Whatever the size of a central angle in a circle, it will intercept an arc that contains the same number of arc degrees as the angle contains angle degrees. For this reason, we can say that in any circle a *central angle is equal, in the number of degrees, to the intercepted arc.*

We must be careful about how we make this statement. When we say a central angle of 25 angle degrees intercepts an arc of 25 arc degrees, we might be tempted to say that the angle equals the arc. Yet an angle cannot equal an

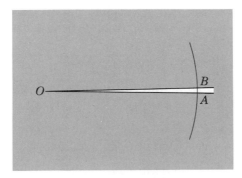

Fig. 29.5. $\overset{\frown}{AB}$ is one arc degree.

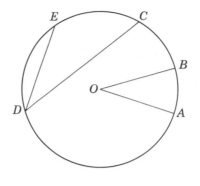

Fig. 29.6

arc. The two things are not comparable. It is no more correct to say that an angle equals an arc than to say, for instance, that your weight is equal to one week. Let us suppose you weigh 168 pounds. There are 168 hours in one week. How can we state any equality between these two quantities? The only thing equal about them is the number 168. We can say that the number of hours in one week is the same as the number of pounds in your weight. In any other manner the two quantities are not equal at all. In the same way, an angle cannot equal an arc. We can say, however, that the number of *angle degrees* in a central angle is equal to the number of *arc degrees* in the intercepted arc. In this manner *a central angle is said to be measured by the intercepted arc.*

An *inscribed angle* is an angle formed by two chords drawn from the same point on the circumference of a circle. In Fig. 29.6 angle *CDE* is an inscribed angle. *An inscribed angle is measured by one-half the intercepted arc.* This means that an inscribed angle contains one-half as many angle degrees as the number of arc degrees in the intercepted arc. If an inscribed angle intercepts an arc of 80 arc degrees, then the angle contains 40 angle degrees. If an inscribed angle contains 30 angle degrees, then it intercepts an arc of 60 arc degrees. Any angle inscribed in a semicircle intercepts an arc of 180°. The angle is therefore 90°, or a right angle.

29.2 MEASUREMENTS IN A CIRCLE: CIRCUMFERENCE

In any circle we are usually concerned with measurements that involve the diameter, the radius, the circumference, and the area. In the formulas concerning the circle we use the following notation:

C represents the number of *linear units* in the circumference.
D represents the number of *linear units* in the diameter.

r represents the number of *linear units* in the radius.

A represents the number of *square units* in the area.

We have already pointed out the fact that since the diameter is equal to twice the radius we have the two formulas

$$D = 2r \quad \text{and} \quad r = \frac{D}{2}$$

The circumference of any circle always has a fixed ratio to the diameter. This ratio is called π (pronounced *pie*). The value of π is *approximately* equal to $3\frac{1}{7}$. It is more nearly equal to 3.1416. However, you should remember that this number, 3.1416, is *not* the exact value of π. For a long time people believed that π could be written as an exact decimal or common fraction. Now it is known that the exact value of π cannot be so written. It is an unending decimal fraction. The value to 30 decimal places is

3.141592653589793238462643383280 (rounded off)

There is seldom any need for this extreme accuracy. In most problems in science π is rounded off to 3.14159 or 3.1416 (on a slide rule we use the value 3.14). As a student you should understand and use both 3.1416 and 3.14 from time to time. Then, in an actual problem in your work, you should use the value that in your judgment is the best value for that particular problem.

If we know the diameter of a circle, we can find the circumference by multiplying the diameter by the number 3.1416, or 3.14, depending on the degree of accuracy we want. Representing this number by π, we have the formula

$$C = \pi D$$

Since the diameter is twice the radius, or $D = 2r$, we can substitute $2r$ for D in the formula and get, upon rearranging the values,

$$C = 2\pi r$$

The second form of the formula for the circumference, $C = 2\pi r$, is the most useful form in most mathematics and engineering.

These formulas, of course, can be used in reverse; that is, if the circumference of a circle is known and we wish to find the diameter or radius, we reverse the procedure. If we know the circumference of a circle, we divide the circumference by π to find the diameter. If the circumference of a circle is measured as 74.56 inches, then

$$D = 74.56 \div \pi = 74.56 \div 3.1416 = 23.733 \text{ in.}$$

The radius can be found by taking $\frac{1}{2}$ of the diameter.

The reverse formulas can be written as follows:

$$D = \frac{C}{\pi} \qquad r = \frac{C}{2\pi}$$

29.3 AREA OF A CIRCLE

Perhaps many people still remember from their grade school days the formula $A = \pi r^2$ for the area of a circle. This formula can be derived exactly only by more advanced mathematics. However, the meaning of the rule is not difficult to understand. Let us see why the rule is reasonable.

If we imagine a circle divided into any number of sectors, resembling triangles (Fig. 29.7), the altitude of these triangles is equal to the radius of the circle, and the sum of the bases is equal to the circumference. The total area of the triangles can then be found by the rule for the area of a triangle. The area is equal to $\frac{1}{2}$ the altitude times the sum of the many bases; or,

$$A = \tfrac{1}{2}(\text{radius})(\text{circumference})$$
$$A = \tfrac{1}{2}(r)(2\pi r)$$
$$A = \pi r^2$$

Of course, in this reasoning each sector is not a true triangle. However, if we imagine that the number of sectors increases, the base of each sector becomes a smaller and smaller arc that approaches the condition of a straight line. The sum total of the bases of the sectors is still equal to the circumference of the circle.

If the area of a circle is known, the formula can be reversed, and we get

$$r^2 = \frac{A}{\pi} \qquad \text{or} \qquad r = \sqrt{\frac{A}{\pi}}$$

Another formula for the area of a circle is obtained by substituting the value $D/2$ for the radius r. The formula then becomes

$$A = \pi\left(\frac{D}{2}\right)^2 \qquad \text{or} \qquad A = \frac{\pi}{4}D^2$$

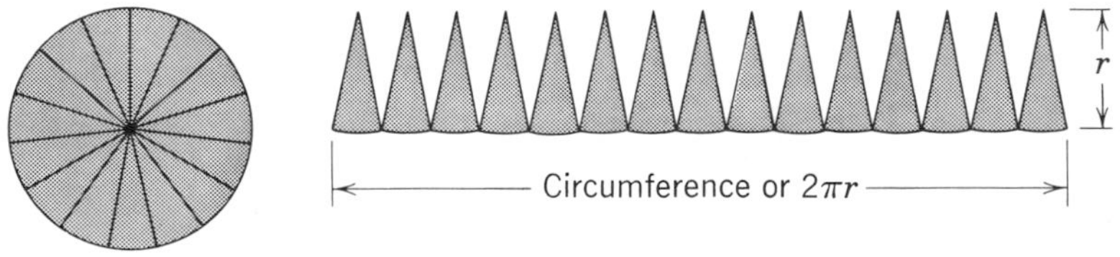

Circumference or $2\pi r$

Fig. 29.7

This formula can be used when the diameter is known. When the formula involving the diameter is used, then $\pi/4$ is usually taken as 0.7854. The area of a circle is therefore equal to 0.7854 times the area of the circumscribed square, or $A = 0.7854D^2$.

29.4   AREA OF A RING

By the area of a ring we mean the area between two concentric circles. It is often necessary to find such an area, as, for instance, in finding the area of a 4-foot side-walk laid around a circular fountain, 20 feet in diameter (Fig. 29.8). If the area of the inner circle is subtracted from the area of the outer or larger circle, the remainder is the area of the ring.

The method may be stated as a formula. We let R represent the radius of the outside or large circle, and r represent the radius of the small inner circle. Now, if we let A_L represent the area of the large circle and A_S represent the area of the small circle, we can say

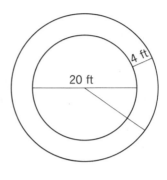

Fig. 29.8

$$A_L = \pi R^2 \quad \text{and} \quad A_S = \pi r^2$$
(area of large circle)   (area of small circle)

Then the area of the ring can be stated as the difference between the areas of the two circles:

$$A \text{ (of ring)} = \pi R^2 - \pi r^2$$

The formula can be written: $A \text{ (of ring)} = \pi(R^2 - r^2)$, or in factored form:

$$A = \pi(R + r)(R - r).$$

In the problem in Fig. 29.8 the radius R of the large circle is 14 feet; the radius r of the smaller circle is 10 feet. Using the formula

$$A = \pi(R^2 - r^2)$$

we have
$$A = \pi(196 - 100)$$
$$= \pi(96)$$
$$= (96)(3.1416)$$
$$= 301.6 \text{ (rounded off)}$$

If the ring is very narrow (for instance, a ring $\frac{1}{16}$ of an inch wide around a circle 6 inches in diameter), then the approximate area of the ring can be found by a short method (Fig. 29.9).

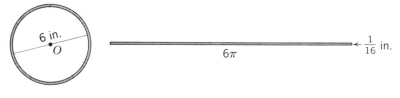

Fig. 29.9

Let us assume that we cut the ring at some point and lay it out along a straight line. We can say that the ring is now a long narrow rectangle. The width of the rectangle is $\frac{1}{16}$ of an inch and the length is equal to 6π inches, the circumference of the circle. We can find the area of this rectangle by multiplying the length by the width; that is,

$$A = (\tfrac{1}{16})(6\pi) = 1.178 \text{ sq in.}$$

The error, of course, is in assuming that the ring forms a perfect rectangle. However, the difference is slight. In fact, if the area of the ring were originally computed as the difference between two circles, it would be 1.190 square inches. The short method is in error by 0.012 sq in. If the ring were still narrower, or the circle larger, then the error would be much less. If the ring were wide, as compared with the size of the circle, then the short method would result in an error too great to be useful.

29.5   AREA OF A SECTOR

The area of a sector can be computed if the number of degrees in the angle of the sector and the radius of the circle are known. We know that a central angle of 90° intercepts an arc equal in length to one-fourth of the circumference. In fact, an intercepted arc bears the same relation to the entire circumference as the central angle does to 360°. In the same way, the area of a sector has the same ratio to the entire circle as the central angle has to 360°.

As an example, suppose a sector has a central angle equal to 20° in a circle whose radius is 12 in. We know the circumference is equal to $(2)(3.1416)(12) = 75.3984$ in. The area of the entire circle is equal to 452.3904 sq in. The sector contains an arc that is $\frac{20}{360}$ of the circumference, or 4.1888 in. The area of the sector is $\frac{20}{360}$ of the area of the circle, or 25.1328 sq in.

29.6   AREA OF A SEGMENT

A segment is a part of a circle bounded by a chord and an arc. There is no simple accurate formula for the area of a segment of a circle. One of the simplest formulas depends on the *width* and the *height* of the segment. The width w is the length of the chord forming part of the boundary of the segment. The height h is the perpendicular distance from the midpoint of the chord to the arc. The height represents the greatest distance of the arc from the chord. A formula for a good approximation for the area of a segment is the following:

$$A = \frac{2}{3}hw + \frac{h^3}{2w}$$

Exercise 29.1

1. Find the area and the circumference of each of the following:
   (a) A round table top 42 in. in diameter.
   (b) A circle made with a compass set at 9.2 cm.
   (c) A circular window $4\frac{1}{2}$ ft in diameter.
   (d) A circular mirror $27\frac{3}{4}$ in. in diameter.
   (e) A circular signboard 8 ft, 10 in. in diameter.
   (f) A circular clock dial whose radius is 53 mm.
   (g) A skating rink 120 ft in diameter.
   (h) A coin whose diameter is 30 mm.
2. The diameter of a drumhead is 26.3 in. Find the number of square inches in both heads.
3. A circular race track has a radius of 136.5 ft. How many turns does it take to run a mile?
4. On a merry-go-round you sit 16 ft from the center post. How far do you ride in making 20 complete revolutions?
5. The distance around a large tree is 11 ft, 4 in. What is the diameter of the tree?
6. A cream separator bowl makes 165 revolutions per second (rps). The diameter of the bowl is 4.75 in. What is the speed of a point on the rim of the bowl in miles per hour?
7. A bicycle wheel has a radius of 13 in. How many turns will it make in going a mile if no allowance is made for slipping?
8. An automobile tire is 28.4 in. in diameter and the wheel makes 3 revolutions per second. How far does the car move in 1 hour if no allowance is made for slipping?
9. A circular race track is 770 ft long. Find the area of the land enclosed by the track.
10. A locomotive wheel is 68 in. in diameter. If no allowance is made for slipping, how many revolutions does the wheel make per second when the train travels 60 mph?
11. A circular skating rink has a radius of 64 ft. The rink is surrounded by a 10-ft sidewalk. Find the number of square feet in the sidewalk.
12. A circular fountain having a diameter of 23 ft, 4 in. is surrounded by a cement walk 9 ft wide. Find the area of the walk in square yards.
13. The area of a circular skating rink is approximately 10,000 sq ft. What is its diameter?
14. A circular running track is $\frac{1}{8}$ mile long. How many square rods are enclosed by the track?

15. A belt pulley makes 30 rps. The pulley is 8.5 in. in diameter. If slipping is disregarded, how fast is the belt traveling in miles per hour?

16. A circle is inscribed in a square that is 16 in. on a side. Find the area of each corner of the square that is outside the circle.

17. Four concentric circles are drawn with radii of 4, 6, 8, and 10 in., respectively. Find the area of the innermost circle and the area between each of the other circles; that is, the area of each ring. (Concentric circles are circles having the same center.)

18. A certain 12-in. record plays for 15 min at a rate of $33\frac{1}{3}$ revolutions per minute. The center hole measures $\frac{9}{32}$ in. across. The distance from the edge of the hole to the outside of the recording is $5\frac{23}{32}$ in., and the distance from the edge of the hole to the inside of the recording is $2\frac{19}{32}$ in. What is the width of each groove in the record?

19. Two ventilating pipes, each 6 in. in diameter, are joined to form one single large pipe having the same capacity as the combined capacity of the two single pipes. What is the diameter of the single large pipe?

20. A square tube 8 in. on a side is to be replaced with a circular tube having the same capacity as the square tube. What is the diameter of the circular tube?

21. A circular water main 24 in. in diameter branches off into two equal circular mains having the same combined capacity as the larger main. What is the diameter of each of the smaller mains?

22. If a 24-in. circular water main branches off into 4 smaller circular mains with the same total combined capacity as the 24-in. main, what is the diameter of each of the smaller mains?

23. If a wire $\frac{1}{16}$ in. in diameter carries 6 amperes under a certain electromotive force (emf), what current will a wire $\frac{1}{32}$ in. in diameter carry under the same emf? (Current carrying capacity is proportional to the cross-sectional area.)

24. The hour hand of a clock is 10.3 cm long. How far does a point on the tip travel between 2 o'clock and 3 o'clock? How much area does the hand sweep over in 1 hr?

25. A circle 20 in. in diameter has a chord 16 in. long. How far is the center of the circle from the chord? Find the area of the circle cut off by the chord.

26. How much area can be enclosed by a wire 60 in. long if it is bent to form each of the following:
   (a) A rectangle 4 in. wide   (b) A rectangle 5 in. wide
   (c) A rectangle 8 in. wide   (d) A rectangle 10 in. wide
   (e) An equilateral triangle   (f) A square
   (g) A regular hexagon   (h) A circle

27. A company wishes to put up a fence around a circular storage tank 32 ft in diameter. If the fence is to be placed 6 ft from the tank, what will the length of the fence be? What will the area between the tank and the fence be?

28. A golfer has decided to put in a circular putting green in his back yard. What will the area of the green be if the diameter is 24.5 ft?

29. A ship's rudder has jammed and the ship is traveling in a circle with a radius of $\frac{1}{2}$ mile at the rate of 5 mph. How many minutes will it take for the ship to travel once around its circular path?

30. Three circular table tops each 4 ft in diameter are to be cut from a single board measuring 4 by 14 ft. What will the area of the scrap material be?

30
Geometric Solids: Prisms

30.1 POLYHEDRON

The figures we have studied up to this point do not occupy space. All can be drawn on a plane and are understood to have no thickness. *Solid geometry*, or space geometry, as it is sometimes called, is the study of figures that occupy space. Such figures are called *geometric solids*.

A *polyhedron* is a geometric solid bounded by planes. (The prefix "poly" means many, and "hedron" refers to faces.) The plane surfaces of a polyhedron are called *faces*. Any two faces intersect in a straight line called an *edge*. The intersection of three or more edges is called a *vertex*. Figure 30.1 shows several polyhedrons.

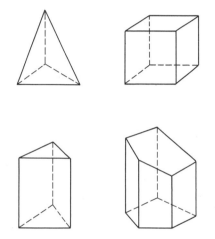

Fig. 30.1. Polyhedrons.

30.2 PRISM

A *prism* is a special kind of polyhedron. In a prism two of the faces, called bases, are congruent and parallel polygons. The other faces, called *lateral faces*, are parallelograms formed by joining the corresponding vertices of the bases with straight lines. Figure 30.2 shows several kinds of prisms.

The bases of a prism may be triangles, quadrilaterals, pentagons, or any other kind of polygon. Notice that the two bases, or two ends, of each prism are polygons of exactly the same size and shape. The lateral faces are parallelograms.

A *right* prism is a prism having its edges perpendicular to the bases. (Figs. 30.2*a*, *c*, *d*, *f*). If the edges are not perpendicular to the bases, the prism is called an *oblique* prism (Figs. 30.2*b*, *e*, *g*).

441

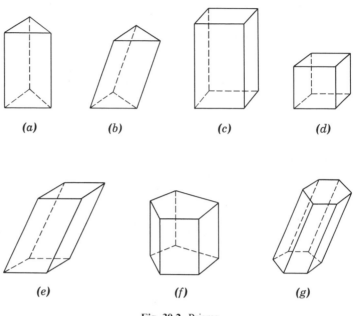

Fig. 30.2. Prisms.

The most common prism is the *rectangular solid,* such as an ordinary box. Such a prism (Figs. 30.2c, *d*) has six faces, all of which are rectangles. A *cube* is a special rectangular solid whose faces are squares. A cube is an example of a solid called a *regular polyhedron.* In a regular polyhedron all the angles are equal and all the faces are congruent regular polygons. There are in all only five possible regular polyhedrons.

30.3 VOLUME OF A PRISM

Volume refers to the amount of space occupied by a geometric solid. In order to understand the method of finding the volume of any prism, as well as other solids, we begin with a rectangular solid.

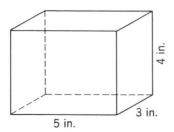

Fig. 30.3

Suppose we have a rectangular solid 5 inches long, 3 inches wide, and 4 inches high (Fig. 30.3). We wish to find its volume. Perhaps everyone who reads this sentence knows the rule for finding the volume of a rectangular solid. To find the volume we say "multiply the length, the width, and the height together. The result is the volume." (5)(3)(4) = 60, volume (in cubic inches).

The answer is correct, but does it not seem strange that we can multiply *lines* together and get *volume*, which occupies space? We multiply *linear* measurements, yet the result becomes *cubic units*, or volume. If you take a moment to analyze the problem, you will get a better understanding of the methods for finding the volumes of *all* kinds of prisms as well as cylinders and other solids.

To measure volume we must use a small amount of volume as a unit of measure. The most convenient unit of volume is one that has the shape of a cube. A common unit for measuring a solid of this size is a cubic inch. A *cubic inch* is a cube 1 inch long, 1 inch wide, and 1 inch high.

To measure the volume of this particular rectangular solid, we determine how many times the unit is contained in the solid. We begin by placing the units along one side at the bottom (Fig. 30.4). We find that we can place 5 cubic-inch units in one row. In the bottom layer there will be 3 rows. Then the bottom layer will contain

$$(3)(5 \text{ cu in.}) = 15 \text{ cu in.}$$

Since the solid is 4 inches high, there will be 4 layers. Then the volume of the entire solid is

$$(4)(15 \text{ cu in.}) = 60 \text{ cu in.}$$

One advantage of using a cubic unit to measure volume is that we can measure the length in *linear* units, the width in *linear* units, and the height in *linear* units. When we multiply these *linear* units together, we get the number of corresponding *cubic units* of volume. The rule may be stated as a formula:

$$V = lwh$$

If the volume of a rectangular solid is known, together with two dimensions, then the unknown dimension can be found by using the formula

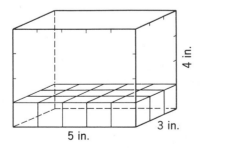

1 cu in.

Fig. 30.4

in reverse. Solving the formula for each dimension, we have

$$l = \frac{V}{wh} \qquad w = \frac{V}{lh} \qquad h = \frac{V}{lw}$$

If we know the area of the base of a rectangular solid, together with the height, we can find the volume without knowing the length and the width. For example, if the base contains 24 square inches, we know that 24 cubic inches can be placed in 1 layer. Then, if the altitude is 15 inches, the volume is

$$(15)(24 \text{ cu in.}) = 360 \text{ cu in.}$$

This example illustrates a very useful formula for finding the volume of a prism. If we let B represent the *area of the base*, we have

$$V = Bh$$

This formula can be used to find the volume of any prism, even an oblique prism, regardless of the shape of the base. Of course, in an oblique prism, the altitude must be measured perpendicular to the bases.

30.4 LATERAL AREA OF A PRISM

The *lateral area* of a prism is found by computing the area of each side, or lateral face, and then adding these areas. If the prism is a right prism, the lateral area can be found by multiplying the height by the perimeter of the base. The *total area* is found by adding twice the area of the base to the lateral area.

In the case of a rectangular solid, which has six rectangular faces, probably the best way to get the *total* area is to find separately the area of the two sides, the two ends, and the top and bottom and then add these areas together. The total area can also be found by adding the area of one side, one end, and the bottom and then multiplying by 2.

30.5 THE CUBE

Since a cube is a rectangular solid whose length, width, and height are equal, the formula for the volume becomes very simple. If we use the letter e to represent the length of one edge, then the formula for a rectangular solid $V = lwh$ is replaced by the formula

$$V = (e)(e)(e)$$

or

$$V = e^3$$

Each face of the cube is a square whose side is equal to the length of the edge of the cube (Fig. 30.5). The area of each face, therefore, is e^2. For the entire surface area of the six faces of the cube we have the formula

$$A = 6e^2$$

Each face has an area $\frac{1}{6}$ of the entire area of the cube.

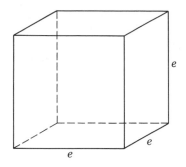

Fig. 30.5. The cube.

30.6 THE VOLUME OF IRREGULAR SOLIDS

The volume of an irregular solid can be found by immersing the solid in a liquid and noting the rise of the liquid in the container. Of course, this cannot be done if the solid is soluble in the liquid or if the object is porous.

Exercise 30.1

1. The base of a rectangular solid contains 29 sq ft. The solid is $4\frac{1}{2}$ ft high. Find its volume in cubic feet.
2. A school room is 33.2 ft long, 27.4 ft wide, and 11.5 ft high. Find the number of cubic feet of air for each of 40 people in the room.
3. How many cubic yards of concrete are needed for a driveway 15.3 yd long, 10.2 ft wide, and 4 in. deep?
4. A prism has a trapezoidal base whose area is 132 sq in. The prism is $4\frac{1}{2}$ ft high. How many cubic feet does it contain?
5. An aquarium is 28 in. long, $20\frac{1}{2}$ in. wide, and 15 in. high. How many gallons will it hold if it is filled up to 2 in. from the top? How many square inches of glass are in the four sides? (One gal holds 231 cu in.)
6. A rectangular box is 6 in. long, $4\frac{1}{4}$ in. wide, and $3\frac{1}{2}$ in. high. How many cubic centimeters does it hold?
7. Find the weight of a solid bar of iron 4 in. square and 24 ft long if the specific gravity of the iron is 6.8. (Water weighs 62.4 lb per cu ft. Specific gravity of 6.8 means 6.8 times as heavy as water.)
8. A basement 36 ft long, 26 ft wide, and 7 ft, 4 in. high contains how many square yards in the floor and four walls?
9. A rectangular box measures 29.4 cm long, 21.3 cm wide, and 16.1 cm high. Find its volume in cubic inches. How long a string will be needed to tie the box with one strand around the box in each of the three directions?
10. Find the weight of a block of gold 6 in. long, 2 in. wide, and $1\frac{1}{2}$ in. thick if the specific gravity of gold is 19.3. (That is, gold is 19.3 times as heavy as water.)

11. A 300-ft ditch is 9 ft wide at the top, $5\frac{1}{2}$ ft at the bottom, and $6\frac{1}{4}$ ft deep. How many cubic yards of dirt were removed in digging it?

12. A swimming pool is 30 ft wide and 80 ft long. It is 3 ft deep at one end and 11 ft deep at the other. How many gallons does it hold? How long will it take to fill the tank if water flows in at the rate of 15 gal per sec?

13. The volume of Lake Mead (Hoover Dam Lake) is 29,830,000 acre-feet (1 acre-foot is the volume needed to cover an acre 1 foot deep.) The area of the lake is 247 sq miles. What is the average depth in feet? What is its volume in gallons? (One cu ft holds $7\frac{1}{2}$ gal.)

14. The area of the six faces of a rectangular solid is 384 sq in. What is its volume if the base is a square 8 in. long and 8 in. wide? What is its volume if the base is 12 in. long and 4 in. wide? (The area of the six faces is still 384 sq in.)

15. The volume of a rectangular solid is 216 cu in. What is its surface area if it is a cube?

16. What is the surface area of the rectangular solid in Problem 15 if the base is 9 in. long and 6 in. wide?

17. What is the surface area (Problem 15) if the base is 12 in. long and 6 in. wide?

18. What is the surface area (Problem 15) if the base is 12 in. long and 9 in. wide?

19. Our number system contains only ten digits, yet with only these ten digits we can write a number of any size, no matter how large. Archimedes, over 2000 years ago, computed the number of grains of sand in the known universe of the time to show that the number could be expressed. It may be interesting to compute the following: how many drops of water fall on a square mile when the rainfall is $\frac{1}{2}$ inch? (Count 8000 drops in 1 pint and 231 cubic inches in 1 gallon.)

31
Cylinders

31.1 DEFINITIONS

A *cylindrical surface* is a curved surface formed by a moving straight line that moves in such a way that it is always parallel to another fixed straight line. A *cylinder* is a geometric solid bounded by a closed cylindrical surface and by portions of two parallel planes (Fig. 31.1).

The plane surface boundaries of a cylinder are called the *bases*, or the two ends, of the cylinder. If the bases are circles, then the cylinder is called a *circular cylinder*. Figs. 31.1*a* and *b* show circular cylinders. Both ends of a circular cylinder are therefore equal and parallel circles.

A cylinder need not be circular. The bases may be in the shape of an ellipse or some other odd-shaped curve (Figs. 31.1*c, d*). However, according to the definition, both bases of the cylinder are exactly the same size and shape.

When we say *cylinder*, we usually mean a *right circular cylinder*, since this is the most common form of cylinder (Fig. 31.1*a*). The word *right* refers to perpendicularity. In a *right* circular cylinder a straight line segment connecting the centers of the circular bases is perpendicular to the bases. If this line is not perpendicular to the bases, then the cylinder is called an *oblique* cylinder (Fig. 31.1*b*).

The radius, *r*, of a circular cylinder is the radius of one of the circular ends. The altitude, or height, *h*, is the perpendicular distance between the ends of the cylinder.

  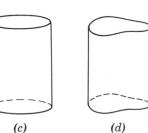

(*a*)　　　　　(*b*)　　　　　(*c*)　　　　　(*d*)

Fig. 31.1

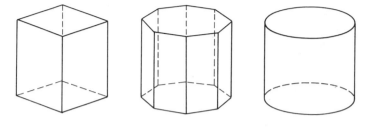

Fig. 31.2

If we form a right prism whose bases are *regular* polygons of three or more sides and then increase the number of sides, without limit, always keeping the base in the form of a regular polygon, the prism will become more and more nearly a cylinder. A right circular cylinder may then be thought of as a right prism whose bases are regular polygons of an infinite number of sides (Fig. 31.2).

Right circular cylinders are numerous in our everyday life. They have many uses. Much of our canned food is put up in cylindrical cans. Storage tanks often have the shape of a cylinder. A round pencil is a cylinder except for the tip. We see cylinders of all sizes, from the very small, such as a shaft for a small wheel in a wrist watch, to a city's large gas storage tank, perhaps 100 ft in diameter. Some cylinders, such as a coin, have a large diameter compared with the length (height) of the cylinder. In contrast, a round wire is a cylinder whose diameter is very small compared with its length (height) (Fig. 31.3).

31.2 VOLUME OF A CYLINDER

Since a cylinder may be considered a prism with an infinite number of sides, then the volume of the cylinder is found by the same formula used for

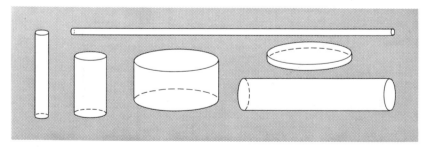

Fig. 31.3. Cylinders (circular).

the volume of a prism:

$$V = Bh$$

For instance, if the base of a cylinder contains 19 square inches (Fig. 31.4), then 19 cubic inches can be placed in one layer on the bottom. If the cylinder is 8 inches high, the volume can be found by multiplying the area of the base, 19, by the height, 8. The volume is $(19)(8) = 152$ cu in.

The base of a circular cylinder is a circle (Fig. 31.5). Therefore, the area of the base can be found by the formula for the area of any circle: $A = \pi r^2$. If we substitute the value πr^2 for the area of the base B in the formula $V = Bh$, we get the formula for the volume of any circular cylinder:

$$V = \pi r^2 h$$

This is an important formula. It applies to all circular cylinders, regardless of the size or shape. It also applies to oblique circular cylinders if we remember to take h as the perpendicular distance between the bases.

Notice that in the formula we are again multiplying together three linear measurements:

$$(\pi)(\text{radius})(\text{radius})(\text{height}) = \text{volume}$$

$$\left(\frac{\text{linear}}{\text{units}}\right)\left(\frac{\text{linear}}{\text{units}}\right)\left(\frac{\text{linear}}{\text{units}}\right) = \left(\frac{\text{cubic units}}{\text{or volume}}\right)$$

The result of the multiplication is units of volume, which has three dimensions and occupies space.

Example 1. Find the volume of a right circular cylinder whose diameter is 8.2 ft and whose altitude is 12.5 ft.

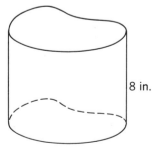

8 in.

Fig. 31.4

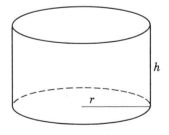

h

r

Fig. 31.5

Solution. In order to use the formula, we must first find the radius r, which is one half the diameter.

$$r = \tfrac{1}{2} \text{ of } 8.2 = 4.1 \qquad\qquad \text{radius}$$
$$r^2 = (4.1)^2 = 16.81 \qquad\qquad \text{square of the radius}$$
$$\pi r^2 = (3.1416)(16.81) = 52.81 \qquad\qquad \text{area of the base}$$
$$\pi r^2 h = (52.81)(12.5) = 660.125 \text{ cu ft} \qquad \text{volume}$$

If the answer is rounded off to five significant digits, we have 660.12.

In a problem such as Example 1 we would probably assume that the given numbers are correct only to three significant digits. If the value 3.14 is used for π and the numbers are rounded off to three significant digits, as is usually done in computation by slide rule, then the computation becomes

$$r = 4.10$$
$$r^2 = 16.8$$
$$\pi r^2 = (3.14)(16.8) = 52.8$$
$$\pi r^2 h = (52.8)(12.5) = 660 \text{ cu ft}$$

If a problem is first written out in the form of the formula with the given quantities in place of the letters, the computation can often be done much more easily. This is especially true in problems containing common fractions. We shall work the next example by this method.

Example 2. Find the number of cubic inches of copper in a copper wire $\tfrac{3}{8}$ in. in diameter and $\tfrac{1}{2}$ mile long.

Solution. The wire is a cylinder whose diameter is $\tfrac{3}{8}$ in. and whose altitude is $\tfrac{1}{2}$ mile. First, the length, or altitude, $\tfrac{1}{2}$ mile, must be expressed in the same units as the diameter. To state $\tfrac{1}{2}$ mile in inches we write

$$\tfrac{1}{2} \text{ mile} = \tfrac{1}{2}(5280)(12) \text{ in.}$$

This product need not be expanded. Computation is simpler if the product is left in the form shown here.

The formula for the volume of a cylinder is

$$V = \pi r^2 h$$

In the example $r = \tfrac{3}{16}$ in., $h = \tfrac{1}{2}(5280)(12)$ in. Substituting numerical values in the formula, we get

$$V = (3.1416)\left(\frac{3}{16}\right)\left(\frac{3}{16}\right)\left(\frac{1}{2}\right)(5280)(12)$$

If the problem is written out in this form, some factors can be "canceled" in numerator and denominator.

$$V = \overset{.3927}{(\cancel{3.1416})}\left(\frac{3}{\cancel{16}}\right)\left(\frac{3}{\cancel{16}}\right)\left(\frac{1}{\cancel{2}}\right)\overset{330}{(\cancel{5280})}\overset{\overset{3}{\cancel{6}}}{(\cancel{12})}$$

$$V = 3498.957 \text{ cu in.}$$

or

$$V = 3499 \text{ cu in., rounded off to four digits.}$$

31.3 LATERAL AREA OF A CYLINDER

It is often necessary to compute the lateral area of a cylinder. By *lateral area* we mean the area of the curved surface. We may wish to paint the outside surface of a cylindrical gasoline storage tank, to find the amount of heating surface of a steam pipe, or to find the number of square inches of metal required in the manufacture of cylindrical tin cans.

In order to arrive at a formula for finding the lateral area, consider the cylinder in Fig. 31.6. Let us assume that the lateral area is cut along one side and spread out flat like a sheet of paper. The lateral area, then, has the form of a rectangle. The length of the rectangle is the circumference C of the cylinder. The width of the rectangle is the altitude, or height h of the cylinder. The area of a rectangle is given by the formula

$$A = (\text{length})(\text{width})$$

The lateral area (LA) of the cylinder now becomes the area of a rectangle. If we substitute the measurements of the cylinder, we get

$$LA = (\text{circumference})(\text{altitude})$$

or

$$LA = (2\pi r)(h)$$

or

$$LA = 2\pi rh$$

This formula can be used to find the lateral area of any right circular cylinder, large or small. Notice that we have in this formula the *product* of *two linear measurements*. The answer will therefore be stated in terms of *square units*.

The total surface of a cylinder must take into account not only the lateral area but also the area of both ends. If the cylinder, such as a wire, has a very small diameter compared with its length, then the area of the two ends is

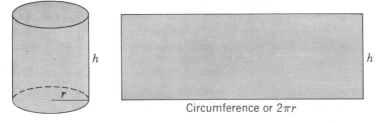

Circumference or $2\pi r$

Fig. 31.6

small enough to be negligible. However, in other cylinders the total area must include the area of both ends. Each end is a circle, and its area can be found by the formula $A = \pi r^2$. The total area is then found by the rule and formula

$$\text{total area} = \text{lateral area} + \text{area of both ends}$$

or

$$TA = 2\pi rh + 2\pi r^2$$

or, factoring,

$$TA = 2\pi r(h + r)$$

31.4 HOLLOW CYLINDER

By the volume of a hollow cylinder we mean the volume of the solid, or shell, between two concentric cylinders; that is, cylinders with the same axis but different radii (Fig. 31.7). As an example, we may wish to find the amount of metal in a hollow iron pipe.

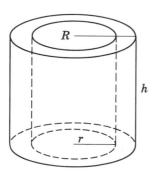

Fig. 31.7

In order to find the volume of a hollow cylinder, or shell, we can compute the volume of the large cylinder, then the volume of the small inner cylinder, or hollow, and then find the difference between the two volumes. The difference will be the volume of material in the shell.

Let us call the radius of the larger, or outer, cylinder R and the radius of the smaller, or inner, cylinder r. The altitude h is the same for both cylinders. Now, if we let V_L represent the volume of the large cylinder and V_s represent the volume of the small cylinder, we have, for the volume of each cylinder,

$$V_L = \pi R^2 h \qquad \text{and} \qquad V_s = \pi r^2 h$$

The volume of the shell is the difference between the two:

$$V \text{ (of shell)} = V_L - V_s$$

or

$$V \text{ (of shell)} = \pi R^2 h - \pi r^2 h$$

The formula may be written

$$V \text{ (of shell)} = \pi(R^2 - r^2)h \qquad \text{or} \qquad V = \pi h(R + r)(R - r)$$

Example 1. Find the volume of an iron shell 15 in. long if the inside diameter is 10 in. and the metal is 2 in. thick.

Solution. In this example the radius of the inner, or small, cylinder is 5 in. Since the metal is 2 in. thick, the radius of the large outer cylinder is 7 in. (The outer diameter is 14 in.) The height, or altitude, h is the same for both: 15 in. We use the formula

$$V \text{ (of shell)} = \pi h(R^2 - r^2)$$

Substituting the given values, we have

$$V = \pi(15)(7^2 - 5^2)$$
$$V = \pi(15)(49 - 25)$$
$$V = \pi(15)(24) = 360\pi$$
$$V = (360)(3.1416) = 1130.976 \quad \text{or} \quad 1131 \text{ cu in.}$$

Warning. The student is warned that he must not subtract the small radius from the large radius before squaring the two.

In a hollow cylinder, if the metal is very thin, for example, $\frac{1}{32}$ inch thick in an 8-inch shell, the approximate volume can be found by a short method. Let us assume that the shell is cut along one side and laid out flat in the form of a rectangular solid.

The volume of the rectangular solid is found by multiplying its area by the thickness. This is the same as multiplying the lateral area of the cylinder by the thickness of the shell. Therefore, we have

approximate volume of shell = (lateral area)(thickness)

or

$$V \text{ (approx.)} = (2\pi rh)(\text{thickness})$$

Example 2. Find the volume of the iron in a hollow iron cylinder having an outside diameter of 8 in. and a length of 24 in. if the metal is $\frac{1}{32}$ in. thick.

Solution. $V \text{ (approx.)} = (2\pi rh)(\text{thickness})$
$$V = 2(3.1416)(4)(24)(\tfrac{1}{32}) = 18.8496 \text{ cu in.}$$

Exercise 31.1

The following containers are cylindrical unless otherwise stated:

1. A hot-water tank has a diameter of 13 in. and is 5 ft high. How many gallons will it hold? (One gal holds 231 cu in.)
2. An oil tank is 22 ft long and has a diameter of 9.5 ft. How many gallons will it hold? (One cu ft holds $7\frac{1}{2}$ gal.)
3. An oil can has a radius of 5 in. and is 15 in. high. Does it hold 5 gal?
4. An oil tank car is 38 ft long and 7 ft, 2 in. in diameter. How many gallons will it hold?

5. A 5-gal can has a radius of 4.8 in. Find its height.

6. A roll of wrapping paper has a diameter of 8 in. and is 42 in. long. Find the number of turns required to cover six picnic tables, each 30 ft long and 40 in. wide.

7. Find the number of cubic inches of copper in a copper wire $\frac{3}{16}$ in. in diameter and 1 mile long. How much does it weigh if the specific gravity of the copper is 8.8?

8. How many square feet of asbestos are needed to wrap a hot-water furnace 5 ft high and 38 in. in diameter (lateral area and top)?

9. A rectangular gasoline tank on a car is 3 ft 6 in. long, 13 in. wide, and 7 in. deep. On another car the cylindrical tank is 3 ft, 2 in. long and has a diameter of 9 in. Which holds more and how much?

10. A road blacktop roller is $4\frac{1}{2}$ ft in diameter and 12 ft long. How many turns will it have to make to roll a blacktop strip *once* if the road is 28 ft wide and $\frac{1}{4}$ mile long?

11. A steam boiler has 24 flues, each 2 in. in diameter and 10 ft long. Find the total number of square inches of heating surface of the 24 flues.

12. One mile of water main is 15 in. in diameter. If water flows at the rate of 3 ft per sec, how much water flows in 1 hr?

13. A rectangular block of copper is 4 ft long and has a square cross section 6 in. on a side. What is its volume in cubic feet? What is the surface area of the block of copper? Surface area is important if we consider the exposure to the air. If the copper in this block were formed into a solid cube 1 ft long, 1 ft wide, and 1 ft high, what would the surface area be? Compare with the present surface area. Can you explain the difference? What is the surface area if this block of copper is drawn into the form of a wire $\frac{1}{4}$ in. in diameter?

14. If 10 gal of hot water are placed in a rectangular metal container 11 by 14 by 15 in., how much is the radiating surface? How much surface is exposed for radiating heat if the water is placed in a cylindrical pipe 3 in. in diameter?

15. A container labeled "1 quart" has a diameter of 10.3 cm and a height of 16.8 cm. Another container marked "1 quart" has a diameter of 8.2 cm and a height of 18.6 cm. Do they hold the same amount? Which one requires more tin (total area)?

16. Find the total piston displacement in an 8-cylinder engine if each cylinder has a diameter of 7.62 cm and a stroke of 9.48 cm.

17. A hollow circular concrete tube is 20 ft long. The inside diameter of the tube is 26 in., and the concrete shell is 4 in. thick. Find the number of cubic feet of concrete in the tube.

18. An iron water pipe has an inside diameter of $\frac{7}{8}$ in. If the metal is $\frac{1}{8}$ in. thick and the specific gravity of the iron is 6.8, find the weight of a hundred feet of pipe.

19. Find the approximate number of cubic inches of metal in an iron shell 12 in. long with an inside diameter of 6 in., if the metal is $\frac{1}{16}$ in. thick.

20. A manufacturer makes some quart tin cans with a diameter of 4 in. and other quart cans with a diameter of 3 in. Which size of can requires more metal for the total area? How many more square inches of metal are required for 10,000 cans of one size than for the other?

Quiz No. 1.   Geometry (Plane).   Form A.

1. The length of a rectangle is 27.3 cm, and the length of the diagonal is 34.2 cm. Find the width of the rectangle, the perimeter, and the area.

2. State the length and width of the rectangle in No. 1 in inches and the area in square inches.
3. The hypotenuse of a right triangle measures 23.6 inches and one leg measures 15.8 inches. Find the perimeter and the area of the triangle.
4. The side of a square measures 14.3 inches. Find the length of the diagonal (in inches); then change this to centimeters.
5. The area of a triangle is 46.7 sq in., and the base is 12.4 inches. Find the altitude of the triangle.
6. Find the two base angles of an isosceles triangle whose vertex angle is 44°.
7. In a 30°-60° right triangle, the shortest side is 14.2 inches. Find the area of the triangle.
8. The two bases of a trapezoid measure 45 inches and 29 inches, respectively. If the altitude is 19.3 inches, find the area of the trapezoid.
9. Find the area of a circular ring whose outside diameter is 24 inches and whose inside diameter is 23 inches. First find the exact area as the difference between two circles. Then imagine the ring is cut and laid out in the form of a rectangle whose length is equal to the outside circumference. In this form find the approximate area of the ring, and tell by how much this result differs from the exact area.
10. A circle is inscribed in a square 18 inches on a side. Find the area of each corner of the square that is outside the circle.
11. Find the area of a sector of 40° in a circle whose diameter is 12 inches.
12. To brace a telegraph pole 80 feet of wire is available. If 5 feet of wire is used for fastening, and one end of the wire is to be fastened to a stake 45 feet from the foot of the pole, how far up on the pole should the wire be fastened to the pole? Assume the pole is perpendicular to the ground.

Quiz No. 1.   Geometry (Plane).   Form B.

1. The width of a rectangle is 22.6 inches, and the length of the diagonal is 37.8 inches. Find the length, the perimeter, and the area of the rectangle.
2. State the length and width of the rectangle in No. 1 in centimeters, and the area in square centimeters.
3. The hypotenuse of a right triangle measures 21.8 cm and one leg measures 17.4 cm. Find the perimeter and the area of the triangle.
4. The side of a square measures 16.2 centimeters. Find the length of the diagonal (in cm); then change this to inches.
5. The area of a triangle is 54.3 sq cm, and the base is 14.2 cm. Find the altitude of the triangle.
6. One base angle of an isosceles triangle is 73°. Find the other angles.
7. In a certain 30°-60° right triangle, the hypotenuse is 26.8 inches. Find the area of the triangle.
8. The two bases of a trapezoid measure 39 inches and 33 inches, respectively. If the altitude is 17.4 inches, find the area of the trapezoid.
9. Find the area of a circular ring whose outside diameter is 25 inches and whose inside diameter is 24 inches. First find the exact area as the difference between two circles. Then imagine the ring is cut and laid out in the form of a rectangle whose

length is equal to the outside circumference. In this form, find the approximate area of the ring, and tell by how much this result differs from the exact area.

10. Four 8-inch circles are drawn inside a 16-inch square so that the circles just touch one another. Find the area inside the square and outside the circles.

11. Find the area of a 30° sector of a circle whose diameter is 18 inches.

12. To brace a light pole, a wire cable is fastened to the pole 56 feet above the ground. The other end is fastened to a stake in the ground 42 feet from the foot of the pole. If an extra length of 6 feet is required for fastening the ends, how long a wire cable is required? Assume the pole perpendicular to the ground.

32
Pyramids and Cones

32.1 THE PYRAMID

The *pyramid* is a geometric solid that has important applications in certain topics in mathematics and engineering. It is related to the measurements in a sphere which, in turn, has certain relations to magnetism and to such problems as the storage of radioactive materials.

A *pyramid* is a polyhedron whose base is a triangle, quadrilateral, or some other polygon and whose sides, called *lateral faces*, are triangles having one vertex in common at a point opposite the base. This point is called the *apex* of the pyramid (Fig. 32.1). Notice that the base of a pyramid may have the

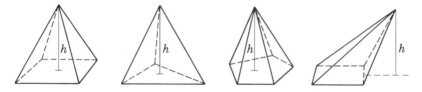

Fig. 32.1. Pyramids.

shape of any polygon. The *altitude h* of a pyramid is the straight line segment from the apex perpendicular to the base.

If the base of a pyramid is a regular polygon and if the apex is directly opposite the center of the base, then the pyramid is called a *regular pyramid* (Fig. 32.2). In a regular pyramid the line segment from the apex to the center of the base is the altitude.

In a regular pyramid all the lateral faces are isosceles triangles, such as triangle *ABC*. The altitude of one of these triangles, *FA*, is called the *slant height* of the pyramid. The intersection,

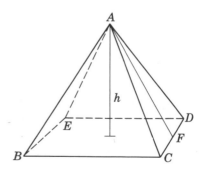

Fig. 32.2

457

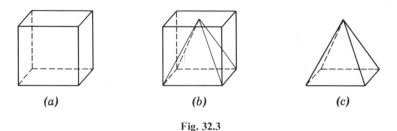

(a)   *(b)*   *(c)*

Fig. 32.3

DA, of two lateral faces is called a *lateral edge* of the pyramid. The inter-section, *BC*, of a lateral face with the base of the pyramid is called the *base edge* of the pyramid.

32.2 VOLUME OF A PYRAMID

In order to get an understanding of the volume of a pyramid, let us begin with a right prism. Suppose we begin with a rectangular solid (Fig. 32.3*a*). For the volume of this prism we have the formula

$$V = Bh$$

Now, if we cut away part of the prism on each side at a slant from a point in the top down to each of the lower edges, as shown in Fig. 32.3*b*, we have a pyramid left. The question is: how much of the prism has been cut away and how much remains? The remaining pyramid is shown (Fig. 32.3*c*).

The pyramid (*c*) has the same base and the same altitude as the correspond-ing prism (*a*). It has been found that the volume of the pyramid is exactly one-third as much as the volume of the corresponding prism. That is, the volume of a pyramid is equal to one-third of the product of the altitude *h* and the area of the base *B*. The rule may be stated as a formula:

$$V = \frac{1}{3}Bh \qquad \text{or} \qquad V = \frac{Bh}{3}$$

The total volume of several pyramids having the same altitude *h* can be found by computing the volume of each pyramid separately and then adding the volumes, or the bases can first be added and the sum of these bases

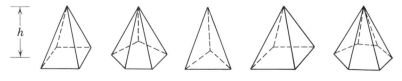

Fig. 32.4

multiplied by the altitude. Suppose we have the pyramids shown in Fig. 32.4 with bases equal to 10, 17, 5, 13, and 18 sq in., respectively, and each pyramid having an altitude of 4 in.

The simplest way to find the total volume of all the pyramids is to find the sum of the bases first. This is 63 sq in. Then we take the sum of the bases as one single base in the formula:

$$\text{total volume} = \frac{1}{3}(63)(4) = 84 \text{ cu in.}$$

32.3 LATERAL AREA OF A REGULAR PYRAMID

In a regular pyramid all the lateral faces are congruent isosceles triangles. Therefore, we can find the area of one and then multiply by the number of faces. Each isosceles triangle has a base equal to the base edge of the pyramid (Fig. 32.5). The altitude of each triangle, FA, is the slant height of the pyramid. We can find the area of a lateral face by taking one-half the product of the slant height and the base edge. Then we can find the total lateral area by multiplying by the number of faces.

However, since all the lateral-face triangles have the same altitude, we can first find the sum of the bases, which is equal to the perimeter of the pyramid base. Then we can find the total lateral area by the following:

$$\text{total lateral area} = \frac{1}{2}(\text{perimeter of base})(\text{slant height})$$

or, as a formula,

$$LA = \frac{1}{2}ps$$

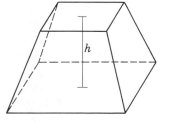

Fig. 32.5   Fig. 32.6

32.4 FRUSTUM OF A PYRAMID

The *frustum* of a pyramid is the part of a pyramid that remains when the top is cut off by a plane parallel to the base (Fig. 32.6). Such a figure may appear, for example, as the box containing a loudspeaker.

The top of the frustum is a polygon of exactly the same shape as the base but smaller in size. The top is sometimes called the *top base*. The two bases are often denoted by B and b, respectively.

The volume of a frustum of a pyramid can be found by the following formula:

$$V = \frac{1}{3}h(B + b + \sqrt{Bb})$$

In the formula V represents the volume in cubic units, h represents the altitude in linear units, B the area of one base in square units, and b the area of the other base in square units.

In the frustum of a pyramid all the lateral faces are trapezoids. Therefore, we can find the lateral area by using the formula for the area of a trapezoid. Instead of finding the area of each trapezoid separately for the frustum of a regular pyramid, we find the sum of the top bases and the sum of the bottom bases of the trapezoids. These bases form the perimeters of the top base and the bottom base of the frustum. If P represents the perimeter of one base and p represents the perimeter of the other base, we use P and p in the formula for the area of a trapezoid. The altitude of each trapezoidal face is the slant height, s, of the frustum of a regular pyramid. Then, for the lateral area of a frustum, we have

$$LA = \frac{1}{2}s(P + p)$$

32.5 THE CONE

A cone is a geometric solid that has many applications in science and in everyday life. We have conical tents, conical speakers in radios, conical containers, ice cream cones, etc. A *cone* is a solid bounded by a plane forming the base and by a lateral curved surface that comes to a point called the *apex*. A cone might be said to be a pyramid with an infinite number of lateral faces. Fig. 32.7 shows several cones.

If the base of a cone is a circle, the cone is called a *circular cone* (Figs. 32.7a, b). A cone need not be circular. The base may have other shapes, such as an ellipse or some other odd-shaped curve (Figs. 32.7c, d).

The *altitude* of a cone is a straight line segment, h, from the apex perpendicular to the base. In a *right circular cone* the base is a circle and the altitude

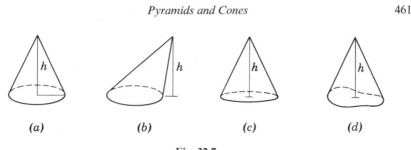

(a) (b) (c) (d)

Fig. 32.7

connects the center of the circular base with the apex. Fig. 32.7*a* shows a right circular cone. If a right triangle is rotated around one of its legs, a right circular cone is generated.

32.6 VOLUME OF A CONE

A cone bears the same relation to a cylinder as a pyramid bears to a prism. In order to get an understanding of the volume of a cone, let us start with a right circular cylinder (Fig. 32.8*a*). For the volume of a cylinder we have the formula

$$V = \pi r^2 h$$

If we begin at a point in the top of the cylinder and cut away part of the cylinder sloping downward to the circumference of the base (Fig. 32.8*b*), the part that remains is a cone (Fig. 32.8*c*). Now, our question is, how much of the cylinder has been cut away and how much remains?

The cone has the same base and the same altitude as the corresponding cylinder (*a*). It has been found that the volume of a cone is exactly one-third as much as the volume of a corresponding cylinder, that is, a cylinder having the same base and the same altitude as the cone. Therefore, the volume of the cone can be found by the formula

$$V \text{ (of cone)} = \frac{1}{3}\pi r^2 h \qquad \text{or} \qquad V = \frac{\pi r^2 h}{3}$$

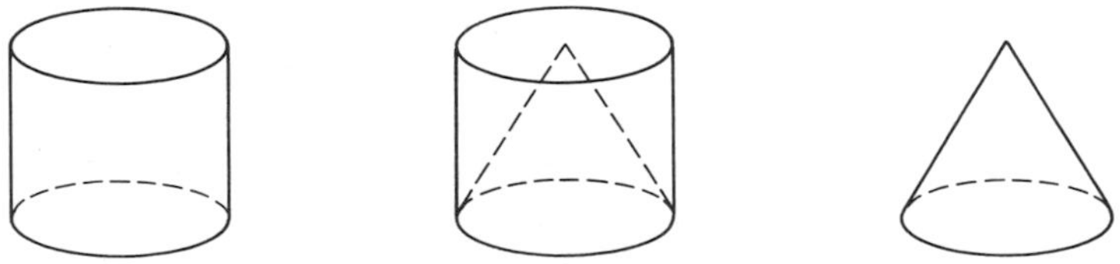

(a) (b) (c)

Fig. 32.8

32.7 LATERAL AREA OF A CONE

The lateral area of a right circular cone is found by the same formula as that used for the lateral area of a regular pyramid:

$$LA = \frac{1}{2}sp$$

However, for a circular cone, the perimeter is called the circumference, which is equal to $2\pi r$. The formula for the lateral area then becomes

$$LA = \frac{1}{2}(\text{slant height})(\text{circumference})$$

The formula reduces to

$$LA = \pi rs$$

We have said that a right circular cylinder may be thought of as a right prism in which the number of sides has increased without any limit until the lateral surface is curved. In the same way, a right circular cone may be thought of as a regular pyramid in which the number of sides of the polygon forming the base has increased without any limit until the base is a circle.

32.8 FRUSTUM OF A CONE

The *frustum* of a cone is the part that remains when the top is cut off by a plane parallel to the base (Fig. 32.9). Such a geometric form appears in many familiar objects, such as paper drinking cups, buckets, pails, containers of many kinds, dishes, lamp shades, and megaphones.

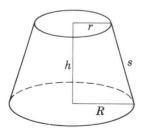

The two plane boundaries of a frustum of a cone are called the bases. In the frustum of a right circular cone one base is a smaller circle than the other. The radius of one base may be denoted by R and the radius of the other base by r. The altitude of the frustum is the perpendicular distance between the bases. The slant height s is the distance from one circumference to the other in the lateral surface.

Fig. 32.9

If we denote the area of one base of the frustum of the cone by B and the area of the other base by b, then for the volume we have the same formula as that used for the volume of the frustum of a pyramid:

$$V = \frac{1}{3}h(B + b + \sqrt{Bb})$$

However, in the case of the frustum of a right circular cone the bases are circles and the formula can be changed to

$$V = \frac{1}{3}\pi h(R^2 + r^2 + Rr) \qquad \text{(for the frustum of a cone)}$$

The lateral area of a frustum of a cone may be found in a way that is similar to the method used for finding the lateral area of the frustum of a pyramid. However, the perimeters are now called circumferences. Otherwise, the formula is similar. For the lateral area of the frustum of a cone, we have the formula

$$LA = \frac{1}{2}s(2\pi R + 2\pi r)$$

The formula reduces to

$$LA = \pi s(R + r)$$

in which s is the slant height.

Exercise 32.1

1. A rectangular prism and a corresponding pyramid both have square bases 8 in. on a side and each is 20 in. high. Find the volume of each in cubic centimeters.
2. A pyramidal monument made of granite has a base of 14 sq ft and is 18 ft high. What is the weight of the monument if granite weighs 170 lb per cu ft?
3. A pyramid contains 87 cu in. Its height is 18 in. If the base is square, find one side of the base.
4. A pyramid has a rectangular base 28 × 24 in. If the pyramid is 12 ft high, how many cubic feet does it contain?
5. A marble pyramid has a base 16 in. square and is 8 ft high. Find its weight if marble has a specific gravity of 2.7. (Water weighs 62.4 lb per cu ft.)
6. Imagine that you are standing 10 ft from a wall on which a picture is hung flat against the wall. The picture is 28 in. wide and 24 in. high. Your eye follows the perimeter of the picture once around. What is the volume of the geometric solid that your line of sight encloses?
7. A tent in the shape of a pyramid has a square base 9 ft on a side. The apex of the tent is 11 ft above the base. Find the number of cubic feet of air in the tent. Also find the number of square feet of canvas needed for the four sides and for the floor of the tent.
8. A pile of sand in the shape of a right circular cone has a base whose diameter is 9.2 ft The altitude of the cone is 2.5 ft. How many cubic yards of sand are there in the pile?
9. A paper cup in the shape of a right circular cone has a diameter of 8.2 cm and an altitude of 10.4 cm. How many cubic inches does it hold? Is this more or less than $\frac{1}{2}$ pint and how much more or less?

10. Some grain piled in one corner of a bin has the shape of a quarter cone with a radius of 5.4 ft and an altitude of 3.5 ft. How many cubic feet of grain are there in the pile?

11. Imagine that you are standing 8 ft from a wall on which hangs a circular mirror 26 in. in diameter flat against the wall. As your eye sweeps around the circumference of the mirror, what is the volume of the conical geometric solid that your line of sight generates?

12. A pyramid has a base in the shape of a triangle. The base of the triangle is 5 in. and the altitude of the triangular base is 3.5 in. Its volume is 35 cu in. Find the height or altitude of the pyramid.

13. A regular tetrahedron is a solid having four faces, all of which are equilateral triangles. This solid might be called a triangular pyramid whose base is an equilateral triangle and all of whose lateral faces are also equilateral triangles of exactly the same size and shape as the base. Find the volume of a regular tetrahedron whose base is 6 in. on a side.

14. A regular pyramid has a base that is a regular hexagon 6 in. on a side. The pyramid is 24 in. high. Where should the pyramid be divided by a plane parallel to the base so that the two parts will have the same volume?

15. A box for a radio speaker is in the shape of the frustum of a pyramid. The front opening (one base) is 18 in. square. The back (the other base) is 6 in. square. If the slant height is 11 in., find the lateral area.

16. A waste basket has the shape of the frustum of a square pyramid. The bottom is $9\frac{1}{2}$ in. square and the top 12 in. square. If the slant height is 14 in., find the volume. Another circular basket has a top 13.5 in. in diameter and a bottom 10 in. in diameter. Its slant height is 15 in. Which has the greater volume?

17. The main part of a monument is the frustum of a pyramid whose lower base is a square 24 in. on a side and whose top base is a square 12 in. on a side. The altitude of this portion of the monument is 14 ft. This frustum is surmounted by a pyramid with an altitude of 12 in. Find the weight of the monument if the stone of which it is formed has a specific gravity of 2.75.

18. A paper drinking cup has a top 6.5 cm in diameter and a bottom of 5.3 cm in diameter. The altitude of the cup is 7.2 cm. How many cups can be filled from 6 qt of coffee?

19. One end of a megaphone has a diameter of 3 in. and the other end has a diameter of 12 in. The altitude is 24 in. How many square inches of surface are there on the outside of the megaphone?

20. Try to derive the formula for the volume of the frustum of a pyramid. To do so, imagine the completed pyramid. Let x equal the altitude of the small pyramid cut off the top. The ratio of the altitudes as well as all corresponding lines in the two pyramids is $x : (x + h)$. Now the volumes of the two pyramids (small and large) can be computed, and then the top part subtracted from the large complete pyramid to get the formula for the frustum.

21. Derive the formula for the volume of the frustum of a cone.

22. Show, in general terms, that the volume of several pyramids having equal altitudes can be found by first adding the bases and then multiplying the result by $h/3$.

33

The Sphere

33.1 DEFINITIONS

A *sphere* is a solid bounded by a curved surface such that every point on the surface is the same distance from a point within called the *center*. If a circle is rotated about one of its diameters as an axis, a sphere is generated (Fig. 33.1).

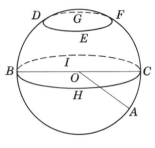

Fig. 33.1

A *radius* of the sphere is a straight line segment joining the center with any point on the surface, OA. A *diameter* is a straight line segment through the center with its ends on the surface, BOC. A diameter is therefore equal to twice the radius.

If a plane cuts through a sphere, the cut surface is circular; that is, the section is a circle, $DEFG$. If a thin slice is cut off one side of a sphere, the section is a *small circle*. As the intersecting plane moves close to the center of the sphere, the sections become larger circles. The largest circle that can be cut by a plane intersecting a sphere is a section through the center of the sphere, $BHCI$. Such a circle is called a *great circle* of the sphere. The length of a minor arc of a great circle is the shortest distance between two points on the surface of a sphere.

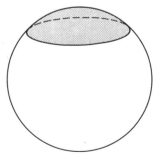

Fig. 33.2

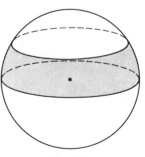

Fig. 33.3

The portion of a sphere cut off by a plane is called a *segment* of the sphere (Fig. 33.2). If two parallel planes cut through a sphere, the portion of the sphere between the planes is called a segment of two bases (Fig. 33.3).

33.2   MEASUREMENTS IN A SPHERE

In connection with a sphere, there are two measurable quantities in which we are interested. They are the volume of the sphere and the surface area.

In stating the size of a sphere, we need state only one measurement. That measurement may be the radius, the diameter, or the circumference. If the radius of a sphere is 5 inches, then the sphere is completely determined in size, and all measurable facts can be computed from this one measurement alone.

To measure the size of a sphere, we might place a plane (flat) surface on each side of the sphere so that the planes are parallel and touching the sphere. Then we measure the perpendicular distance between the planes. This distance is the diameter of the sphere. The diameter may also be measured in some instances by a set of plane calipers.

Practically, it is impossible to measure the radius of a solid sphere directly simply because we cannot get to the center. However, the formulas connected with the sphere, such as the formula for the surface area and the formula for the volume, are usually stated in terms of the radius rather than the diameter. In almost all mathematics, the formulas for a circle and a sphere are more convenient when stated in terms of the radius rather than the diameter.

33.3   SURFACE AREA OF A SPHERE

The formula for the area of a sphere can be derived only by more advanced mathematics. However, the formula itself is not difficult to understand. It is easy to memorize and use, but you should also try to see why it is reasonable.

Suppose we have a sphere with center at point O and radius equal to 6 in. (Fig. 33.4a). If we cut the sphere in two by a plane passing through the center, we have a hemisphere (Fig. 33.4b). The hemisphere resembles a kettledrum. The plane surface of the hemisphere, $CDEF$ (the head of the kettledrum), is a great circle of the sphere. Its radius is 6 inches, the radius of the sphere.

Now we can find the area of this great circle, the head of the kettledrum. It is πr^2, or 36π.

Let us look now at the curved surface of the hemisphere, that is, the bottom of the kettledrum. This curved surface, clearly, has a greater area than the flat top, the head of the drum. In fact, it can be proved that the

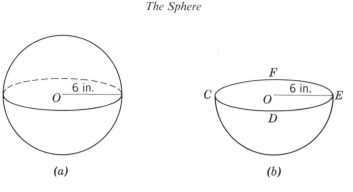

(a)   (b)

Fig. 33.4

curved surface of the hemisphere, (b) is exactly twice the area of the great circle of the sphere, or $2\pi r^2$. This fact is sometimes illustrated in the following manner.

We place a peg in the center of the circular flat top of the hemisphere. Then, starting at the peg, we wind a string of firm texture carefully around the peg, covering the flat part of the hemisphere with a single layer of string. Let us assume that 20 feet of string are required to cover the great circle, the plane surface of the hemisphere. Then we remove the string and wind it around on the curved surface in such a way that the surface is covered with a single layer of string. We discover that the 20 feet of string will cover only half the curved surface. In fact, to cover the curved surface of the hemisphere, 40 feet of string are required.

The area of the hemisphere is twice the area of the great circle. Therefore, the entire area of the whole sphere is four times the area of a great circle. The area of the great circle is given by the formula

$$A = \pi r^2$$

Therefore, the formula for the area of the entire sphere is

$$A \text{ (of sphere)} = 4\pi r^2$$

In the sphere shown in Fig. 33.4a the radius is 6 inches. For the area of the sphere, we have

$$A = 4\pi r^2 \qquad A = 4\pi 6^2 = 144\pi \qquad \text{or} \qquad 452.39 \text{ (approx.)}$$

33.4 THE UNIT SPHERE

A unit sphere is a sphere whose radius is 1 unit in length. The unit may be any measurement, 1 centimeter, 1 inch, 1 foot, and so on. The unit sphere is an important concept in many of the relations of the sphere in scientific study.

Let us suppose we have a sphere whose radius is 1 centimeter. This is a sphere about the size of a fairly large marble. The total area of the sphere is shown by the formula

$$A = 4\pi r^2$$

Since $r = 1$, we have

$$A = 4\pi 1^2$$

or

$$A = 4\pi \text{ sq cm}$$

This sphere is a unit sphere. Its entire surface area is equal to 4π sq cm, or approximately 12.57 sq cm.

Now, suppose we have straight lines or rays emanating outward in all directions from the center of the sphere and of such number that each square centimeter on the surface is pierced by only one line. Then the number of lines extending outward from the center is 4π. The idea of one and only one line from the center piercing each square centimeter on the surface of a sphere of this particular size is an important concept in the study of magnetism.

33.5 VOLUME OF A SPHERE

In trying to understand the formula for the area of a circle, we imagined the circle divided into many sectors, resembling triangles. We can think of the sphere in a similar way. A sphere may be thought of as being composed of many pyramids (Fig. 33.5). The pyramids, of course, have slightly curved bases. However, we can assume that the number of pyramids can be increased until the bases are practically flat.

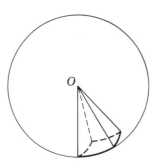

Fig. 33.5

The formula for the volume of a pyramid is, as we have seen,

$$V = \frac{1}{3}Bh$$

In all the pyramids that make up the sphere the altitude is the same, the radius of the sphere. For many pyramids, all having the same altitude, we can say the total volume is given by the rule

$$\text{total volume of pyramids} = \frac{1}{3}(\text{sum of bases})(\text{altitude})$$

The altitude of the pyramids is the same as the radius of the sphere, r. The sum of the bases is the surface area of the sphere, $4\pi r^2$. Therefore, the volume of all the pyramids, or the total volume of the sphere, is given by the formula

$$V(\text{of sphere}) = \frac{1}{3}(4\pi r^2)(r) \qquad \text{or} \qquad V = \frac{4}{3}\pi r^3$$

The formula may be stated in terms of the diameter. If we replace r with its equivalent $\dfrac{D}{2}$, we get

$$V = \frac{\pi D^3}{6} \qquad \text{or} \qquad V = 0.5236\,D^3$$

Exercise 33.1

1. Find the volume and the surface area of the following spheres:
   (a) A globe 16 in. in diameter.
   (b) An iron ball 3 in. in diameter.
   (c) A tennis ball 8.25 in. in circumference.
   (d) A baseball 9 in. in circumference.
   (e) A polo ball, radius equal to $1\frac{5}{8}$ in.
   (f) A basketball 29.75 in. in circumference.
   (g) A beach ball 18.4 in. in diameter.
2. A glass globe 12 in. in diameter is filled with water. How many gallons does it contain?
3. Find the weight of a hollow iron sphere if the outside diameter of the sphere is 16 in. and the metal is $1\frac{1}{2}$ in. thick. The specific gravity of the iron in the hollow ball is 6.8.
4. A croquet ball is $8\frac{7}{8}$ in. in circumference. What is its volume? Its surface area? Its weight? (Specific gravity: 0.72.)
5. Could you lift a sphere of gold 6 in. in diameter? (Specific gravity: 19.3.)
6. You are shown a sphere of gold 4 in. in diameter and you are told that you have a choice of taking only an outside shell $\frac{1}{2}$-in. thick or the remainder of the sphere. Which would you choose?
7. What is the diameter of a 16-lb iron shot if the specific gravity of the iron used is 6.8?
8. The total surface area of a geometric solid is 384 sq in. What is its volume if the figure is a cube? What is its volume if it is a rectangular solid 12 in. long and 9 in. wide? What is its volume if the solid is a sphere? (Remember the area is still 384 sq in.)
9. The volume of a rectangular solid is 216 cu in. What is the surface area if the solid is 12 in. long and 9 in. wide? What is the surface area if the figure is a cube? What is the surface area of a sphere containing the same volume? Can you tell from your answer why all soap bubbles are round?

Quiz No. 2. Geometry (Solid). Form A.

1. A rectangular aquarium measures 28 inches long by 16 inches wide. It is 12 inches deep. Find the volume, and the area of the four glass sides.

2. A bar of iron is 6 feet long. Its cross section is a rectangle 6 inches by 4 inches. Find the volume of the bar (in cubic inches). What is the weight of the bar if the specific gravity of the iron is 7.7. (Water weighs 62.4 pounds per cubic foot.)

3. What is the total surface area of the bar in No. 2? What would be the surface area if the amount of iron were in the shape of a cube?

4. Find the number of cubic feet in the volume of an oil tank car 6 feet in diameter and 38 feet long. How many gallons will it hold if 1 cubic foot is equivalent to 7.5 gallons?

5. Find the weight of $\frac{2}{3}$ mile of copper wire $\frac{1}{4}$ inch in diameter if the specific gravity of copper is 8.8.

6. A right circular cone has an altitude 27.6 cm and a base 22.4 cm in diameter. Find the volume of the cone.

7. A tent has the shape of a square pyramid with the length of a side of 10 feet and an altitude of 12 feet. Find the volume of the tent.

8. How many square feet of canvas are required for the tent in No. 7, including the four walls and the floor?

9. Find the volume of the frustum of a right circular cone having a top base 16 inches in diameter, a bottom base 26 inches in diameter, and an altitude of 12 inches.

10. Find the number of cubic inches of metal in a hollow iron sphere having an outside diameter of 24 inches and an inside diameter of 23 inches.

Quiz No. 2. Geometry (Solid). Form B.

1. A rectangular room measures 32 feet long, 18 feet wide, and 13 feet high. Find the volume of the room, and the area of the four walls and ceiling.

2. A bar of copper is 4 feet long. Its cross section is a rectangle 12 inches by 3 inches. Find the volume of the bar (in cubic inches). What is the weight of the bar if the specific gravity of the copper is 8.8. (Water weighs 62.4 pounds per cubic foot.)

3. What is the total surface area of the bar in No. 2? What would be the surface area if the amount of copper were in the shape of a cube?

4. Find the number of cubic inches in the volume of a hot-water tank in the shape of a right circular cylinder 5.2 feet high and 18 inches in diameter. How many gallons will it hold if 1 gallon is equivalent to 231 cubic inches?

5. Find the weight of $\frac{3}{4}$ mile of steel wire $\frac{1}{3}$ inch in diameter if the specific gravity of the metal is 7.7.

6. A right circular cone has an altitude 34.2 cm and a base 24.2 cm in diameter. Find the volume of the cone.

7. A tent has the shape of a square pyramid. The length of a side is 18 feet and the altitude is 12 feet. Find the volume of the tent.

8. How many square feet of canvas are required for the four walls and the floor of the tent in No. 7?

9. Find the volume of the frustum of a regular square pyramid having an altitude of 15 inches, a top edge of 14 inches, and a bottom edge of 24 inches.

10. Find the number of cubic inches of metal in a hollow metal sphere having an outside diameter of 22 inches and an inside diameter of 21 inches.

Part IV

LOGARITHMS

34
Introduction

34.1 THE MEANING OF LOGARITHMS

Logarithms are used in computation. Long problems in multiplication, division, and in finding powers and roots can be made very simple by means of logarithms. For instance, suppose we have the following problem:

Find $\quad \sqrt{\dfrac{(38.92)^3(0.00879)^4(96800)}{(587.2)(4.987)^2}}\quad$ *Answer:* 0.048299

The ordinary method of making this computation would take a very long time. We shall see that this problem can be worked by logarithms in about four minutes.

The first thing that we must do is to understand the meaning of logarithms and how they can be used.

We have seen the use of exponents in writing numbers. Suppose we wish to write $5 \cdot 5 \cdot 5 = 125$. We can write

$$5^3 = 125$$

In this case the 3 is called an *exponent*. It is placed on the 5 to show how many times the number 5 is to be used as a *factor*. In this example 5 is called the *base*.

An exponent, then, is a number placed at the right and a little above another number (the base) to show how many times the base is to be used as a factor. An exponent implies multiplication of a number by itself. The particular position of the exponent is not the essential thing about it. Its *meaning* is important.

Here are some examples that show uses of exponents.

$$4^3 = 4 \cdot 4 \cdot 4 = 64 \qquad 2^5 = 2 \cdot 2 \cdot 2 \cdot 2 \cdot 2 = 32$$
$$6^2 = 6 \cdot 6 = 36 \qquad 10^4 = 10 \cdot 10 \cdot 10 \cdot 10 = 10,000$$

In the foregoing examples the exponents are 3, 2, 5, and 4. These numbers are also logarithms. A *logarithm* is an *exponent*.

473

Although logarithms are exponents, there is a slight difference in the way each is stated. Let us take a specific example:

$$5^3 = 125$$

In this example 3 is the exponent, but it is also the logarithm. We say 3 is the *exponent on* 5, but it is the *logarithm of* 125. Other examples:

$7^2 = 49$; here 2 is the exponent on 7, but it is the logarithm of 49.
$4^3 = 64$; here 3 is the exponent on 4, but it is the logarithm of 64.
$2^5 = 32$; here 5 is the exponent on 2, but it is the logarithm of 32.
$10^4 = 10,000$; here 4 is the exponent on 10, but the logarithm of 10,000.

34.2 NOTATION USED IN LOGARITHMS

The word *logarithm* is usually abbreviated "log." Now, consider a little more carefully two examples:

In the statement, $9^2 = 81$, the log of 81 is 2.
In the statement, $3^4 = 81$, the log of 81 is 4.

Here we first say the log of 81 is 2, and then immediately we say it is 4. Note that the logarithm depends on what base we use. To make each statement clear, we must indicate the base. That is,

the log of 81 is 2 when the base is 9;
the log of 81 is 4 when the base is 3

In a logarithmic statement, the base is usually indicated by a subscript to the word *log*. The word *of* is omitted. Then we can write

$$\log_9 81 = 2 \quad \text{and} \quad \log_3 81 = 4$$

The same statements may be written in exponential form with the same meaning:

$$\log_9 81 = 2 \quad \text{means} \quad 9^2 = 81; \quad \log_3 81 = 4 \quad \text{means} \quad 3^4 = 81$$

Any expression in logarithmic form may be written in exponential form with the same meaning as shown by these examples:

Logarithmic Form		Exponential Form with Same Meaning
$\log_6 36$	$= 2$	$6^2 = 36$
$\log_5 625$	$= 4$	$5^4 = 625$
$\log_{10} 1000$	$= 3$	$10^3 = 1000$
$\log_2 8$	$= ?$	?
$\log_3 3$	$= 1$	?
$\log_2 128$	$= 7$	$2^7 = 128$
$\log_b N$	$= x$	?
	?	$8^3 = 512$

As a definition then we have: *If*

$$b^y = x$$

then we say y is the logarithm of x to the base b.

Exercise 34.1

In each of the following examples find the indicated power as shown in the first two examples. Then write each in logarithmic form.

1. $5^2 = 25$ **2.** $6^3 = 216$ **3.** $12^2 =$ **4.** $11^3 =$
5. $8^4 =$ **6.** $3^5 =$ **7.** $2^{11} =$ **8.** $7^3 =$
9. $4^4 =$ **10.** $(\frac{1}{2})^3 =$ **11.** $9^3 =$ **12.** $10^5 =$
13. $(\frac{1}{3})^4 =$ **14.** $10^{-3} =$ **15.** $2^{-5} =$ **16.** $16^{\frac{1}{2}} =$
17. $8^{\frac{1}{3}} =$ **18.** $5^0 =$ **19.** $10^0 =$ **20.** $10^1 =$

Express each of the following in logarithmic form:

21. $N^x = y$ **22.** $b^x = K$ **23.** $5^x = z$
24. $7^a = b$ **25.** $3^x = 28$ **26.** $4^y = 382$
27. $5^z = 41.2$ **28.** $x^3 = y$ **29.** $3^{2.5} = 15.59$ (approx.)
30. $2^{4.3} = 19.7$ (approx.)   **31.** $10^{1.5} = 31.63$ (approx.)   **32.** $2^{\frac{3}{2}} = 2.828$ (approx.)

Express each of the following in exponential form:

33. $\log_8 512 = 3$ **34.** $\log_3 27 = 3$ **35.** $\log_2 512 = 9$
36. $\log_5 3125 = 5$ **37.** $\log_4 \frac{1}{2} = -\frac{1}{2}$ **38.** $\log_9 1 = 0$
39. $\log_{10} 1 = 0$ **40.** $\log_3 \frac{1}{9} = -2$ **41.** $\log_b A = c$
42. $\log_c xy = a$ **43.** $\log_x (a + b) = y$ **44.** $\log_{10} 0.001 = -3$

Find the value of x in each of the following examples:

45. $\log_4 64 = x$ **46.** $\log_5 625 = x$ **47.** $\log_3 x = 4$
48. $\log_2 x = 6$ **49.** $\log_7 x = 4$ **50.** $\log_{16} x = \frac{1}{2}$
51. $\log_x 36 = 2$ **52.** $\log_x 0.25 = 2$ **53.** $\log_x 1000 = 3$

34.3   THE BASE AS A BUILDING BLOCK

Let us compare three specific examples:

$$8^2 = 64, \quad \text{then} \quad \log_8 64 = 2$$
$$4^3 = 64, \quad \text{then} \quad \log_4 64 = 3$$
$$2^6 = 64, \quad \text{then} \quad \log_2 64 = 6$$

Here we have three different logarithms of 64. The logarithm of 64 is either 2, 3, or 6, depending on the base used.

Notice that when the base is large, the logarithm is small, and when the base is small, the logarithm is large. This simply means that if we use a small base, we must use a large exponent on the base to bring the base up to any desired value.

We might look upon the base as a sort of "building block." If we wish to erect a certain building, the number of building blocks we shall need will depend on the size of the blocks used. If we start with a large base or "building block," such as 8, then we shall need to build it up only twice (by multiplication) to reach 64. If we use a small base, such as 2, we must build it up six times (by multiplication) to reach 64. In other words, the smaller the base, the more times it must be used to build it up to any desired value.

34.4 ANY NUMBER EXPRESSED AS A POWER OF ANOTHER NUMBER

It can be shown that any number can be expressed as a power of another number. We have expressed the number 64 as a power of 8, 4, and 2. Yet the number 64 can also be expressed as a power of some other number, say 7, if we wish. In this case the power will not be a whole number but instead a mixed number including a fraction.

We know that if we build up the base 7 twice we will reach 49, and we know that the third power of 7 is 343. Therefore, if we wish to say that 64 is some power on the base 7, this power must be more than 2 and less than 3. Actually, in order to build 7 up to 64, we must use an exponent *approximately* equal to 2.137. In other words

$$7^{2.137} = 64$$

or, in log form,

$$\log_7 64 = 2.137$$

These values are only approximate.

Any number, such as 64, can also be expressed as a power of 10. If we wish to build the base 10 up to 64, we must use an exponent greater than 1 and less than 2. The necessary exponent is approximately 1.8062; that is,

$$10^{1.8062} = 64$$

or, in log form,

$$\log_{10} 64 = 1.8062$$

The first question that comes to mind might be, why bother with all this? Are we just doing a lot of unnecessary work? On the contrary, we shall soon find that it will often save a lot of time in many problems involving much computation. We know that when we multiply two numbers expressed as powers of the same base, we add the exponents. In this way multiplication is actually reduced to addition. When we wish to multiply two numbers, we may add their exponents, or logarithms, since logarithms are simply exponents. This advantage will become clearer as we get further along in our study of the subject.

34.5 USE OF 10 AS A BASE IN COMMON LOGARITHMS

The first step in the study and use of logarithms is to understand what they are. We have seen that a number may be expressed as a power of another number. Any number (except 0 and 1) may be used as a base and any number may be considered as a power of this base. Moreover, any particular number, such as 64, may be considered as a power of any base, such as 2, 4, 8, 7, or 10.

In most computation the base used is 10. This base is so convenient and so common that it is not usually written as a subscript but is understood if no base is mentioned. Here are some numbers expressed as powers of 10. They may be written in exponential or logarithmic form. The base 10 is understood.

Exponential Form	Logarithmic Form
$10 = 10^1$	$\log 10 = 1$
$100 = 10^2$	$\log 100 = 2$
$1000 = 10^3$	$\log 1000 = 3$
$64 = 10^{1.8062}$	$\log 64 = 1.8062$
$42 = 10^{1.62325}$	$\log 42 = 1.62325$
$527.4 = 10^{2.72214}$	$\log 527.4 = 2.72214$
$34 = 10^{1.53148}$	$\log 34 = 1.53148$
$30,000 = 10^{4.47712}$	$\log 30,000 = 4.47712$

Exercise 34.2

Express each of the following statements in logarithmic form. (Exponents and logarithms are approximate.)

1. $10^{1.92942} = 85$ **2.** $10^{2.96942} = 932$ **3.** $10^{3.39794} = 2500$

4. $10^{0.68124} = 4.8$ **5.** $10^{2.90956} = 812$ **6.** $10^{4.89209} = 78000$

7. $10^{2.53148} = 340$ **8.** $10^{1.69897} = 50$ **9.** $10^{1.26482} = 18.4$

10. $10^{0.77815} = 6$ **11.** $10^{1.77815} = 60$ **12.** $10^{2.77815} = 600$

Express each of the following statements in exponential form as above:

13. $\log 470 = 2.67210$ **14.** $\log 6800 = 3.83251$ **15.** $\log 59.2 = 1.77232$

16. $\log 9.15 = 0.96142$ **17.** $\log 336 = 2.52634$ **18.** $\log 75 = 1.87506$

19. $\log 61.7 = 1.79029$ **20.** $\log 1550 = 3.19033$ **21.** $\log 1.87 = 0.27184$

22. $\log 248 = 2.39445$ **23.** $\log 24.8 = 1.39445$ **24.** $\log 2.48 = 0.39445$

34.6 TWO PARTS OF A LOGARITHM

It will be noted that the logarithm of a number is often a mixed number consisting of a whole number part and a decimal fraction part. The decimal part is, of course, rounded off. In fact, most logarithms are not rational numbers. For instance, the logarithm of 34 is 1.53148, rounded off to five decimal places.

In order to find and work with the logarithms of numbers, we distinguish between the whole number part and the decimal part. The whole number part is called the *characteristic* of the logarithm. The decimal part is called the *mantissa* of the logarithm. To find the complete logarithm of a number we must find both the characteristic and the mantissa. For instance, in the logarithm of 34, the characteristic is 1 and the mantissa is 0.53148. The reason that the two parts are carefully distinguished is that they are found in different ways.

34.7 SCIENTIFIC NOTATION

Before we try to find the logarithm of a number, let us review the meaning of *scientific notation*. In science we often work with numbers that are very large or very small. For instance, the distance from the earth to the sun is approximately 92,000,000 miles. Such a number is written in a special way called *scientific notation*.

The number is written by placing a decimal point just to the right of the first significant digit, such as 9.2. This is called the *standard position* for the decimal point. The number 9.2 is then multiplied by the proper power of 10.

This power of 10 is determined by counting the number of places from standard position to the decimal point in the original number. In the number 92,000,000 the decimal point is 7 places to the right of standard position. Remember, in a whole number in which a decimal point is not shown it is understood that the decimal point is at the right of the number. The number 92,000,000 is written in scientific notation thus:

$$92,000,000 = (9.2)(10^7)$$

A decimal fraction can be written in the same way, but the power of 10 will be negative. Example: 0.0000435 is written

$$(4.35)(10^{-5})$$

Exercise 34.3

Express the following numbers in scientific notation:

1. 186,000	**2.** 75,460	**3.** 0.00253
4. 4960	**5.** 39.37	**6.** 0.00058
7. 3.1416	**8.** 25,463,000	**9.** 0.000000634
10. 950,000,000,000	**11.** 10,000,000	**12.** 0.000036652

13. 300,000,000   **14.** 0.0000000073   **15.** 872,300

16. 57.3   **17.** 4.378   **18.** 980

19. 16.534   **20.** 0.50   **21.** 0.06325

22. The radius of the earth is approximately 3959 miles. Write this number in scientific notation.

23. One inch is equal to 25,400,000 nanometers. Write this number in scientific notation.

24. The constant of gravitation is approximately the $(6.67)(10^{-8})$. Express this number in expanded form.

25. Express the density of dry air, 0.001293, in scientific notation.

26. The velocity of sound is approximately 33,136 cm per sec. How is this number expressed in scientific notation?

27. The coefficient of expansion of gases is 0.003665. Express this number in scientific notation.

28. The length of a wave of sodium light is approximately 0.0000005893 meters. Express this number in scientific notation.

29. The number of electrons in 1 coulomb is approximately $(6.28)(10^{18})$. Write the number in expanded form.

30. The weight of 1 electron is about 10^{-28} gram. Write the number in expanded form.

34.8 FINDING THE CHARACTERISTIC OF A LOGARITHM

When a number is written in scientific notation, the power of 10 is the characteristic of the logarithm. Therefore, to find the characteristic of a logarithm, count the number of places from standard position to the decimal point in the number. For instance, if we wish to find the logarithm of 5280, we notice that the standard position of the decimal point is between 5 and 2. This is three places from the decimal point in the number. Therefore, the characteristic is 3. For the number 758.6 the characteristic is 2. For the number 0.000836 the characteristic is -4.

34.9 FINDING THE MANTISSA OF A LOGARITHM

To find the mantissa of the logarithm of any number, we use a table of mantissas. These tables are found in many mathematics books. The mantissas are decimal fractions, but the decimal point is not printed.

Mantissas are irrational numbers and have been rounded off. Some tables have mantissas rounded off to 3, 4, 5, or more places. In much engineering work five-place tables are used. If five-place tables are used, the entire mantissa as a rule is not printed in every column. The first two digits are shown only in the first column. This is done to save space.

To find the mantissa for a number such as 5762, we look in the left-hand column, headed N, for the first three digits of the number (576). When we find this number in the first column, we follow directly across the page until we come to the column headed 2, the fourth digit. There we find the number 057. However, the first two digits of the mantissa are not printed in this column. The complete mantissa is 76057.

If the fourth digit of a number is 0, such as 2670, we find the mantissa in the first column headed 0. The mantissa for 2670 is 42651. If a mantissa has a star before it, the first two digits of the mantissa are taken from the next row below. For instance, the mantissa for 5627 is 75028. The mantissa for 2189 is 34025.

34.10 MANTISSA NOT AFFECTED BY THE DECIMAL POINT

We shall point out in a moment that the position of the decimal point in a number does not affect the mantissa for that number. (This is true only when the base is 10.) The mantissa of a logarithm is determined only by the succession of digits in the number. For instance, if any number has as its first four significant digits 3, 2, 7, 6, then the mantissa will be 51534, no matter where the decimal point happens to be. The following numbers have logarithms with the same mantissas:

$$3276 \qquad 327.6 \qquad 327600 \qquad 32.76 \qquad 0.003276 \qquad 3.276$$

Of course, the characteristic will be different for each of the foregoing numbers. The complete logarithm consists of characteristic and mantissa. These are shown here.

$$\log 3276 = 3.51534 \qquad \log 32.76 = 1.51534$$
$$\log 327.6 = 2.51534 \qquad \log 0.003276 = 0.51534 - 3$$
$$\log 327600 = 5.51534 \qquad \log 3.276 = 0.51534$$

Let us see why the position of the decimal point in a number does not affect the mantissa. We start with an example.

$$\log 32.64 = 1.51375$$

We write this in exponential form: $32.64 = 10^{1.51375}$
Suppose we multiply both sides of the equation by 10^2

$$(10^2)(32.64) = (10^2)(10^{1.51375})$$

Expanding and adding exponents,

$$3264. = 10^{3.51375}$$

Multiplying the left side by 10^2 moves the decimal point two places to the right. Multiplying the right side by the same factor, 10^2, simply adds 2 to the characteristic of the exponent. The decimal part of the exponent is *not* changed. Therefore,

$$\log 32.64 = 1.51375$$
$$\log 3264 = 3.51375$$

Multiplying the left side of the exponential equation by any integral power of 10 simply moves the decimal point in the number. Multiplying the right side by the same integral power of 10 simply adds this whole number to the characteristic of the exponent, or logarithm.

From the foregoing example we see that $\log 3.264 = 0.51375$

Let us write this in exponential form: $3.264 = 10^{0.51375}$

Now, what happens if we multiply both sides of the equation by a negative power of 10? Let us multiply both sides of the equation by 10^{-3}. We get

$$(10^{-3})(3.264) = (10^{-3})(10^{0.51375})$$

Expanding and adding exponents,

$$0.003264 = 10^{0.51375-3}$$

All mantissas in the table are *positive*. Therefore, we wish to leave the mantissa positive and make only the characteristic negative. In computation we always leave the mantissa positive. Later we shall find that it is sometimes desirable to combine the positive mantissa and the negative characteristic algebraically.

34.11 HOW TO WRITE A NEGATIVE CHARACTERISTIC

The best way to write a negative characteristic is to place it at the right of the mantissa and to indicate that it is negative. This is shown in the preceding example. In some cases it is desirable to make the negative part minus 10 (-10). This can be done by making the characteristic partly positive, as shown here.

$$\log 0.003276 = 0.51534 - 3$$

This can be written

$$\log 0.003276 = 7.51534 - 10$$

It will be seen in the foregoing example that the *net* characteristic is still -3. If necessary, we can make the negative part of the characteristic anything we wish, provided that we compensate for any change by a positive portion of the characteristic. This is sometimes necessary. For instance, the logarithm of 0.003276 can be written in any of the following forms, as well as others:

$0.51534 - 3$	$1.51534 - 4$	$6.51534 - 9$
$2.51534 - 5$	$4.51534 - 7$	$27.51534 - 30$

In each case the net characteristic is -3.

Exercise 34.4

Find the complete logarithm of each of the following numbers. Then write each as a power of 10.

1. 178200	**2.** 26.51	**3.** 0.003523	**4.** 5.958
5. 758.6	**6.** 0.9779	**7.** 6726000	**8.** 0.0004834
9. 0.8915	**10.** 1054	**11.** 702.7	**12.** 8.273
13. 0.5012	**14.** 120200	**15.** 0.0000214	**16.** 41690
17. 1420000	**18.** 0.06027	**19.** 3.313	**20.** 63.09
21. 9.705	**22.** 0.0000024	**23.** 15080	**24.** 104.8
25. 520000000	**26.** 0.00002694	**27.** 0.007499	**28.** 3
29. 4.008	**30.** 9.304	**31.** 0.8	**32.** 10020000

34.12   INTERPOLATION

It often happens that we need to find the logarithm of a number containing five significant digits, such as 16,375. We see that its characteristic is 4. However, this five-digit number is not found in the table of mantissas. We find the mantissa for 16370 in the table, but the next entry is for 16380. Then

$$\log 16370 = 4.21405$$
$$\log 16380 = 4.21431$$

Now, we know that the logarithm of a number increases as the number itself increases. Therefore, it is reasonable that the logarithm of 16375 should lie between the logarithms of 16370 and 16380. In fact, we can safely guess that the logarithm of 16375 is about midway between the two given logarithms. A good guess would be that the logarithm of 16375 is approximately 4.21418.

Interpolation may be defined as simply a good guess or a good estimate for a number lying between two other numbers. In making this estimate, all we need to consider is often only the last two or three digits of the mantissas.

It should be mentioned that in making this estimate we are assuming that the logarithm of a number increases in direct proportion to the increase in the number itself. It is *not* true that logarithms increase in exactly the same ratio as the numbers, but if the difference between the two numbers is small the error is negligible. If the difference between two numbers is large, then the error in interpolation would be too great. For example, it would not be correct to assume that the logarithm of 700 lies midway between the logarithms of 600 and 800. The error would be too great. However, we can safely say that the logarithm of 16375 lies approximately midway between the logarithms of 16370 and 16380, since the difference between the numbers is small.

Suppose we wish to find the logarithm of 16373. This number lies closer to 16370 than to 16380. In fact, it lies three-tenths of the way from the first number to the second. It is reasonable to assume that the logarithm is approximately 0.3 of the way from the first logarithm to the second. To estimate the logarithm of 16373, we proceed as follows:

$$\log 16370 = 4.21405$$
$$\log 16380 = 4.21431$$

The difference between the logarithms is 26 points or steps. (Actually, the difference is 0.00026, but we need consider only the last two or three digits.) Now, we want to move three-tenths of the way from the first logarithm to the second. So we find 0.3 of the 26-point difference:

$$(0.3)(26) = 7.8$$

The number of points is rounded off to 8. This number is then added to the first logarithm, and we get 4.21413.

The actual work of interpolation may be simplified by considering the mantissas only. To do this, we write down the numbers and their corresponding mantissas, as shown here. (Be careful not to place an equal sign ($=$) between a number and its mantissa).

Number	Mantissa		
16370	21405		
16373	?	Difference is	26 points
		Multiply by	0.3
16380	21431	Round this	7.8
		off to	8

The first mantissa is now increased by 8 points:

$$21405 + 8 = 21413$$

The complete logarithm of 16373 is therefore 4.21413.

For a better understanding of interpolation, the student may find it profitable to work out the logarithms for all integers from 16370 to 16380; that is, 16371, 16372, 16373, 16374, 16375, 16376, 16377, 16378, 16379.

In actual computation most interpolating is done mentally, especially when the numbers involved are small. At first each step in the process of interpolation may be written down as shown in the foregoing outline. However, as a student, you should try as soon as possible to develop the ability to interpolate mentally without writing down each step. With practice, you will soon find it possible to do so quickly and thus save much time in computation.

34.13 ANTILOGARITHMS

An antilogarithm (usually called *antilog*) is the opposite of a logarithm. If we are asked to find an antilogarithm, this means only that we must find the number of which the logarithm is given. As an example, the logarithm of 163700 is 5.21405. Therefore, the antilogarithm of 5.21405 is 163700.

Now suppose we are told that the logarithm of some number is 5.62459. We need to find the number that corresponds to this logarithm. To find the antilogarithm, we use the same table but *in reverse*.

Remember, the table contains only mantissas. Therefore, we first look up the mantissa 62459 in the *body of the table*. When we have located the mantissa, the row and column in which it is found will indicate the proper *four digits* for the required number, or antilogarithm.

We find that the mantissa 62459 is opposite the number 421 and in column 3. Therefore, the required number has as its *first four significant digits* 4, 2, 1, 3. However, we still have not established the position of the decimal point. The decimal point is determined by the characteristic 5, which means that the decimal point is five places to the right of standard position. The required number, or antilogarithm, is 421300.

Notice that if a number is given and we wish to find its logarithm we first find the number at the left and then move across the page *to the right*. On the other hand, if the logarithm is given and we wish to find the antilogarithm, we first find the logarithm in the body of the table and then move to the left side of the page for the number, that is, from *right to left*.

Interpolation is also often necessary in finding an antilogarithm. We illustrate the method by an example. Suppose the logarithm of some number is 6.37683. We wish to find the corresponding antilogarithm. Since the table contains mantissas only, we look for the mantissa 37683 *in the body of the table*. This particular mantissa is not found in the table. We find one mantissa slightly smaller, 37676, and another slightly larger, 37694. These two mantissas correspond to the numbers 2381 and 2382, respectively.

The given mantissa 37683 lies between the two we find in the table. Therefore, the antilogarithm should lie between the two numbers 2381 and 2382. The difference will be indicated by the fifth digit. The two mantissas in the table can also correspond to 23810 and 23820, since the mantissa does not affect the position of the decimal point.

Let us set up the two mantissas from the table with their corresponding antilogarithms, or numbers. We also show the given mantissa for which we wish to find the antilogarithm. Read from right to left.

Number	Mantissa
23810	37676 ⎫ 7 ⎫
?	37683 ⎭ ⎬ 18
23820	37694 ⎭

Notice that the given mantissa lies between two mantissas found in the table. The difference between the two enveloping mantissas is 18 points. However, the given mantissa, 37683, is only 7 points from the first. Therefore, we can say that our given mantissa lies $\frac{7}{18}$, or approximately 0.4, from the first to the second. Then the antilogarithm lies 0.4 of the way from the first antilogarithm to the second. The required number has the succession of digits, 23814. The decimal point, being determined by the characteristic, is six places to the right of standard position. Therefore, the number itself, or the antilogarithm is 2381400.

Exercise 34.5

Find the logarithm of each of the following numbers:

1. 27.963	**2.** 138.36	**3.** 2.4102	**4.** 0.32783
5. 11654	**6.** 0.0024314	**7.** 30077	**8.** 3.9845
9. 48.701	**10.** 0.056015	**11.** 0.50997	**12.** 60.259
13. 6.4863	**14.** 4269.2	**15.** 777.77	**16.** 0.00073106
17. 82694000	**18.** 9.1512	**19.** 0.00085355	**20.** 0.096989
21. 3.1416	**22.** 2.7183	**23.** 0.31831	**24.** 6.2832
25. 0.10101	**26.** 989.99	**27.** 6.6075	**28.** 0.93333

Find the antilogarithm of each of the following given logarithms.

29. 2.12463	**30.** 1.13268	**31.** 2.24650
32. 3.01512	**33.** 4.20729	**34.** 0.25460 − 3
35. 0.29610 − 1	**36.** 0.41500 − 5	**37.** 0.47112 − 4
38. 0.66178 − 2	**39.** 5.39045	**40.** 0.36126
41. 6.50000	**42.** 2.55555	**43.** 0.62003
44. 0.73622 − 6	**45.** 0.79217 − 1	**46.** 2.88652
47. 4.94182	**48.** 2.98481 − 10	**49.** 6.20000 − 10

35
Computation by Logarithms

35.1 MULTIPLICATION

Logarithms are used to simplify computation in arithmetic. By use of logarithms, the processes of multiplication, division, and finding powers and roots of numbers can be made very simple. To show the use of logarithms in computation, we begin with multiplication.

In algebra we learn that $(x^3)(x^4) = x^7$; that is, when two quantities expressed as powers of the same base are multiplied together, the exponents are added. In general terms, we have the rule

$$x^a \cdot x^b = x^{a+b}$$

This rule holds true for any and all kinds of exponents; positive, negative, and fractional. When no exponent is expressed, the exponent is understood to be 1. Here are some examples showing the rule:

$$x^2 \cdot x^3 = x^5; \qquad 10^3 \cdot 10^5 = 10^8; \qquad (10^{2.1352})(10^{1.4134})(10) = 10^{4.5486}$$

Now suppose we have the problem of multiplying together two numbers, such as

$$(764)(875)$$

Instead of multiplying the numbers in the usual way, we express both numbers as powers of 10:

$$764 = 10^{2.88309} \qquad \text{and} \qquad 875 = 10^{2.94201}$$

The product can now be expressed as a power of 10 by adding the exponents, or logarithms, of the numbers. The product is

$$(10^{2.88309})(10^{2.94201}) = 10^{5.82510}$$

The result means that the logarithm of the product is 5.82510. To find the product itself, (764)(875), we look up the *antilogarithm* of 5.82510. In other words, we find the number that has this logarithm. The antilogarithm is 668,500. This is the product of the two numbers: (764)(875) = 668,500.

486

The work is best arranged as shown here:

$$\log 764 = 2.88309$$
$$\log 875 = 2.94201$$

Adding, we get $\log$ of product = 5.82510

product = 668,500

Note especially that when we add the two logarithms, we do *not* get the product of the two numbers. Instead, we get the *logarithm* of the product; that is, we get the logarithm of (764)(875). This fact can be stated in the following equation form:

$$(\log \text{ of } 764) + (\log \text{ of } 875) = \log \text{ of } (764)(875)$$

Stated in words: *When we add the logarithms of two numbers, we get the logarithm of the product of the two numbers.* Note the following examples:

(a) $\log 48 + \log 85 = \log (48)(85)$;　(b) $\log (25)(37) = \log 25 + \log 37$

From these examples, we may formulate the first principle of logarithms:

Principle 1. *The logarithm of a product of two or more factors is equal to the sum of the logarithms of the factors.* In general,

$$\log xy = \log x + \log y$$

Proof. To prove this principle, let

$$\log x = m \qquad \text{and} \qquad \log y = n$$

Then, in exponential form,

$$x = 10^m \qquad \text{and} \qquad y = 10^n$$

Multiplying,

$$xy = (10^m)(10^n) \qquad \text{or} \qquad xy = 10^{m+n}$$

Then, by definition,

$$\log xy = m + n$$

Substituting equivalents,

$$\log xy = \log x + \log y$$

The principle may be extended to several factors:

$$\log xyz = \log x + \log y + \log z$$

Examples.　(a) $\log (25)(40)(15) = \log 25 + \log 40 + \log 15$; (b) $\log 2 + \log 3 = \log 6$;
(c) $\log 4 + \log 5 + \log 7 = \log 140$.

In *multiplication by logarithms,* we observe *the following steps*:

1. *Find the logarithms of the numbers.*
2. *Add the logarithms.*
3. *Find the antilogarithm.* This is the product of the numbers.

In adding several logarithms that contain positive and negative characteristics, we add the negative characteristics separately. The positive characteristics are added with the mantissas.

Example 1.   Multiply by logarithms: (38.79)(6896).

Work:
$$\begin{aligned}
\log 38.79 &= 1.58872 \\
\log 6896 &= 3.83860 \\
\log \text{ of product} &= 5.42732 \\
\text{product (or antilog)} &= 267{,}500 \quad \text{or} \quad (2.675)(10^5)
\end{aligned}$$

The answer is correct to five significant digits, as can be seen if the problem is worked out by the usual method of multiplication.

Example 2.   Multiply by logs: $(0.4122)(3142)(0.002302)(10^2)(5.111)$.

Work:
$$\begin{aligned}
\log 0.4122 &= 0.61511 - 1 \\
\log 3142 &= 3.49721 \\
\log 0.002302 &= 0.36211 - 3 \\
\log 10^2 &= 2.00000 \\
\log 5.111 &= 0.70851 \\
\log \text{product} &= 7.18294 - 4 \quad \text{(net characteristic is 3)} \\
\text{product} &= 1523.9 \quad \text{or} \quad (1.5239)(10^3)
\end{aligned}$$

In Example 2, note that the logarithm of the product is $7.18294 - 4$. In an example of this kind in which the logarithm of the product contains both a positive and a negative characteristic, the form may be changed to show a single characteristic:

$$\log \text{product} = 3.18294$$

However, this change is not necessary. All we need to do is to observe that the *net characteristic* is $+3$.

35.2 AMOUNT OF ERROR IN LOGARITHMIC COMPUTATION

In Example 2, we found the product of the five numbers to be 1523.9. If the numbers are multiplied by the usual long method, the actual product is

$$1523.79087451128$$

Rounding off this product to five significant digits, we get 1523.8. Using logarithms, we get 1523.9. Let us see why there is a slight difference.

Mantissas, in general, are irrational numbers and have been rounded off. In some tables they are shown to six, seven, or even ten or more places. Since they have been rounded off, there is actually a slight error in the values shown in the table. Now, if several mantissas are combined, these errors may be accumulated in such a way that there is a greater error in the mantissa of the answer. For this reason the answer may not be accurate to more than four significant digits even though we use a five-place table. This is what happened in Example 2. However, even this fifth-place difference is only one point. Usually the difference is even less or none at all.

Exercise 35.1

Multiply the following using logarithms:

1. $(148.82)(0.028067)(47606)$ **2.** $(30.84)(0.8312)(2495.5)$
3. $(0.54837)(85.179)(0.0017613)$ **4.** $(0.35205)(6.8718)(0.016291)$
5. $(0.001907)(63.584)(0.084)$ **6.** $(1.3424)(0.72457)(23546)$
7. $(98)(86.5)(740)(0.00123)$ **8.** $(8)(0.694)(7300)(10.02)$
9. $(91.291)(0.000049449)(1.5653)(10^3)(0.000588)$
10. $(5.7034)(0.26363)(9008)(0.00021115)(10^{-2})$
11. $(2073.5)(9.6349)(0.000006)(0.807)(10)$
12. $(75.03)(0.097)(0.10034)(308)(5.6072)$
13. $(1124.8)(0.20695)(7.67)(10^{-4})(45.053)$
14. $(3.1416)(1.4142)(2.7183)(5280)$
15. $(287000)(0.043697)(360.85)(0.00079461)$
16. $(1.2025)(0.40765)(6166)(0.00045928)$
17. Write the proof of Principle 1, using the general base b.

35.3 NEGATIVE NUMBERS

Sometimes computation involves negative numbers. For example, we may have problems like the following:

$$\text{multiply:} \quad (-3.7)(85.2); \qquad \text{divide:} \quad (-894.2) \div (-27.6)$$

In any computation involving negative numbers we proceed just as though the numbers were positive. After the answer has been found by logarithms, it is given the proper sign according to the rules for signs in algebra. You will notice that this is exactly what we do if we perform the computation in the ordinary long way. For instance, let us multiply $(-3.7)(85.2)$ in the usual way:

$$
\begin{array}{r}
85.2 \\
3.7 \\
\hline
5964 \\
2556 \\
\hline
31524
\end{array}
$$

Now, since we have the multiplication of a negative number ($-$) by a positive number ($+$), we give the answer a negative sign; then

$$(-3.7)(85.2) = -315.24$$

That is, when we do any computation by the usual arithmetic method, we disregard the signs until we get the answer. We do the same in computation by means of logarithms.

35.4 ADDITION AND SUBTRACTION

Logarithms are not used to perform actual addition or subtraction of numbers. Suppose we have this problem in addition:

$$325.4 + 49.32$$

The sum of the two numbers is found by simple addition

$$
\begin{array}{r}
325.4 \\
49.32 \\
\hline
374.72
\end{array}
$$

If you add the logarithms of the two numbers, you get the logarithm of their *product*, not their *sum*.

Example.   Find $(43.2)(5.86) + 62.3$.

Solution.   Let us work the first part of the problem by logarithms.

$$
\begin{array}{rl}
\log 43.2 = & 1.63548 \\
\log 5.86 = & 0.76790 \\
\hline
\log (43.2)(5.86) = & 2.40338
\end{array}
$$

Product $(43.2)(5.86) = 253.15$
Now we add $\underline{62.3}$
Answer 315.45

We need not find the logarithm of 62.3.

In working any problem, you must be sure to perform exactly the operations called for in the problem. In other words, do exactly what the problem says.

Exercise 35.2

Use logarithms to find the following:
1. $(-4.2)(-56.3)(706)(-0.96)$
2. $(8400)(-1.35)(-0.62)(56.97)$

3. $(+980)(0.824)(-2.54)(30000)$
4. $(2.718)(-0.73)(0.00512)(-0.306)(0.9)$
5. $(-5.838)(63.7)(-0.4928)(-90600)(10^2)$
6. $(10^6)(-72.69)(-5.32)(10^{-4})(68.42)$
7. $(-33.418)(-2.968)(0.00617)(-8)(-10^{-6})$
8. $(3.1416)(0.0027)(-0.0365)(-1.3427)(8800)$
9. $(-10^{-3})(78.54)(1728)(-10^4)(-1.073)(10)$
10. $(-3.5624)(-78.083)(14796)(-0.006934)$
11. $(65.2)(47.3) + 864$
12. $(3.964)(1280) + (24.75)(532.1)$
13. $(0.714)(512) - (84.5)(6.24)$
14. $(58.77)(0.473) + (643.7)(5.929)$
15. $(-0.238)(0.0814) - (0.312)(0.00089)$
16. $(87.32)(5.814) + (0.6329)(0.492)(7.3)$
17. $(5.933)(-43.72) - (0.6541)(-0.9688)$
18. $91.35 - (4.087)(130.2)$
19. Find the area of a field whose length is 87.43 rd and whose width is 46.82 rd.
20. If light travels 186,000 miles per sec, how far will it travel in 8.314 min?

35.5 DIVISION BY LOGARITHMS

In algebra we learn that $x^8 \div x^2 = x^6$; that is, when two quantities expressed as powers of the same base are divided, the exponent of the divisor is subtracted from the exponent of the dividend. In general terms,

$$x^a \div x^b = x^{a-b}$$

The rule is true for all kinds of exponents. Here are examples showing the rule:

$$x^6 \div x^2 = x^4; \qquad y^9 \div y^3 = y^6; \qquad (5^{4.76}) \div (5^{1.34}) = 5^{3.42}$$
$$x^5 \div x^{-2} = x^7; \qquad (10^{4.786}) \div (10^{1.2718}) = 10^{3.5142}$$

Now suppose we have the following problem in division:

$$76400 \div 216$$

Instead of dividing in the usual way, we first express both numbers as powers of 10:

$$76400 = 10^{4.88309} \qquad \text{and} \qquad 216 = 10^{2.33445}$$

The quotient can now be expressed as a power of 10 by subtracting the exponents, or logarithms. The quotient is

$$(10^{4.88309}) \div (10^{2.33445}) = 10^{2.54864}$$

The result means that the logarithm of the quotient is 2.54864. To find the quotient itself, $(76400) \div (216)$, we look up the antilogarithm. That is, we find the number whose logarithm is 2.54864. The antilog is 353.7. This is the desired quotient. The work should be arranged as shown here:

$$\log 76400 = 4.88309$$
$$\log 216 = 2.33445$$

Subtracting,   log of quotient = 2.54864
                          quotient = 353.7

Note especially that when we subtract the logarithms, we do not immediately get the quotient of the numbers. Instead, we get the logarithm of the quotient; that is, we get

$$\text{the logarithm of } \frac{76400}{216}$$

This fact can be stated in the following equation form:

$$\log 76400 - \log 216 = \log \left(\frac{76400}{216}\right)$$

Stated in words: *When we subtract the logarithm of one number from the logarithm of another number, we get the logarithm of the quotient of the numbers.* Note the following examples:

(a) $\log 68 - \log 17 = \log \dfrac{68}{17}$ (b) $\log \dfrac{487}{23} = \log 487 - \log 23$

From these examples we can formulate the second principle of logarithms:

Principle 2.   *The logarithm of the quotient of two numbers is equal to the logarithm of the dividend minus the logarithm of the divisor.* In general,

$$\log \frac{x}{y} = \log x - \log y$$

The proof of this principle is left to the student. The proof is similar to the proof of Principle 1.

35.6 CHANGING THE FORM OF A LOGARITHM

In using logarithms for division, we often run into difficulties that we do not meet in multiplication. It is often necessary to make some adjustment in the characteristic of a logarithm. It must be remembered that no matter what changes are made, the *net value* of the characteristic must not be changed.

Suppose the logarithm of some number is, say, 3.46528. We see that the characteristic is +3.

Now, if for some reason it should be necessary to change the form of the characteristic, the foregoing logarithm might be written in any of the following forms:

$$
\begin{array}{rl}
\text{a logarithm such as} & 3.46528 \\
\text{can be written} & 4.46528 - 1 \\
\text{or} & 5.46528 - 2 \\
\text{or} & 9.46528 - 6 \\
\text{or} & 13.46528 - 10
\end{array}
$$

or any other similar form. Each of the forms of the logarithm is exactly equal to the original form. No matter which form is used, the *net characteristic* is still $+3$.

If the logarithm of some number has a negative characteristic (which is true for a decimal fraction), then the form may also be changed if necessary. For instance, the logarithm of 0.03786 is $0.57818 - 2$. This logarithm may be written in any of the following forms:

$$
\begin{array}{rl}
\text{a logarithm such as} & 0.57818 - 2 \\
\text{may be written} & 1.57818 - 3 \\
\text{or} & 2.57818 - 4 \\
\text{or} & 5.57818 - 7 \\
\text{or} & 8.57818 - 10
\end{array}
$$

In any of these forms the net characteristic is -2.

It is a common practice with many people to write a negative characteristic in such a way that -10 is always written at the right of the mantissa. The proper adjustment is then made in the remaining part of the logarithm. This form is shown in the last of the foregoing examples.

$$\log 0.03786 = 8.57818 - 10$$

However, it is not necessary to use -10 in this way, since any one of the forms shown is correct for the logarithm of 0.03786.

In most instances, in the examples that are worked out, the simplest form is used:

$$\log 0.03786 = 0.57818 - 2$$

This form is changed only when necessary.

There are other ways of showing negative characteristics. These methods are not recommended but are mentioned here only because they are encountered in books on logarithms.

One important fact must be remembered: the mantissa is a *positive* decimal fraction. If the characteristic of a logarithm is $+3$ and the mantissa is some decimal, such as 0.62751, for example, then the entire logarithm can be written as an entire positive number:

$$+3.62751$$

However, if the characteristic is negative, such as -3, and the mantissa is positive, such as 0.62751, then the two combined *cannot* be written -3.62751. This would indicate that both parts of the logarithm are negative. The negative characteristic must somehow be separated from the positive mantissa.

A logarithm consisting of a negative characteristic and a positive mantissa is sometimes written $-3 + 0.62751$. It is also sometimes written with a minus sign $(-)$ over the characteristic: $\bar{3}.62751$. The last two forms of writing negative characteristics are *not* recommended.

It might be mentioned here that the practice of using only *positive* mantissas and setting up tables of mantissas that are all positive is followed only when 10 is used as a base. If any other base is used, such as 2, 5, or e, as in natural logarithms, then the logarithms are always written as *entirely positive* or *entirely negative*. In such systems there is no separation of characteristic from the mantissa.

35.7   EXAMPLES SHOWING STEPS IN DIVISION BY LOGARITHMS

As we have stated, when we divide two numbers by using logarithms, it is often necessary to make some change in the form of the characteristic. In order to show how these changes may be made, we shall work out several examples in division and comment on each one.

Remember that the mantissas found in the table are all *positive*. Remember also the following *steps in division*:

1. *Find the logarithm of the dividend and the logarithm of the divisor.*
2. *Subtract the logarithm of the divisor from the logarithm of the dividend.*
3. *Find the antilogarithm.*

Example 1.   Divide 27380 by 87.91.

Work:
$$\begin{aligned}
\log 27380 &= 4.43743 \\
\log 87.91 &= 1.94404 \\
\log \text{quotient} &= 2.49339 \\
\text{quotient} &= 311.45
\end{aligned}$$

In this example the entire logarithm of the dividend and the logarithm of the divisor are positive. Since the logarithm of the dividend is the greater, we can subtract the two logarithms as they stand and still get a positive logarithm of the quotient. No adjustment is necessary.

Example 2. Divide 0.008733 by 3.196.

Work:
$$\log 0.008733 = 0.94116 - 3$$
$$\log 3.196 = \underline{0.50461}$$
$$\log \text{quotient} = \overline{0.43655 - 3}$$
$$\text{quotient} = 0.0027324$$

In this example we simply subtract the mantissas as they stand and bring down the negative characteristic -3. We are subtracting a smaller mantissa from a larger one, and therefore we still get a positive mantissa. This agrees with the table, which has only positive mantissas.

Example 3. Divide 8.984 by 21260.

Work:
$$\log 8.984 = 0.95347$$
$$\log 21260 = \underline{4.32756}$$

If, in this example, we were to subtract the logarithms as they stand, we should get a negative logarithm; that is, the mantissa as well as the characteristic would be negative. Since the mantissas in the table are all positive, we cannot look up the antilogarithm of a negative mantissa. For this reason, it is necessary to make a change in the form of the logarithm.

There is one basic rule to follow in division. When logarithms are subtracted, *the mantissa must still remain positive.* Therefore, the logarithm of the dividend must be such that the mantissa of the divisor may be subtracted from it without resulting in a negative mantissa.

In Example 3 we change the form of the logarithm of the dividend by adding 4 and subtracting 4:

$$\begin{array}{r} 4 \\ \log 8.984 = \cancel{0}.95347 - 4 \\ \log 21260 = \underline{4.32756} \\ \log \text{quotient} = \overline{0.62591 - 4} \\ \text{quotient} = 0.00042258, \\ \text{or} \quad (4.2258)(10^{-4}) \end{array}$$

The answer is very small, as we should expect when we divide a number that is approximately equal to 9 by 21,000.

Example 4. Divide 3.809 by 69320.

Work:
$$\begin{array}{r} 5 \\ \log 3.809 = \cancel{0}.58081 - 5 \\ \log 69320 = \underline{4.84086} \\ \log \text{quotient} = \overline{0.73995 - 5} \\ \text{quotient} = 0.000054948 \quad \text{or} \quad (5.4948)(10^{-5}) \end{array}$$

In Example 4 it is necessary to add 5 and to subtract 5 from the first logarithm in order to be able to subtract the logarithm of the divisor. The answer is very small, as we should expect when we divide a number less than 4 by 69,000.

Example 5. Divide 0.0002588 by 690.7.

$$
\begin{array}{r}
\phantom{\text{Work:}}\quad \overset{3}{}\qquad\qquad \overset{7}{}\\
\log 0.0002588 = \cancel{0}.41296 - \cancel{4}\\
\log 690.7 = \underline{2.83929}\\
\log\text{quotient} = \overline{0.57367} - 7\\
\text{quotient} = 0.00000037469
\end{array}
$$
or $(3.7469)(10^{-7})$

Work:

In Example 5 it is necessary to adjust the logarithm of the dividend by adding and subtracting 3. The answer is a very small number, as we should expect when we divide a small number by a much larger number.

Example 6. Divide 7624 by 0.02038.

Work:
$$
\begin{array}{r}
\log 7624 = 3.88218\\
\log 0.02038 = \underline{0.30920 - 2}\\
\log\text{quotient} = \overline{3.57298 + 2}\\
\text{quotient} = 374090
\end{array}
$$
or $(3.7409)(10^5)$

In Example 6 we need not make any adjustment in the logarithm of the dividend. The negative characteristic -2 is simply subtracted from zero, which makes $+2$. The *net characteristic* is $+3 + 2$, or $+5$.

Example 7. Divide 0.08916 by 0.0000198.

Work:
$$
\begin{array}{r}
\log 0.08916 = 0.95017 - 2\\
\log 0.0000198 = \underline{0.29667 - 5}\\
\log\text{quotient} = \overline{0.65350 + 3}\\
\text{quotient} = 4503.0
\end{array}
$$
or $(4.5030)(10^3)$

In Example 7 we subtract the negative characteristics algebraically. The result is $+3$. It is not necessary to make any adjustment in the logarithm of the dividend.

Example 8. Divide 0.0000276 by 0.07692.

$$
\begin{array}{r}
\overset{1}{}\qquad\qquad \overset{6}{}\\
\log 0.0000276 = \cancel{0}.44091 - \cancel{5}\\
\log 0.07692 = \underline{0.88604 - 2}\\
\log\text{quotient} = \overline{0.55487 - 4}\\
\text{quotient} = 0.00035882
\end{array}
$$
or $(3.5882)(10^{-4})$

Work:

In Example 8 we cannot subtract the mantissas as they stand. Therefore, we adjust the logarithm of the dividend by adding and subtracting 1.

Example 9. Divide 0.0413 by 0.0000748.

$$
\begin{array}{r}
\overset{1}{}\qquad\qquad \overset{3}{}\\
\log 0.0413 = \cancel{0}.61595 - \cancel{2}\\
\log 0.0000748 = \underline{0.87390 - 5}\\
\log\text{quotient} = \overline{0.74205 + 2}\\
\text{quotient} = 552.14
\end{array}
$$
or $(5.5214)(10^2)$

Work:

In Example 9 we are unable to subtract the mantissas as they stand. Therefore, we change the form of the logarithm of the dividend by adding and subtracting 1. By subtracting the negative characteristics algebraically, we get $+2$.

Example 10. Divide 0.0003506 by 0.08573.

$$
\begin{array}{r}
& \overset{1}{} \qquad \overset{5}{} \\
\text{Work:} \qquad \log 0.0003506 = \cancel{0}.54481 - \cancel{4} \\
\log 0.08573 = 0.93313 - 2 \\
\log \text{quotient} = \overline{0.61168 - 3} \\
\text{quotient} = 0.0040896 \qquad \text{or} \qquad (4.0896)(10^{-3})
\end{array}
$$

In Example 10 we change the form of the logarithm of the dividend in order to subtract mantissas. The logarithm is changed by adding and subtracting 1.

Remember that a logarithm may be changed to any form desired or necessary by adding and subtracting the same number. The new form must be exactly equivalent to the original.

It often happens that we have a problem involving a combination of multiplication and division. In such a problem we find the logarithms of the numbers as usual. We add the logarithms of the numbers to be multiplied. From this sum we subtract the logarithms of the numbers to be used as divisors.

Example 11. Find $\dfrac{(3472)(0.5684)}{(73.85)(0.006891)}$.

If we write these numbers as powers of 10, we have

$$
\frac{(10^{3.54058})(10^{.75465-1})}{(10^{1.86835})(10^{.83828-3})}
$$

Now we add the exponents in the numerator and add the exponents in the denominator of the fraction. We then subtract one sum from the other. The result will be the exponent or the power of 10 for the answer.

In logarithmic form we have

$$
\begin{array}{ll}
\log 3472 = 3.54058 & \log 73.85 = 1.86835 \\
\log 0.5684 = \underline{0.75465 - 1} & \log 0.006891 = \underline{0.83828 - 3} \\
\log \text{numerator} = 4.29523 - 1 & \log \text{denominator} = 2.70663 - 3
\end{array}
$$

$$
\begin{array}{r}
\log \text{numerator} = 4.29523 - 1 \\
\log \text{denominator} = \underline{2.70663 - 3} \\
\log \text{answer} = 1.58860 + 2 \\
\text{answer} = 3877.9
\end{array}
$$

You will note that it is not necessary to find the antilogarithm until the final step. You will also note that the *actual numerator or denominator does not appear in the work* and that it is nowhere necessary to combine negative and positive characteristics of the same number.

Exercise 35.3

Perform the indicated operations by logarithms.

1. $58340 \div 21.73$

2. $7.182 \div 2457$

3. $575.9 \div 24760$

4. $(-363.7) \div 55.78$

5. $(-48.31) \div 93350$

6. $(-0.0638) \div (-7245)$

7. $0.003203 \div 705700$

8. $803.9 \div 0.003738$

9. $0.9125 \div (-0.0004194)$

10. $0.01486 \div 0.00003972$

11. $0.2483 \div 0.000947$

12. $(-0.0003759) \div 0.08455$

13. $(-6422.4) \div (-20.953)$

14. $5.6238 \div 229.82$

15. $611.06 \div 3134.9$

16. $2807.5 \div 5471.7$

17. $(-15.204) \div 6639.6$

18. $(-33665) \div (-0.070012)$

19. $\dfrac{0.000072481}{0.018637}$

20. $\dfrac{0.0043209}{78548}$

21. $\dfrac{-0.049883}{0.000012647}$

22. $\dfrac{0.0040993}{-3721.8}$

23. $\dfrac{-0.011351}{-506.24}$

24. $\dfrac{0.00002384}{0.07046}$

25. $\dfrac{(37.49)(80960)}{(453.8)(0.09751)}$

26. $\dfrac{(0.7394)(61500)}{(824.7)(0.002437)}$

27. $\dfrac{(680)(0.00087)(493)}{(7.85)(0.0966)(18400)}$

28. $\dfrac{(0.0598)(6004)(0.372)}{(447.6)(0.0819)(20600)}$

29. $\dfrac{(52.56)(0.9118)(10^3)}{(0.00007)(860)(0.00264)}$

30. $\dfrac{(0.7004)(94200)(10^{-2})}{(668.4)(0.0053)(49700)}$

31. Prove Principle 2, using the general base b.

35.8 THE EXPANDED LOGARITHMIC FORM

We have seen by Principle 1 that the *logarithm of the product* of two or more factors is equal to the *sum of the logarithms of the factors*. That is,

$$\log ab = \log a + \log b$$

This is called the *expanded form* of the logarithm. In a similar way we can expand the form of the following by Principle 2:

$$\log \frac{m}{n} = \log m - \log n$$

Now suppose we have a fraction containing two or more factors in numerator or denominator or both. Then, in writing the logarithm of the fraction, we can expand the log form by adding the logarithms of numerator factors and subtracting the logarithms of the denominator factors. For example, let us write the expanded log form of the following:

$$\log \frac{ab}{xy}$$

By Principle 2, we can write this as

$$\log ab - \log xy$$

Then by Principle 1, we can write the sum of the logs of the factors:

$$\log \frac{ab}{xy} = \log ab - \log xy = (\log a + \log b) - (\log x + \log y)$$

$$= \log a + \log b - \log x - \log y$$

We might also use the same principles in reverse to combine several logarithms into a single logarithm, as in this example:

$$\log 60 + \log 140 - \log 80 - \log 15 = \log \frac{(60)(140)}{(80)(15)} = \log 7$$

Exercise 35.4

Write each of the following in expanded logarithmic form:

1. $\log (5)(7)$ **2.** $\log abcd$ **3.** $\log (25)(38)(42)$
4. $\log vwxyz$ **5.** $\log (47.2)(68)(3.9)$ **6.** $\log (0.28)(250)(16)$

7. $\log \dfrac{p}{q}$ **8.** $\log \dfrac{4680}{21}$ **9.** $\log \dfrac{34}{17}$

10. $\log \dfrac{cd}{r}$ **11.** $\log \dfrac{mn}{rs}$ **12.** $\log \dfrac{(50)(40)}{16}$

13. $\log \dfrac{(4.3)(72)}{(1.3)(31)}$ **14.** $\log \dfrac{485}{(51)(0.8)}$ **15.** $\log \dfrac{(7.92)(36.8)}{(97)(41.5)}$

16. $\log \dfrac{(55)(36)(0.24)}{(22)(18)(0.06)}$ **17.** $\log \dfrac{(60)(6)(8)(7)}{(14)(12)(40)}$ **18.** $\log \dfrac{(2)(3)(5)(7)}{(3)(5)(7)(2)}$

Write each of the following expressed as a single logarithm. Simplify if possible.

19. $\log 72 + \log 36$ **20.** $\log 1.5 + \log 28$
21. $\log 400 + \log 0.05$ **22.** $\log r + \log a + \log t$
23. $\log 580 + \log 4.59 + \log 50$ **24.** $\log 20 + \log 6 + \log 5 + \log 8$
25. $\log f + \log g + \log h + \log k$ **26.** $\log 25 + \log 30 + \log 0.004$
27. $\log 48 - \log 3$ **28.** $\log 648 - \log 12$
29. $\log 16.83 - \log 7.1$ **30.** $\log 25 - \log 483$

31. $\log 840 + \log 7 - \log 60$ **32.** $\log 52.5 + \log 96 - \log 75$

33. $\log 39.4 - \log 2.8 - \log 4.5$ **34.** $\log 28 - \log 42 + \log 15$

35. $\log 84 + \log 0.00025 + \log \frac{1}{7} + \log \frac{1}{3} + \log 40000$

36. $\log 30 - \log 25 + \log 45 - \log 36 + \log 18 - \log 3$

37. $\log a - \log b + \log c - \log d + \log f - \log g$

38. $\log 50 + \log 200 + \log 0.5 + \log 0.002 + \log 1000$

39. $\log 18 - \log 40 - \log 27 + \log 32 + \log 45 - \log 24$

40. $\log 28 - \log 50 - \log 60 + \log 0.8 - \log 56 + \log 75$

35.9 FINDING POWERS BY MEANS OF LOGARITHMS

In algebra we have seen that $(x^5)^3 = x^{15}$; that is, to find the power of a power, we multiply the powers. As another example,

$$(10^{2.1342})^4 = 10^{8.5368}$$

In general terms, the rule may be stated

$$(x^a)^b = x^{ab}$$

If we wish to find the power of any number, we first write the number itself as a power of 10. Then we multiply the exponent on 10 by the required power. We then have the power of the number expressed as a power of 10.

Suppose we have the problem

$$(453)^3$$

Instead of multiplying three factors together, we first express the number 453 as a power of 10:

$$453 = 10^{2.65610}$$

The answer can now be expressed as a power of 10 by multiplying the exponent by 3. We get

$$(453)^3 = (10^{2.65610})^3 = 10^{7.96830}$$

The logarithm of the power is 7.96830. To find the answer itself, $(453)^3$, we look up the antilogarithm of 7.96830. It is 92,960,000. That is,

$$(453)^3 = 92,960,000 \qquad \text{or} \qquad 9.296(10^7) \quad \text{(approx.)}$$

For the work we use the following form:

$$\log 453 = 2.65610$$
$$\times 3$$

Multiplying, we get $\log (453)^3 = \overline{7.96830}$

Then $(453)^3 = 92,960,000$

Note especially that when we multiply the logarithm by 3, we do not immediately get the answer to the problem. Instead, we get the logarithm of the answer; that is, we get the log of $(453)^3$. We can state this fact in the following equation form:

$$3 \times \log 453 = \log(453)^3$$

Stated in words: *When we multiply the logarithm of a number by 3, we get the logarithm of the cube of the number.* The rule applies to any power.

(a) $4 \times \log 15 = \log 15^4$;   (b) $5 \times \log 2 = \log 2^5$;

(c) $2(\log 7) = \log 7^2$

From these examples we can formulate the third principle of logarithms:

Principle 3.   *The logarithm of the power of a number is equal to the exponent times the logarithm of the number.* In general,

$$\log x^n = n \log x$$

Proof.   The proof of this principle involves the use of exponential forms. First we shall let

$$y = \log x$$

In exponential form,

$$10^y = x$$

Raising both sides of the equation to the nth power,

$$(10^y)^n = x^n$$

This can be written

$$10^{ny} = x^n$$

By definition, ny is the logarithm of the left side. Taking the logarithm of both sides, we get

$$ny = \log x^n$$

Substituting the equivalent of y,

$$(n)(\log x) = \log x^n$$

Steps in finding powers by use of logarithms.

1. *Find the logarithm of the number to be raised to a power.*
2. *Multiply the logarithm by the exponent of the indicated power.*
3. *Find the antilogarithm.* This is the required power.

Example 1.   Find $(87.36)^4$.

   Solution. $\log 87.36 = 1.94131$

$$\frac{\quad\quad\quad\quad\quad\times\,4}{}$$

$$\log (87.36)^4 = \overline{7.76524}$$

$$(87.36)^4 = 58{,}242{,}000$$

Example 2.   Find $(89.76)^8$.

   Solution.   In finding powers of numbers, we may realize for the first time the tremendous saving of time through the use of logarithms in computation. Consider, for example, the amount of work involved in this problem by the usual long method of multiplication. Using logs we have,

$$\log 89.76 = \quad 1.95308$$

$$\frac{\quad\quad\quad\quad\quad\times\,8}{}$$

$$\log (89.76)^8 = \overline{15.62464}$$

$$(89.76)^8 = 4{,}213{,}500{,}000{,}000{,}000$$

$$\text{or}\quad (4.2135)(10^{15})$$

Example 3.   Find $(0.05182)^4$.

   Solution.   In powers of decimal fractions, both mantissa and characteristic (that is, the entire logarithm) must be multiplied by the required power.

$$\log 0.05182 = 0.71450 - 2$$

$$\frac{\quad\quad\quad\quad\quad\times\,4}{}$$

$$\log (0.05182)^4 = \overline{2.85800 - 8} \quad \text{(net characteristic is } -6)$$

$$(0.05182)^4 = 0.000007211 \quad \text{or} \quad 7.211(10^{-6})$$

Exercise 35.5

Compute by logarithms:

1. $(147.3)^3$	**2.** $(39.87)^4$	**3.** $(8.739)^5$
4. $(0.00651)^4$	**5.** $(0.0427)^6$	**6.** $(0.0078)^9$
7. $(8760)^5$	**8.** $(0.7948)^4$	**9.** $(0.09378)^7$
10. $(32.5)^{2.13}$	**11.** $(18.67)^{1.42}$	**12.** $(492000)^{\frac{2}{3}}$

13. $(28.41)^2(37.19)^3$ **14.** $(0.0069)^4(53.7)^2$

15. $(940000)^3(.0008)^5$ **16.** $(769.2)^3(0.000469)^4$

17. $(-347.8)^2(-2.145)^3$ **18.** $(85.9)^2 + (63.7)^2$

19. $(-7.503)^2(0.6844)^5$ **20.** $(-5.8)^3 - (3.67)^2$

21. $(241.8)^2 + (187.6)^2$ **22.** $(-0.097)^2 + (0.32)^3$

23. $(48.6)^2 + (63 - 24)^2$ **24.** $(78.463)^2 + (59.018)^2$

25. $\dfrac{(39.71)^3(7.243)}{(6.078)^2}$ **26.** $\dfrac{(0.09842)^2(8.035)^3}{(48.2)(0.00572)^2}$

27. $\dfrac{(1.8687)^3(0.0789)^4}{(0.6107)^2(9073)}$ **28.** $\dfrac{(14.9)^2(0.7)^4(0.0035)^3}{(297)^3(9.108)^2(0.0024)}$

29. Write the proof of Principle 3, using the general base b.

35.10 FINDING ROOTS OF NUMBERS BY LOGARITHMS

We know that finding the square root of a number, such as the square root of 1376.48, is not an easy process in arithmetic. To find the cube root of a number is still more difficult. If we wish to find other roots of numbers, such as $\sqrt[7]{487.39}$, the problem is practically impossible by the use of arithmetic alone. Such problems are easily worked by logarithms.

In algebra we have seen that

$$\sqrt{x^{10}} = x^5; \qquad \sqrt[3]{x^6} = x^2; \qquad \sqrt[4]{x^{12}} = x^3; \qquad \sqrt[3]{10^{4.864}} = 10^{1.621}$$

That is, when we wish to find the root of a number expressed with an exponent, we divide the exponent by the index of the root.

Now suppose we have the following problem: $\sqrt[3]{9650}$. We first express the radicand, 9650, as a power of 10:

$$9650 = 10^{3.98453}$$

Then the cube root can also be expressed as a power of 10:

$$\sqrt[3]{9650} = \sqrt[3]{10^{3.98453}} = 10^{1.32818}$$

The logarithm of the root is 1.32818. To find the cube root itself, that is, $\sqrt[3]{9650}$, we look up the antilogarithm of 1.32818. It is 21.29. This is the answer to the problem; that is,

$$\sqrt[3]{9650} = 21.29$$

For the work we use the following form:

$$\log\ 9650 = 3.98453$$

Dividing the log by 3, $\quad \log \sqrt[3]{9650} = 1.32818$

$$\sqrt[3]{9650} = 21.29 \text{ (approx.)}$$

Note especially that when we divide the logarithm by 3, we do not at once get the cube root: $\sqrt[3]{9650}$. Instead, we get the logarithm of the cube root. This fact may be stated in the following equation form:

$$\log \sqrt[3]{9650} = (\log 9650) \div 3 \qquad \text{or} \qquad \frac{\log 9650}{3}$$

In the same way,

$$\log \sqrt[4]{78} = (\log 78) \div 4; \qquad \log \sqrt[7]{684} = \frac{\log 684}{7}$$

From the example shown we may formulate a fourth principle for the use of logarithms:

Principle 4.   *The logarithm of a root of a number is equal to the logarithm of the number divided by the index of the root.* In general,

$$\log \sqrt[r]{N} = (\log N) \div r = \frac{\log N}{r}$$

In algebra we have seen that a root may be written as a fractional power. That is, $\sqrt[3]{9650}$ may be written as $(9650)^{\frac{1}{3}}$

Then we can apply *Principle 3*. If we work this problem by Principle 3, we have

$$\log 9650 = 3.98453$$

Multiplying the log by $\frac{1}{3}$, $\log (9650)^{\frac{1}{3}} = 1.32818$

$$(9650)^{\frac{1}{3}} = 21.29$$

To prove Principle 4, we let

$$\log N = x$$

Writing in exponential form, $10^x = N$

Taking the rth root of both sides, $\sqrt[r]{10^x} = \sqrt[r]{N}$

That is, $10^{x/r} = \sqrt[r]{N}$

Then, by definition of a log, $\dfrac{x}{r} = \log \sqrt[r]{N}$

Replacing x with its equivalent, $\dfrac{\log N}{r} = \log \sqrt[r]{N}$

The result can also be stated in the form of Principle 3, with a fractional power:

$$\log N^{1/r} = \frac{1}{r}(\log N)$$

Steps in finding roots by logarithms:

1. *Find the logarithm of the number, the radicand.*
2. *Divide the logarithm by the index of the root.*
3. *Find the antilogarithm.* This is the required root of the number.

Since a root is equivalent to a fractional power, then in finding a root of a number, we can make use of Principle 3 which refers to finding powers.

Example 1.   Find $\sqrt[3]{47120}$ in two ways: Principle 4 and Principle 3.

Solution. $\log \quad 47120 = 4.67321$

Dividing the logarithm by 3, $\log \sqrt[3]{47120} = 1.55774$
   (Principle 4)

then $\sqrt[3]{47120} = 36.119$

For Principle 3: the problem can be stated as $(47120)^{\frac{1}{3}}$.

$$\log 47120 = 4.67321$$
Multiplying the logarithm by $\frac{1}{3}$, $\quad \log (47120)^{\frac{1}{3}} = 1.55774$
then $\qquad\qquad\qquad\qquad (47120)^{\frac{1}{3}} = 36.119$

In finding the root of a decimal fraction, we must divide the entire logarithm, including mantissa and characteristic, by the index of the root. In many problems it is necessary to make some adjustment in the negative characteristic. The following rule must be observed:

Rule. *The negative characteristic must be exactly divisible by the index of the root.*

The characteristic always, whether negative or positive, indicates the number of places from standard position to the decimal point in the number. Therefore, *the characteristic can never be a fraction.* It must be a whole number, positive or negative, or zero.

Example 2. Find $\sqrt[3]{0.007326}$.
Work: $\qquad\qquad\qquad\qquad \log 0.007326 = 0.86487 - 3$
Dividing the logarithm by 3, $\quad \log \sqrt[3]{0.007326} = 0.28829 - 1$
$$\sqrt[3]{0.007326} = 0.19422$$

In Example 1 no adjustment is necessary, since the negative characteristic -3 is exactly divisible by the index 3.

Example 3. Find $\sqrt[3]{0.0007326}$.
Work: $\qquad\qquad\qquad\qquad \log 0.0007326 = 0.86487 - 4$

At this point in this example we notice that the characteristic is -4. This number is not exactly divisible by the index 3. Therefore, the characteristic must be changed in form so that the negative part is divisible by 3. The negative part may be changed to -6, -9, or any negative multiple of 3. Of course, we must make a corresponding change in the positive part of the logarithm.

The form of the characteristic is easily changed by adding and subtracting 2: $0.86487 - 4$ is the same as $2.86487 - 6$. The negative part of the characteristic is now divisible by 3. We now show the work:

$$\log 0.0007326 = \overset{2}{\cancel{0}}.86487 - \overset{-6}{\cancel{4}}$$
Dividing the entire logarithm by 3, $\quad \log \sqrt[3]{0.0007326} = 0.95496 - 2$
$$\sqrt[3]{0.0007326} = 0.090148$$

Note. It goes without saying that in the division of the positive portion of the logarithm any remainder must *not* be carried over to the negative characteristic.

35.11   FRACTIONAL EXPONENTS IN GENERAL

In problems involving any type of fractional exponent such as $(815.6)^{\frac{2}{3}}$ we first find the logarithm of 815.6 as usual. The logarithm of 815.6 is 2.91148. Now we are to multiply this logarithm by the fraction $\frac{2}{3}$. This involves two separate steps.

Example 1.   Find $(815.6)^{\frac{2}{3}}$.

Work:

To multiply the logarithm by $\frac{2}{3}$, we first multiply by 2 and then divide by 3.

$$
\begin{aligned}
\log 815.6 &= 2.91148 \\
&\underline{\times\,2} \\
\div 3)&\overline{5.82296} \\
\log (815.6)^{\frac{2}{3}} &= 1.94099 \\
(815.6)^{\frac{2}{3}} &= 87.296
\end{aligned}
$$

In the foregoing example you will note than when we first multiply the logarithm by 2 we get 5.82296. This number is really the logarithm of the power $(815.6)^2$.

Note.   In multiplying a logarithm by a fractional power, as in Example 1, we might have first divided by 3 and then multiplied by 2. However, it is usually best to do the multiplication first.

Example 2.   Find $(0.001837)^{\frac{3}{4}}$.

Work:

Multiplying the logarithm by 3,

Before dividing by 4, the form must be changed to

Dividing the logarithm by 4,

$$
\begin{aligned}
\log 0.001837 &= 0.26411 - 3 \\
&\underline{\times\,3} \\
&\overline{0.79233 - 9} \\
&3.79233 - 12 \\
\log (0.001837)^{\frac{3}{4}} &= 0.94808 - 3 \\
(0.001837)^{\frac{3}{4}} &= 0.0088732
\end{aligned}
$$

Example 3.   Find $(0.006342)^{\frac{4}{7}}$.

Work:

Multiplying the logarithm by 4,

Before dividing by 7, the form must be changed to

Dividing the logarithm by 7,

$$
\begin{aligned}
\log 0.006342 &= 0.80223 - 3 \\
&\underline{\times\,4} \\
&\overline{3.20892 - 12} \\
&5.20892 - 14 \\
\log (0.006342)^{\frac{4}{7}} &= 0.74413 - 2 \\
(0.006342)^{\frac{4}{7}} &= 0.055479
\end{aligned}
$$

In a problem in which the power is a decimal fraction, we proceed in the same manner as in finding any other power.

Example 4.   Find $(263.4)^{2.142}$.

Work:

Multiplying the logarithm by 2.142,

The new logarithm is rounded off.

$$
\begin{aligned}
\log 263.4 &= 2.42062 \\
&\underline{\times\,2.142} \\
&\overline{5.18496804} \\
\log (263.4)^{2.142} &= 5.18497 \\
(263.4)^{2.142} &= 153100
\end{aligned}
$$

Note. In Example 4 the multiplication (2.42062)(2.142) may itself be done by logarithms if so desired; that is, we may find the logarithms of 2.42062 and 2.142, add these logarithms, and finally find the antilogarithm. However, it is important to note that this antilogarithm will not be the answer to the problem.

35.12 NEGATIVE LOGARITHMS

It is sometimes desirable to combine a positive mantissa with a negative characteristic into a single negative number. Consider the example,

$$\log 0.004238 = 0.62716 - 3$$

or, in exponential form,

$$0.004238 = 10^{0.62716-3}$$

Here we see that the power of 10 is part positive and part negative. If we wish, we can combine the positive mantissa with the negative characteristic into one number that is entirely negative. This is done simply by algebraic addition. The two parts of the logarithm $0.62716 - 3$ may be combined into the single negative number -2.37284.

$$
\begin{array}{r}
-3.00000 \\
+0.62716 \\
\hline
-2.37284
\end{array}
$$

Adding

Then we may write $0.004238 = 10^{-2.37284}$ or $\log 0.004238 = -2.37284$. This single number, -2.37284, may be called the *actual* logarithm of 0.004238. It is *all negative*. It is sometimes desirable to make this change, as we shall see.

The reverse change is also necessary at times. If we have given a logarithm that is entirely negative, such as -4.75326, the antilogarithm cannot be found in the table of mantissas since all the table mantissas are positive. In the logarithm, -4.75326, both parts are negative.

Before looking up the antilogarithm, we must change the form of the logarithm in such a way that the mantissa, or decimal part, is positive. Only the characteristic can be negative.

To change a negative logarithm, such as -4.75326, we note that this logarithm lies between the two negative numbers -4 and -5. Therefore, if the mantissa, or decimal part, is to be positive, the characteristic must be large enough negatively to offset any positive part. The characteristic may be -5, -6, -7, or some such negative number.

The form of the logarithm is changed by adding and subtracting 5 or more:

$$5 - 4.75326 - 5$$

Now $+5$ is combined with -4.75326, which becomes $+0.24675$: thus

$$-4.75326 = +5 - 4.75326 - 5 = 0.24674 - 5$$

To find the antilogarithm, we look up the positive mantissa 0.24674 in the table as usual.

Remember that the number we add and subtract must be greater *numerically* than the given logarithm.

Example 1.   Find $(27.57)^{-3}$.

Work: We begin as usual

$$\log 27.57 = 1.44044$$
$$\times \quad -3$$

Multiplying the logarithm by -3, $\log (27.57)^{-3} = -4.32132$

Here we see that the logarithm of the answer is entirely negative. We cannot look up the antilogarithm of this number in the table because all the table mantissas are positive. We change the form of the logarithm in such a way that the decimal part will be positive.

The negative logarithm -4.32132 is changed by adding and subtracting 5, which does not alter the value:

$$-4.32132 = +5 - 4.32132 - 5 = 0.67868 - 5$$

The problem now becomes, $\log (27.57)^{-3} = 0.67868 - 5$
$$(27.57)^{-3} = 0.000047718$$

The student should always check the final form of the logarithm to be sure it represents exactly the *same value as the original form.*

Example 2.   Find $(0.005788)^{2.431}$.

Work: We begin as usual, $\log 0.005788 = 0.76253 - 3$.

In finding a power, we recall that the entire logarithm, both mantissa and characteristic, must be multiplied by the indicated power 2.431. A glance will show us that the product will be a combination of positive and negative decimal fractions and whole numbers.

The best procedure to follow in a problem of this kind is to change the form of the logarithm *before* multiplying. First we combine the positive and negative parts into the *actual* logarithm. The actual logarithm is the negative number, -2.23747, obtained by algebraic addition of the two parts:

$$-3.00000$$
$$+0.76253$$
$$-2.23747$$

In Example 2 we start with $\log 0.005788 = 0.76253 - 3$
Changing to a negative logarithm, $\log 0.005788 = -2.23747$
Multiplying the logarithm by 2.431, $\times 2.431$
$$-5.43928957$$

Rounding off $\log (0.005788)^{2.431} = -5.43929$
Changing to a positive mantissa, $\log (0.005788)^{2.431} = 0.56071 - 6$
$$(0.005788)^{2.431} = 0.0000036368$$

35.13 COMBINATION OF PROCESSES

Suppose we have a problem involving a combination of the processes of multiplication, division, powers, and roots. By using logarithms, the problem is reduced to the simpler processes of addition, subtraction, multiplication, and division, respectively. The antilogarithm is found as a final step.

Example 1. Find $\dfrac{(7.344)^3(0.000486)}{(61590)(0.367)}$.

Work:

$\log 7.344 = 0.86593$

$\log (7.344)^3 = 2.59779$

$\log 0.000486 = 0.68664 - 4$

$\log \text{numerator} = 3.28443 - 4$

$\log 61590 = 4.78951$

$\log 0.367 = 0.56467 - 1$

$\log \text{denominator} = 5.35418 - 1$

or: 4.35418

$$\log \text{numerator} = \overset{5}{\cancel{3}}.28443 - \overset{-6}{\cancel{4}}$$

$\log \text{denominator} = 4.35418$

$\log \text{fraction} = 0.93025 - 6$

$\text{answer} = 0.0000085162$

Example 2. Find $\sqrt[5]{\dfrac{(2.678)^2(0.00874)^3(753)}{(42.9)^2(0.003164)^2}}$.

Work:

$\log 2.678 = 0.42781$

$\log (2.678)^2 = 0.85562$

$\log 0.00874 = 0.94151 - 3$

$\log (0.00874)^3 = 2.82453 - 9$

$\log 753 = 2.87679$

$\log 42.9 = 1.63246$

$\log (42.9)^2 = 3.26492$

$\log 0.003164 = 0.50024 - 3$

$\log (.003164)^2 = 1.00048 - 6$

$\log (2.678)^2 = 0.85562$

$\log (0.00874)^3 = 2.82453 - 9$

$\log 753 = 2.87679$

$\log \text{numerator} = 6.55694 - 9$

$\log (42.9)^2 = 3.26492$

$\log (0.003164)^2 = 1.00048 - 6$

$\log \text{denominator} = 4.26540 - 6$

$\log \text{numerator} = 6.55694 - 9$

$\log \text{denominator} = 4.26540 - 6$

$\log \text{fraction} = 2.29154 - 3$

Since we must find the fifth root in Example 2, the negative characteristic must be divisible by 5. If the net characteristic had been zero or positive, no adjustment would be necessary. However, in this example we change the form of the logarithm so that the negative characteristic is divisible by 5.

$\log \text{fraction} = 2.29154 - 3$

Change this to $\log \text{fraction} = 4.29154 - 5$

Dividing the logarithm by 5, $\log \sqrt[5]{\text{fraction}} = 0.85831 - 1$

Answer to the problem is the antilogarithm $\quad 0.72162$

Exercise 35.6

Compute the following by logarithms:

1. $\sqrt{238.6}$
2. $\sqrt[3]{498100}$
3. $\sqrt[5]{65100}$
4. $\sqrt{0.007418}$
5. $\sqrt[3]{0.005089}$
6. $\sqrt[3]{0.0005089}$
7. $\sqrt[3]{0.00005089}$
8. $\sqrt[4]{0.00001802}$
9. $\sqrt[5]{0.8917}$
10. $\sqrt[3]{(73.2)(57)}$
11. $(2.72)^{3.14}$
12. $(6930)^{0.233}$
13. $(49.8)^{-2}$
14. $(513)^{-1.4}$
15. $(0.00237)^{3.142}$
16. $(81540)^{\frac{2}{3}}$
17. $(0.00724)^{\frac{3}{4}}$
18. $(0.000382)^{1.45}$
19. $\sqrt[4]{(8.49)^2(0.4735)}$
20. $\sqrt[3]{(0.0325)^4(7.98)^2}$

21. $\sqrt[4]{\dfrac{(197)^2(0.4435)^3}{(24.9)^2(0.06)^5}}$

22. $\sqrt[5]{\dfrac{(28.8)^2(0.000349)^2}{(0.578)^3(8.63)^4}}$

23. $\sqrt[2]{\dfrac{(9.26)^4(0.132)^6(0.8)^5}{(87000)^3(0.0069)^2}}$

24. $\left(\dfrac{(3.142)^3(2.72)^4(0.09)^6}{(0.488)^5(730.6)^2}\right)^{\frac{3}{8}}$

25. Work out the example in the first paragraph in Section 34.1.
26. Write the proof of Principle 4, using the general base b.

Exercise 35.7

Write in expanded logarithmic form:

1. $\log x^4$
2. $\log (23)^3$
3. $\log (58)^{\frac{1}{2}}$
4. $\log (5.92)^{-2}$
5. $\log x^2 y^3$
6. $\log (39)^4(47)^3$
7. $\log \dfrac{(3.7)^2}{(52)^3}$
8. $\log \dfrac{(28.6)^3}{(0.37)^4}$
9. $\log \dfrac{(\pi r^2 h)}{7(33)}$
10. $\log \dfrac{2\pi r^2}{12^2}$
11. $\log \dfrac{\pi r^3}{3}$
12. $\log \dfrac{(68)^2(7)^3}{(8.9)^4(0.5)^6}$
13. $\log (3.7)^{\frac{1}{2}}(52)^{\frac{1}{3}}$
14. $\log \sqrt{xy}$
15. $\log \sqrt[3]{0.012}$
16. $\log \sqrt[4]{1024}$
17. $\log \sqrt[5]{4.32}$
18. $\log \sqrt[7]{0.003}$
19. $\log \sqrt{abc}$
20. $\log \sqrt{(23)(31)}$
21. $\log (3.2)^3\sqrt{42}$
22. $\log \dfrac{(38)^{\frac{1}{3}}}{\sqrt{47}}$
23. $\log \dfrac{\sqrt{67.3}}{4.38}$
24. $\log \dfrac{\sqrt{34}\sqrt[3]{45}}{(15^{-3})(16^{-2})}$

Write each of the following as a single logarithm with a coefficient of 1.

25. $5 \log 20$
26. $7 \log 33.4$
27. $\frac{1}{2} \log 64$
28. $\frac{3}{2} \log 25$
29. $\frac{3}{4} \log 16$
30. $\frac{2}{5} \log 32$
31. $2 \log 5 + 3 \log 49 + 4 \log 3$
32. $\frac{1}{3} \log 64 + 4 \log 5 - 5 \log 2$
33. $3 \log 40 - 2 \log 25 + \frac{1}{2} \log 81$
34. $\frac{3}{2} \log 9 - 2 \log 3 + \frac{1}{4} \log 16$
35. $\frac{1}{3} \log 8 + \frac{1}{2} \log 9 - \frac{1}{5} \log 32 - \frac{1}{3} \log 27$
36. $\frac{1}{3} \log 15 + \frac{1}{3} \log 24 - \frac{1}{3} \log 9$
37. $\frac{1}{2} \log 64 + \frac{1}{3} \log 512 - \frac{1}{4} \log 256$
38. $\frac{2}{3} \log 27 + \frac{5}{6} \log 64 - \frac{1}{2} \log 36$

35.14 SUMMARY OF PRINCIPLES OF LOGARITHMS

Now that we have used logarithms to find products, quotients, powers, and roots of numbers, let us summarize the principles involved. First, let us restate the definition of a logarithm. If any number N is stated as a power with the exponent x on a base b, then x is defined as the logarithm of the number N to the base b. That is,

$$\text{if} \quad b^x = N, \qquad \text{then} \qquad \log_b N = x$$

Any number, except 1 or zero, can be used as the base for a system of logarithms. The base of common logarithms is 10. This system is most convenient for computation. Common logarithms consist of two parts: *characteristic* and *mantissa*. The characteristic is determined by the position of the decimal point and is equal to the power of 10 for a number written in scientific notation. All mantissas shown in the table are positive. The mantissa is not affected by the decimal point of a number, but is dependent upon the succession of digits alone. Negative numbers have no real logarithms, but logarithms themselves may be negative.

In computation by logarithms we use the following principles:

Principle 1. *The logarithm of the product of two or more factors is equal to the sum of the logarithms of the factors.* That is,

$$\log xy = \log x + \log y$$

This is the principle we have used in multiplication. For example, to multiply (23)(14), we

(a) find the logarithms of the numbers, 23 and 14
(b) add the logarithms
(c) find the antilogarithm.

In the second step (b), when we add the logarithms of the numbers, we get, not the product (23)(14), but the *logarithm of the product*. That is,

$$\log 23 + \log 14 = \log (23)(14)$$

As an application of this principle, $\log 5 + \log 7 = \log 35$.

Principle 2. *The logarithm of the quotient of two numbers is equal to the logarithm of the dividend minus the logarithm of the divisor.* That is,

$$\log \frac{x}{y} = \log x - \log y$$

This is the principle we have used in division. For example, to divide $(480) \div (15)$, we

(a) find the logarithms of the numbers, 480 and 15
(b) subtract the logarithm of the divisor from the logarithm of the dividend
(c) find the antilogarithm.

In the second step (b), when we subtract the logarithms, we get, not the quotient of the numbers, but the *logarithm of the quotient*. That is,

$$\log 480 - \log 15 = \log \frac{480}{15}$$

As an application of this principle, $\log 18 - \log 3 = \log 6$.

Principle 3.   *The logarithm of a power of a number is equal to the logarithm of the number multiplied by the exponent of the power.* That is,

$$\log x^n = (n)(\log x)$$

This is the principle we have used in finding powers. For example, to find the power, 24^3, we

(a) find the logarithm of the base 24
(b) multiply the logarithm by 3, the exponent of the power
(c) find the antilogarithm.

In the second step (b), when we multiply the logarithm by the exponent, we get, not the power itself, but the *logarithm of the power*, 24^3. That is,

$$(3)(\log 24) = \log 24^3$$

As an application of this principle, $(5)(\log 2) = \log 32$.

Principle 4.   *The logarithm of a root of a number is equal to the logarithm of the number divided by the index of the root.* That is,

$$\log \sqrt[r]{N} = \frac{1}{r} \log N$$

This is the principle we have used in finding roots of numbers. For example, to find the root, $\sqrt[3]{512}$, we

(a) find the logarithm of the radicand, 512
(b) divide the logarithm by 3, the index of the root
(c) find the antilogarithm.

In the second step (b), when we divide the logarithm by the index of the root, we get, not the root of the number, but the *logarithm of the root*. That is,

$$\tfrac{1}{3}\log 512 = \log \sqrt[3]{512}$$

As an application of this principle, $\tfrac{1}{4}\log 16 = \log 2$.

The four principles of logarithms that we have stated enable us to compute some logarithms from certain known logarithms. In fact, in the actual computation of a table of logarithms, a few of them are computed by formulas in calculus. Then most of them are computed from these few by using the four principles we have stated. For example, suppose we know that the logarithm of 5 is 0.69897, and the logarithm of 7 is 0.84510. Knowing these two logarithms, we can compute many others.

For example, we can compute the logarithm of 35 by use of Principle 1:

$$\log 35 = \log (5)(7) = \log 5 + \log 7 = 1.54407$$

Also, we can compute the logarithm of 25 by use of Principle 3:

$$\log 25 = \log 5^2 = (2)(\log 5) = (2)(0.69897) = 1.39794$$

Now we can compute the logarithm of 175, which is (7)(25):

$$\log 175 = \log (7)(25) = \log 7 + \log 25 = 2.24304$$

By Principle 2, $\log 1.4 = \log (\frac{7}{5}) = \log 7 - \log 5 = 0.14613$. Of course, since the values given are rounded off to five digits, there may be an error in the last digit.

Exercise 35.8

Given: $\log 2 = 0.30103$ and $\log 3 = 0.47712$. From these two given logs, find the following without using a table:

1. log 6	**2.** log 9	**3.** log 4	**4.** log 12
5. log 5	**6.** log 36	**7.** log 8	**8.** log 16
9. log 32	**10.** log 25	**11.** log 27	**12.** log 108
13. log 54	**14.** log 144	**15.** log 81	**16.** log 432
17. log 324	**18.** log 1728	**19.** log 9216	**20.** log 600000
21. log 1.5	**22.** log 3.75	**23.** log 11.25	**24.** log 13.333

25. If $7^4 = 2401$, this is near 2400. Find the approximate logarithm of 7 by finding the prime factors of 2400, and expressing 2400 as the product of powers of 2, 3, and 5.

Quiz No. 1 on Logarithms. Computation. Form A.

1. Multiply by logarithms: (2198.3)(0.000033528)(8.6324).
2. Divide by logarithms: (88740) ÷ (38.5).
3. Divide by logarithms: (0.06874) ÷ (18700).
4. Divide by logarithms: (0.0002856) ÷ (0.4873).
5. Use logarithms to find the following powers:

   (a) $(87.96)^4$ (b) $(0.02538)^6$ (c) $(24.73)^{1.32}$

6. Use logarithms to find the following:

   (a) $\sqrt[5]{278.3}$ (b) $\sqrt[4]{0.002873}$ (c) $(0.0384)^{\frac{1}{3}}$

7. Compute by logarithms: $\dfrac{(3.63)(0.00527)}{(73.4)(0.000173)}$

8. Compute by logarithms: $\sqrt[7]{\dfrac{(4.52)^3(0.005)^2}{(32.4)^4(0.0713)}}$

9. If $V = 315.2$, find the value of r in the formula: $r = \sqrt[3]{\dfrac{3V}{4\pi}}$.

10. Given: $\log 3 = 0.47712$, and $\log 8 = 0.90309$, find the logarithms of the following numbers from these two given logarithms without a table:

$$9; \quad 64; \quad 24; \quad \tfrac{3}{8}; \quad 2; \quad 6; \quad 27; \quad 72$$

(Show the work.)

Quiz No. 1 on Logarithms. Computation. Form B.

1. Multiply by logarithms: $(2.6373)(0.0037835)(674.29)$.
2. Divide by logarithms: $(58200) \div (24.58)$.
3. Divide by logarithms: $(0.4736) \div (19.8)$.
4. Divide by logarithms: $(0.0000478) \div (0.08437)$.
5. Use logarithms to find the following powers:

(a) $(837.8)^3$ (b) $(0.3847)^6$ (c) $(32.56)^{2.31}$

6. Use logarithms to find the following:

(a) $\sqrt[4]{548.2}$ (b) $\sqrt[5]{0.007374}$ (c) $(0.439)^{\frac{4}{7}}$

7. Compute by logarithms: $\dfrac{(52.3)(0.0463)}{(0.0836)(51.6)}$

8. Compute by logarithms: $\sqrt[6]{\dfrac{(53.2)^3(0.0006)^2}{(41.6)^4(0.0237)}}$

9. If $V = 247.3$ and $h = 6.5$, find r in the formula: $r = \sqrt{\dfrac{3V}{\pi h}}$.

10. Given: $\log 4 = 0.60206$, and $\log 7 = 0.84510$, find the logarithms of the following numbers from these two given logarithms without a table:

$$16; \quad 49; \quad 28; \quad \tfrac{4}{7}; \quad 2; \quad 14; \quad 32; \quad 112$$

(Show the work.)

36
Applications of Logarithms

36.1 SOLVING STATED PROBLEMS BY USE OF LOGARITHMS

We have seen that logarithms can facilitate computation. By means of logarithms the operations of multiplication, division, and finding powers and roots can be made relatively simple. We shall now see how logarithms can be used in the solution of stated word problems.

We should mention, however, that logarithms do not now hold the same importance they once held in computation. In modern times, they have been replaced by the much more efficient methods of calculators and computers. At the present time, logarithms are more important for their theoretical implications than for computational purposes. Yet some practice in connection with their use in solving stated problems will probably help to make their importance better understood.

There is one point we must keep in mind in working problems. Logarithms are in most instances irrational numbers. For use in computation, they have been rounded off to three, four, five, or more decimal places. The numbers we use (that is, those that appear in a table) are only approximate values. For this reason the answers obtained through their use are only approximate.

Logarithms should not be used when exact answers are required. For example, suppose we have the problem of computing the payroll for a certain construction job. Suppose this project requires the labor of 671 employees for an 8-hour day. The hourly pay rate is, say, $2.34, and 13 days are required to complete the work. If the payroll is computed correctly, it is exactly $163,294.56. We cannot use logarithms to find the answer to this problem unless we are prepared to round off the total to $163,290.00, if we use a 5-place table. To compute the exact payroll by logarithms, we should need a table of 8-place or 9-place mantissas. The number of places in the table must be at least as many as the number of places of accuracy required in the answer and preferably one more.

Briefly, logarithms should not be used in computation involving numbers arrived at by counting, unless we wish to state approximate answers. As a general rule, they should be used only in connection with numbers obtained through measuring. Counting is exact, whereas all measurement is only approximate.

36.2   SETTING UP THE PROCEDURE FOR SOLVING

In solving problems by logarithms, it is usually best to try to set up the procedures involved before actually beginning the computation. After analyzing a problem, we try to set up the various steps in the form of a formula for the solution. Here are some examples to show how this is done.

Example 1.   Find the number of square centimeters in the area of a rectangle 32.6 in. long and 23.9 in. wide (1 in. = 2.54 cm).

Solution.   We know the area of a rectangle can be found by the formula $A = LW$. The area of this rectangle can be expressed as the product $(32.6)(23.9)$. If we multiply the two given measurements, we shall have the number of square inches in the area.

However, before we work out this multiplication, let us see what else must be done in the problem. The problem calls for square centimeters. Therefore, after we have found the number of square inches, we must multiply this number by the number or square centimeters in a square inch.

Since 1 in. equals approximately 2.54 cm, then 1 sq in. is approximately equal to $(2.54)^2$ sq cm. In order to convert square inches to square centimeters, we must multiply by $(2.54)^2$. Therefore, we can say

$$\text{area (in sq cm)} = L \cdot W \cdot (2.54)^2$$

The problem then becomes

$$\text{area (in sq cm)} = (32.6)(23.9)(2.54)^2$$

Solution by logarithms:

$$
\begin{aligned}
\log 32.6 &= 1.51322 \\
\log 23.9 &= 1.37840 \\
\log (2.54)^2 &= 0.80966 \\
\log \text{answer} &= 3.70128 \\
\text{answer} &= 5026.7 \text{ sq cm}
\end{aligned}
\qquad
\begin{aligned}
\log 2.54 &= 0.40483 \\
& \times 2 \\
\log (2.54)^2 &= 0.80966
\end{aligned}
$$

This is usually written 5026.7 cm^2.

Example 2.   Find the number of cubic feet in a rectangular box 74.82 in. long, 38.65 in. wide, and 9.75 in. high.

Solution.   We know that the volume of a rectangular solid is given by the formula

$$\text{volume} = (\text{length})(\text{width})(\text{height}) \qquad \text{or} \qquad V = lwh$$

If we multiply the three given measurements together, we shall have the number of cubic inches in the volume.

However, the problem asks for the number of cubic feet. When we have found the number of cubic inches, we must divide this number by 1728, or 12^3. Therefore, we can say

$$\text{volume (in cu ft)} = \frac{lwh}{12^3} \qquad \text{or} \qquad \frac{lwh}{1728}$$

The problem then becomes

$$\text{volume (in cu ft)} = \frac{(74.82)(38.65)(9.75)}{1728}$$

Solution by logarithms:

$$\log 74.82 = 1.87402 \qquad \log 12 = 1.07918$$
$$\log 38.65 = 1.58715 \qquad \log 12^3 = 3.23754$$
$$\log 9.75 = 0.98900$$
$$\log \text{numerator} = 4.45017$$
$$\log \text{denominator} = 3.23754$$
$$\log \text{volume} = 1.21263$$
$$\text{volume} = 16.317 \text{ cu ft}$$

We round off the answer to 16.32 cu ft, since the measurements are correct only to two decimal places.

The logarithm of the denominator might have been found by looking up the log of 1728 directly instead of finding the log of 12 and then multiplying this log by 3.

Warning. A common error is to multiply a logarithm by some small number, such as 2 or 3, when a power is not indicated, as in finding the logarithm of 2π. The following example is an illustration of this kind of problem.

Example 3. The formula for the lateral area of a right circular cylinder is

$$A = 2\pi r h$$

Suppose we are told that the lateral area is 574.2 sq in. and the height h is 15.3 in. Our problem is to find the radius.

Solution. First we solve the formula for r:

$$r = \frac{A}{2\pi h}$$

If we supply the given values, we get the problem

$$r = \frac{574.2}{2\pi(15.3)}$$

Solution by logarithms:

$$\log 574.2 = 2.75906 \qquad\qquad \log 15.3 = 1.18469$$
$$\log \text{denominator} = 1.98287 \qquad\qquad \log \pi = 0.49715$$
$$\log \text{radius} = 0.77619 \qquad\qquad \log 2 = 0.30103$$
$$\text{radius} = 5.973 \qquad\qquad \log \text{denominator} = 1.98287$$

A common mistake is to add or subtract two logarithms when a problem calls for the addition or subtraction of the antilogarithms, as illustrated in the following example:

Example 4. In a certain right triangle, ABC, the legs a and b measure 45.2 and 63.8 in., respectively. Find the length of the hypotenuse, c.

Solution. By the Pythagorean rule, we have

$$c^2 = a^2 + b^2$$

Solving for c,

$$c = \sqrt{a^2 + b^2}$$

Substituting numerical values, we get

$$c = \sqrt{(45.2)^2 + (63.8)^2}$$

Solving by logarithms,

$$\log 45.2 = 1.65514$$
$$\log (45.2)^2 = 3.31028$$
$$\log 63.8 = 1.80482$$
$$\log (63.8)^2 = 3.60964$$

At this point in the solution, a common mistake is to add the two logarithms.

$$\log (45.2)^2 = 3.31028$$
$$\log (63.8)^2 = \underline{3.60964}$$

If we add these logarithms, we get the logarithm of the product

$$(45.2)^2(63.8)^2$$

However, we do not want this product. The problem calls for the *sum* of the *two quanti-ties*: $(45.2)^2 + (63.8)^2$.

In order to add these quantities, we must find the antilogarithm of 3.31028 and of 3.60964. The proper form and procedure is shown here:

$$\log (45.2)^2 = 3.31028$$
Taking antilogarithm,
$$(45.2)^2 = 2043.0*$$
$$\log (63.8)^2 = 3.60964$$
Taking antilogarithm,
$$(63.8)^2 = 4070.5*$$

Now, we add the numbers indicated by asterisks.

$$(45.2)^2 + (63.8)^2 = 6113.5$$

The problem reduces to the matter of finding

$$\sqrt{6113.5}$$

To complete the solution, we find

$$\log 6113.5 = 3.78629$$
$$\log \sqrt{6113.5} = 1.89314$$
$$c = \sqrt{6113.5} = 78.188$$
$$c = 78.2 \text{ in. (rounded off)}$$

Exercise 36.1

Solve the following problems by logarithms:

1. Find the number of square yards in a rectangular floor that is 83.48 ft long and 52.12 ft wide.
2. Find the number of square feet in a plot of ground that is a rectangle, 49.4 yd long and 35.2 yd wide.
3. A rectangular field measures 617.4 ft long and 367.0 ft wide. How many square rods does it contain? (1 rd is equal to $16\frac{1}{2}$ ft.)
4. A rectangular solid is 17.26 in. long, 13.84 in. wide, and 8.93 in. high. What is its volume in cubic centimeters? (1 in. is equal to 2.54 cm.)
5. A rectangular solid is 36.42 cm long, 23.56 cm wide, and 15.98 cm high. Find its volume in cubic inches.
6. A man drives an average of 43.6 mph for 9.4 hr and uses 26.7 gal of gasoline. Find his average milage per gallon.
7. If a man drives 1438 miles in three days, averaging 9.8 hr a day, what is his average speed in miles per hour?
8. Find the number of cubic centimeters in the volume of a rectangular solid, 28.4 in. long, 19.5 in. wide, and 8.63 in. high.
9. Find the area of a circle whose radius is 16.3 in. ($A = \pi r^2$.)
10. Find the number of square centimeters in the area of a circle whose diameter is 35.6 in.
11. The area of a circle is 582 sq cm. Find its diameter in inches.
12. The two legs of a right triangle measure 24.6 and 37.2 in., respectively. Find the hypotenuse, the perimeter, and the area of the triangle.
13. A rectangle is 32.5 in. long and 21.4 in. wide. What is the length of the diagonal?
14. A rectangle has a length of 63.2 cm and an area of 2780 sq cm. Find the width of the rectangle and the length of the diagonal.
15. One leg of a right triangle is 26.8 cm long and the hypotenuse is 35.3 cm. Find the length of the other leg. What is the area of the triangle?
16. How long a cable will be required to brace a TV tower if one end of the cable is fastened to the two 385 ft from the ground and the other end of the cable is fastened at a point on the ground level 412 ft from the foot of the tower?
17. A radio antenna is to be braced with a cable 153 ft long. The cable is to be fastened at ground level 112 ft from the foot of the tower. How high up on the tower should the cable be fastened?
18. A rectangular bar of iron has a cross section that is a rectangle $1\frac{3}{32}$ in. long and $\frac{52}{64}$ in. wide. Find its cross-sectional area in square centimeters.
19. The diameter of a right circular cylinder measures 83.72 in. Its height measures 173.4 in. How many gallons will it hold? Formula: $V = \pi r^2 h$ (1 gal holds 231 cu in.).
20. The altitude of a right circular cone measures 23.15 in. and its diameter is 16.43 in. How many pints will it hold? Formula: $V = \frac{1}{3}\pi r^2 h$.
21. A right circular cylinder holds 495 gal. If the height measures 67.3 in., find the diameter.
22. The diameter of a sphere measures 9.45 in. What is the volume of the sphere in cubic centimeters? Formula: $V = \frac{4}{3}\pi r^3$.

23. If a spherical container holds 3 gal, what is its diameter?

24. The area of an ellipse is given by the formula $A = \pi ab$, in which a is the semimajor axis and b is the semiminor axis. Find the area of an ellipse with a major axis of 458 ft and a minor axis of 371 ft.

25. Find the number of centimeters in 15 miles.

26. If light travels 300,000,000 m per sec, find the number of miles in 1 light-year (use 1 m = 39.37 in.).

27. The formula for the approximate area of the segment of a circle is

$$A = \frac{2hw}{3} + \frac{h^3}{2w}$$

in which h = the height of the segment and w the width. Find the area of a circular segment with a height of 7.8 in. and a width of 48.3 in.

28. The formula for the volume of a frustum of a right circular cone is

$$V = \tfrac{1}{3}\pi h(R^2 + r^2 + Rr)$$

In the formula R represents the radius of one base and r represents the radius of the other. The altitude is represented by h. If the radius of the bottom is 8.4 in., the radius of the top is 5.2 in., and the altitude is 11.6 in., find the volume of the frustum.

29. The radius of a circle inscribed in a triangle whose sides are a, b, and c is given by the formula

$$r = \frac{\sqrt{s(s-a)(s-b)(s-c)}}{s}$$

in which $s = \tfrac{1}{2}(a + b + c)$. Find the radius of a circle inscribed in a triangle whose sides are 17.3 in., 23.2 in., and 32.7 in., respectively.

30. The radius of a circle circumscribed around a triangle is given by the formula

$$R = \frac{abc}{4\sqrt{s(s-a)(s-b)(s-c)}}$$

Find the radius of the circle circumscribed around the triangle in Problem 29.

31. Using Hero's formula $A = \sqrt{s(s-a)(s-b)(s-c)}$, find the area of a triangle with sides equal, respectively, to 15.46, 12.13, and 21.69 in.

32. The area of the curved surface of a right circular cone whose base-radius is r and whose altitude is h is given by the formula

$$A = \pi r \sqrt{r^2 + h^2}$$

Find the area of the curved surface of a cone with an altitude of 53.2 in. and a base radius of 21.4 in.

33. The formula for the distance of a freely falling body is

$$S = \tfrac{1}{2}gt^2$$

in which S represents distance in feet and t represents time in seconds. If $g = 32.2$ ft per sec per sec, how far, according to the formula, will an object fall from rest in 47.5 sec?

34. A formula that occurs often in the theory of alternating currents is

$$i = \frac{E}{R}\left(1 - e^{-(R/L)t}\right)$$

If $E = 110$ volts, $R = 480$ ohms, and $L = 0.152$ henrys, find the current (in amperes) at the end of $t = 0.0035$ sec. (In this problem e is the base of natural logarithms, 2.7183. See Sec. 36.6).

35. The time for one cycle of a pendulum is given by the formula

$$T = 2\pi\sqrt{L/G}$$

If $T = 1.24$ sec, π is taken as 3.1416, and $G = 32.16$, find L.

36. If $R = 5.2$ ohms, $X_L = 15.3$ ohms, and $X_C = 7.4$ ohms, find Z in the formula

$$Z = 2\pi\sqrt{R^2 + (X_L - X_C)^2}$$

36.3 LOGARITHMS AS PARTS OF PROBLEMS

In many problems in science a logarithm itself forms part of the problem. Then we must be sure we understand the problem as it is given. One way to make sure that you are working a problem correctly is to understand the exact meaning of the written statement of the problem.

For example, suppose we are trying to determine the number of square inches in a certain area, and we have discovered that the area can be found by the formula:

$$A = 8 + 3 \log 29 \qquad \text{(square inches)}$$

Of course, this happens to be the answer just for this particular problem. Now our problem is to try to determine the area stated as a number of square inches, correct to four or five places.

Our first problem is to determine the value of the second term: $3 \log 29$.

$$\log 29 = 1.4624$$

Now we multiply this log by 3, and get

$$\frac{3}{4.3872}$$

Then the problem becomes: $A = 8 + 4.3872 = 12.3872$, area in sq in.

The following examples involve logarithms as part of the problem.

Example 1.   Find $\log 48 + \log 324$.

Solution.   This problem does not tell you to add 48 and 324. It does not even tell you to multiply 48 by 324. All it says is to add the two logarithms. The only arithmetic process indicated is addition ($+$). The logarithm of 48 is 1.68124. The logarithm of 324 is 2.51055. Therefore, the statement says only: add $1.68124 + 2.51055$. The answer is 4.19179.

Example 2.   Divide $\dfrac{\log 48}{\log 6}$.

Solution.   We know that the line separating numerator from denominator means division. In other words, the numerator is to be divided by the denominator.

The problem does not ask you to find the logarithm of 48/6. It does *not* mean $(48) \div (6)$. The numerator of the fraction is not 48. It is simply the logarithm of 48, or 1.68124. The denominator of the fraction is not 6. It is the logarithm of 6, or 0.77815. The problem is essentially the following problem in division:

$$\frac{1.68124}{0.77815}$$

Right at this point, many students make the mistake of subtracting. The arithmetic process here indicated is *division*, not subtraction. If the problem were $(48) \div (6)$, then we should find the logarithms of 48 and 6, subtract the logarithms, and then find the antilogarithm. But the problem is not one of dividing 48 by 6. It is a problem of *dividing one logarithm by another logarithm.*

If the problem is rewritten in complete words, the meaning may be clearer:

$$\frac{\text{the logarithm of } 48}{\text{the logarithm of } 6} = \frac{1.68124}{0.77815}$$

The statement means

$$(\log 48) \div (\log 6) \qquad \text{or} \qquad (1.68124) \div (0.77815)$$

The answer is approximately equal to 2.1606.

This problem in division might itself be worked by using logarithms:

$$\begin{array}{r} 1 \\ \log 1.68124 = \cancel{0}.22563 - 1 \\ \log 0.77815 = \underline{0.89106 - 1} \\ \log \text{quotient} = 0.33457 \\ \text{quotient} = 2.1606 \end{array}$$

Note that in both cases we have found a logarithm of a logarithm.

Exercise 36.2

Use tables of logarithms to find the following:

1. $\log 48.3 + \log 53.9$ 2. $(48.3)(53.9)$
3. $(742) \div (19.2)$ 4. $\log 742 - \log 19.2$
5. $\log 68.4 - \log 21.3$ 6. $\log (68.4 - 21.3)$
7. $\log (54.8 + 3970)$ 8. $\log 54.8 + \log 3970$
9. $\log (18.2)(31.4)$ 10. $(\log 18.2)(\log 31.4)$
11. $3 \log 128$ 12. $5 + 2 \log 23.1$

13. $\log \dfrac{843}{19}$ 14. $\dfrac{\log 843}{\log 19}$

15. $(\log 21.4)^2$

16. $\log (31.5)^2$

17. $\dfrac{\log 684}{\log 31}$

18. $\log \dfrac{684}{31}$

19. $\log 15 + \log 0.082$

20. $\log 0.0032 - \log 34$

21. $23 \log 482$

22. $32 \log 0.038$

23. $\dfrac{\log 563}{4}$

24. $\dfrac{\log 0.00487}{6}$

25. $\log (\log 89600)$

26. $\log (23 \log 62)$

27. $3 \log 128 + 2 \log 79$

28. $5 \log 73 - \frac{1}{3} \log 56$

29. $\dfrac{4 \log 48 + \frac{1}{2} \log 16.8}{2 + \log 23.4}$

30. $\dfrac{3 \log 3.2 - \log 0.023}{\log 46 - \log 15}$

36.4 LOGARITHMIC AND EXPONENTIAL EQUATIONS

A *logarithmic equation* is an equation containing the indicated logarithm of an unknown, such as x, in some form. The following is an example of a logarithmic equation, since it involves the logarithm of the unknown x.

$$5 \log x = 8.4621 + \log x^2$$

An *exponential equation* is an equation in which x (or some other unknown) appears in the exponent of a power, as in the example

$$7^{3x} = 487$$

Logarithms are used to solve logarithmic and exponential equations. They may also be used to solve another type of equation containing a constant exponent on an unknown base, as in the equation

$$x^{2.4} = 59.62$$

This kind of equation can easily be changed to a logarithmic equation which can then be solved for x.

We now solve the three preceding examples to show the procedure that may be used in each type of equation.

Example 1. Solve the equation $5 \log x = 8.4621 + \log x^2$.

Solution. First we rewrite the equation and change the expression $\log x^2$ to its equivalent, $2 \log x$. The equation then becomes

$$5 \log x = 8.4621 + 2 \log x$$

Transposing, $\quad\quad 5 \log x - 2 \log x = 8.4621$

Combining, $\quad\quad\quad\quad\quad 3 \log x = 8.4621$

Dividing both sides by 3, $\quad\quad \log x = 2.8207$

Taking antilog of both sides, $\quad\quad x = 661.76$

Example 2. Solve the equation $7^{3x} = 487$.

Solution. As a general rule, when solving an exponential equation of this kind, we first take the logarithm of both sides of the equation.

$$\log 7^{3x} = \log 487$$

The equation can be written $\qquad 3x \log 7 = \log 487$

In this equation the coefficient of x is the quantity $3 \log 7$.

Dividing both sides by $(3 \log 7)$, $\qquad x = \dfrac{\log 487}{3 \log 7}$

$$x = \dfrac{2.68753}{3(0.84510)}$$

$$x = 1.060$$

Example 3. Solve the equation $x^{2.4} = 59.62$.

Solution. Here, again, we first take the logarithm of both sides.

$$\log x^{2.4} = \log 59.62$$

The equation can be written $\qquad 2.4 (\log x) = \log 59.62$

In this equation, the coefficient of $(\log x)$ is the quantity 2.4.

Dividing both sides by 2.4, $\qquad \log x = \dfrac{\log 59.62}{2.4}$

$$\log x = \dfrac{1.77539}{2.4}$$

$$\log x = 0.73975$$

Taking antilog of both sides, $\qquad x = 5.4922$

36.5 CHANGE OF BASE OF LOGARITHMS

It is sometimes necessary to change the base of a logarithm. Suppose we have the logarithm of a number to the base 10, which, of course, can be found in the table of common logarithms. For instance, from the table we find that the logarithm of 87.2 is 1.94052.

Now suppose we wish to know the logarithm of 87.2 when we use 5 as a base; that is, we wish to find

$$\log_5 87.2$$

As in solving any problem in algebra, we let x represent the number we wish to find. Using the letter x, then, as the unknown quantity, we write the equation

$$\log_5 87.2 = x$$

Our problem now is simply to solve for x in the equation.

First, we write the equation in exponential form:

$$5^x = 87.2$$

At this point we note that the exponent placed on 5 that will produce 87.2 must be greater than 2 and less than 3, since $5^2 = 25$ and $5^3 = 125$. Therefore, we expect to find that x will equal the integer 2 plus some fraction. Now we take the logarithm (base 10) of both sides of the equation.

$$\log 5^x = \log 87.2$$

The equation can be written $\quad x \log 5 = \log 87.2$

In this equation the coefficient of x is the quantity $(\log 5)$.

Dividing both sides by $(\log 5)$, $\qquad x = \dfrac{\log 87.2}{\log 5}$

$$x = \frac{1.94052}{0.69897}$$

By division, we get $\qquad\qquad x = 2.776 \text{ (approx.)}$

That is to say, $\qquad\qquad \log_5 87.2 = 2.776$

or, in exponential form, $\qquad\qquad 87.2 = 5^{2.776}$

Exercise 36.3

Solve the following equations for the unknowns:

1. $\log x + 3 \log x = 4$

2. $\log 5x + 2 \log x = 5$

3. $\log \dfrac{M}{15} = 1.4$

4. $\log \dfrac{250}{x} = 1.324$

5. $\log t^2 = \log 2t + 0.862$

6. $\log x^3 + 1.4352 = \log x^2$

7. $\log y + \log 4y = 5.324$

8. $\log x^2 = 1.347 + 5 \log x$

9. $\log (3x + 2) = 1 + \log x$

10. $\log (2x + 3) = \log x + \log 5x$

11. $3^x = 42$

12. $4^{2x} = 583$

13. $5^{3x-2} = 482$

14. $(1.5)^{2x-3} = 57.3$

15. $x^{1.7} = 2.56$

16. $x^{-1.2} = 789$

17. $x^{3.4} = 56.8$

18. $(5x)^{2.35} = 672.4$

19. Find $\log_5 37$

20. Find $\log_3 184$

21. Find $\log_8 5.27$

22. Find $\log_{2.4} 53.8$

23. Find $\log_{10} 4.1$

24. Find $\log_{4.1} 10$

25. Find $\log_6 1.73$

26. Find $\log_7 0.254$

27. Solve for x: $\log_x 723 = 3.25$

28. Solve for y: $\log_y 2.35 = -4.6$

29. Show that $\log_{10} 7 = \dfrac{1}{\log_7 10}$

30. Show that $\log_3 5 = \dfrac{1}{\log_5 3}$

36.6 NATURAL LOGARITHMS

Up to this point in our computation by means of logarithms we have used 10 as a base. Logarithms based on 10 are called *common* logarithms and are used almost exclusively in computation because they are more convenient than any other system of logarithms in multiplication, division, and in finding powers and roots.

There is another number that is often used as a base for a system of logarithms. It is an irrational number that is equal approximately to 2.718281828459045. This number is usually rounded off to 2.71828 or, in some cases, to 2.718. For convenience, this base is usually represented by the letter e (though sometimes by the Greek letter epsilon, ε).

Logarithms based on this number are called *natural* logarithms. They are sometimes called Napierian logarithms in honor of John Napier, the inventor of logarithms.

You may wonder why such an irrational number should be used as a base for a system of logarithms. Natural logarithms are not often used for computation, although they can be so used. However, they force themselves into many problems in science, particularly in physics and in electricity. The number represented by e appears in many problems in alternating currents, transmission lines, antennas, and in other physical problems. This irrational number is the basis of the laws of growth and decay. It is sometimes called the compound interest law. In the computation of the numerical values of logarithms, the natural logarithms are actually computed first and are then converted to common logarithms.

36.7 THE USE OF e AS A BASE FOR LOGARITHMS

We have seen that any number may be expressed as a power of another number. For instance, to take an example we have already used, the number 64 can be expressed as a power of 8, 4, 2, or some other base. The exponent of the power is the same as the logarithm to that particular base.

Examples.

$64 = 8^2$	or	$\log_8 64 = 2$
$64 = 4^3$	or	$\log_4 64 = 3$
$64 = 2^6$	or	$\log_2 64 = 6$

We have said that the base is a sort of building block to be used in the building of a number, such as 64. If we use a large block, such as 8, we need an exponent of only 2 in order to build the base up to 64. If we use a smaller building block, such as 4, for a base, we need an exponent of 3 in order to build the 4 up to 64. If we use 2 as a base, we need a larger exponent, 6, to build the smaller base up to 64.

If we wish to build a base up to any desired number, the exponent will depend upon the base we use. When the base is large, the exponent is small; when the base is small, the exponent must be large.

We have also seen that we may use the number 10 as a base and that 10 may be built up to the number 64, although the power on 10 will be a mixed decimal; that is,

$$64 = 10^{1.80618} \quad \text{or} \quad \log_{10} 64 = 1.80618$$

Now, suppose we use the number e as a base. Remember that e is a rather small number between 2 and 3. To build the number 10 up to 64 we needed an exponent of 1.80618. If we wish to build the number e up to 64, we need a larger exponent. In fact, we need an exponent equal approximately to 4.15888. To see the comparison, note these two statements:

$$64 = 10^{1.80618} \qquad 64 = e^{4.15888}$$

In logarithmic form the two statements are

$$\log_{10} 64 = 1.80618 \qquad \log_e 64 = 4.15888$$

If the base 10 and the base e are each built up to any particular number, then the power on e must be larger than the power on 10. If $\log_{10} 300 = 2.47712$, then $\log_e 300$ must be larger than 2.47712.

If N is any particular number in the two statements below, then which is larger, x or y?

$$N = 10^x \qquad N = e^y$$

As we have stated, the number e (that is, 2.71828 ...) appears naturally in connection with logarithms in many problems in science and mathematics. For this reason, this number is called a *natural base* for logarithms. To indicate the natural logarithm of a number N, we can write

$$\log_e N$$

However, we often use a somewhat different notation. Instead of writing $\log_e$, we use the notation "ln" to denote a *natural logarithm*. Then we need not show the base, just as we need not write the base 10 for common logarithms. For example, we write

$$\log 64 = 1.80618 \quad \text{(base 10)}$$
$$\ln 64 = 4.15888 \quad \text{(base } e\text{)}$$

Tables of natural logarithms have been constructed for convenience in more advanced work in mathematics. Such a table is not essential for most practical work. However, in practical problems it is sometimes desirable and necessary to determine the natural logarithm of a number. This can be done without the use of a table if the need should arise.

We must keep a few points in mind in working with natural logarithms. Natural logarithms are not separated into characteristic and mantissa. The whole-number part of the logarithm cannot be determined by inspection as is done in the system of common logarithms. Therefore, in any table of natural logarithms, *the entire logarithm (whole number and decimal part) is printed in the table.* In fact, we do not speak of characteristic and mantissa in connection with natural logarithms. Moreover, if the natural logarithm is negative, then *the entire logarithm is stated as negative* and it is so printed in a table. For example, the natural logarithm of 0.243 is -1.41469.

If we wish to determine the natural logarithm of any number, we first find the common logarithm (base 10) in the table of common logarithms. We can then convert this common logarithm to the natural logarithm of the same number by simple formula. On the other hand, it sometimes happens that we know the natural logarithm of a number and find it necessary to convert this value to the common logarithm. Let us, therefore, derive two formulas for making these changes.

Let us assume we know the common logarithm (base 10) of a number N, and let us denote this known common logarithm by the letter a. Then we have

$$\log_{10} N = a$$

In exponential form,
$$N = 10^a$$

Now we take the *natural logarithm* of both sides of the equation:

$$\ln N = \ln 10^a$$

This can be written

$$\ln N = (a) \ln 10$$

The left side of the equation is precisely what we wish to find. The right side of the equation shows that the known common logarithm, a, must be multiplied by the natural logarithm of 10. The natural logarithm of 10 is approximately equal to $2.302585\ldots$, rounded off to 2.3026. That is

$$\ln 10 = 2.3026$$

In a similar manner, it can be shown that if the natural logarithm of a number is known, then the common logarithm can be found by multiplying the known natural logarithm by the common logarithm of e, which is approximately equal to 0.4343; that is, $\log_{10} e = 0.4343$.

Therefore, in converting logarithms from base 10 to base e and from base e to base 10, we use the following factors:

$$0.4343 \quad \text{and} \quad 2.3026$$

These two factors should be memorized. They are actually irrational numbers but are usually rounded off as shown. These factors are the *multipliers* to be used in converting logarithms. Which factor will be needed will depend on the logarithm given. Moreover, it will depend on your own judgment and on these two principles:

1. *If you wish to increase the size of a logarithm, you must use the multiplier 2.3026, which is more than 1.*

2. *If you wish to decrease the size of a logarithm, you must use the multiplier 0.4343, which is less than 1.*

To show how these factors are applied, we work out two examples.

Example 1. Suppose we know that $\log 73.2 = 1.86451$. If we wish to change this common logarithm to the natural logarithm of 73.2, we first recall that e is a smaller base than 10. Therefore, the logarithm will be larger, and we use the multiplier 2.3026.

$$(2.3026)(1.86451) = 4.29322 \text{ (rounded off)}$$

This means that $\ln 73.2 = 4.29322$

or, in exponential form, $73.2 = e^{4.29322}$

Note. The multiplication itself can actually be done by common logarithms.

Example 2. Suppose we know that $\ln 342 = 5.83481$. If we wish to change this natural logarithm to the common logarithm of 342, we first recall that 10 is a larger base than e. Therefore, the logarithm will be smaller, and we must use the multiplier 0.4343.

$$(0.4343)(5.83481) = 2.53406 \text{ (rounded off)}$$

This means that $\log 342 = 2.53406$

or, in exponential form, $342 = 10^{2.53406}$

The procedure outlined for changing logarithms from base 10 to base e and from base e to base 10 can be summarized in the following two rules.

Rule 1. *To change a common logarithm (base 10) to a natural logarithm (base e), multiply the common logarithm by 2.3026.*

Rule 2. *To change a natural logarithm (base e) to a common logarithm (base 10), multiply the natural logarithm by 0.4343.*

Exercise 36.4

Find the common logarithm of each of the following numbers by use of a table. Then change the common logarithm to the natural logarithm by using the proper multiplier.

1. 31.71	**2.** 6.421	**3.** 1480
4. 86400	**5.** 257.4	**6.** 2.163

7. 41700   **8.** 0.726   **9.** 0.046
10. 0.000533   **11.** 1878000   **12.** 2.7183

The following are natural logarithms of numbers. Change each natural logarithm to the corresponding common logarithm by using the proper multiplier. Then find the antilogarithm of each.

13. 4.1463   **14.** 2.1102   **15.** 6.3315
16. 3.5582   **17.** 6.8533   **18.** 0.3001
19. −0.3524   **20.** −1.4065   **21.** −1.8708
22. −3.91202   **23.** 5.24321   **24.** −2.4567

Work out the following exercises by using the conversion factors 0.4343 and 2.3026.

25. If $\log A = 1.37291$, find $\ln A$.
26. If $\ln B = 2.1471$, find $\log B$; then find B.
27. If $\ln C = 4.358$, find $\log C$; then find C.
28. If $\log D = 0.03784 - 2$, find $\ln D$.
29. If $\ln M = -2.7181$, find $\log M$; then find M.
30. If $\ln N = -1.1301$, find $\log N$; then find N.
31. If $\ln K = 9.312$, find $\log K$; then find K.
32. If $\log X = 0.39794 - 3$, find $\ln X$.
33. If $\ln Y = -5.234$, find $\log Y$; then find Y.
34. If $\log Z = 0.9425$, find $\ln Z$.

Quiz No. 2 on Logarithms. Form A.

1. Write the following in expanded logarithmic form:

  (a) $\log \dfrac{4\pi r^3}{9x^2 y}$ (b) $\log \dfrac{(20)^3 (45)^4 \sqrt{35}}{(18)^{\frac{2}{3}} (52)^{\frac{1}{4}}}$

2. Write the following as a single logarithm with a coefficient of 1:

$$3 \log x + 5 \log y - \tfrac{1}{4} \log z - 4 \log a$$

3. Write the following as a single logarithm and simplify:

$$2 \log 5 + 3 \log 4 - \tfrac{1}{3} \log 8$$

4. Find the following, using tables:

  (a) $\log 34 + \log 14$ (b) $(\log 7)^2$ (c) $(\log 24)(21)$

  (d) $\dfrac{\log 88}{\log 4}$ (e) $\log (38 + 12)$ (f) $\log 56^2$

5. (a) $2 \log 46 - \tfrac{1}{2} \log 84$ (b) $\dfrac{4 \log 21 - \tfrac{1}{3} \log 210}{\log 3}$

6. State the value of x in each of the following:

  (a) $\log_2 8 = x$ (b) $\log_3 x = 4$ (c) $\log_x 32 = 5$
  (d) $\log_6 6 = x$ (e) $\log_5 1 = x$ (f) $\log_9 3 = x$

7. Solve for x:

  (a) $x^{2.3} = 77$ (b) $\log_x 42 = 1.3$ (c) $\log (x^2 - 1) = 1 + \log (x + 1)$

8. If the common logarithm of a number is 3.5302, find the number and also find the natural logarithm of the number.

9. A right circular cone has an altitude of 27.3 inches and a diameter of 16.4 inches. Find the number of cubic centimeters in its volume.

Quiz No. 2 on Logarithms. Form B.

1. Write the following in expanded logarithmic form:

(a) $\log \dfrac{5a^2b}{2\pi rh}$ (b) $\log \dfrac{(15)^4(78)^2(14)^{\frac{1}{3}}}{(25)^{\frac{3}{4}}\sqrt{43}}$

2. Write the following as a single logarithm with a coefficient of 1:

$$4 \log b + \tfrac{1}{3} \log c - 3 \log d - 2 \log x$$

3. Write the following as a single logarithm and simplify:

$$3 \log 5 + 2 \log 6 - \tfrac{1}{2} \log 9$$

4. Find the following, using tables:

(a) $\log 240 - \log 17$ (b) $\log 12^2$ (c) $(\log 13)(\log 15)$

(d) $\dfrac{\log 48}{6}$ (e) $\log (28)(30)$ (f) $(\log 20)^2$

5. (a) $3 \log 18 + \tfrac{1}{2} \log 14$ (b) $\dfrac{5 \log 16 - \tfrac{1}{4} \log 320}{\log 4}$

6. State the value of x in each of the following:

(a) $\log_3 9 = x$ (b) $\log_6 x = 3$ (c) $\log_x 16 = 4$
(d) $\log_7 1 = x$ (e) $\log_4 2 = x$ (f) $\log_8 x = 0$

7. Solve for x:

(a) $x^{2.1} = 74$ (b) $\log_x 84 = 1.2$ (c) $\log (x^2 - 4) = 1 + \log (x + 2)$

8. If the natural logarithm of a number is 5.0814, find the common logarithm of the number. Then find the number.

9. A right circular cylinder has an altitude of 31.8 centimeters and a diameter of 25.6 centimeters. Find its volume (in cubic inches).

Part V
TRIGONOMETRY

37

The Trigonometric Ratios

37.1 IMPORTANCE OF TRIGONOMETRY

Trigonometry is one of the most useful forms of mathematics. It has many applications in science and engineering as well as in theoretical mathematics. It forms the basis of *indirect* as contrasted with *direct* measurement. That is, it is used to measure *indirectly* distances that are difficult or impossible to measure *directly*, such as the height of a flagpole or the distance across a river. It is essential in practically all engineering. Much advanced work in mathematics is dependent upon trigonometry.

37.2 DEFINITION

For our purpose here, we define trigonometry as the study of *angles*. Historically, it is true that trigonometry arose out of the need to find unknown sides of triangles. It is still sometimes used for this purpose. Yet, for the many applications of trigonometry in engineering, it seems best to define trigonometry as the study of angles rather than of triangles. In fact, the trigonometric ratios refer to angles, not triangles. We speak of the sine, the cosine, and the tangent of angles, not of triangles.

37.3 ANGLE

What, then, is an angle? It is important that we have a clear and correct definition of the term *angle*. We know that if we have two lines drawn from the same point, such as line *AB* and line *AC*, an angle is formed (Fig. 37.1). But what exactly is the angle?

One definition often given is: "An angle is the amount of opening between two lines drawn from the same point." This definition is satisfactory if we limit the size of angles to less than 180°, but it would not be satisfactory for all angles, for example, an angle of 390°.

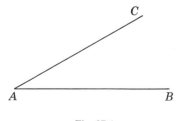

Fig. 37.1

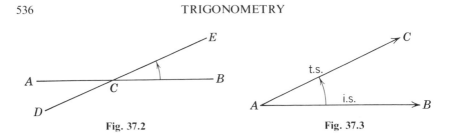

Fig. 37.2   Fig. 37.3

To get a satisfactory definition that would apply to all angles, suppose the straight line *AB* is rotated about the point *C* on the line until the line has reached the new position *DE* (Fig. 37.2). Then we say *the angle is the amount of rotation of the line AB about point C*, as shown by the curved arrow.

Of course, a line is understood to have no end. It has unlimited extent in both directions. Now, instead of starting with a line of unlimited extent, we can start with what is called a *half-line*, or *ray*. A ray is understood to have one end point and unlimited extent in one direction. Suppose we have the ray *AB* with end point at *A* and unlimited extent in the direction of *B* (Fig. 37.3). Now, if this ray is rotated about its end point *A*, an angle is formed. Again, the angle is the *amount of rotation*. The sides of the angle are the two *positions* of the rotating ray. The original position, *AB*, is called the *initial side* (*i.s.*) of the angle; the final position, *AC*, is called the *terminal side* (*t.s.*) of the angle. The *vertex* of the angle is the end point *A* around which the ray is rotated.

We often think of the two sides of an angle as being two separate lines. However, it is sometimes better to consider the two sides, not as two separate lines, but rather as *two different positions* of the *same rotating line*.

If we agree to begin with the fundamental definition that "an angle is the amount of rotation of a ray," then we may let the ray rotate to any position we wish and as far as we wish. There is, then, no limit to the size of an angle.

37.4   POSITIVE AND NEGATIVE ROTATION

If a rotating ray, in generating an angle, rotates in a *counterclockwise* direction, the rotation is called *positive*. If the rotation is clockwise, it is called *negative* rotation.

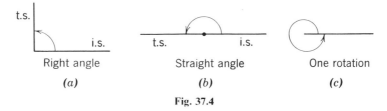

Right angle   Straight angle   One rotation

(a)   (b)   (c)

Fig. 37.4

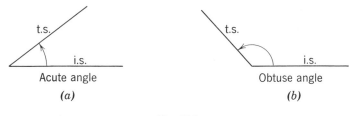

Fig. 37.5

37.5 KINDS OF ANGLES

When the rotating ray reaches a position perpendicular to its original position, the angle is called a *right angle* (Fig. 37.4a). A right angle forms what is usually called a square corner. When the rotating ray has reached a position so that the two sides point in opposite directions, the angle is called a *straight angle* (Fig. 37.4b). When the rotating ray reaches its original position, the angle is called one *revolution* (or *rotation*) (Fig. 37.4c).

If the rotating ray is in any position before it has generated a right angle, the angle formed is called an *acute angle* (Fig. 37.5a). An *obtuse angle* is greater than a right angle but less than a straight angle (Fig. 37.5b).

If the angle formed by the rotating ray is equal to three right angles, the sides of

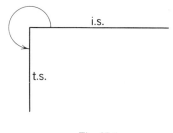

Fig. 37.6

the angle are again perpendicular to each other (Fig. 37.6). In this instance we must be careful to call the angle three right angles, not simply one right angle.

37.6 MEASUREMENT OF ANGLES

The amount of rotation of a ray (or half-line) is often measured in *degrees*. One degree (1°) is the name given to $\frac{1}{360}$ of a revolution. A revolution is called 360°. A right angle is therefore called 90°. A straight angle is called 180°. When measured in degrees, an acute angle is less than 90°. An obtuse angle is greater than 90° and less than 180°.

37.7 THE NATURE OF AN ANGLE

It should be observed that the size of an angle cannot be determined simply by looking at the initial side and the terminal side. The position of the sides

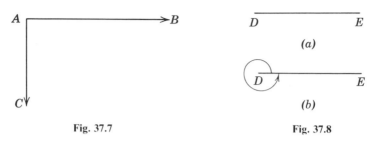

Fig. 37.7   Fig. 37.8

alone tells nothing about the amount of rotation. An angle, as here considered, should not be looked upon as something static. Instead, it should be considered as the result of some action or motion.

For example, if two rays are drawn perpendicular to each other from the point A (Fig. 37.7), the figure may look like one right angle. However, if we are told that the ray AB has rotated counterclockwise (positive rotation) until it has reached the position AC, we see that the angle BAC is not one right angle but *three* right angles.

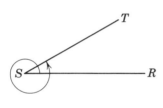

Fig. 37.9

If we look at the line DE (Fig. 37.8a), we see no angle at all. However, if the line has rotated about point D just once (Fig. 37.8b), then the angle is one complete revolution, or 360°. Suppose we measure the angle RST (Fig. 37.9) with a protractor and find that it measures 30°. However, we cannot tell the size of the angle until we know the amount of rotation. The side SR may have made one revolution or several. If it has made one revolution and 30° more, the sides of the angle will be in the position shown, yet the angle will contain 390°, not only 30°. The curved arrow shows the direction and the amount of rotation.

With this understanding of the meaning of an angle, it will make sense when an engineer speaks of an angle of 450°, 3600°, or 21,600°. An angle of 540° is one and one-half revolutions, or six right angles (Fig. 37.10a). An angle of 1800° is an angle of five complete revolutions (Fig. 37.10b).

540°   1800°

(a)   (b)

Fig. 37.10

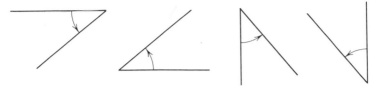

Fig. 37.11. Angles of 40°.

37.8 STANDARD POSITION OF AN ANGLE

Angles are found in many different positions. For example, an angle of 40° may have its vertex pointing in any direction as in Fig. 37.11. However, angles are best studied in what is called *standard position* of the angle. Standard position refers to a certain definite position on the rectangular coordinate system.

To place an angle in standard position, first, place the *vertex* of the angle at the *origin* (0, 0). Then swing the angle around so that the *initial* side falls along the *positive direction* of the x-axis. An angle of 30° is in standard position in Fig. 37.12.

Exercise 37.1

1. Sketch the following angles (approximately to size) in standard position on the x- and y-axes. Show the initial side and the terminal side of each and show the direction and the amount of rotation by a curved arrow: 45°, 225°, 135°, 315°.

2. Do the same for the following angles (sketch these four angles on one graph): 30°, 150°, 240°, 300°.

3. Sketch the following angles on one graph. Notice that some angles have their terminal sides in the same place. Such angles are called *coterminal* angles: 60°, 420°, −300°, 120°, −240°. (A negative angle indicates clockwise rotation.)

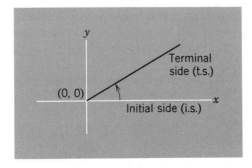

Fig. 37.12

4. Sketch the following angles in standard position, showing the initial and the terminal sides and showing the direction and amount of rotation (these need not be on the same graph). Which are coterminal? $-45°$, $-30°$, $-120°$, $-210°$, $180°$, $-180°$, $270°$, $-90°$.

5. On one graph show the following angles, with the use of a protractor if necessary: $10°$, $20°$, $30°$, $40°$, $50°$, $60°$, $70°$, $80°$. Now try to draw each of the following angles, using your eye as a guide: $20°$, $70°$, $10°$, $80°$, $30°$, $60°$, $40°$, $50°$.

37.9 TRIGONOMETRIC RATIOS OR FUNCTIONS

Suppose that some angle such as A is in standard position (Fig. 37.13). Let us further suppose that the point (8, 6) lies on the terminal side of the angle. Then the abscissa of the point is 8 and the ordinate of the point is 6.

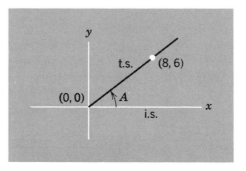

Fig. 37.13

The distance from the origin out to the point is called the *radius vector* of the point. The radius vector can be computed by the Pythagorean rule. In the case of the angle A, the radius vector is 10. The three lengths, abscissa, ordinate, and radius vector, represent three distances; and the numbers 8, 6, and 10 represent the number of units in these distances, respectively.

Now, it is possible to state six and only six *ratios* between these three values: abscissa, ordinate, and radius vector. These six ratios are known as the six *trigonometric ratios* or *functions*. They have been given names as follows:

The ratio $\dfrac{ordinate}{radius\ vector}$ is called the *sine* of angle A (pronounced sine to rhyme with "mine").

The ratio $\dfrac{abscissa}{radius\ vector}$ is called the *cosine* of angle A (pronounced *co-sine*).

The ratio $\dfrac{ordinate}{abscissa}$ is called the *tangent* of angle A.

The ratio $\dfrac{abscissa}{ordinate}$ is called the *cotangent* of angle A (pronounced *co-tangent*).

The ratio $\dfrac{radius\ vector}{abscissa}$ is called the *secant* of angle A (pronounced *see-cant*).

The ratio $\dfrac{radius\ vector}{ordinate}$ is called the *cosecant* of angle A (pronounced *co-secant*).

For brevity, the ordinate is often called y, the abscissa is called x, and the radius vector is called r. The names of the ratios are abbreviated by using the first three letters, except for cosecant, which is abbreviated "csc." The word

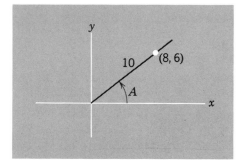

Fig. 37.14

"of" is also omitted. In abbreviated form, the foregoing definitions then become

$$\frac{y}{r} = \sin A \text{ (pronounced sine } A)$$

$$\frac{x}{r} = \cos A \text{ (pronounced co-sine } A)$$

$$\frac{y}{x} = \tan A \text{ (pronounced tangent } A)$$

$$\frac{x}{y} = \cot A \text{ (pronounced co-tangent } A)$$

$$\frac{r}{x} = \sec A \text{ (pronounced see-cant } A)$$

$$\frac{r}{y} = \csc A \text{ (pronounced co-secant } A)$$

It should be noted especially that the names of the functions in the abbreviated form are still pronounced as though written out in full.

The foregoing definitions hold true for any angle in standard position. If an angle is in standard position and a point on the terminal side is known, then all the ratios can be computed for that angle.

Consider again the angle A in standard position with point $(8, 6)$ on the terminal side (Fig. 37.14). From the definitions of the trigonometric ratios, the following values can be found:

$$\sin A = \frac{y}{r} = \frac{6}{10} = \frac{3}{5} = 0.6000$$

$$\cos A = \frac{x}{r} = \frac{8}{10} = \frac{4}{5} = 0.8000$$

$$\tan A = \frac{y}{x} = \frac{6}{8} = \frac{3}{4} = 0.7500$$

$$\cot A = \frac{x}{y} = \frac{8}{6} = \frac{4}{3} = 1.3333$$

$$\sec A = \frac{r}{x} = \frac{10}{8} = \frac{5}{4} = 1.2500$$

$$\csc A = \frac{r}{y} = \frac{10}{6} = \frac{5}{3} = 1.6667$$

It must be understood that the trigonometric ratios do not indicate inches, feet, degrees, or measurements of any kind. Instead, they are pure ratios and are, therefore, pure numbers without any denomination. *Trigonometry is concerned with these six ratios for any angle.*

To consider another example, suppose an angle is in standard position and the point $(-7, 3)$ is on its terminal side (Fig. 37.15). Now we wish to

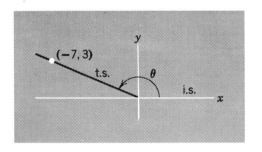

Fig. 37.15

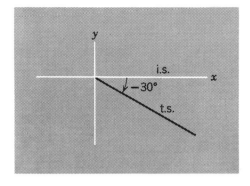

Fig. 37.16

find the values of the six trigonometric ratios for the angle. Let us call the angle *theta* (θ). The first thing to do is to sketch the angle in standard position (the angle should be indicated by a curved arrow).

In this example the abscissa is -7, the ordinate is 3, and the radius vector, determined by the Pythagorean rule, is $\sqrt{58}$. Then the six trigonometric ratios for the angle θ are

$$\sin \theta = \frac{3}{\sqrt{58}} \qquad \tan \theta = \frac{3}{-7} \qquad \sec \theta = \frac{\sqrt{58}}{-7}$$

$$\cos \theta = \frac{-7}{\sqrt{58}} \qquad \cot \theta = \frac{-7}{3} \qquad \csc \theta = \frac{\sqrt{58}}{3}$$

The foregoing values can be changed to decimal form if it is so desired. It will be noted that some of these functions are negative. A trigonometric ratio will always be negative when the two terms have opposite signs. The ratio will be positive when it is the quotient of like signs. This is simply the application of the rule for the division of signed numbers in algebra.

37.10 NEGATIVE ANGLE IN STANDARD POSITION

By *negative* angle, we mean that the angle is formed by a *clockwise* rotation of a line. If a negative angle is placed in standard position, its initial side is along the x-axis, just as it is with a positive angle. However, the direction of rotation is clockwise. For instance, an angle of $-30°$ in standard position has its terminal side in the fourth quadrant (Fig. 37.16).

Exercise 37.2

Each of the following angles, indicated by letter, is in standard position, and the given point is on the terminal side. Find the numerical and signed values of the six trigonometric functions of each angle. Consider all angles positive. Make a sketch of each angle in standard position.

Angle	Point on Terminal Side	Angle	Point on Terminal Side	Angle	Point on Terminal Side
A	8, 6	K	5, 5	U	$\sqrt{3}, 1$
B	$-12, 5$	L	6, 6	V	1, 1
C	$4, -3$	M	$4, -4$	W	$5, \sqrt{11}$
D	$-6, -8$	N	$-6, 6$	X	$-5, 10$
E	$5, -12$	O	$7, -3$	Y	$8, -4$
F	8, 15	P	$-2, 1$	Z	$2\sqrt{3}, 2$
G	$-24, 7$	Q	$-3, -2$	α	4, 5
H	6, 4	R	$-30, -40$	β	$-3, 5$
I	8, 2	S	$-5, 3$	θ	$4, 2\sqrt{5}$
J	3, 6	T	7, 1	ϕ	$\sqrt{3}, \sqrt{3}$

38
Tables of Trigonometric Ratios

38.1 THE TRIGONOMETRIC RATIOS AS FUNCTIONS OF AN ANGLE

The numerical values of the trigonometric ratios for any angle do not depend on the lengths of the sides of the angle but only on *the size of the angle*. For this reason, we say the trigonometric ratios are *functions of the angle*.

To show that this is true, suppose we have an angle in standard position with the point (8, 6) on the terminal side, as shown in Fig. 38.1. Let us call the angle *alpha* (α). We find that the radius vector is 10 units. Then the sine of α is $\frac{6}{10}$, $\frac{3}{5}$, or 0.6000. Now we shall find that the terminal side of α passes through the point (4, 3) also. This can be proved from the fact that the right triangles formed are similar. Therefore, their corresponding sides are proportional. If we take the point (4, 3), the radius vector is 5. The sine of α is $\frac{3}{5}$, the same as before.

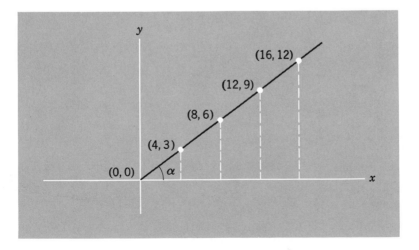

Fig. 38.1

The terminal side will also pass through the points (12, 9) and (16, 12). If we compute the radius vector correctly for each point, we shall find that the sine for this particular angle (α) always has the value $\frac{3}{5}$ or 0.6000.

In fact, no matter what point is taken on the terminal side of an angle, the sine value for that angle will always remain the same. The numerical value of the sine will not change unless the angle changes in size. In the same way, all the other trigonometric ratios will also remain the same for any particular angle no matter what point is chosen on the terminal side of the angle.

Since the trigonometric ratios depend only on the size of the angle, they are called *functions of the angle*.

Now, it can be shown that the angle whose sine value is 0.6000 or $\frac{3}{5}$ is an angle of approximately 36.9°. In other words, the sine value of an angle of 36.9° is approximately 0.6000 no matter what point is taken on the terminal side.

Suppose we have another angle, say, an angle of 20°, in standard position (Fig. 38.2). The trigonometric ratios of this angle will remain constant whatever point we choose on the terminal side. We take the general point (x, y), and indicate the radius vector by r. Now let us estimate the value of the sine of 20°. For the sine ratio for any angle, we have

$$\frac{\text{ordinate}}{\text{radius vector}}$$

Note in Fig. 38.2 that the ordinate is approximately $\frac{1}{3}$ of the radius vector. This ratio is true no matter where we take the point (x, y). Then we can conclude that the sine of 20° is approximately $\frac{1}{3}$. Computed by advanced formulas, the value has been found to be approximately 0.3420.

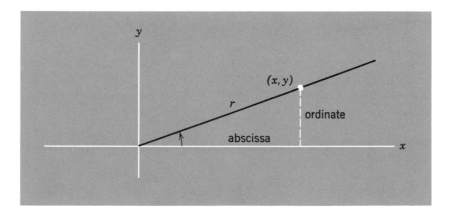

Fig. 38.2

Let us in the same way estimate the value of the cosine of 20°. Note that for any position of the point (x, y), the abscissa is almost as great as the radius vector. Therefore the cosine ratio is almost 1. Actually, the cosine of 20° is approximately 0.9397.

38.2 TABLES: FOUR AND FIVE PLACE

The numerical values of all trigonometric ratios have been computed for angles from zero to 90°. These values are usually listed in tabular form. The values are often given for tenths of a degree or for minutes. An angle of one minute (1′) is $\frac{1}{60}$ of a degree. An angle of one second (1″) is $\frac{1}{60}$ of a minute, or $\frac{1}{3600}$ of a degree.

One of the most useful tables for most work in engineering is a table of trigonometric ratios for degrees and tenths of a degree.

In most tables the function values are arranged so that angles may be read downward at the left side and upward at the right. To find the functions of all angles from zero to 45°, find the angle in the *left-hand* column and read the function value *under* the proper heading. For angles of 45 to 90°, read *upward* at the *right of the table for the angle* and read the *footings* instead of headings.

Examples.

sin 13.8° = 0.2385	sin 56.4° = 0.8329
cos 27.2° = 0.8894	cos 71.8° = 0.3123
tan 38.4° = 0.7926	tan 64.9° = 2.1348
cot 21.7° = 2.5129	cot 47.7° = 0.9099

In some problems it is necessary to use greater accuracy than tenths of a degree. In the table showing tenths of a degree we find consecutive angles such as 28.3° and 28.4°. Suppose we wish to find the functions of an angle between 28.3° and 28.4°. We may interpolate, or we may use a table showing angles by minutes. Since one degree is equal to 60 minutes, then one-tenth of a degree is equal to 6 minutes. An angle of 28.3° is equivalent to an angle of 28° 18′. An angle of 28.4° is equal to 28° 24′. An angle of 31° 42′ is equal to 31.7°.

If we wish to find the sine of an angle of 28° 19′, we may use a table showing angles by minutes, in which the sine of 28° 19′ is 0.47434. If we interpolate for 28° 19′, which lies between 28.3° and 28.4°, we get a sine value of 0.47435.

Even for an angle of 24.3°, compared with the same angle stated in degrees and minutes, there is a slight difference in the values found in the five-place and the four-place tables. In a table showing angles by degrees and tenths of a degree, the sine of 24.3° is shown as 0.4115. In a table showing division by minutes, the value is shown as 0.41151. The only difference is that the second value indicates greater accuracy because an angle showing minutes indicates greater accuracy than one showing only tenths of a degree.

The tables of trigonometric ratios can also be used in *reverse*; that is, when a certain function value is known, the angle itself may be found in the table. For instance, if we know that the sine of an angle is 0.3322, we can look this value up under the heading "sine." There we discover that the angle corresponding to this sine value is 19.4°.

In using the table in reverse, we must sometimes use *footings* instead of headings. For example, suppose we know that the tangent of angle A is 1.5340. Then we find that angle A is 56.9°.

If the exact value of a function as given is not found in the table, we may take the nearest angle shown or we may estimate by interpolation the angle lying between two known angles.

Exercise 38.1

For the first 24 examples, use a table showing tenths of a degree. For Examples 25 through 48, use a table showing minutes or interpolate.

Find the value of each of the following functions:

1. sin 23.4°	**2.** cos 17.2°	**3.** tan 35.6°
4. cot 12.3°	**5.** sin 9.8°	**6.** cot 43.5°
7. cos 7.1°	**8.** sin 48.2°	**9.** cot 73.8°
10. cos 52.3°	**11.** tan 57.3°	**12.** sin 81.9°
13. cos 82.1°	**14.** cot 69.7°	**15.** sin 0.9°
16. tan 0.9°	**17.** sin 89.4°	**18.** tan 89.9°
19. sin 35°	**20.** cos 55°	**21.** tan 69°
22. cot 21°	**23.** cos 0.4°	**24.** cos 0°
25. sin 18° 25'	**26.** cos 23° 14'	**27.** tan 31° 17'
28. cot 43° 13'	**29.** sin 57° 18'	**30.** cos 61° 38'
31. cot 77° 53'	**32.** tan 84° 6'	**33.** sin 54° 44'
34. tan 38° 15'	**35.** cos 76° 21'	**36.** cot 67° 45'
37. tan 13° 13'	**38.** cos 17° 17'	**39.** sin 7° 9'
40. cot 14° 15'	**41.** sin 38° 27'	**42.** cos 4° 3'
43. cot 20° 37'	**44.** tan 44° 17'	**45.** cot 45° 43'
46. cos 58° 26'	**47.** sin 83° 15'	**48.** tan 89° 59'

Use a table of secants and cosecants to find the following:

49. sec 13.4°	**50.** csc 37.3°	**51.** csc 42.6°
52. sec 48.2°	**53.** sec 68.9°	**54.** csc 72.8°

Find the angle for each of the following given functions:

55. sin A = 0.1805	**56.** cos B = 0.9259	**57.** tan C = 0.2905
58. cot D = 1.946	**59.** sin E = 0.8950	**60.** tan F = 2.059
61. cot G = 0.2830	**62.** sin H = 0.9444	**63.** cos J = 0.1925

64. tan K = 1.3649   **65.** cot L = 1.2431   **66.** cos M = 0.4815
67. sin N = 0.9899   **68.** tan P = 12.410   **69.** cos Q = 0.3800
70. cot R = 0.2659   **71.** sec S = 1.1270   **72.** csc T = 1.7000

38.3 ARC-FUNCTIONS OR INVERSE FUNCTIONS

At this point in our study it is necessary that we understand the terms *arcsine*, *arctangent*, and so on. Such expressions mean *angles*. The term *arc* can be used as a prefix to any of the names of trigonometric functions. Such expressions are sometimes called *inverse functions*.

To see what is meant by this notation, let us first consider the arcsine (usually written *arcsin*). Suppose we know that the sine of some particular angle is $\frac{2}{3}$, or 0.6667. Then we can write the equation

$$\sin \theta = \tfrac{2}{3}$$

Now, we may ask, how large is angle θ? From the table, we find that the angle θ is approximately 41.8°. This is a problem we faced in the preceding assignment.

However, there is a way of stating the size of the angle without looking it up in the table. Notice these two equations:

If $\qquad\qquad \sin \theta = \tfrac{2}{3}$,
then $\qquad\qquad \theta = $ the angle whose sine is $\tfrac{2}{3}$

You will notice that the first equation tells what "*sin θ*" equals. The second equation tells what "*θ*" equals.

The student will probably object and say, "But the second equation doesn't tell anything new. It still doesn't tell the size of the angle." That is true. Yet there are many times when it is convenient to use the second form. The two equations can be shortened as follows:

If $\qquad\qquad \sin \theta = \tfrac{2}{3}$
then $\qquad\qquad \theta = $ arcsin $\tfrac{2}{3}$

The word *arcsine* (pronounced ark-sine) means "the angle whose sine is." A similar expression is used in connection with all the trigonometric functions. Their abbreviated forms are as follows:

> *arccos* (pronounced ark-cosine)
> *arctan* (pronounced ark-tangent)
> *arccot* (pronounced ark-cotangent)
> *arcsec* (pronounced ark-secant)
> *arccsc* (pronounced ark-cosecant).

The *arc-functions*, often called *inverse functions*, are sometimes indicated by

-1 written in the same position as an exponent. Thus arcsin x is often written $\sin^{-1} x$. If this form is used, the -1 must *not* be taken as a negative exponent. It is probably less confusing to the student to use the form *arcsin*. If it is necessary to use a negative exponent on a trigonometric function, it should be written as shown here:

$$\frac{1}{\sin x} = (\sin x)^{-1}$$

It must be understood that this expression does *not* mean *arcsin*. In our discussion here we use the forms *arcsin*, *arctan*, and so on.

Here are some examples showing the meaning of these expressions:

1. If $\tan A = \frac{1}{2}$, then angle $A = \arctan \frac{1}{2}$. This expression means "A is the angle whose tangent is $\frac{1}{2}$."

2. If $\sec B = \frac{5}{3}$, then $B = \text{arcsec} \frac{5}{3}$. This means "$B$ is the angle whose secant is $\frac{5}{3}$."

3. If we know that $\cos E = 0.7230$, then $E = \arccos 0.7230$; that is, "E is the angle whose cosine is 0.7230."

Of course, if we wish to know the size of an angle in degrees, we must look it up in the table. If $\cos E = 0.7230$, then $E = \arccos 0.7230$. From the table, we find that the angle is 43.7°; that is, arccos $0.7230 = 43.7°$. In the same way we find that

$$\text{arcsin } 0.5635 = 34.3°$$
$$\text{arctan } 1.5051 = 56.4°$$

Exercise 38.2

Find the following angles:

1. arcsin 0.3355	**2.** arccos 0.7157	**3.** arctan 0.5704
4. arccot 1.6128	**5.** arctan 2.023	**6.** arcsin 0.8231
7. arccos 0.2890	**8.** arccot 0.2642	**9.** arctan 0.8162
10. arccot 3.513	**11.** arccos 0.8947	**12.** arcsin 0.2350
13. arccos 0.2040	**14.** arcsin 0.9464	**15.** arccot 0.3880
16. arctan 4.370	**17.** arctan $\frac{3}{4}$	**18.** arcsin $\frac{2}{5}$
19. arccot $\frac{5}{12}$	**20.** arctan 1.5	

39

The Right Triangle

39.1 DEFINITIONS OF THE TRIGONOMETRIC FUNCTIONS IN TERMS OF A RIGHT TRIANGLE

The trigonometric functions are often defined in terms of the sides of a right triangle without regard to the x and y axes. Let us see how this is done.

Consider, again, an angle in standard position on the rectangular coordinate system. Suppose we have an angle, A, in standard position, with point (8, 6) on the terminal side (Fig. 39.1). The abscissa of the point is 8 units, the ordinate is 6 units, and the radius vector is 10 units.

From our definitions of the trigonometric functions, we have

$$\sin A = \frac{3}{5} \qquad \cos A = \frac{4}{5} \qquad \tan A = \frac{3}{4}$$

We have seen that in this case angle A is approximately 36.9°.

Now, suppose we erase the x-axis and the y-axis. Then we have only a right triangle with two sides and hypotenuse (Fig. 39.2). We still have the same angle A, which is still the same size. The sides of the triangle are 6 units, 8 units, and 10 units, respectively.

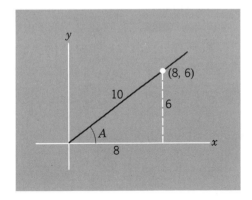

Fig. 39.1

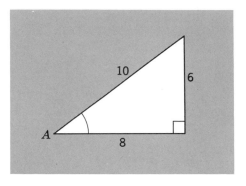

Fig. 39.2

However, we now have no x-axis, no y-axis, and no origin. Therefore, we have no ordinate, no abscissa, and no radius vector. We can no longer define the sine of the angle as y/r. The same is true for the other functions. We have neither x nor y nor r. The definitions of the trigonometric functions must now be stated in terms of these three sides of the triangle.

From the position of angle A, we can tell which side of the triangle was formerly the ordinate, which was the abscissa, and which was the radius vector. The hypotenuse was formerly the radius vector. To distinguish between the other two sides, we call one of them the side *opposite* angle A and the other the side *adjacent* to angle A. The side adjacent to angle A, is the side which, with the hypotenuse, forms angle A.

Our former definitions of sine, cosine, tangent, and so on, now become new definitions in terms of *hypotenuse, side opposite*, and *side adjacent*. Corresponding to our former definitions, we have

$$\sin A = \frac{\text{side opposite}}{\text{hypotenuse}} \qquad \cot A = \frac{\text{side adjacent}}{\text{side opposite}}$$

$$\cos A = \frac{\text{side adjacent}}{\text{hypotenuse}} \qquad \sec A = \frac{\text{hypotenuse}}{\text{side adjacent}}$$

$$\tan A = \frac{\text{side opposite}}{\text{side adjacent}} \qquad \csc A = \frac{\text{hypotenuse}}{\text{side opposite}}$$

The foregoing definitions hold true for any *acute* angle in a right triangle. The definitions are often abbreviated. Suppose *theta* (θ) is any acute angle in a right triangle; then the definitions of the trigonometric functions are as follows:

$$\sin \theta = \frac{\text{opp}}{\text{hyp}} \qquad \cos \theta = \frac{\text{adj}}{\text{hyp}} \qquad \tan \theta = \frac{\text{opp}}{\text{adj}}$$

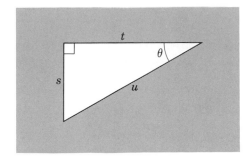

Fig. 39.3

$$\cot \theta = \frac{\text{adj}}{\text{opp}} \qquad \sec \theta = \frac{\text{hyp}}{\text{adj}} \qquad \csc \theta = \frac{\text{hyp}}{\text{opp}}$$

To illustrate these ratios, suppose we have a right triangle (Fig. 39.3) with sides lettered s, t, and u, in which u represents the hypotenuse and the angle θ is opposite the side s. Then, from the foregoing definitions, we have

$$\sin \theta = \frac{s}{u} \qquad \tan \theta = \frac{s}{t} \qquad \sec \theta = \frac{u}{t}$$

$$\cos \theta = \frac{t}{u} \qquad \cot \theta = \frac{t}{s} \qquad \csc \theta = \frac{u}{s}$$

It is important that the definitions of the trigonometric ratios be thoroughly understood and remembered; it is equally important that they should *not* be memorized in *a particular order*. Each function, by itself, should be recognized instantly.

39.2 THE FUNCTION VALUES IN ANY PARTICULAR RIGHT TRIANGLE

If we know the hypotenuse and the two sides of a right triangle, we can easily state the six trigonometric ratios between the sides. For instance, in the triangle shown in Fig. 39.4, suppose the sides are 5 and 12 inches, respectively, and the hypotenuse is 13 inches. If we let angle R be the angle opposite the 5-inch side, then we can state the six trigonometric ratios for angle R as follows:

$$\sin R = \frac{\text{opp}}{\text{hyp}} = \frac{5}{13} \qquad \tan R = \frac{\text{opp}}{\text{adj}} = \frac{5}{12} \qquad \sec R = \frac{\text{hyp}}{\text{adj}} = \frac{13}{12}$$

$$\cos R = \frac{\text{adj}}{\text{hyp}} = \frac{12}{13} \qquad \cot R = \frac{\text{adj}}{\text{opp}} = \frac{12}{5} \qquad \csc R = \frac{\text{hyp}}{\text{opp}} = \frac{13}{5}$$

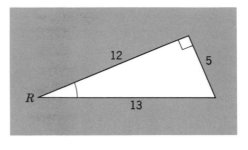

Fig. 39.4

In a given right triangle one side may be unknown. Then it is first necessary to find the length of the unknown side before the numerical values can
be stated. As an example, suppose we have the right triangle shown in Fig.
39.5, with sides of 2 inches and 6 inches, respectively. The hypotenuse, found
by the Pythagorean rule, is $\sqrt{40}$.

Now, using the definitions previously given, we can state the numerical
values of all the trigonometric ratios for either of the two acute angles of the
triangle. For instance, for angle M we have

$$\sin M = \frac{2}{\sqrt{40}} \qquad \tan M = \frac{2}{6} \qquad \sec M = \frac{\sqrt{40}}{6}$$

$$\cos M = \frac{6}{\sqrt{40}} \qquad \cot M = \frac{6}{2} \qquad \csc M = \frac{\sqrt{40}}{2}$$

These numerical values can be reduced to lower terms and also to decimal
fractions if desired.

If we wish, we can also find the size of angle M. We see that the tangent
of angle M is $\frac{2}{6}$, or $\frac{1}{3}$, or, in decimal form, 0.3333. From the table, we find that
arctan 0.3333 is an angle of 18.4°. If we wish a more accurate answer, we
find that angle M equals 18° 26′.

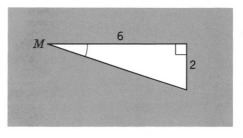

Fig. 39.5

Again, it should be clearly understood that the values of the trigonometric ratios are *not measurements*, such as feet, inches, or degrees, but pure numbers. In the last example given, one side of the triangle is 2 inches, and the other side is 6 inches. The tangent is the ratio of 2 inches to 6 inches, but this ratio, $\frac{1}{3}$, is not inches, but simply the pure number $\frac{1}{3}$.

Exercise 39.1

In each of the right triangles in Fig. 39.6:

1. Find the length of the unknown side.
2. Then state the value of the sine, cosine, and the tangent of each of the lettered angles.
3. Finally, tell the approximate size of the lettered angle by use of the table. In finding the size of the angle, use the function involving the two *given* sides.

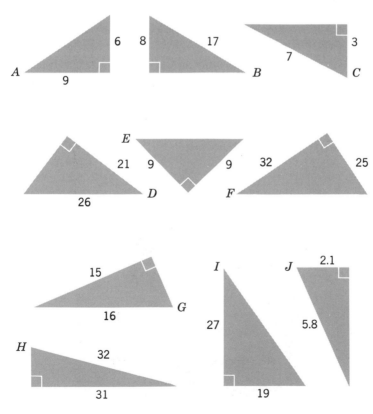

Fig. 39.6

39.3　SOLVING RIGHT TRIANGLES

Every triangle has three sides and three angles. The three sides and three angles are called the six *elements* of a triangle. The three angles are customarily named by the capital letters, A, B, and C, respectively. Each side is named by the small letter that corresponds to the opposite angle. In a right triangle the right angle is often called C. The hypotenuse is labeled c.

Although this is the usual method of naming the elements of a triangle, the student should not get the idea that they must be so named. An angle may be given any name we wish.

To "solve" a triangle means to find all the unknown elements. At least three of the six elements must be known, one of which must be a side. In a right triangle we know one angle is a right angle, or 90°. Therefore, in a right triangle two more elements must be known, one of which must be a side.

In finding the unknown elements of a right triangle, we make use of the trigonometric ratios. In all cases we *set up a ratio between two sides*, one of which is known. Then we equate this ratio to the correct trigonometric function. To show how this is done, we use an example.

Example.　Solve the right triangle, ABC, in which angle C is the right angle, angle $B = 57.1°$, and side $a = 15.2$ in. To solve the triangle, we must find the three unknown parts: angle A and sides b and c.

Solution.　The first step in the solution is to make a sketch of the triangle, labeling all parts, including those given and those to be found (Fig. 39.7). Next, we set up a ratio between an *unknown side* and the *known side*:

$$\frac{b}{a}$$

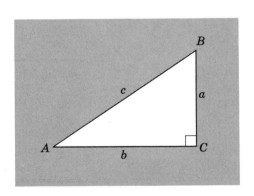

Fig. 39.7

Now we notice that this ratio is the tangent of the angle B. This fact is then stated as an equation:

$$\frac{b}{a} = \tan B$$

We substitute known values and solve the resulting equation.

We may solve the equation for b at once or after substituting the value of $\tan 57.1°$

$$\frac{b}{15.2} = \tan 57.1°$$

$$b = (15.2)(\tan 57.1°)$$
$$b = (15.2)(1.5458)$$
$$b = 23.496 \qquad \text{or} \qquad 23.50$$

To find c, we may write

$$\frac{c}{a} = \sec B$$

Let us assume that we have no table of secants. Then we rewrite the ratio

$$\frac{a}{c} = \cos B$$

Substituting given values,

$$\frac{15.2}{c} = \cos 57.1°$$

Solving for c,

$$c = \frac{15.2}{\cos 57.1°}$$

From the table we find that $\cos 57.1°$ is 0.5432. Therefore,

$$c = \frac{15.2}{0.5432} = 27.982 \qquad \text{or} \qquad 27.98$$

Angle A is found by subtracting angle B from $90°$:

$$A = 90° - 57.1° = 32.9°$$

The work may be checked by the Pythagorean rule:

$$a^2 + b^2 = c^2$$

Since the values we have used are only approximate, the two sides of the equation will not be exactly equal. Let us ask

Squaring,

does $(15.2)^2 + (23.496)^2 = (27.982)^2$?
does $231.04 + 552.05 \quad = 782.99$?
does $\qquad\quad 783.09 \quad = 782.99$?

Since the two sides of the equation are approximately equal, the work may be considered correct.

Exercise 39.2

Solve the following right triangles. Each triangle is understood to be lettered ABC, with angle C as the right angle and the sides lettered with small letters that correspond, respectively, to the opposite angles.

1. $A = 34.4°$; $a = 16.8$ in.
2. $A = 14.3°$; $c = 31.4$ in.

3. $A = 62.5°; b = 21.4\,\text{ft}$ **4.** $B = 59.2°; c = 23.1\,\text{cm}$
5. $B = 29.6°; b = 106\,\text{ft}$ **6.** $B = 12.3°; a = 320\,\text{ft}$
7. $a = 3.23\,\text{in.}; b = 5.11\,\text{in.}$ **8.** $b = 28\,\text{ft}; c = 115\,\text{ft}$
9. $a = 89\,\text{cm}; c = 125\,\text{cm}$ **10.** $b = 47\,\text{in.}; a = 212\,\text{in.}$
11. $A = 38.2°; c = 112.3\,\text{ft}$ **12.** $A = 27.9°; b = 43.2\,\text{ft}$
13. $B = 53.4°; c = 245\,\text{ft}$ **14.** $B = 18.6°; b = 162.5\,\text{ft}$
15. $a = 39.3\,\text{ft}; b = 51.6\,\text{ft}$ **16.** $a = 25.8\,\text{in.}; c = 32.1\,\text{in.}$
17. $b = 31.7\,\text{cm}; c = 40.5\,\text{cm}$ **18.** $A = 72.3°; a = 24.7\,\text{ft}$
19. $a = 32.4\,\text{ft}; b = 21.2\,\text{ft}$ **20.** $B = 57.3°; a = 38.6\,\text{in.}$
21. $A = 19.2°; a = 32.4\,\text{cm}$ **22.** $a = 58.7\,\text{cm}; b = 14.2\,\text{cm}$
23. $B = 5.7°; a = 45.6\,\text{in.}$ **24.** $A = 12.8°; c = 36.4\,\text{in.}$
25. $a = 53.1\,\text{cm}; c = 62.5\,\text{cm}$ **26.** $b = 43.2\,\text{cm}; c = 45.8\,\text{cm}$
27. $A = 21.9°; c = 45.8\,\text{in.}$ **28.** $B = 81.1°; c = 132\,\text{ft}$
29. $B = 4.8°; b = 83.5\,\text{ft}$ **30.** $a = 13.1\,\text{cm}; b = 65.5\,\text{cm}$

*39.4 LOGARITHMS OF FUNCTIONS

Logarithms can be used to simplify much of the work in trigonometry. For instance, in the foregoing worked-out example, we have

$$b = (15.2)(\tan 57.1°)$$

or

$$b = (15.2)(1.5458)$$

We may now use logarithms to perform the computation.

Using logarithms, we have
$$\log 15.2 = 1.18184$$
$$\log 1.5458 = 0.18915$$

For a product, we add logarithms:
$$\log b = 1.37099$$
$$b = 23.496 \quad \text{or} \quad 23.50$$

In this example we have $b = (15.2)(\tan 57.1°)$. Note that in order to find the logarithm of the second factor we must use two steps. We must first look up the tangent of $57.1°$, which is 1.5458. Then we must find the logarithm of 1.5458, which is 0.18915; that is,

$$\tan 57.1° = 1.5458$$
$$\log 1.5458 = 0.18915$$

Actually, what we wish to find is the logarithm of the tangent of $57.1°$

Tables have been constructed to show the logarithms of the trigonometric functions *directly*; that is, we look up the angle $57.1°$ and find directly, *not* the tangent, but the *logarithm* of the tangent, which is 0.18915. Using such a

* This section may be omitted if these tables are not available.

table, we have

$$b = (15.2)(\tan 57.1°)$$

$$\log 15.2 = 1.18184$$
$$\log \tan 57.1° = 0.18914$$
$$\overline{\log b = 1.37098}$$
$$b = 23.495 \quad \text{or} \quad 23.50$$

The advantage of these tables lies in the fact that one table takes the place of two.

Many logarithms of trigonometric functions have negative characteristics. This is true in all cases in which the value of the function is less than 1. It is true for all the sine and cosine values, for tangent values from zero to 45°, and for cotangent values from 45 to 90°.

For instance, if we look up the sine of 20°, we find that it is 0.3420. The logarithm of this number is $0.53403 - 1$. This may be written

$$\log \sin 20° = 9.53403 - 10$$

In the table, the -10 is omitted from such logarithms.

We shall use logarithms of the functions to solve an example.

Example. Given a right triangle ABC, C = the right angle, $a = 87.1$ ft, $b = 142.7$ ft, find A, B, and c.

Solution. *Step 1.* Sketch the triangle (Fig. 39.8).

Step 2. Label the parts.

Step 3. Set up a ratio between sides: $\dfrac{87.1}{142.7}$

Step 4. If we wish to find A, we write $\dfrac{87.1}{142.7} = \tan A$

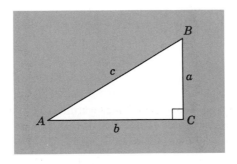

Fig. 39.8

Step 5. Solve, using logarithms:

In dividing quantities, we subtract their logarithms:
$$\log 87.1 = 1.94002$$
$$\log 142.7 = 2.15442$$
$$\log \tan A = \overline{9.78560 - 10}$$

Angle A is found directly from log tan A $A = 31°\ 24'$ or $31.4°$

Angle B is found by subtraction: $B = 90° - 31.4° = 58.6°$

Side c could be found by the Pythagorean rule, since both a and b are known. However, we find c by trigonometry and then use the Pythagorean rule for a check. We write

$$\frac{a}{c} = \sin A \qquad \text{or} \qquad c = \frac{a}{\sin A}$$

Filling in given values, we have
$$c = \frac{87.1}{\sin 31.4°}$$

Solving for c, using logarithms,
$$\log 87.1 = 1.94002$$
$$\log \sin 31.4° = \overline{9.71685 - 10}$$
$$\log c = 2.22317$$
$$c = 167.2$$

For a check, we may use $a^2 + b^2 = c^2$. However, if logarithms are used in the check, a better form of the Pythagorean rule is the following:

$$a^2 = c^2 - b^2$$
or
$$a^2 = (c + b)(c - b)$$

Taking the logarithm of both sides, $\log a^2 = \log [(c + b)(c - b)]$

So we ask,   does $2 \log a = \log (c + b) + \log (c - b)$?

does $2 \log 87.1 = \log 309.9 + \log 24.5$?

does $2(1.94002) = (2.49122) + (1.38918)$?

does $3.88004 = 3.88039$?

The two sides of the equation are sufficiently close to serve as a check.

Note. Any unknown value should be found by using only given values if possible. However, sometimes it is necessary to use one of the values that have been found previously, as we have done in finding the value of c in the foregoing example.

Exercise 39.3

Solve the following right triangles by using logarithms of the trigonometric functions. Each right triangle is understood to be lettered ABC, with angle C as the right angle and the sides lettered a, b, and c opposite corresponding angles.

1. $A = 16.3°$; $b = 24.8$ ft   **2.** $A = 25.7°$; $c = 340$ ft

3. $B = 38.2°$; $a = 12.6$ in.   **4.** $B = 42.6°$; $c = 204$ ft

5. $A = 51.9°; a = 32.2$ ft

6. $B = 68.4°; b = 52.4$ in.

7. $A = 73.5°; b = 420$ ft

8. $B = 81.8°; a = 3.24$ cm

9. $a = 264$ ft; $b = 721$ ft

10. $a = 129$ ft; $c = 153$ ft

11. $b = 58$ in.; $c = 181$ in.

12. $b = 81$ ft; $a = 75$ ft

39.5 SOLVING STATED WORD PROBLEMS

In stated word problems we usually wish to find only one or two particular unknown quantities. All the problems we are considering here involve a right triangle. In solving any stated word problem, the following steps will serve as a guide:

1. *First, sketch a figure showing the right triangle involved.*
2. *Label all parts, showing given values and the part to be found.*
3. *Set up a ratio between two sides (at least one known).*
4. *Equate this ratio to a function of some angle.*
5. *Solve the resulting equation for the unknown value.*

Example 1.   Suppose we wish to measure the height of a flagpole simply by making certain measurements from the ground. We first measure a distance, say, 120 ft, along the ground from the foot of the pole. From this point it is possible, by means of an instrument, to measure the angle of elevation of the top of the pole. Suppose the angle of elevation is 24.3°. Call the height h.

Solution.   *Step 1.*   We make a sketch of the right triangle involved (Fig. 39.9).

Step 2.   We label all parts.

Step 3.   Now we set up a ratio between two sides: $\dfrac{h}{120}$

Step 4.   Express this ratio as a function of the given angle and solve the resulting equation for the unknown:

$$\frac{h}{120} = \tan 24.3° \qquad h = 120 \tan 24.3°$$

$$h = (120)(0.4515) \qquad h = 54.18 \qquad \text{or} \qquad 54.2 \text{ ft}$$

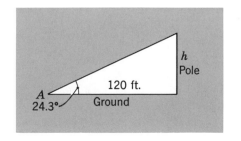

Fig. 39.9

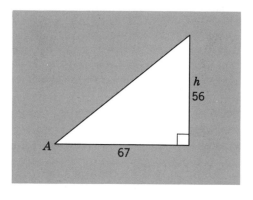

Fig. 39.10

If the measurement of angle A is made from a point some distance above the level of the foot of the pole, this distance must be added to the answer in order to obtain the height of the pole. In some problems this extra distance is negligible.

Example 2. Find the angle of elevation of the sun when a flagpole 56 ft high casts a shadow 67 ft long (Fig. 39.10).

Solution.

$$\tfrac{56}{67} = \tan A$$
$$\tan A = 0.8358$$
$$\text{angle } A = \arctan 0.8358 = 39.9°$$

Example 3. From the top of a cliff, 400 ft above the edge of a lake, a small boat is observed out on the lake at an angle of depression of 15.6°. How far is the boat from the foot of the cliff?

Solution. First, make a sketch of the right triangle in the problem and label all parts (Fig. 39.11). Next, set up the ratio $\dfrac{d}{400} = \cot\theta$. The angle θ is the same size as

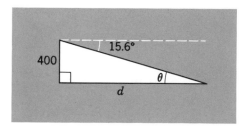

Fig. 39.11

the angle of depression. Therefore,

$$\frac{d}{400} = \cot 15.6°$$

$$d = (400)(\cot 15.6°) = (400)(3.582) = 1432.8$$

The answer can reasonably be rounded off to 1430 ft.

Exercise 39.4

1. A ladder 32 ft long leans up against a vertical wall and makes an angle of 17.4° with the wall. How high up on the wall does the ladder reach? How far is the foot of the ladder from the wall?

2. An escalator from the first floor to the second floor of a building is 43.2 ft long and makes an angle of 35.7° with the floors. Find the vertical distance between the floors.

3. A road has a uniform elevation of 6.2°. Find the increase in elevation in driving one quarter of a mile along the road.

4. The shadow of a tree is 72 ft long when the sun is at 43.7° elevation. Find the height of the tree.

5. An inclined railway is built to the top of a hill whose elevation is 364 ft above the level of the bottom of the railway. If the angle of elevation of the railway is 35.8°, how long is the railway?

6. A chandelier hangs on a 52-ft chain from a high ceiling. If the chandelier is pulled aside so that the chain forms an angle of 25.8° with its vertical position, how much is the chandelier raised vertically?

7. A plank 18 ft long is used to roll a barrel onto a truck. If the platform of the truck is 5.4 ft above the ground, what angle does the plank form with the ground?

8. A bridge is 24 ft above the surrounding ground level. An approach to the bridge is to be built so that the angle of elevation of the approach is not over 7.1°. How far from the bridge must the approach be started?

9. How long a shadow will be cast by the Washington Monument (height 555 ft) when the elevation of the sun is 41.7°?

10. From the top of a cliff, 850 ft above the level of the sea, the angle of depression of a small boat on the water is found to be 16.3°. Some time later the angle of depression is found to be 36.7°. How far has the boat traveled toward the cliff? How could you determine the speed of the boat by observation from the top of the cliff?

11. A 24-ft ladder is placed against a vertical wall so the foot of the ladder is 5.9 ft from the wall. What angle does the ladder make with the ground? How high on the wall does the ladder reach?

12. A man sees a flagpole on top of a building. He wishes to calculate the length of the flagpole. He walks 240 ft away from the building. (Assume the ground is level.) From his new position he finds that the angle of elevation of the bottom of the flagpole is 28.4° and the angle of elevation of the top of the pole is 36.8°. What is the length of the flagpole?

13. Observing a tower in the distance, a man measures the angle of elevation of the top and finds that it is 17.6°. He then walks directly toward the tower for a distance of 300 ft. From this position he finds that the angle of elevation is 39.3°. Find the height of the tower.

14. Two observation posts, A and B, are 4500 ft apart. A helicopter is directly above a straight line connecting A and B. From point A the helicopter appears at an elevation of 54.3° and from point B it appears at an elevation of 43.7°. Find the height of the helicopter. Also find the line-of-sight distance from each post to the helicopter.

15. From the top of a 70-ft building it is observed that the angle of depression of the far side of a street is 34.7° and the angle of depression of the near side of the street is 55.2°. Find the width of the street.

16. A motorist sees a tower in the distance directly east. He drives 6.3 miles directly north and then notices that the tower appears at a direction 38.1° south of east. How far is he then from the tower?

17. Standing on top of a building, a man observes a flagpole on another building. By measurement he finds that the top of the pole has an elevation of 19.5° and the bottom has an angle of depression of 8.2°. If the pole is 60 ft high, how far away is the pole?

18. Show how you might compute the distance across a river. Make a diagram showing the parts of a right triangle that might be involved. Show what measurements might conveniently be made directly. Then supply some reasonable numbers for these values, and, from these values, compute the width of the river.

40

Functions of Angles of Any Size

40.1 INTRODUCTION

Up to this time we have used a table to find the function values of any angle from zero to 90°. However, we know that angles are not limited to 90°. An angle may be any size, and it may have its terminal side in any quadrant. For example, an angle of 257° has its terminal side in the third quadrant when the angle is in standard position.

Our problem now is to see how we can use the same table for angles greater than 90° and for negative as well as positive angles. We shall see, moreover, that the same table can be used for angles greater than 360°.

To begin with, we go back to our original definitions of the functions of any angle in standard position on the x and y coordinate system. If θ is any angle in standard position, and point (x, y) is on the terminal side, then, by definition,

$$\sin \theta = \frac{y}{r} \qquad \tan \theta = \frac{y}{x} \qquad \sec \theta = \frac{r}{x}$$

$$\cos \theta = \frac{x}{r} \qquad \cot \theta = \frac{x}{y} \qquad \csc \theta = \frac{r}{y}$$

40.2 TERMINAL SIDE IN FIRST QUADRANT

Let us first consider an angle less than 90°. Such an angle is called a *first-quadrant* angle. Any *acute* angle is a first-quadrant angle, wherever it appears. Suppose we have a first-quadrant angle in standard position with the point (12, 5) on its terminal side (Fig. 40.1). Call the angle *alpha* (α). Then for angle α we have

$$y = 5, \qquad x = 12, \qquad r = 13$$

From the definition of the sine of an angle, we see that

$$\sin \alpha = \frac{y}{r} = \frac{5}{13}; \qquad \text{or} \qquad 0.3846 \text{ (approx.)}$$

From the table, we find that α is approximately 22.6°.

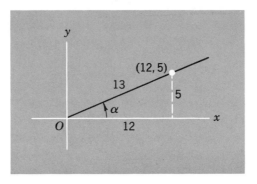

Fig. 40.1

In Fig. 40.1 note that a right triangle is formed by the line segments indicating the *x*, *y*, and *r* distances, respectively. This triangle may be called a "5-12-13" right triangle. The angle α is opposite the shortest side. Now keep in mind that in a right triangle of this particular shape, the smallest angle contains 22.6° In other words, we can say that in any "5-12-13" right triangle the angle opposite the shortest side is 22.6°. This is true no matter where this particular triangle appears.

40.3 ANGLE WITH ITS TERMINAL SIDE IN THE SECOND QUADRANT

Next consider an angle in standard position with its terminal side in the second quadrant. Such an angle is called a *second-quadrant* angle.

Suppose we have a second-quadrant angle with the point $(-12, 5)$ on its terminal side (Fig. 40.2). Let us call the angle beta (β). Note that angle β is

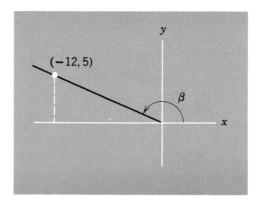

Fig. 40.2

greater than 90° and less than 180°. For angle β we have

$$y = 5 \qquad x = -12 \qquad r = 13$$

Again, from the definition of the sine of an angle,

$$\sin \beta = \frac{y}{r} = \frac{5}{13}$$

If we show the distances represented by y, x, and r, we see the same right triangle that we saw in the first quadrant. In this "5-12-13" right triangle, we found that the smallest angle is 22.6°. Since the same triangle appears in the second quadrant, the smallest angle is 22.6°.

In Fig. 40.2, this small angle is called the *reference* angle because we can refer to it to find angle β. However, it must be remembered that this reference angle is *not* β. Yet it has the same sine value; that is, $\frac{5}{12}$. Here we see that the sine of β is the same as the sine of the reference angle. Knowing the reference angle, we find that β is 157.4°.

40.4 TERMINAL SIDE IN THIRD QUADRANT

An angle in standard position with its terminal side in the third quadrant is called a *third-quadrant* angle. Suppose a third-quadrant angle has the point $(-12, -5)$ on its terminal side (Fig. 40.3). Let us call the angle θ (theta). Note that θ is greater than 180° and less than 270°. For angle θ we have

$$y = -5, \qquad x = -12 \qquad r = 13 \qquad (r \text{ is always positive})$$

Then

$$\sin \theta = \frac{y}{r} = -\frac{5}{13} \qquad \text{or} \qquad -0.3846 \quad (\text{approx.})$$

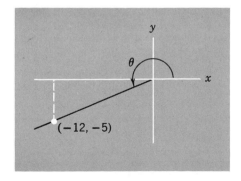

Fig. 40.3

Here again is the same triangle seen in the first and second quadrants. The smallest angle is therefore 22.6°. This angle, the reference angle, enables us to find θ. We see that θ is 202.6°.

It is important to keep in mind that the reference angle, 22.6°, is *not* the angle θ. The angle θ is in standard position whereas the reference angle is *not*. Note that the sine of θ has the same *numerical value* as the sine of the reference angle. However, if any angle in standard position has its terminal side in the

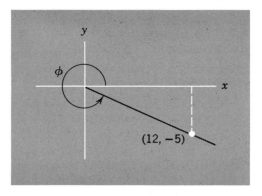

Fig. 40.4

third quadrant, then for any point on the terminal side, the ordinate will be negative. Since r is always positive, the sine value of a third-quadrant angle is negative. This is simply the application of the rule for the division of signed numbers in algebra. It is therefore important that we hold to the definition that the sine of an angle is always equal to the ratio, y/r, in order that the function has the proper sign, positive or negative.

40.5 TERMINAL SIDE IN FOURTH QUADRANT

An angle in standard position with its terminal side in the fourth quadrant is called a *fourth-quadrant* angle. Suppose we have a fourth-quadrant angle with the point $(12, -5)$ on its terminal side (Fig. 40.4). Let us call the angle ϕ (phi). If we assume that ϕ is a positive angle, it is greater than 270° and less than 360°. Then for angle ϕ we have

$$y = -5 \qquad x = 12 \qquad r = 13$$

Then

$$\sin \phi = \frac{y}{r} = -\frac{5}{13}$$

Here again the abscissa, the ordinate, and the radius vector form the same

"5-12-13" right triangle that appeared in the other quadrants. Therefore, the smallest angle is 22.6°. We refer to this small angle to find ϕ but we must remember that the reference angle is *not* ϕ. We see that ϕ is 337.4°. Note that the sine of 337.4° has the same *numerical value* as the sine of the reference angle, 22.6°. However, the sine of ϕ is negative.

Note. We have used various letters, including θ, to refer to various angles. However, when we wish to refer to *any general angle*, we often call it θ.

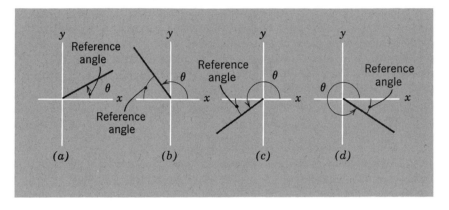

Fig. 40.5

40.6 REFERENCE ANGLE AND ITS USE

We have mentioned the use of the reference angle in determining the value of a trigonometric function. It is necessary to define carefully what is meant by the reference angle. For any given angle in standard position, the *reference angle* is the *acute* angle between the terminal side and the *x*-axis. It is a common mistake to consider the reference angle adjacent to the *y*-axis. The reference angle is always an *acute* angle, and it is always adjacent to the *x*-axis.

It will be observed that the reference angle is sometimes within the given angle and at other times outside it. This has nothing to do with its meaning or use. In Fig. 40.5 we see the angle theta (θ) ending in different quadrants. Also shown is the reference angle in each case.

We have seen that the sine of any angle ending in any quadrant has the same numerical value as the sine of the reference angle. This is true also with regard to all the other functions.

Therefore, to find a function of any angle in standard position ending in any quadrant, it is necessary only to find the *reference angle* and then to use the table to find the numerical value of the function of the reference angle. The function of the given angle will have the *same numerical* value as the function of the reference angle. The final step is to determine whether the function value will be positive or negative for the given angle. This can be determined by observing the signs for x and y for the particular quadrant.

It should be remembered that the reference angle is always an *acute* angle; that is, it is less than 90°. It is considered a positive angle. Therefore, the reference angle is actually what is called a "first-quadrant angle," no matter where it appears. Its functions are always positive. It might be mentioned that the reference angle is sometimes called the *related* angle.

In determining the sine, cosine, or other function of an angle, it makes no difference whether the angle is positive or negative. It makes no difference whether the angle is more or less than 360°. The only thing that determines the value of a function of any angle is the position of the terminal side.

For example, if the terminal side of any angle in standard position passes through the point $(-4, -3)$, the sine of that angle is $-3/5$, whether the angle is positive or negative, or whether it is more or less than 360°. It may be an angle of 216.9°, or $-143.1°$, or 1656.9°.

We need only one rule, or two at most:

1. The reference angle will determine the numerical value of any function. For this we use the table of values for angles from zero to 90°.

2. The quadrant in which the terminal side falls will determine whether the function will be positive or negative according to the signs of x and y, since r is always positive.

To find the functions of an angle ending in any quadrant, we have the following steps:

1. *Draw the given angle in standard position, showing the terminal side and showing the direction and amount of rotation by a curved arrow.*

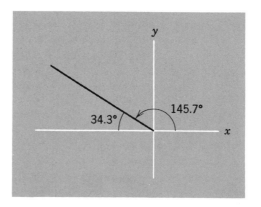

Fig. 40.6

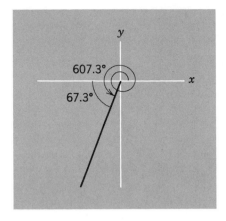

Fig. 40.7

2. *Show the reference angle and state its size.*
3. *From the table, find the functions of the reference angle.*
4. *Give the functions of the given angle the same numerical values as the functions of the reference angle. Then give each function its proper sign, positive or negative, depending on the signs for x and y for the position of the terminal side.*

Example 1. Find sine, cosine, tangent, and cotangent of 145.7° (Fig. 40.6).
Reference angle = 34.3°.

$$\begin{array}{ll}
\sin 34.3° = 0.5635 & \sin 145.7° = +0.5635 \\
\cos 34.3° = 0.8261 & \cos 145.7° = -0.8621 \\
\tan 34.3° = 0.6822 & \tan 145.7° = -0.6822 \\
\cot 34.3° = 1.4659 & \cot 145.7° = -1.4659
\end{array}$$

Example 2. Find sine, cosine, and tangent of 607.3° (Fig. 40.7).
Reference angle = 67.3°.

$$\begin{array}{ll}
\sin 67.3° = 0.9225 & \sin 607.3 = -0.9225 \\
\cos 67.3° = 0.3859 & \cos 607.3 = -0.3859 \\
\tan 67.3° = 2.391 & \tan 607.3 = +2.391
\end{array}$$

Example 3.*

Suppose we have the formula $e = 80 \sin \omega t$. This is a common formula in alternating currents in which e represents the instantaneous voltage at any particular instant, and ωt is the angle in which ω (omega) represents *angular velocity* and t represents *time*. For instance, if the angular velocity (ω) of a generator is 21,600° per sec and if the time

* Optional. May be omitted by students unfamiliar with alternating-current theory.

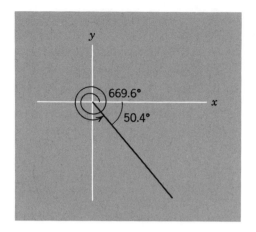

Fig. 40.8

elapsed is 0.031 sec, the angle can be found by multiplying the *angular velocity* by the *time*. Suppose we wish to find the instantaneous voltage at the end of exactly 0.031 sec.

Solution. Let us call the angle theta (θ) (Fig. 40.8). We know that

$$\theta = \omega t$$
$$\theta = (21,600°)(0.031)$$
$$\theta = 669.6°$$

Then we have
$$e = 80 \sin 669.6°$$

The reference angle is 50.4°.

$$\sin 50.4° = 0.7705$$
$$\sin 669.6° = -0.7705$$

Now we see that
$$e = (80)(-0.7705)$$
$$e = -61.64 \text{ volts}$$

Exercise 40.1

Find the sine, cosine, tangent, and cotangent of each of the following angles:

1.	156.3°	**2.**	344.8°	**3.**	243.9°
4.	285.5°	**5.**	96.7°	**6.**	−131.4°
7.	−38.5°	**8.**	232.1°	**9.**	318.9°
10.	143.6°	**11.**	192.7°	**12.**	161.1°
13.	206.5°	**14.**	164.7°	**15.**	209.2°
16.	324.3°	**17.**	221.8°	**18.**	248.1°
19.	334.2°	**20.**	154.9°	**21.**	377.4°
22.	566.8°	**23.**	505.3°	**24.**	676.1°

25. 754.2°	**26.** 951.6°	**27.** −235.3°
28. −54.3°	**29.** −332.7°	**30.** −169.9°

Find the same four functions for the following angles:

31. 127° 14′	**32.** 156° 43′	**33.** 211° 15′
34. 163° 20′	**35.** 285° 18′	**36.** 226° 37′
37. 308° 23′	**38.** −147° 16′	**39.** 834° 46′

Find e or i in each of the following problems:

40. $e = 60 \sin 168.2°$	**41.** $e = 120 \sin 243.8°$
42. $i = 20 \sin 134.3°$	**43.** $i = 15 \cos 257.3°$
44. $e = 80 \cos 323.8°$	**45.** $i = 12 \sin 304.4°$

In the following problems* find e or i if omega (ω) is 21,600° per sec. (The angle $\theta = \omega t$.)

46. If $e = 60 \sin \omega t$, find e when $t = 0.008$ sec.
47. If $i = 12 \sin \theta$, find i when $t = 0.012$ sec.
48. If $e = 150 \cos \omega t$, find e when $t = 0.07$ sec.
49. If $e = 50 \cos \theta$, find e when $t = 0.043$ sec.
50. If $i = 30 \cos \theta$, find i when $t = -0.002$ sec.

40.7 FINDING AN ANGLE FROM A GIVEN FUNCTION VALUE

It is often necessary to find an angle when its function is given. In Chapter 38 we saw that the problem presents no difficulty if the angle is an acute angle (that is, less than 90°). We simply use the table of function values in reverse. We look up the function value in the proper column of the table and then find the angle opposite this value.

However, when we also wish to consider angles greater than 90°, the problem is a little more involved. We have seen that angles of 22.6° and 157.4° have the same sine value, 0.3846. Now, if we are asked what angle has a sine of 0.3846, we can say that the angle is either 22.6° or 157.4°. In fact, both answers are correct. In other words, there are two angles whose sines are equal to 0.3846.

Actually, there are other angles, both positive and negative, with the same sine value, such as −202.6° or +742.6°. However, if we confine the angles to positive angles less than 360° whose sines are equal to 0.3846, then we can state that there are two answers to the question.

In the same way (see Sections 40.4 and 40.5), we find that there are two positive angles less than 360° whose sines are equal to −0.3846. They are 202.6° and 337.4°.

We must remember that there are many angles with the same function values. However, there are always just two positive angles of less than 360° with the same function values. In stating the angles for a given function

---

* Optional. May be omitted by students unfamiliar with alternating-current theory.

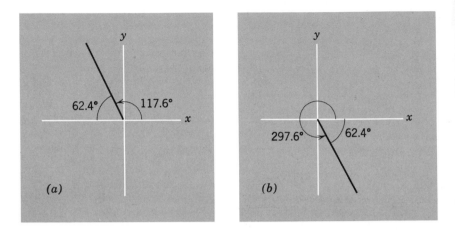

Fig. 40.9

value, we should always list these two angles. If only one answer is required, then additional information must be known.

Example. Find two positive angles of less than 360° whose tangent is − 1.913.

Solution. The tangent of the reference angle has the same numerical value; that is, 1.913. We look for this value in the table under the heading tangent and find

arctan 1.913 = 62.4°

We know then that the reference angle is 62.4°. Since the angles we are seeking have a negative tangent value, the angles must end in the second or fourth quadrant. Therefore, we place the reference angle in the proper position in the second and the fourth quadrants. The position of the reference angle will show the terminal side of the required angle. This is shown in Fig. 40.9.

From the reference angle we can compute the size of the two required angles. They are 117.6° and 297.6°.

Now, if we have the additional information that the required angle has its terminal side in the second quadrant, then the answer is 117.6°.

Exercise 40.2

Find two positive angles of less than 360° that correspond to each of the given function values.

1. sin A = − 0.4210
2. cos B = − 0.8771
3. tan C = − 0.6420
4. cot D = − 1.1423
5. sec E = − 1.1412
6. sin F = 0.9432
7. cos G = 0.4321
8. tan H = 2.808
9. cot I = 0.6950
10. sin J = − 0.4763

40.8 FINDING THE VALUES OF ALL THE FUNCTIONS OF AN ANGLE FROM ONE GIVEN FUNCTION VALUE

If the numerical value of one trigonometric function is known, the value of each of the other functions can be found from the known value. As an example, suppose we know that the sine of an angle θ is equal to $\frac{3}{5}$, or 0.6000. Let us assume that the angle is an acute angle of a right triangle, as shown in Fig. 40.10. We place the numerator, 3, and the denominator, 5, of the fraction in the correct positions on the sides of the triangle to represent the sine ratio for θ. From these two values we can find the unknown side by the Pythagorean rule.

$$\sqrt{5^2 - 3^2} = \sqrt{25 - 9} = \sqrt{16} = 4$$

Now, since we know the length, 4, of the side adjacent to angle θ, we can write the value of each of the six functions. For example, $\cot \theta = \frac{4}{3}$.

If the value of a function is given as a decimal fraction or a mixed decimal, we simply write this value over the denominator 1 and then proceed as in the foregoing example. For instance, if we know that the secant of an angle ϕ is 2.31, we can write this number as 2.31/1. We sketch a right triangle and call one of the angles ϕ. We place the two numbers, 2.31 and 1, on the hypotenuse and side adjacent, respectively, so that the ratio, 2.31/1 will represent the secant of ϕ. The length of the unknown side, the side opposite ϕ, can now be found by use of the Pythagorean rule.

$$\sqrt{2.31^2 - 1^2} = \sqrt{5.3361 - 1} = \sqrt{4.3361} = 2.08$$

Knowing the two sides and the hypotenuse of the right triangle, we can write the value of each of the six functions of ϕ.

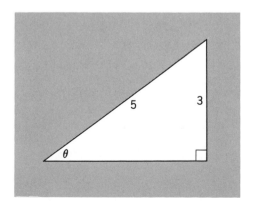

Fig. 40.10

Exercise 40.3

Find the other five function values from the given function value. Consider only the acute angle. The angle itself need not be found.

1. $\tan A = \dfrac{3}{4}$ **2.** $\sin B = \dfrac{5}{13}$ **3.** $\cos C = 0.6$

4. $\cot D = \sqrt{3}$ **5.** $\sin E = \dfrac{8}{17}$ **6.** $\cot F = \sqrt{2}$

7. $\tan G = 1$ **8.** $\cos H = \dfrac{24}{25}$ **9.** $\sec I = 2$

10. $\csc J = \sqrt{2}$ **11.** $\sin K = \dfrac{x}{4}$ **12.** $\cos L = \dfrac{2}{x}$

13. $\tan M = \dfrac{v}{3}$ **14.** $\cot N = 0.34$ **15.** $\sec P = 1.5$

16. $\csc Q = 2.1$ **17.** $\sin R = 0.5$ **18.** $\cos S = 0.75$

19. $\tan T = 1.3$ **20.** $\sec U = \dfrac{3x}{2}$

21. Find $\sin \arctan \frac{4}{3}$. (First show the angle whose tangent is $\frac{4}{3}$. Remember, $\arctan \frac{4}{3}$ is an angle. Now find the sine of this angle.)

22. Find $\tan \arcsin \dfrac{1}{2}$.   **23.** Find $\cot \arctan \dfrac{5}{8}$.

24. Find $\arctan \dfrac{4}{3} - \arctan \dfrac{1}{2}$.   **25.** Find $\arctan 1 - \arcsin 0.5$.

41

Trigonometric Identities

41.1 MEANING OF IDENTITY

There are certain relations between the trigonometric functions that are always true. Such relations are called *trigonometric identities*.

In algebra we learned that an identity is an equation that is always true for all values of a variable. For example, take the equation

$$3x + 2x = 5x$$

This equation is true no matter what value we give to x. It is an identity. An identity is often indicated by three parallel lines instead of two, as in the usual *equal* sign; that is,

$$3x + 2x \equiv 5x$$

The symbol means that the expression is an identity.

Compare the foregoing equation with the following:

$$3x + 2 = 17$$

This equation is true only on the condition that $x = 5$. It is a *conditional equation*. The root of a conditional equation is the value of the unknown that makes the equation true.

In trigonometry certain relations are true for all values of an angle. Other relations are conditional equations and call for a solution. As an example, let us ask the question:

$$\text{does} \quad \sin \theta = \cos \theta?$$

The equation is true if θ is 45° or 225°, as well as for some angles greater than 360°. Yet it is *not* true for all values of θ. For example, if θ is equal to, say, 20°, then the statement is not true. That is,

$$\sin 20° \neq \cos 20°$$

Therefore the equation is *not* an identity.

However, there are certain relations in trigonometry that are always true regardless of the size of the angle. For example, there is a definite relation between the sine and the cosecant of any particular angle, no matter what the size of the angle. There are certain definite relations between all the trigonometric functions whatever the size of the specific angle. These relations are called *identities*. The trigonometric identities are useful in many ways in mathematics. Some identities are very simple, and others are more complicated. A few identity relations should be understood and memorized. You will find the trigonometric identities very helpful in simplifying much of the work in mathematics.

41.2   RECIPROCAL RELATIONS

Certain relations in trigonometry are called *reciprocal relations*. Let us recall the meaning of *reciprocal*.

In arithmetic and algebra we learned that the reciprocal of a number is *1 divided by the number*. The reciprocal of 5 is $\frac{1}{5}$; the reciprocal of -7 is $\frac{1}{-7}$. The reciprocal of $\frac{2}{5}$ is $1 \div \frac{2}{5}$, which is $\frac{5}{2}$. The reciprocal of a fraction is the fraction *inverted*. In arithmetic and algebra we make use of the reciprocal in the division of fractions.

When we say that "the sine of an angle, θ, is the reciprocal of the cosecant of the same angle, θ," we mean that the following relation exists:

$$\sin \theta = \frac{1}{\csc \theta}$$

To make the relation still clearer, let us take a specific example. Suppose θ is an angle of 18.2°. Then the statement means

$$\sin 18.2° = \frac{1}{\csc 18.2°}$$

Let us see if this is true when we substitute numerical values. The cosecant of 18.2° is approximately 3.2017. The sine of 18.2° is 0.3123. Then the expression

$$\frac{1}{\csc 18.2°} \quad \text{means} \quad \frac{1}{3.2017}$$

If we work out the division, $1 \div 3.2017$, we get 0.3123, rounded off to four digits.

Now, we know that the sine of 18.2° is 0.3123. Therefore, we see that

$$\frac{1}{\csc 18.2°} = \sin 18.2°$$

Let us consider again the relation

$$\sin \theta = \frac{1}{\csc \theta}$$

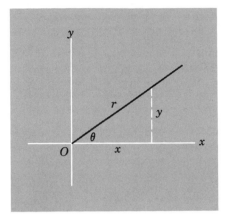

Fig. 41.1

We have seen that this relation is true for a particular angle, that is, if θ is 18.2°. However, this does *not* make the statement an identity. To be an identity, it must be true for *all values* of θ. Our problem now is: can this statement be shown to be true for all angles?

We might go on to show that it is true for some other values of the angle, say, for two, three, or a hundred angles, such as 61.2°, 47.3°, or any other particular angle. However, it should be remembered that any so-called "proof" of a trigonometric identity by the use of a specific example is not a proof at all but only an illustration. To prove an identity, we must show it to be true for *all* angles.

This is not so difficult as it might seem. An identity can be proved by using a *general* angle rather than a specific angle. If we use a general angle, this general angle represents all specific angles. Then, if the statement can be proved to be true for the general angle, it will be true for all angles.

Let us see why the relation is true for all angles. We might rather phrase the statement as a question and ask, "For any general angle, θ, is it true always that

$$\sin \theta = \frac{1}{\csc \theta} \,?"$$

Suppose we take a general angle in standard position, as shown in Fig. 41.1. We call the angle θ. Remember, θ represents all angles. We already know from the definitions of the functions that

$$\sin \theta = \frac{y}{r} \qquad \csc \theta = \frac{r}{y}$$

If we work out the meaning of $\dfrac{1}{\csc \theta}$, we have

$$\frac{1}{\csc \theta} = \frac{1}{r/y} = 1 \div \frac{r}{y} = 1 \cdot \frac{y}{r} = \frac{y}{r}$$

But we already know that the ratio y/r is the sine of θ. Therefore, we see that the relation is true no matter what the size of θ. Then we can say that the relation is an identity; that is,

$$\frac{1}{\csc \theta} \equiv \sin \theta \qquad \text{(for all values of } \theta\text{)}$$

If any particular relationship has been proved to be true for all angles, it can be checked by showing that it is true for some specific angle. For instance, since we have proved that the foregoing relation is identically true for all angles, we can show that it works out for some particular angle, such as 15°, 21.4°, or 27° 19′. If the statement fails for a single angle, it is not an identity. Remember, however, that the values in the table are only approximate.

Here is a list of the six reciprocal relations. We have proved the first one. Now, using a general angle, try to show that the rest are also identities.

1. $\sin \theta \equiv \dfrac{1}{\csc \theta}$ 2. $\cos \theta \equiv \dfrac{1}{\sec \theta}$ 3. $\tan \theta \equiv \dfrac{1}{\cot \theta}$

4. $\cot \theta \equiv \dfrac{1}{\tan \theta}$ 5. $\sec \theta \equiv \dfrac{1}{\cos \theta}$ 6. $\csc \theta \equiv \dfrac{1}{\sin \theta}$

Exercise 41.1

Check each of the foregoing identities by showing it to be true for some particular angle. Remember that the values in the table are only approximate. You may use a different angle to check each identity. Then prove that each is true for all angles by using a general angle.

41.3 COFUNCTION RELATIONS

Other identities are the so-called "co-function" relations. There is a definite relation between a function of any angle and the cofunction of that angle. For instance, there is a definite relation between the sine and the cosine of any angle, regardless of the size of the angle.

We see from the table that the sine of 20° is the same as the cosine of 70°. Also the sine of any angle, for instance, 31.6°, is the same as the cosine of its

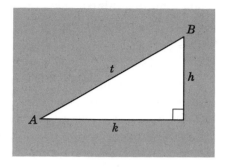

Fig. 41.2

complement, 58.4° ; that is, *the sine of any angle is always equal to the cosine of the complementary angle.* (Complementary angles are two angles whose sum is 90°.)

The same is true with regard to the other functions. The tangent of 15° is the same as the cotangent of 75°. The secant of 34° is the same as the cosecant of 56°. To summarize, we can say that *any function of an angle is equal to the cofunction of the complementary angle.*

It is the relation between cofunctions that enables us to arrange a table of values reading angles from top to bottom on one side and from bottom to top on the other side. You may wonder why this relation is true.

Probably the best way to understand the reason for this cofunction relation is to make use of a right triangle and the corresponding definitions. In the right triangle shown in Fig. 41.2, we have, by definition,

$$\sin A = \frac{\text{opposite}}{\text{hypotenuse}} = \frac{h}{t} \qquad \cos A = \frac{\text{adjacent}}{\text{hypotenuse}} = \frac{k}{t}$$

For angle *B* we have

$$\sin B = \frac{\text{opposite}}{\text{hypotenuse}} = \frac{k}{t} \qquad \cos B = \frac{\text{adjacent}}{\text{hypotenuse}} = \frac{h}{t}$$

Here we see that the sine of *A* has the same value as the cosine of *B*, regardless of the size of either angle. Also, $\cos A = \sin B$.

We know that angles *A* and *B* are complementary; that is, $A + B = 90°$. Therefore, $A = 90° - B$ and $B = 90° - A$.

Since	$\sin A = \cos B$
then	$\sin A = \cos (90° - A)$
In the same way	$\cos A = (90° - A)$

Here are some examples showing this cofunction relation:

$$\sin 42° = \cos 48° \qquad \tan 23.6° = \cot 66.4°$$
$$\sin 17.4° = \cos 72.6° \qquad \sec 31.8° = \csc 58.2°$$
$$\cos 25.2° = \sin 64.8° \qquad \cot 41.7° = \tan 48.3°$$

The relation between the cofunctions might be better understood if we realize that the present names were not always used for the cofunction relations. For instance, the word *cosine* has not always been used for this particular ratio. For some time the cosine ratio was called the *complementary sine*. Instead of $\sin 20° = \cos 70°$, this relation was expressed as $\sin 20° =$ complementary sin 70°. In time, the words "complementary sine" led to the shortened form, *cosine*.

Exercise 41.2

Fill in the blanks in the following exercises, showing cofunction relations:

1. $\tan 37.9° = \cot$ _____   **2.** $\csc 27.4° = \sec$ _____

3. $\sin 12.8° = \cos$ _____   **4.** $\cot 25.1° = \tan$ _____

5. $\sec 42.6° = \csc$ _____   **6.** $\cos 18° 27' = \sin$ _____

7. $\sin \theta = \cos$ _____   **8.** $\cos A = \sin$ _____

9. $\tan \varphi = \cot$ _____   **10.** $\cot B = \tan$ _____

11. $\sin 90° = \cos$ _____   **12.** $\sin 130° = \cos$ _____

13. $\tan 25° =$ _____ $65°$ **14.** $\sin 15° = \dfrac{1}{\sec \text{\_\_\_\_\_}}$

15. $\sin 15° = \dfrac{1}{\csc \text{\_\_\_\_\_}}$ **16.** $\sec A =$ _____ $(90° - A)$

17. $\csc M = \sec$ _____   **18.** $\cos (90° - C) =$ _____

19. $\sec (90° - X) =$ _____   **20.** $\cot (90° - Y) =$ _____

21. $\tan (90° - \phi) =$ _____   **22.** $\sin (90° - \theta) =$ _____

23. $\csc (90° - 17°) =$ _____   **24.** $\sin 35° 42' = \cos$ _____

25. $\cos 4.3° = \sin$ _____   **26.** $\tan 0° = \cot$ _____

27. $\cos 270° = \sin$ _____   **28.** $\sec 20° =$ _____ $70°$

29. $\tan 25° = \dfrac{1}{\text{\_\_\_\_\_} 65°}$ **30.** $\sec 20° = \dfrac{1}{\sin \text{\_\_\_\_\_}}$

41.4 IDENTITIES INVOLVING SQUARES

There are three important identities involving squares of functions. These should be thoroughly understood and then memorized. Here, again, we should not only know these identities but we should see that they are true for any particular angle as well as for a general angle.

Suppose we take some particular angle, say, 28.3°. The sine of 28.3° is approximately 0.4741, and the cosine is approximately 0.8805. Now, suppose we wish to find the square of the sine value, that is, $(0.4741)^2$, indicated in the following manner:

$$(\sin 28.3°)^2$$

However, in most cases, the exponent 2 is written next to the word *sine*. To indicate the square of the sine of an angle, we write

$$\sin^2 \theta$$

No parentheses are needed when this form is used. The same notation is used to indicate any power of any trigonometric function.

Squaring the sine of 28.3°, we have

$$(0.4741)^2 = 0.22477081$$

The square of the cosine of 28.3° is $(0.8805)^2 = 0.77528025$. If we add the square of the sine and the square of the cosine, we get 1.00005106. We might guess that the value would be exactly 1 if we had the exact values for the sine and cosine.

In fact, the following relation can be shown to be true for any value of the angle θ:

$$\sin^2 \theta + \cos^2 \theta = 1$$

This relation, involving the squares of the sine and cosine of any angle, can be checked for any particular angle. However, if we use the values for a particular angle shown in the table, we find that the sum is not exactly 1. That is because the values in the table are only approximate. Most of the values of trigonometric functions are irrational numbers.

The actual proof that the foregoing relation is an identity is derived by taking a *general* angle, θ, in standard position, as shown in Fig. 41.3. Let us state the relation as a question: is it always true that $\sin^2 \theta + \cos^2 \theta = 1$?

We begin with a statement that we know to be true always; that is, by the Pythagorean rule, we know that

$$y^2 + x^2 \equiv r^2$$

We may divide both sides of the identity by anything we wish except zero. Suppose we divide both sides of the equation by r^2. We get

$$\frac{y^2}{r^2} + \frac{x^2}{r^2} \equiv \frac{r^2}{r^2}$$

In the resulting equation note that the first term is actually the square of the sine, the second term is the square of the cosine, and the right side of

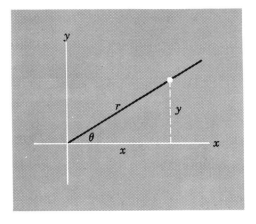

Fig. 41.3

the equation is equivalent to 1. This proves that

$$\sin^2 \theta + \cos^2 \theta \equiv 1$$

Other relations involving squares of functions are

$$\tan^2 \theta + 1 \equiv \sec^2 \theta$$
$$\cot^2 \theta + 1 \equiv \csc^2 \theta$$

These identities can be proved in the same way as the preceding identity.

The student should work out the proofs for all the identities involving squares of functions. The proofs can easily be worked out by starting with the Pythagorean relation that is always true for any angle:

$$y^2 + x^2 \equiv r^2$$

If we divide both sides of the equation by r^2, we get the first of the identities. If we divide both sides of the equation by x^2, we are led to the second. If we divide by y^2, we get the third identity.

The method shown is the general proof for these three identities. However, we should also show that the identities hold true for some particular angle. An identity is often more readily understood and remembered if it is shown to be true for a particular angle. For instance, we might show that the identity $\tan^2 \theta + 1 = \sec^2 \theta$ is true if θ is an angle of, say, 25.2°.

It should be noted that the foregoing identities are often seen in a slightly different form. For instance, instead of

$$\sin^2 \theta + \cos^2 \theta = 1$$

we may have

$$\sin^2 \theta = 1 - \cos^2 \theta$$

or

$$\cos^2 \theta = 1 - \sin^2 \theta$$

The student should write out the relations involving squares in as many forms as possible. The difference between two squares may also be written in factored form.

41.5 TWO SPECIAL RELATIONS

Two other important relations should be understood and memorized. They are (for any angle, θ)

$$\frac{\sin \theta}{\cos \theta} \equiv \tan \theta \qquad \frac{\cos \theta}{\sin \theta} \equiv \cot \theta$$

The proofs for these identities can be derived by taking a general angle, θ, and using the following definitions:

$$\sin \theta \equiv \frac{y}{r} \qquad \cos \theta \equiv \frac{x}{r} \qquad \tan \theta \equiv \frac{y}{x}$$

These should also be shown to be true for some particular angle.

Exercise 41.3

1. Write out a list of the 17 general identities mentioned in this chapter.
2. Check each one of the 17 identities by using a particular angle, say, $\theta = 32.8°$, $64.7°$, or some other angle.

41.6 PROVING IDENTITIES

An identity, as we have said, is an equation that is true for all values of the variable. A *trigonometric identity* is an equation that is true for all values of an angle.

To prove that an equation is an identity, we need only show that the equation can be transformed into one of the known identities we have already shown to be true. In some cases this is simple. In others the identity may be more involved and therefore more difficult to prove.

Given an equation in trigonometry, we might prove that it is an identity in one of three ways:

1. Transform the left side of the equation and try to make it exactly like the right side.

2. Transform the right side of the equation and try to make it exactly like the left side.

3. Transform both sides into new forms so that the new equation shows one of the known identities.

There is no rule that will always lead to success in proving an identity easily. One rule that may help when other attempts fail is to change all terms into sines and cosines. If an equation can be transformed in such a way that it will show one of the known identities, its identity is considered proved.

Example. Show that the following equation is true for all angles:

$$\tan \theta + \cot \theta = (\sec \theta)(\csc \theta)$$

Solution. In proving an identity, the best approach is to ask yourself, is this statement always true for all values of the angle? In other words, for all values of θ,

$$\text{does} \qquad \tan \theta + \cot \theta = (\sec \theta)(\csc \theta)?$$

Let us change all terms to some form of sine or cosine. The problem then is as follows:

$$\text{does} \qquad \frac{\sin \theta}{\cos \theta} + \frac{\cos \theta}{\sin \theta} = \left(\frac{1}{\cos \theta}\right)\left(\frac{1}{\sin \theta}\right)?$$

Multiply both sides of the equation by the quantity $(\sin \theta)(\cos \theta)$.

$$\text{does} \qquad \sin^2 \theta + \cos^2 \theta = 1? \qquad \text{Yes.}$$

This last form is known to be true for all values of θ. Therefore, the identity is proved.

Exercise 41.4

Prove each of the following identities or show that it is not an identity:

1. $\sin A \csc A = 1$

2. $\tan B \cos B = \dfrac{1}{\csc B}$

3. $\dfrac{1}{\sin^2 \theta} - 1 = \dfrac{\cos^2 \theta}{\sin^2 \theta}$

4. $\cos^2 M = 1 - \tan^2 M$

5. $\sin^2 x (\cot^2 x + 1) = 1$

6. $\dfrac{\sin A}{\csc A} + \dfrac{\cos A}{\sec A} = 1$

7. $\tan^2 \phi - \sin^2 \phi = \sin^2 \phi \tan^2 \phi$

8. $(\sin x)(\cot x)(\sec x) = 1$

9. $(\sin A)(1 + \cot^2 A) = \csc A$

10. $\sin t = \csc t - (\cos t)(\cot t)$

11. $\csc^2 Y \sec^2 Y = \csc^2 Y + \sec^2 Y$

12. $\csc^4 A - \cot^4 A = \csc^2 A + \cot^2 A$

13. $(\cot x)(\csc x) = \dfrac{\cos x}{1 - \cos^2 x}$

14. $\dfrac{1 + \sin \theta}{1 - \sin \theta} = \dfrac{\csc \theta + 1}{\csc \theta - 1}$

15. $\sin x \cos x (\tan x + \cot x) = 1$

16. $2 - \sin^2 \phi - \cos^2 \phi = \sec^2 \phi - \sin^2 \phi \sec^2 \phi$

Simplify the following expressions. State each one in the simplest form possible without fractions.

17. $\sec x \cot x$

18. $\tan B \csc^2 B$

19. $\sec^3 \phi \cot \phi$

20. $\dfrac{\cot^3 \theta}{\csc^5 \theta}$

21. $\dfrac{\tan^2 M}{\sec^3 M}$

22. $\dfrac{1 + \tan^2 x}{\tan^2 x}$

23. $\dfrac{\cos^2 A}{\sin^3 A}$

24. $\dfrac{\sin^3 B}{\cos^5 B}$

25. $\dfrac{\tan^3 A}{\sec^2 A}$

26. $\tan^2 \theta \csc^2 \theta$

27. $\cot^3 Z \sec^2 Z$

28. $\tan^4 T \csc^3 T$

29. $\dfrac{\sec^3 \phi}{\tan^3 \phi}$

30. $\dfrac{\csc^3 \phi}{\cot^2 \phi}$

31. $\dfrac{\tan^5 \theta}{\sec^3 \theta}$

Quiz No. 1. Trigonometry. Form A.

1. Each of the following angles, A and B, is in standard position with the given point on the terminal side. State the numerical value (with proper sign) of each of the six trigonometric functions of each angle.

(a) Angle A: point $(-8, 2)$ (b) Angle B: point $(-3, -5)$

2. State the numerical value of the six trigonometric functions of angle T in the right triangle shown below (Fig. 41.4). Leave answers in fractional and radical form. First find the value of the unknown side.

3. In a certain right triangle, DEF, angle F is the right angle, $D = 36.2°$, and side $e = 66$ inches. Solve the triangle (that is, find E, d, and f).

4. At a certain time of day a flagpole 64 feet high casts a shadow 51.4 feet long. Find the angle of elevation of the sun at that time.

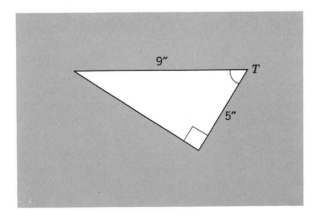

Fig. 41.4

5. A man stands on the top of a 70-foot building. From this position, the angle of depression of the near side of the street is 62.3°, and the angle of depression of the far side is 33.1°. How wide is the street?

6. Using the tables, find the sine, cosine, and tangent of the following:

$$\text{(a) } 264.3° \qquad \text{(b) } 342.6° \qquad \text{(c) } -193.8°$$

7. Find the smallest positive angle for each of the following:

(a) arcsin 0.8554   (b) arccos 0.9527   (c) arctan 1.6909   (d) arccot 0.5820

8. Find two positive angles less than 360° for each of the following:

$$\text{(a) } \cos \theta = -0.3681 \qquad \text{(b) } \tan \phi = 0.3191$$

9. Using the definitions in terms of x, y, and r, show that each of the following is true:

(a) $\dfrac{\sin \theta}{\cos \theta} = \tan \theta$ (b) $\dfrac{1}{\sec \theta} = \cos \theta$ (c) $\sec^2 \theta - \tan^2 \theta = 1$

10. Prove the following identity:

$$\sec^2 \theta + \csc^2 \theta = (\sec^2 \theta)(\csc^2 \theta)$$

Quiz No 1. Trigonometry. Form B.

1. Each of the following angles, A and B, is in standard position with the given point on the terminal side. State the numerical value (with proper sign) of each of the six trigonometric functions of each angle.

(a) Angle A: point $(6, -3)$ (b) Angle B: point $(-2, -7)$

2. State the numerical value of the six trigonometric functions of angle R in the right triangle shown below (Fig. 41.5). Leave answers in fractional and radical form. First find the value of the unknown side.

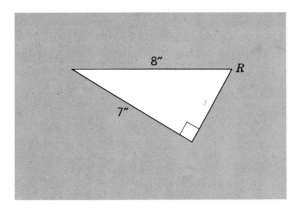

Fig. 41.5

3. In a certain right triangle, *RST*, angle *T* is the right angle, $S = 65.1°$, and side $s = 77$ feet. Solve the triangle (that is, find *R*, *r*, and *t*).

4. A 40-foot ladder leans up against a vertical wall. The foot of the ladder is 7.9 feet from the wall. What angle does the ladder make with the wall?

5. Standing on the ground 90 feet from a building, a man sees a flagpole on the top of the building. The angle of elevation of the bottom of the pole is 37.6°, and the angle of elevation to the top of the pole is 49.6°. Find the length of the flagpole.

6. Using the table, find the sine, cosine, and tangent of the following:

(a) 117.6°   (b) 309.2°   (c) −158.3°

7. Find the smallest positive angle for each of the following:

(a) arcsin 0.5835   (b) arccos 0.4163   (c) arctan 0.5727   (d) arccot 0.3327

8. Find two positive angles less than 360° for each of the following:

(a) $\sin \theta = -0.4019$ (b) $\cot \theta = 0.4942$

9. Using the definition in terms of *x*, *y*, and *r*, show that each of the following is true:

(a) $\dfrac{\cos \theta}{\sin \theta} = \cot \theta$ (b) $\dfrac{1}{\csc \theta} = \sin \theta$ (c) $\csc^2 \theta - 1 = \cot^2 \theta$

10. Prove the following identity:

$$\cos^2 \theta + (\cos^2 \theta)(\tan^2 \theta) + \cot^2 \theta = \csc^2 \theta$$

42
Radian Measure

42.1 DEFINITION OF RADIAN

The size of an angle is usually measured in degrees. Angles may also be measured in right angles. For instance, we can say that the size of an angle is 2 right angles, 3.5 right angles, or 0.24 right angles. Since most tables give angles in degrees, we usually express angular measurement in degrees before looking up the values of the functions in a table; that is, the sine of 0.3 right angles is the same as the sine of 27°, which is 0.4540.

Angles may also be measured in *radians.* The radian is so important in work in trigonometry and in all engineering that we should understand clearly the meaning of the term. A radian is an angle of a definite size, just as one degree is an angle of a definite size.

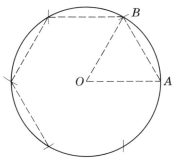

Fig. 42.1

It happens that a radian is an angle of approximately 57.3°; that is, it is a little less than 60°. This will be better understood when we learn the definition of the term. When we say that one radian is an angle of approximately 57.3°, that is a fact, but it is *not* a definition.

Let us see, then, what we mean by the term *radian.* Suppose that we have a circle of any convenient size, such as the circle with center point O (Fig. 42.1). Starting at any point on the circumference, such as A, let us mark off arcs on the circumference, using the same radius as the radius of the circle; that is, the compass is set at length OA, so that $AB = OA$.

The circumference will be divided into six equal arcs. Of course, in actual construction the six points may not turn out to be evenly spaced. Yet it can be proved that an absolutely accurate construction will produce six evenly spaced points.

590

If the six points are joined successively and then each point is joined to the center of the circle by straight lines, six equilateral triangles will be formed. The triangles are also equiangular.

In Fig. 42.1 each angle at the center is 60°. The six angles at the center will add up to 360°, or one complete revolution; that is, by using the radius as the chord *AB*, we *must* get 60° angles at the center. Therefore, there will be exactly six such angles at the center.

Now, if we look at the *arc AB*, we realize that it is slightly longer than the *chord AB*, since a straight line is the shortest distance between two points. We see that the 60° angle at the center cuts off an arc that is slightly more than the radius of the circle. Whatever the size of the circle, a 60° angle at the center will cut off on the circumference an arc slightly greater than the radius of that circle.

Suppose we wish to have an angle at the center of a circle so that the intercepted arc will be *exactly as long as the radius of the circle*; that is, in Fig. 42.2 we want *arc AC* exactly equal in length to the radius *OA*.

Let us assume that the angle *R* at the center does cut off an arc, *AC*, that is equal in length to the radius *r*. Then *angle R is one radian.*

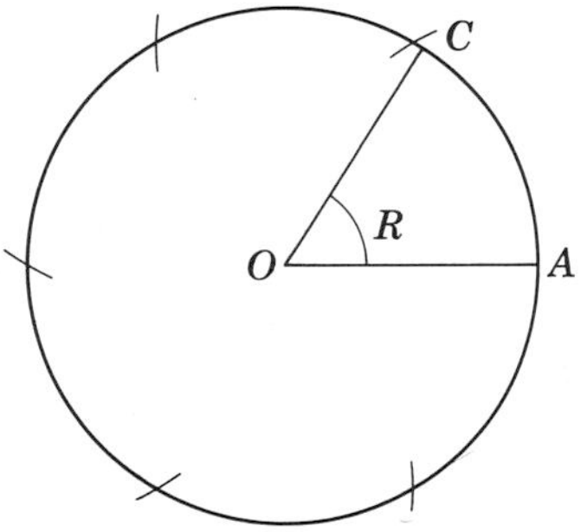

We see that angle *R* must be slightly less than 60°. Actually, one radian is approximately 57.3°. Remember, the radian is *not* the circle; it is *not* the center. It *is* the *angle* which, if placed at the center of the circle, will cut off an arc equal in length to the radius.

A radian need not be at the center of any circle. It may be found anywhere, just as any other angle may be found anywhere. No matter where it is seen, a radian is always a certain size, approximately 57.3°. However, we define a radian with reference to the central angle of a circle and the intercepted arc.

Fig. 42.2

The size of the circle does not affect the size of a radian. One radian at the center of any circle will be just large enough to cut off on the circumference an arc exactly as long as the radius. For instance, if we have a circle whose radius is 6 inches, one radian at the center will intercept an arc 6 inches long. In a circle with a 10-inch diameter, one radian at the center will cut off an arc exactly 5 inches long.

In Fig. 42.3 we see an angle of one radian at the center of concentric circles. In each circle the intercepted arc is exactly equal in length to the radius of that circle.

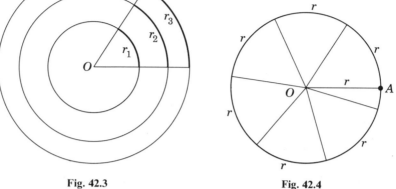

Fig. 42.3   Fig. 42.4

42.2 MEASUREMENT OF ANGLES IN RADIANS

In 180° there are a little over three radians. Actually, 180° is equal to approximately 3.14159 radians, or *exactly* π radians. One revolution, or 360°, is equal to 2π radians. Let us see why this is so.

Suppose we have a circle with center at O, as shown in Fig. 42.4. Let us lay off the radius successively on the circumference starting at any point, A. For each radius length that we lay off on the circumference, we have one radian at the center. We know that the circumference is always 2π times the radius.

$$\text{If} \qquad C = 2\pi \cdot \text{radius,}$$
$$\text{then} \qquad 360° = 2\pi \text{ radians}$$
$$\text{Therefore,} \quad 180° = \pi \text{ radians}$$

In radian measure we often omit the word *radian*; that is, instead of saying 180° = π radians, we say 180° = π.

Exercise 42.1

Fill in the blanks in the following. Work out each answer by *inspection*. For instance, if $\pi = 180°$, then $2\pi = 360°$. State radians in terms of π.

1. 3π = ____°   2. 4π = ____°   3. $\dfrac{\pi}{2}$ = ____°

4. $\dfrac{\pi}{3}$ = ____°   5. $\dfrac{\pi}{6}$ = ____°   6. 8π = ____°

7. 10π = ____°   **8.** $\dfrac{2}{3}\pi$ = ____°   **9.** $\dfrac{3}{2}\pi$ = ____°

10. $180°$ = ____ (radians)   **11.** $135°$ = ____ (radians)   **12.** $150°$ = ____ (radians)

13. $18°$ = ____ (radians)   **14.** $15°$ = ____ (radians)   **15.** $720°$ = ____ (radians)

42.3 CHANGING FROM DEGREES TO RADIANS AND FROM RADIANS TO DEGREES

In the preceding exercises we can change radians to degrees and degrees to radians rather easily. However, the conversion of one kind of measure to the other is often more difficult. Let us formulate two rules for making the changes.

We start with $$180° = \pi \text{ radians}$$

Dividing both sides of this equation by 180, we get

$$1° = \frac{\pi}{180} \text{ radians}$$

This means that if we have any number of degrees given we can change this to radians by multiplying the number by $\pi/180$. As an example,

since $$1° = \pi/180 \text{ radians},$$

then $$17° = (17) \cdot \frac{\pi}{180} \text{ radians}$$

Rule 1. *To change degrees to radians, multiply the number of degrees by $\pi/180$. The result is the number of radians.*

Example 1. Change 86.4° to radians.

Solution. $86.4 \cdot \dfrac{\pi}{180} = 1.508$ radians.

The foregoing rule is sometimes simplified by using the number 57.3, the approximate number of degrees in one radian. We may divide the number of degrees by 57.3 to obtain the number of radians.

$$86.4 \div 57.3 = 1.508, \text{ number of radians.}$$

To change radians to degrees, we begin, again, with the equation

$$\pi \text{ radians} = 180°$$

Dividing both sides of the equation by π, we get the equation

$$1 \text{ radian} = \frac{180°}{\pi}$$

Rule 2. *To change radians to degrees, multiply the number of radians by 180/π*. The result is the number of degrees.

Example 2. Change 2.4 radians to degrees.

Solution. $(2.4)\dfrac{180°}{\pi} = 137.5°$.

Here, again, the work may be simplified by using the number 57.3. We have then

$$2.4 \text{ radians} = 2.4 \times 57.3° = 137.5°$$

Note. In the examples shown the answers have been rounded off to four significant digits.

There is one point that must be clearly understood with reference to any number used in connection with a trigonometric function. When we say, for instance, $\sin \theta$, we think of θ as an angle. The angle is usually stated in degrees. For example, suppose we have the equation

$$\sin 45° = 0.7071$$

Note that the number 45 after the trigonometric function states the angle in *degrees*. However, when any number is used in any way to indicate an angle, then, *if the angle is not definitely stated as degrees*, it must be taken to mean *radians*. For instance, the expression, sin 1, means the sine of one radian; that is, sin 1 means

$$\sin 1 \text{ radian} = \sin 57.3° = 0.8415$$

On the other hand, $\sin 1° = 0.01745$.

We must be especially careful with regard to the number π. The number π taken by itself is the irrational number approximately equal to 3.14159265358979323846264338280, or, less accurately, to 3.1416. But when π, or any other number, is used in such a way that an angle is indicated, then the number must be taken to mean *radians* unless it is definitely stated as degrees.

As an example, the expression sin π means sin π radians, which is the same as sin 180°, which is zero; that is,

$$\sin \pi = \sin 180° = 0$$

However,

$$\sin \pi° = \sin 3.14° = 0.0548 \text{ (approx.)}$$

As another example,

$$\sin \frac{\pi}{3} = \sin \frac{3.1416}{3} = \sin 1.0472 \text{ radians} = \sin 60° = 0.866$$

The expression sin 2π means the sine of 360°, which is zero. However, sin $2\pi°$ is simply the sine of 6.28°, which is approximately equal to 0.10939.*

Exercise 42.2

Change the following degree measure to radian measure:

1. 45°	**2.** 210°	**3.** 225°	**4.** 540°
5. 330°	**6.** 1080°	**7.** −90°	**8.** −450°
9. 25°	**10.** 38.2°	**11.** 152°	**12.** 247°
13. 21600°	**14.** 13.5°	**15.** −74.3°	**16.** 318°
17. 270°	**18.** −120°	**19.** 112.5°	**20.** 4.5°

Change the following *radian measure* to degree measure:

21. 5π	**22.** 2	**23.** 3.4	**24.** 0.213
25. 1.32	**26.** 10	**27.** 7.3	**28.** 377
29. 120	**30.** 0.015	**31.** 6.2832	**32.** 1.414

Find the value of each of the following:

33. $\sin \dfrac{\pi}{2}$	**34.** $\cos \dfrac{\pi}{12}$	**35.** $\sin \dfrac{\pi}{3}$
36. $\tan \dfrac{\pi}{6}$	**37.** $\cot \dfrac{\pi}{4}$	**38.** $\cos \dfrac{2\pi}{3}$
39. $\tan \dfrac{3\pi}{4}$	**40.** $\sec \dfrac{\pi}{5}$	**41.** $\sin \pi°$
42. $\sin 1.3$	**43.** $\cos 1.2$	**44.** $\tan 0.4$
45. $\dfrac{\pi}{2} + \sin \dfrac{\pi}{2}$	**46.** $\pi + \cos \pi$	**47.** $3 + \tan 2$
48. $\dfrac{\pi}{4} + \tan \dfrac{\pi}{4}$	**49.** $1.5 + \tan 1.5$	**50.** $\left(\sin \dfrac{\pi}{4}\right)^2$

†42.4 THE SOLID ANGLE

Radian measure is extended to the measurement of *solid angles*. The solid angle is an important concept in science. The concept is useful in connection with such problems as studio lighting, the magnetic force between masses, the storage of fissionable materials, and in other ways. At this point,

---

* In more advanced studies in mathematics it is necessary to extend the meaning of trigonometry to include the functions of *numbers* rather than angles. However, at present we are concerned only with angles.

† This section may be omitted without any discontinuity in the study of trigonometry.

we shall only attempt to make the idea clear. To see what is meant by a solid angle, let us first repeat the definition of a plane angle.

In trigonometry we find it convenient to define a *plane angle* as the amount of rotation of a ray about its end point. However, for our present purpose,

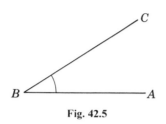

Fig. 42.5

let us go back to an earlier definition and say that a *plane angle* is the *amount of opening between two lines* drawn from a point (Fig. 42.5).

Now let us extend the term *angle* to three dimensions. A *dihedral* angle is a three-dimensional figure formed by two intersecting planes. When we try to represent three-dimensional figures on a plane, we run into trouble. The paper is flat, yet we must try somehow to make a drawing that will represent three dimensions. The result is that we draw figures that are optical illusions. They only *look like* the figures they represent.

Suppose we fold a piece of cardboard and open up the fold as we open the pages of a book. We try to show the result in Fig. 42.6. The figure formed is a *dihedral* angle. (The word *hedral* refers to *side* or *face*.) The two planes forming the angle are called *faces*. The two faces meet in a *line* called the *vertex* of the angle.

We often measure a plane angle in degrees. A dihedral angle can also be measured in degrees. To measure the angle we measure the plane angle between two straight lines in the faces of the dihedral angle from the same

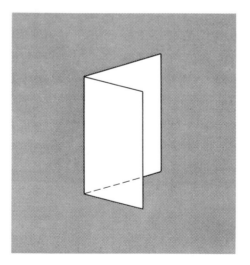

Fig. 42.6

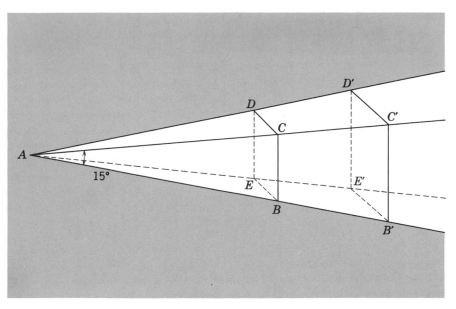

Fig. 42.7

point in the vertex (edge) and perpendicular to the vertex. For example, if the two faces are perpendicular to each other, we say the dihedral angle is 90°.

Now, let us go one step further. Suppose we have three or more planes meeting at a point, such as the apex of a pyramid (Fig. 42.7). The figure formed by these planes outward from their point of intersection will be three-dimensional and, in general, will be pyramidal in shape. Then the *amount of opening* of the planes at the apex is called a *solid angle*.

We have said that a plane angle can be called the amount of opening between two lines drawn from a point. In somewhat the same way, a solid angle is the amount of opening between planes or any other surrounding surfaces coming to a point. The size of a plane angle is not determined by the lengths of the sides. In a similar manner, the amount of opening of a solid angle is not determined by the extent of the planes. Moreover, there may be any number of planes or, in fact, any sort of surrounding surfaces forming the solid angle. A solid angle θ may be denoted by the symbol $\underline{/\theta/}$.

In Fig. 42.7, we have four planes meeting at a point. They are the planes *ABC*, *ACD*, *ADE*, and *AEB*. The four planes meet at point *A*, the apex of the pyramid. Our question now is: How shall we measure the solid angle?

In the figure we might measure several plane angles. For example, we might find that plane angle *BAC* measures 15°. In the same way, we can measure angles *CAD*, *DAE*, and *EAB*. These are plane angles and are measured in

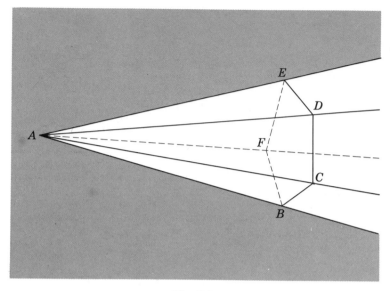

Fig. 42.8

degrees. They may or may not all be equal to each other. Again, we might
measure the dihedral angle formed by two faces of the pyramid. The dihedral
angles can also be measured in degrees.

Now we come to the solid angle. How shall it be measured? It is not the
sum of the plane angles at A, nor is it the sum of the dihedral angles.

Let us take points B, C, D, and E on the edges of the pyramid, respectively,
so that these points are equidistant from A. If the four dihedral angles are
equal, then the figure $BCDE$ is a square. The *area* of this square is a measure
of the size of the solid angle. To be strictly correct, we should assume that the
square surface is curved so that every point on the square is equidistant from
A.

If we take four other points, B', C', D', and E', all equidistant from A, the
area included in the square $B'C'D'E'$ is also a measure of the same solid angle.
The solid angle is still the same size, although the larger square has the greater
area.

Of course, there may be any number of planes meeting at a point. Let us
suppose we have five planes all intersecting at point A (Fig. 42.8). The solid
angle is the amount of opening between the five planes. Let us again take
points B, C, D, E, and F on the edges of the pyramid, all equidistant from A.
Then the solid angle at A is measured by the area of the polygon, $BCDEF$.

We may have any number of planes forming the solid angle. The polygon
whose area we have been considering will have as many sides as the number of

planes forming the solid angle. The area may have any shape. For measuring the size of a solid angle, we consider the particular area intercepted by planes or other surfaces meeting at a point and at a specified distance from the common point.

The unit for measuring solid angles is called a *steradian*. If we think of a solid angle as being located at the center of a sphere, then we take into account the amount of area that the *central solid angle* intercepts on the surface of the sphere. A *central plane angle* of a *circle* intercepts an *arc* on the *circumference* (see Section 29.1). In a similar manner, a *central solid angle* of a *sphere* intercepts an *area* on the *surface* of the *sphere*.

Now, recall that one radian at the center of a circle intercepts an arc equal in length to the radius, by definition. Then we have the following definition of a *steradian*.

Definition. *One steradian is a solid angle of such size that when placed at the center of a sphere, it intercepts on the surface of the sphere an area exactly equal to the square of the radius* (Fig. 42.9).

If the radius of a sphere is 10 inches, then one steradian at the center will intercept an area of 100 square inches on the surface of the sphere. This area, in fact, may be any shape—square, triangular, circular, or irregular. In general, one steradian at the center of a sphere of radius r intercepts an area equal to r^2 on the surface.

The surface area of any sphere is given by the formula: $A = 4\pi r^2$. Since one steradian at the center intercepts an area of r^2 on the surface, the total

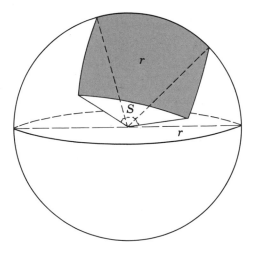

Fig. 42.9

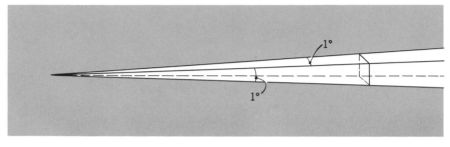

Fig. 42.10

surface of the sphere must be associated with 4π steradians. Therefore, the entire solid angle from any point in space, or the total amount of opening in all directions from a point, is 4π steradians.

For measuring *plane angles*, the radian is a rather large unit. Instead, we often use a smaller unit, the *degree*. In the same way, the steradian is a rather large unit for measuring *solid angles*. It is possible to use a smaller unit. Let us see how this is done.

We have seen that an angle of one degree is called an *angle degree* (Section 29.1). Also, one angle degree at the center of a circle intercepts an arc called one *arc degree* on the circumference.

Consider now a regular square pyramid with its apex at the center of a sphere, and of such size that each plane angle at the apex is 1° (Fig. 42.10). Each plane angle of 1° will intercept one arc degree on a great circle of the sphere. We call the solid angle or amount of opening at the apex of this pyramid one *square degree*. (This is analogous to our definition of a *square inch* as a unit of area.) Then we have the following definition of a square degree.

Definition.   *One square degree is a solid angle equivalent to the opening at the apex of a regular square pyramid each of whose plane angles at the apex is one angle degree.*

We already have the following formulas:

$$\pi \text{ radians} = 180° \qquad 1 \text{ radian} = \frac{180°}{\pi}$$

Therefore, the radius is equal in length to $180/\pi$ arc degrees.

Now we derive the following formulas. Since

$$r = \frac{180}{\pi} \text{ arc degrees in length}, \qquad r^2 = \left(\frac{180}{\pi}\right)^2 \text{ square arc degrees}$$

For the area of a sphere,

$$A = 4\pi r^2 = 4\pi\left(\frac{180}{\pi}\right)^2 \text{ square arc degrees}$$

Then

$$4\pi \text{ steradians} = \frac{129600}{\pi} \text{ square degrees}$$

Therefore, the entire solid angle about any point in space is $\dfrac{129600}{\pi} \text{ deg}^2$.

The size of a solid angle is an important consideration in the size of a TV or movie screen. There is an optimum size of the solid angle for viewing a TV or movie if viewing is to be most comfortable. Sometimes it is a simple matter to compute the size of the solid angle. Suppose you sit directly before a home movie screen that is rectangular in shape. Let us assume that the plane angle between your lines of sight to the left side and the right side is 15° (Fig. 42.11). That is, the horizontal spread of your eyesight to the screen is 15°. Suppose also that the vertical spread of your eyesight to the top and bottom of the screen is 12°. Then, since the screen is rectangular, the solid angle, $\underline{/A/}$, is given by

$$\underline{/A/} = (15°)(12°) = 180 \text{ deg}^2$$

If one is seated about 7 feet from a TV screen that is 15 inches high and 19 inches wide, the solid angle in the viewing is approximately 132 square degrees. If one moves up to a distance of 6 feet from the TV, the solid angle is approximately 179 square degrees. Let us see how the size of a solid angle can be computed.

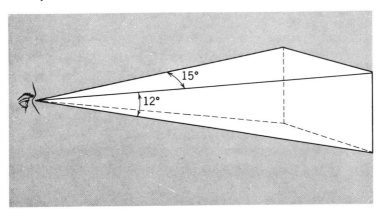

Fig. 42.11

Example 1. Suppose you sit directly in front of a home movie screen that is 4 feet wide and 3 feet high. You sit 15 feet from the screen with the center of the screen on a level with your eyes. What is the size of the solid angle from your eyes to the perimeter of the screen?

Solution. We take the top of the screen at 1.5 feet above eye level and the bottom of the screen at 1.5 feet below eye level (Fig. 42.12). Now let us say 2α is the plane angle between the lines of sight to the top and bottom of the screen. Then we have an angle of α above and α below eye level. Then

$$\tan \alpha = 1.5/15 = 0.1000 \quad \text{or} \quad \alpha = 5.7° \text{ (approx.)}; \quad \text{then } 2\alpha = 11.4°$$

Note that we cannot take 3/15 as the tangent of 2α.

In a similar manner we can find the horizontal angle between the left and right edges of the screen. Calling this angle 2β, we have

$$\tan \beta = 2/15 = 0.13333 \quad \text{or} \quad \beta = 7.6° \text{ (approx.)}; \quad \text{then } 2\beta = 15.2°$$

Now we have a vertical spread of 11.4° and a horizontal spread of 15.2°. Then the solid angle, $\underline{/A\,/}$, is found by

$$\underline{/A\,/} = (11.4°)(15.2°) = 173.3 \text{ deg}^2 \text{ (approx.)}$$

Approximate solution: We can get an approximation to the size of the solid angle without using trigonometry if we consider every point on the screen to be 15 feet from our eyes (which of course is not true). Then the number of square degrees can be computed as a 12-square-feet portion of the entire surface of a sphere having a radius of 15 feet. That is, we take

$$\frac{12}{4\pi 225}\left(\frac{129600}{\pi}\right) = \frac{12}{900}\left(\frac{129600}{\pi^2}\right) = 175.1 \text{ (approx.)}$$

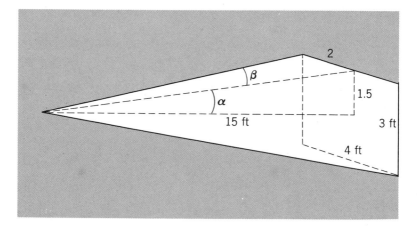

Fig. 42.12

The formula is approximately: $\underline{/A/} = \left(\dfrac{\text{area}}{d^2}\right)(3280)$, where d represents the distance from the viewer to the object.

Example 2. A right circular cone has an altitude of 20 inches and the diameter of its base of 8 inches. Find the solid angle at the apex of the cone.

Solution. Let α be the plane angle between the altitude and an element of the cone. Then

$$\tan \alpha = 4/20 = 0.20000; \qquad \alpha = 11.31°; \qquad 2\alpha = 22.62°$$

Now if the base were a square with 8 inches on a side the solid angle would be

$$(22.62°)^2 \qquad \text{or} \qquad 511.7 \deg^2$$

However, we know the area of a circle is approximately 0.7854 times the area of a circumscribed square. Then, for the solid angle of the cone, we have (0.7854) (512.6) $= 401.9 \deg^2$, the solid angle at the apex of the cone. Using the approximation formula, we get $412.2 \deg^2$ (approx.).

Note that the result from using geometry instead of trigonometry turns out to be slightly greater in each case than the true size of the solid angle. This is because in using geometry, we neglect the fact that the surface we are considering is a plane rather than the curved surface of a sphere. The error becomes greater as the viewed area increases in size with reference to the distance from the viewer. If we take the maximum distance across any viewed area as compared with the distance from the viewer, then, if this ratio is less than $1/4$, there is little error through use of the approximate formula.

Exercise 42.3

Use trigonometry to solve the following problems.

In the first six of the following exercises, find the size of the solid angle from a point directly in front of the center of the object:

1. A picture, 8 feet wide and 6 feet high, from a distance of 20 feet.
2. A rectangular picture, 6 by 4 feet, from a distance of 20 feet.
3. A TV screen, 24 inches wide and 20 inches high, from 12 feet away.
4. A movie screen, 24 feet wide and 15 feet high, from 60 feet away.
5. A circular picture, 36 inches in diameter, from 12 feet away.
6. A speck of uranium, 4 feet from a ball of material 8 inches in diameter.
7. Find the size of the solid angle in No. 1, if the line of sight is perpendicular to the picture at one corner of the picture.
8. Work No. 4 if you sit with your eyes on a level with the bottom of the screen and 4 feet to the right of center.
9. How far from a movie screen, 15 feet high and 24 feet wide, should you sit for a solid angle of 240 square degrees if you sit directly before the center?
10. What should be the size of a TV screen, with a ratio of width to height of 6 to 5, if you wish to sit 6 feet from the TV and the solid angle is to be 270 square degrees?
11. How far should the speck of uranium in Problem No. 6 be placed from the other ball of material if the solid angle is not to exceed 36 square degrees?

43

Special Angles

43.1 THE 30°-60° RIGHT TRIANGLE

If we wish to know the sine, or any function, of an angle, we usually look up the value in a table. Yet it is often desirable to find the value of a trigonometric function without the use of a table. This is especially true with regard to certain angles.

In the case of most angles the computation of the numerical values of the functions is a complicated process. However, for a few special angles we can compute the values rather easily. For instance, one such angle is a 30° angle. Let us see, then, how we might find the sine, cosine, and other functions of a 30° angle without using a table.

Suppose we have a 30° angle in standard position (Fig. 43.1). We take a point, *P*, on the terminal side of the angle and show the ordinate. The triangle formed by the ordinate, the abscissa, and the radius vector has one acute angle of 30°. Therefore, the other acute angle of the triangle is 60°. Here we have what is called a "30°-60° right triangle."

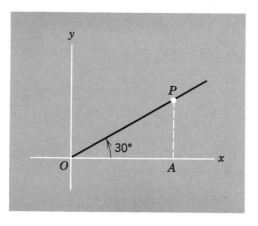

Fig. 43.1

604

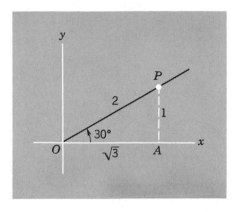

Fig. 43.2

In geometry it is proved that *in any 30°-60° right triangle the hypotenuse is always exactly twice the length of the shortest side.* Therefore, in Fig. 43.1 side *AP* is one-half the length of side *OP*.

If we assume that *AP* is 4 inches, then *OP* is 8 inches. Whatever length we assume for *AP*, the hypotenuse *OP* will always be twice as long. Therefore, the sine of 30° is $\frac{1}{2}$, or 0.5000. We may just as well assume that the length of *AP* is 1 unit and that the length of *OP* is equal to 2 units. The sine of 30° is still $\frac{1}{2}$, or 0.5000.

In order to find the values of the other functions of a 30° angle, we place the numbers 1 and 2 on the triangle in the proper places to represent those lengths (Fig. 43.2). The third side of the triangle is then computed by the Pythagorean rule. It is $\sqrt{3}$. These numbers, 1, 2, and $\sqrt{3}$, are shown in proper positions on the triangle in Fig. 43.2. We must be sure to use the number 1 for the shortest side of the triangle and the number 2 for the hypotenuse.

We can now express the six functions of an angle of 30° or $\pi/6$ radians. From the definitions of the functions, we have

$$\sin \frac{\pi}{6} = \sin 30° = \frac{y}{r} = \frac{1}{2} \qquad \cos \frac{\pi}{6} = \cos 30° = \frac{x}{r} = \frac{\sqrt{3}}{2}$$

$$\tan \frac{\pi}{6} = \tan 30° = \frac{y}{x} = \frac{1}{\sqrt{3}} \qquad \cot \frac{\pi}{6} = \cot 30° = \frac{x}{y} = \sqrt{3}$$

$$\sec \frac{\pi}{6} = \sec 30° = \frac{r}{x} = \frac{2}{\sqrt{3}} \qquad \csc \frac{\pi}{6} = \csc 30° = \frac{r}{y} = 2$$

These values can be changed to decimal form if desired.

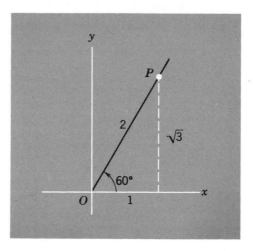

Fig. 43.3

If we have a 60° angle in standard position (Fig. 43.3), the same 30°-60° triangle will appear in the sketch. We can use the same numbers, 1, 2, and $\sqrt{3}$, to find the values of the functions of a 60° angle. For instance, by definition, the sine of 60° $= y/r = (\sqrt{3})/2$.

The same 30°-60° right triangle will appear for several other angles in standard position. As an example, suppose we wish to find the functions of an angle of 240°, which is equal to $4\pi/3$ radians.

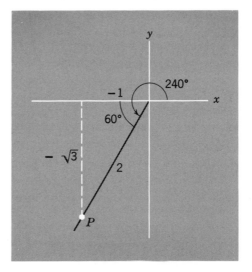

Fig. 43.4

We sketch the 240° angle in standard position (Fig. 43.4). When we draw a vertical line to indicate the ordinate, we see a 30°-60° right triangle in the sketch. In this case the reference angle is 60°. We place the numbers, 1, 2, and $\sqrt{3}$ in the proper positions on the right triangle. Moreover, we must indicate whether these values are positive or negative for the 240° angle. The signs of the numbers will depend on the signs of x and y for the point on the terminal side.

For the 240° angle, $x = -1$, $y = -\sqrt{3}$, and $r = 2$. Then we have the following values for the angle of 240°, or $(4\pi/3)$ radians:

$$\sin \frac{4\pi}{3} = \sin 240° = \frac{y}{r} = \frac{-\sqrt{3}}{2} \qquad \cos \frac{4\pi}{3} = \cos 240° = \frac{x}{r} = \frac{-1}{2}$$

$$\tan \frac{4\pi}{3} = \tan 240° = \frac{y}{x} = \frac{-\sqrt{3}}{-1} \qquad \cot \frac{4\pi}{3} = \cot 240° = \frac{x}{y} = \frac{-1}{-\sqrt{3}}$$

$$\sec \frac{4\pi}{3} = \sec 240° = \frac{r}{x} = \frac{2}{-1} \qquad \csc \frac{4\pi}{3} = \csc 240° = \frac{r}{y} = \frac{2}{-\sqrt{3}}$$

These values can be changed to decimal form and each one given its proper sign.

43.2 THE 45° RIGHT TRIANGLE

Another special angle for which we can easily compute the functions is a 45° angle. Suppose we sketch a 45° angle in standard position (Fig. 43.5). Take point P on the terminal side. In the triangle AOP one acute angle is 45°. Therefore, the other acute angle is also 45°. Therefore, $OA = AP$. The

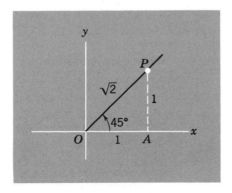

Fig. 43.5

triangle formed is called a "45° right triangle." If we assume that AP is 4 inches, then OA is also 4 inches, and $OP = 4\sqrt{2}$ inches.

We may assume that AP is equal to 1 unit. Then $OA = 1$, and $OP = \sqrt{2}$. The numerical values of the ratios will not change, regardless of the length we assume for OA. Using the numbers 1, 1, and $\sqrt{2}$ for the two sides and the hypotenuse, respectively, we can compute all the values of the functions of the 45° angle, which is equal to $(\pi/4)$ radians:

$$\sin\frac{\pi}{4} = \sin 45° = \frac{y}{r} = \frac{1}{\sqrt{2}} \qquad \cos\frac{\pi}{4} = \cos 45° = \frac{x}{r} = \frac{1}{\sqrt{2}}$$

$$\tan\frac{\pi}{4} = \tan 45° = \frac{y}{x} = 1 \qquad \cot\frac{\pi}{4} = \cot 45° = \frac{x}{y} = 1$$

$$\sec\frac{\pi}{4} = \sec 45° = \frac{r}{x} = \sqrt{2} \qquad \csc\frac{\pi}{4} = \csc 45° = \frac{r}{y} = \sqrt{2}$$

We can use the numbers 1, 1, and $\sqrt{2}$ to find the values of the functions of any angle whenever a 45° angle appears in the sketch of the given angle in standard position. This will be true for an angle of 135°, an angle of 225°, an angle of 315°, or for any angle, positive or negative, whose terminal side falls in one of the corresponding positions.

We must be sure to place the numbers 1, 1, and $\sqrt{2}$ in their proper positions on the right triangle in the sketch. Moreover, we must indicate whether the numbers are positive or negative for the given angle. This will depend upon the signs of x and y for the point on the terminal side.

As an example, let us take an angle of $(-45°)$ in standard position (Fig. 43.6). (Parentheses are often used to enclose a negative angle.) We take any

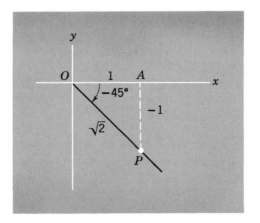

Fig. 43.6

point, P, on the terminal side and show the ordinate length. The triangle formed is a 45° right triangle. We place the numbers 1, 1, and $\sqrt{2}$ on the sides of the triangle in proper positions and with the correct signs. Since point P lies in the fourth quadrant, the abscissa is positive and the ordinate is negative. The radius vector is always positive.

From the values shown, we can write all the function values for $(-45°)$, or $(-\pi/4)$ radians. The values can be reduced to decimal form if desired.

$$\sin\left(-\frac{\pi}{4}\right) = \sin(-45°) = \frac{y}{r} = \frac{-1}{\sqrt{2}} = -0.7071$$

$$\cos\left(-\frac{\pi}{4}\right) = \cos(-45°) = \frac{x}{r} = \frac{+1}{\sqrt{2}} = +0.7071$$

$$\tan\left(-\frac{\pi}{4}\right) = \tan(-45°) = \frac{y}{x} = \frac{-1}{+1} = -1.000$$

$$\cot\left(-\frac{\pi}{4}\right) = \cot(-45°) = \frac{x}{y} = \frac{+1}{-1} = -1.000$$

$$\sec\left(-\frac{\pi}{4}\right) = \sec(-45°) = \frac{r}{x} = \frac{\sqrt{2}}{+1} = +1.414$$

$$\csc\left(-\frac{\pi}{4}\right) = \csc(-45°) = \frac{r}{y} = \frac{\sqrt{2}}{-1} = -1.414$$

43.3 QUADRANTAL ANGLES

We now consider a few angles that require special attention. They are the *quadrantal* angles whose terminal sides fall on one of the coordinate axes, such as 0°, 90°, 180°, 270°, 360°, or any other angles, positive or negative, whose terminal sides fall in like positions. The functions of such angles may be found in the following manner.

Sketch the angle in standard position, showing the terminal side along the axis. Indicate the angle by a curved arrow. Assume some point on the terminal side. Then express the abscissa, the ordinate, and the radius vector of the point. The function values can then be written from the definitions.

Example.   Find the six trigonometric functions of 180°, or π radians.

First, we sketch the angle in standard position (Fig. 43.7). Now we assume some point, say, $(-6, 0)$, on the terminal side. Then, for this angle of 180°, we have

$$x = -6 \qquad y = 0 \qquad r = 6$$

From these values the numerical values of all the functions of 180° can be written.

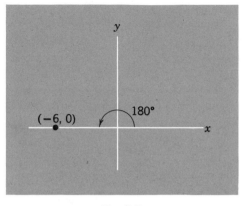

Fig. 43.7

Remember to show the proper sign for each function. If a zero appears in the denominator of a fraction, the function is not defined for the angle. The functions of 180°, or π radians are as follows:

$$\sin \pi = \frac{y}{r} = \frac{0}{6} = 0 \qquad\qquad \cot \pi = \frac{x}{y} = \frac{-6}{0} \quad \text{(not defined)}$$

$$\cos \pi = \frac{x}{r} = \frac{-6}{6} = -1 \qquad \sec \pi = \frac{r}{x} = \frac{6}{-6} = -1$$

$$\tan \pi = \frac{y}{x} = \frac{0}{-6} = 0 \qquad\qquad \csc \pi = \frac{r}{y} = \frac{6}{0} = \text{(not defined)}$$

Exercise 43.1

Find the sine, cosine, tangent, cotangent, secant, and cosecant for each of the following angles. Also sketch each angle in standard position and state each angle in radian measure. Do not use a table of function values here.

1.	0°	**2.**	30°	**3.**	45°	**4.**	60°
5.	90°	**6.**	120°	**7.**	135°	**8.**	150°
9.	180°	**10.**	−150°	**11.**	225°	**12.**	240°
13.	−90°	**14.**	300°	**15.**	−45°	**16.**	−30°
17.	330°	**18.**	−180°	**19.**	450°	**20.**	690°
21.	−60°	**22.**	−120°	**23.**	990°	**24.**	−270°

Find each of the following by the use of special angles:

25. $\sin \dfrac{\pi}{6} + \cos \dfrac{\pi}{3}$

26. $\cos \dfrac{2\pi}{3} + 2 \cos \pi$

27. $\sin \dfrac{5\pi}{6} + \cos \dfrac{4\pi}{3}$

28. $\cos^2 \dfrac{\pi}{4} - \cos \pi$

29. $\tan \dfrac{2\pi}{3} \sec \dfrac{2\pi}{3}$

30. $\sin^2 \dfrac{3\pi}{4} + \cos^3 \dfrac{3\pi}{4}$

31. $\sin \dfrac{5\pi}{4} \cos^3 \dfrac{5\pi}{4}$

32. $\sec^2 \dfrac{7\pi}{6} + \csc^2 \dfrac{7\pi}{6}$

33. $\tan \dfrac{5\pi}{6} + \sec \dfrac{5\pi}{6}$

34. $\sin^3 \dfrac{7\pi}{4} - \cos \dfrac{7\pi}{4}$

35. $\sec^2 \dfrac{5\pi}{4} - \tan^2 \dfrac{5\pi}{4}$

36. $\csc^2 \dfrac{3\pi}{4} - \cot^2 \dfrac{3\pi}{4}$

37. $\tan^3 \dfrac{7\pi}{4} \cot^3 \dfrac{7\pi}{4}$

38. $\sin^2 \dfrac{3\pi}{2} + \cos^2 \dfrac{3\pi}{2}$

39. $\sin \dfrac{\pi}{2} + \tan \dfrac{\pi}{2}$

40. $\tan \dfrac{3\pi}{2} \cot \dfrac{3\pi}{2}$

41. $\sec^2(-45°) - \tan^2(-45°)$

42. $\sin^2 300° \cos^4 300°$

43. $\sec^3 150° \csc^3 150°$

44. $\cot^3 135° - \sin^3 270°$

45. $\cot^3 180° \csc^2 315°$

46. $\csc^2 225° \cot^3 150°$

47. $(\tan^2 300°)(\cot^2 300°) + \sin^2 300° + \cos^2 300°$

48. $(\sin 150°)(\cos 240°) - (\cos 150°)(\sin 240°)$

49. $(\cot 30°)(\csc 60°) + (\tan 60°)(\sec 45°)$

50. $(\sin 120°)(\sec 135°) - (\sec^2 240°)(\csc^2 240°)$

51. If $\theta = \arcsin\left(\dfrac{-\sqrt{3}}{2}\right)$, find two positive values of θ less than 360°.

52. If $\phi = \arctan(-1)$, find two positive values of ϕ less than 360°.

53. Find $\log_e \tan^2 120°$.

54. Find $\log_e \sec 45° + \log_e \csc 135°$.

55. Find $\log_e \cot 210° + \log_e \csc 150°$.

56. Find $\log_e \sin 120° - \log_e \tan 240°$.

43.4   TRIGONOMETRIC EQUATIONS

In Chapter 41 we saw the meaning of a trigonometric identity. An identity is an equation that is true for all values of the angle θ, just as an identity in algebra is true for all values of an unknown, x.

Now, a trigonometric equation may be true for some values but not for all values of the angle θ. Then it is not an identity but a *conditional equation*. Just as a conditional equation in algebra calls for a *solution*, so does a conditional equation in trigonometry.

Consider the following conditional equation in algebra: $x^2 - 2x - 8 = 0$. The equation is true only if $x = -2$ or $x = 4$. These are solutions. To solve a conditional equation, we find values of the unknown that make the equation true.

   In trigonometry we have a similar situation. For example, suppose we have the equation,

$$\sin \theta = \cos \theta$$

This is not an identity because it is not true for all values of θ. Now we try to find the solutions, that is, the values of θ that make the equation true. If we divide both sides of the equation by $\cos \theta$ we get

$$\frac{\sin \theta}{\cos \theta} = 1$$

We can replace the left side of the equation by its equivalent, *tan* θ, and get

$$\tan \theta = 1$$

There are an infinite number of angles θ whose tangent is 1. However, we confine the solutions to values of θ from 0 to 360°, but not including 360°, since the values for 360° are the same as those for zero. Then,

$$\text{if} \quad \tan \theta = 1$$
$$\theta = 45° \text{ and } 225°$$

Checking these values, we find that they both satisfy the original equation.

Example 1.   Find all values of θ from 0° to but not including 360° such that

$$\sin 3\,\theta = \tfrac{1}{2}$$

   Solution.   First, we seek values of the entire angle, $3\,\theta$, having a sine value equal to $\tfrac{1}{2}$. The only angles less than 360° satisfying this condition are angles of 30° and 150°. Then we first say

$$\text{if} \quad \sin 3\,\theta = \tfrac{1}{2}$$
$$\text{then} \quad 3\,\theta = 30° \text{ and } 150°$$

However, these values are not the solutions to the problem. The problem calls for values of θ, not only $3\,\theta$. As values of θ, we get

$$\theta = 10° \text{ and } 50°$$

There are also other values that satisfy the equation. To get all values of θ, we go around the circle three times for $3\,\theta$ and get

$$3\,\theta = 30°\,;\,150°\,;\,390°\,;\,510°\,;\,750°\,;\,870°$$
$$\text{then} \quad \theta = 10°\,;\,50°\,;\,130°\,;\,170°\,;\,250°\,;\,290°$$

Example 2.   Solve the following equation: $\cos^2 \theta = \tfrac{1}{4}$.

   Solution.   Taking the square root, $\cos \theta = \pm\tfrac{1}{2}$. Since we can take positive and negative values, we get

$$\theta = 60°\,;\,120°\,;\,240°\,;\,300°$$

Exercise 43.2

Solve the following equations for all values of the unknown from zero up to but not including 360°.

1. $\sin \theta = \frac{1}{2}$

2. $\sin^2 \theta = 1$

3. $\cos^2 2\phi = 1$

4. $\tan^2 \theta = 1$

5. $\tan^2 \phi = 3$

6. $\sin 3\phi = 1$

7. $\cos 3x = 0$

8. $\sin^2 4x = \frac{3}{4}$

9. $\tan 5x = -1$

10. $\sec 2\phi = 1$

11. $\csc^2 \theta = 4$

12. $\cot^2 3x = 0$

13. $\sin \theta = \sqrt{3} \cos \theta$

14. $3 \cos 2x = 2 - \cos 2x$

15. $4 \cos^2 3x - 3 = 0$

16. $\tan^2 \theta - \tan \theta = 0$

17. $\sin^2 \theta - 2 \sin \theta = 0$

18. $3 \sin^2 \theta - 2 \sin \theta = 1$

19. $\sin^2 \theta + \sin \theta = 2$

20. $\sin^2 2x - 3 \cos^2 2x = 0$

44

Multiple Angle Formulas

44.1 PREASSIGNMENT

In order to understand more clearly the subject of this chapter, the student should first work out the following assignment:

1. Copy in *table form* the sine for each of the following angles:

$$0°, 10°, 20°, 30°, 40°, 50°, 60°, 70°, 80°, 90°$$

Then answer the following questions:

(a) As the angle increases from 0 to 90°, does the sine value increase or decrease?

(b) If an angle is doubled, is its sine doubled?

(c) Is the sine of 80° equal to the sine of 50° plus the sine of 30°; that is, is sin 80° = sin 50° + sin 30°?

(d) If one angle is one-half another angle, is its sine also one-half as much?

(e) Do angles have the same ratio as their sines? For example, if one angle is three-fifths of another angle, is its sine value also three-fifths as great?

2. Copy in table form the cosines of the angles in No. 1.

(a, b, c, d, e) Answer the same questions for the cosine.

3. Copy in table form the tangents of the same angles.

(a, b, c, d, e) Answer the same questions for the tangent.

44.2 SUM AND DIFFERENCE FORMULAS

From the preceding exercises a few facts should be noted. First, we note that the *sine of the sum* of two angles is *not* equal to the *sum of the sines* of the two angles. For instance, the sine of 50° cannot be found simply by adding the sine of 20° to the sine of 30°.

As another example, if we wish to find the sine of 75°, we cannot find it simply by adding the sine of 45° to the sine of 30°. However, it is sometimes convenient and desirable to compute the functions of some angle, such as the sine of 75°, from the functions of other angles.

Let us make one point clear. In most problems, if we wish to find the functions of any angle, we look up the values in a table. We can do the same for an angle of 75°, 15°, or for any other angle. Yet it is possible to find the functions of some angles by using functions of other angles that can be computed *without a table*. Let us see how this is done.

We have seen that we can easily find the functions of 45° and 30° without the use of a table. Now, it happens that the functions of 75° can be computed from the functions of 45° and 30°. Remember, the sine of 75° *cannot* be found simply by adding the sines of the other two angles. Instead, it can be shown that

$$\sin 75° = (\sin 45°)(\cos 30°) + (\cos 45°)(\sin 30°)$$

or

$$\sin (45° + 30°) = (\sin 45°)(\cos 30°) + (\cos 45°)(\sin 30°)$$

By using the values of the sines and cosines of 30° and 45°, we can find the sine of 75°. The following values can be found without a table:

$$\sin 45° = \frac{\sqrt{2}}{2} \qquad \sin 30° = \frac{1}{2}$$

$$\cos 45° = \frac{\sqrt{2}}{2} \qquad \cos 30° = \frac{\sqrt{3}}{2}$$

Substituting numerical values in the foregoing equation, we get

$$\sin 75° = \frac{\sqrt{2}}{2} \cdot \frac{\sqrt{3}}{2} + \frac{\sqrt{2}}{2} \cdot \frac{1}{2}$$

$$= \frac{\sqrt{6}}{4} + \frac{\sqrt{2}}{4} = \frac{\sqrt{6} + \sqrt{2}}{4}$$

$$= \frac{2.449 + 1.414}{4} = \frac{3.863}{4} = 0.966$$

Let us state the rule in words.

Rule.   *The sine of the sum of two angles is equal to the sine of the first angle times the cosine of the second angle, plus the cosine of the first angle times the sine of the second angle.*

If we let A and B represent any two angles, we· may state the rule as a formula:

$$\sin (A + B) = (\sin A)(\cos B) + (\cos A)(\sin B) \qquad \text{(Formula 1)}$$

This is called the formula for the *sine of the sum of two angles.*

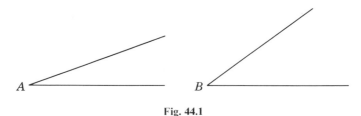

Fig. 44.1

This formula can be used to compute the sine of any angle that can be expressed as *the sum of any two of the special angles we have studied.* For example, we can use the formula to compute the sine of 165°, since 165° may be called (120° + 45°). We have already seen how to find the functions of these two angles.

Note. The formula is an identity and can be used for any angle if the angle is expressed as the sum of two other angles. For instance, it could be used to find the sine of 68° by combining the functions of 47° and 21° in the proper manner. The formula might be checked for any combination of angles. However, it is not used generally, except with reference to a combination of the special angles we have mentioned in Chapter 43, that is, a combination of a 30° and a 45° angle or multiples of these angles.

We shall now show how this formula is derived. Let us start with any two general angles, A and B, as shown in Fig. 44.1.*

To show the sum of the two angles, $A + B$, we add them geometrically and place the sum in standard position. In Fig. 44.2.

$$A + B = \text{angle } COD$$

The sine of $(A + B)$ is the same as the sine of angle COD.

To express the sine of angle COD, take a point P on the terminal side OD. Draw a line PM perpendicular to the x-axis. We then have

$$\sin (A + B) = \frac{MP}{OP}$$

Our problem now becomes a question of expressing the two lengths, MP and OP, as functions of the angles, A and B. To do so, we first draw three other line segments.

1. Draw PQ perpendicular to OE.
2. Draw QN perpendicular to the x-axis.
3. Draw QR perpendicular to MP.

---

* The derivation shown here is geometric in nature. The formula may also be derived by the analytic method which depends on the use of the formula for the distance between two points.

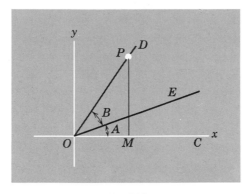

Fig. 44.2

In Fig. 44.3 we see that MR is equal to NQ. Also angle RPQ is equal to the angle A, since their sides, respectively, are perpendicular, right to right, and left to left.

Let us go back to the definition of the sine of $(A + B)$:

$$\sin(A + B) = \frac{MP}{OP}$$

Now, since $MP = MR + RP$, we can write

$$\sin(A + B) = \frac{MR + RP}{OP}$$

Separating the right side into two fractions, we get

$$\sin(A + B) = \frac{MR}{OP} + \frac{RP}{OP}$$

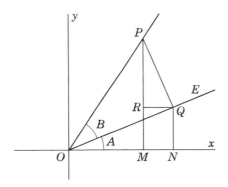

Fig. 44.3

or

$$\sin (A + B) = \frac{NQ}{OP} + \frac{RP}{OP}$$

Sine and cosine functions may now be substituted for the fractions on the right side of the equation. Note that

$$\frac{NQ}{OQ} = \sin A; \qquad \text{therefore, } NQ = OQ \sin A$$

$$\frac{RP}{PQ} = \cos A; \qquad \text{therefore, } RP = PQ \cos A$$

If we replace NQ with its equal, $OQ \sin A$, and replace RP with its equal, $PQ \cos A$, in the formula, we get

$$\sin (A + B) = \frac{OQ \sin A}{OP} + \frac{PQ \cos A}{OP}$$

From Fig. 44.3 we note that

$$\frac{OQ}{OP} = \cos B \qquad \text{and} \qquad \frac{PQ}{OP} = \sin B$$

By substitution of equals, the final formula becomes

$$\sin (A + B) = \sin A \cos B + \cos A \sin B \qquad \text{(Formula 1)}$$

(The parentheses are usually omitted on the right side of the equation.)

To derive the formula for the cosine of $(A + B)$, we also use Fig. 44.3. To express this function, we first write

$$\cos (A + B) = \frac{OM}{OP}$$

From the figure we see that $OM = ON - MN$ and $MN = RQ$. The final formula becomes

$$\cos (A + B) = \cos A \cos B - \sin A \sin B \qquad \text{(Formula 2)}$$

This is the formula for the *cosine* of the *sum* of two angles. The derivation is left as an exercise for the student.

In demonstrating that the foregoing formulas hold true, we have used two angles whose sum is less than 90°; that is, the terminal side of the sum $(A + B)$ still falls in the first quadrant. The angles and the figure we have used do not apply to the cases in which the terminal side of the sum falls in other quadrants. A formula derived from one particular situation cannot always be assumed to be true for a different situation. However, these formulas can be proved true for all cases by using two angles whose sum falls in each of the four quadrants. The complete proof requires four different figures. The student should try to show that the formulas are true for each of the four quadrants.

Other formulas, similar to the foregoing, refer to the *difference* between two angles. In the exercises in the preassignment at the beginning of this chapter it will be noted that we cannot find the sine of the *difference* between two angles simply by subtracting the sines of the two angles. For instance, the sine of 15° cannot be found simply by subtracting the sine of 30° from the sine of 45°.

However, the sine, as well as the other functions, of 15° can be found by the formulas for the functions of the *difference* between two angles. The *difference* formulas can be derived directly from the foregoing *sum* formulas. First, it is necessary to see the relation between functions of negative and positive angles of equal magnitude.

First, we ask: What is the relation between the sine of a negative angle and the sine of the corresponding positive angle of equal magnitude? Let us take a positive angle θ ending in the first quadrant. Then the corresponding negative θ of the same magnitude ends in the fourth quadrant (Fig. 44.4). We take a point (a, b) on the terminal side of θ. Then the corresponding point on the terminal side of $(-\theta)$ is $(a, -b)$. The radius vector r is the same for the

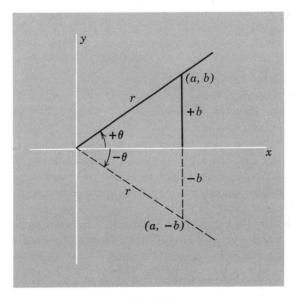

Fig. 44.4

positive and the negative angle. Then we have

$$\sin(+\theta) = \frac{b}{r} \qquad \text{and} \qquad \sin(-\theta) = \frac{-b}{r}$$

In general,

$$\sin(-\theta) = -\sin(+\theta)$$

That is, *the sine of a negative angle is the negative of the sine of the corresponding positive angle.* The statement can be shown to be true for angles ending in any quadrant.

For the cosine of the angles, $+\theta$ and $-\theta$, we note that the abscissa has the same sign for the negative as for the positive angle. Therefore,

$$\cos(+\theta) = \frac{a}{r} \qquad \text{and} \qquad \cos(-\theta) = \frac{a}{r}$$

In general,

$$\cos(-\theta) = +\cos(+\theta)$$

That is, *the cosine of a negative angle has the same sign as the cosine of the corresponding positive angle.* This statement can also be shown to be true for all values of θ.

The student should work out the rules for the remaining functions showing the relations between positive and negative angles.

The formula for the sine of the *difference* between two angles can now be derived by substituting $(-B)$ for $(+B)$ in Formula 1. We get

$$\sin(A - B) = \sin A \cos B - \cos A \sin B \qquad \text{(Formula 3)}$$

Note. The formulas shown here, as well as others to be shown presently, are identities. Therefore they can be used for any combinations of angles, whatever the size. However, in practical use they have little value. If we wish to find the functions of an angle, even of 75 or 15°, we look up the values in a table. Yet it should be remembered that many formulas for which we can see no immediate use turn out to be very important later in our study of trigonometry and other forms of mathematics. One important value of many formulas is that they are necessary in deriving other formulas that are useful in themselves alone.

The formula for the cosine of the *difference* between two angles may be derived by substituting a negative angle $(-B)$ for the $+B$ in the formula for the cosine of the sum of two angles. We get

$$\cos(A - B) = \cos A \cos B + \sin A \sin B \qquad \text{(Formula 4)}$$

The plus sign $(+)$ on the right side of the equation is reasonable if we think of the angle $(A - B)$ as being a small angle whose cosine is therefore comparatively large. Again, we must remember that the formula is true for angles of any size.

To derive the formula for the tangent of $(A + B)$, we begin with the identity

$$\tan \theta = \frac{\sin \theta}{\cos \theta}$$

By using Formulas 1 and 2, we get

$$\tan (A + B) = \frac{\sin (A + B)}{\cos (A + B)} = \frac{\sin A \cos B + \cos A \sin B}{\cos A \cos B - \sin A \sin B}$$

By dividing the entire numerator and denominator of the last fraction by the quantity $\cos A \cos B$, we get the formula for the tangent of the sum of two angles:

$$\tan (A + B) = \frac{\tan A + \tan B}{1 - \tan A \tan B} \qquad \text{(Formula 5)}$$

In the same way we can derive the formula for $\tan (A - B)$:

$$\tan (A - B) = \frac{\tan A - \tan B}{1 + \tan A \tan B} \qquad \text{(Formula 6)}$$

The formulas for the cotangent of the sum and the difference of two angles can be derived in a similar manner. However, these formulas are not used so much as those we have already shown.

44.3 DOUBLE-ANGLE FORMULAS

Another fact to be observed from the preassignment exercises is that if we *double an angle*, we do *not* thereby *double the sine value*. The same is true for the cosine value, the tangent value, or any other function value; that is, the sine of 80° is *not* simply twice the sine of 40°. The tangent of, say, 36° is *not* exactly twice the tangent of 18°. In fact, none of the function values is exactly proportional to the corresponding angle.

However, it is possible, by using the functions of a particular angle, to compute the functions of an angle twice as large. For such computations we have the so-called "double-angle" formulas. These formulas can be derived from Formulas 1, 2, and 5 by assuming that angle B is equal to angle A in each case; then $A + B = 2A$. We get the following double-angle formulas:

$$\sin (A + A) = \sin A \cos A + \cos A \sin A$$

or

$$\sin 2A = 2 \sin A \cos A \qquad \text{(Formula 7)}$$

Also

$$\cos 2A = \cos^2 A - \sin^2 A \qquad \text{(Formula 8)}$$

and

$$\tan 2A = \frac{2 \tan A}{1 - \tan^2 A} \qquad \text{(Formula 9)}$$

As examples of the application of Formula 7, we have

$$\sin 60° = 2\,(\sin 30°)(\cos 30°) = (2) \cdot \frac{1}{2} \cdot \frac{\sqrt{3}}{2} = \frac{\sqrt{3}}{2}$$

Since the formulas are identities, they are true for all angles. For instance,

$$\begin{aligned}
\sin 36.4° &= (2)(\sin 18.2°)(\cos 18.2°) \\
&= (2)(0.3123)(0.9500) \\
&= 0.5934
\end{aligned}$$

44.4 HALF-ANGLE FORMULAS

Still another fact is to be noted from the preassignment: we cannot obtain the functions of half an angle simply by taking half the function value of a given angle. For instance, the sine of 20° is not simply one-half the sine of 40°. Yet it is sometimes desirable to compute the functions of one-half a given angle. To do so, we use the so-called "half-angle" formulas.

To derive the formula for the sine of half a given angle, we begin with Formula 8:

$$\cos 2A = \cos^2 A - \sin^2 A$$

In this formula angle A represents any angle. Then $2A$ represents twice the angle A. Therefore, we can say that angle A is one-half angle $2A$.

First, we recall the identity $\cos^2 A = 1 - \sin^2 A$. For $\cos^2 A$ in Formula 8 we substitute $1 - \sin^2 A$. The formula

$$\cos 2A = \cos^2 A - \sin^2 A$$

then becomes

$$\cos 2A = 1 - \sin^2 A - \sin^2 A$$

or

$$\cos 2A = 1 - 2 \sin^2 A$$

Transposing, $2 \sin^2 A = 1 - \cos 2A$

Dividing by 2, $\sin^2 A = \dfrac{1 - \cos 2A}{2}$

Solving, $\sin A = \sqrt{\dfrac{1 - \cos 2A}{2}}$

If we replace angle $2A$ with any other angle, say, θ, then angle A is equal to $\theta/2$, or one-half θ. In terms of θ, we have the formula for the sine of half an angle:

$$\sin \frac{\theta}{2} = \sqrt{\frac{1 - \cos \theta}{2}}$$ (Formula 10)

The formula may be also stated in terms of A:

$$\sin \frac{A}{2} = \sqrt{\frac{1 - \cos A}{2}}$$

By the use of this formula, the sine of 15° may be computed from the cosine of 30°. Since the formula is an identity, it applies to the half of *any* angle.

Summary of half-angle formulas:

$$\sin \frac{A}{2} = \sqrt{\frac{1 - \cos A}{2}}$$ (Formula 10)

$$\cos \frac{A}{2} = \sqrt{\frac{1 + \cos A}{2}}$$ (Formula 11)

$$\tan \frac{A}{2} = \sqrt{\frac{1 - \cos A}{1 + \cos A}}$$ (Formula 12)

Formula 12 may be written in two other forms:

$$\tan \frac{A}{2} = \frac{\sin A.}{1 + \cos A} = \frac{1 - \cos A}{\sin A}$$

The student should try to work out the derivation of each of the foregoing formulas.

44.5 APPLICATION OF FORMULAS TO PARTICULAR SITUATIONS

Formulas 1 to 12 must be understood to be true for all values of an angle. In other words, they are identities. When we say, as in Formula 7, $\sin 2A = 2 \sin A \cos A$, we must understand that the formula is true for all values of the angle A.

This means, of course, that it is true for any *particular* angle. Now, we might wish to show that it is true when $A = 20°$. The sine of 20° is approximately 0.3420; the cosine of 20° is approximately 0.9397. Therefore, the sine of 40° should be approximately

$$\sin 40° = (2)(0.3420)(0.9397)$$

The product of the three factors on the right is 0.6427548, or, rounded off, 0.6428. If we look up the sine of 40°, we find it is given as 0.6428 to four places. This example shows that the formula is true for this one angle.

However, when we show that a formula is true for a particular angle, the example should not be considered as a proof but only an illustration. An illustration by example is not a proof at all. If the application of a formula turns out to be correct in a particular case, the example itself does not prove the formula to be always true.

Perhaps the chief value of trying out a formula in a particular example is that it helps us to understand the full meaning of the formula. An example or illustration is valuable in that it shows the application of the formula to a special situation. The example may be considered as a check on the formula. If the formula fails in only one instance, then it is not a general formula and it is not an identity.

Example.   From the triangle in Fig. 44.5 show that

$$\cos 2A = \cos^2 A - \sin^2 A$$

To understand our problem better, let us state it in the form of a question: in Fig. 44.5.

$$\text{does} \qquad \cos 2A = \cos^2 A - \sin^2 A?$$

Perhaps the best way is to work out the right side of the equation first. From the figure we see that

$$\cos A = \frac{12}{13} \qquad \cos^2 A = \frac{144}{169}$$

$$\sin A = \frac{5}{13} \qquad \sin^2 A = \frac{25}{169}$$

The right side of the equation becomes

$$\cos^2 A - \sin^2 A = \frac{144}{169} - \frac{25}{169} = \frac{119}{169} = 0.70414$$

Now we shall determine whether the $\cos 2A$ is equal to this value. First, we must find angle A. Angle A is arctan $\frac{5}{12}$, or approximately 22.6°. Then angle $2A$ is approximately 45.2°. The table shows $\cos 45.2°$ to be approximately 0.7046. The two sides of the

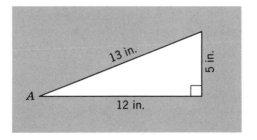

Fig. 44.5

equation are not exactly equal, since only approximate values were used, but they are sufficiently close.

If we had computed angle A more accurately, we should have found it to be about 22° 37.2'. Then angle $2A$ is 45° 14.4'. The table shows the cosine of this angle as 0.70414 by interpolation. The two sides of the equation should be approximately equal up to three or four digits.

Exercise 44.1

1. Find cos 75°, using angles of 45 and 30°.
2. Find sin 105°, using angles of 60 and 45°.
3. Find sin 165°, using angles of 135 and 30°.
4. Find cos 105°, using angles of 60 and 45°.
5. Find cos 165°, using 120 and 45°.
6. Find tan 75°, using 45 and 30°.
7. Find sin 15°, using 45 and 30°; also 60 and 45°.
8. Find cos 15°, using two different sets of angles.
9. Find tan 15°, using two different sets of angles.
10. Find sin 15°, using only a 30° angle.
11. Find the sine, cosine, and tangent of an angle of 7.5° without the use of a table.
12. Find sine, cosine, and tangent of 22.5°; 67.5°.
13. A right triangle has sides equal to 3 in., 4 in., and 5 in., respectively. Angle A is the acute angle opposite the 3-in. side. From this triangle show that Formula 9 is correct, using angle A.
14. A right triangle has sides equal to 5 in., 12 in., and 13 in., respectively. Angle R is the acute angle opposite the 12-in. side. From this triangle, show that Formula 11 is correct, using angle R.
15. A right triangle has sides equal to 7, 24, and 25 in., respectively. Angle S is the acute angle opposite the 24-in. side. From this triangle show that Formula 10 is correct, using angle S.
16. Using angle R in Problem 14, show that Formula 9 is correct.
17. Derive the formula for the tangent of a negative angle.
18. Derive the formula for the secant of a negative angle.
19. Derive the formula for the cotangent of the sum of two angles.
20. Using Formula 1 and Formula 3, combine them in such a way that you get the formula for (sin A cos B).
21. Combine Formula 2 and Formula 4 in such a way that you get a formula for (cos A cos B).
22. Combine Formula 2 and Formula 4 in such a way that you get a formula for (sin A sin B).
23. Combine Formula 1 and Formula 3 in such a way that you get a formula for the difference between two sines; that is, sin M − sin N. (Hint: let $M = A + B$, and let $N = A − B$).
24. Derive the three forms of Formula 12.

45

Solving Oblique Triangles

45.1 TWO KINDS OF OBLIQUE TRIANGLES

An oblique triangle is any triangle that is *not* a right triangle. There are two kinds of oblique triangles. An *acute triangle* is a triangle in which all *three* of its angles are *acute* (Fig. 45.1). An *obtuse triangle* is a triangle with *one obtuse* angle. In an obtuse triangle, of course, two of the angles are acute (Fig. 45.2).

The three sides and the three angles of any triangle are called the six *elements* of a triangle. The three angles are often indicated by capital letters, A, B, and C. The sides are usually indicated by small letters, a, b, and c. Each side is denoted by a small letter that corresponds to the *opposite* angle. Thus side a is opposite angle A.

Oblique triangles can be solved indirectly by using the regular trigonometric functions and by drawing extra line segments in some instances. However, such triangles are often more conveniently solved by using the *sine law* or the *cosine law*.

45.2 THE SINE LAW

Before deriving this law, let us consider an oblique triangle, ABC, as shown in Fig. 45.3. Suppose angle A is equal to 40° and angle B is equal to 80°. Since angle B is greater than angle A, we know from plane geometry that side b is greater than side a. In plane geometry we prove the following theorem:

Fig. 45.1   Fig. 45.2

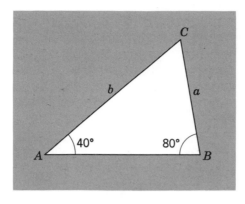

Fig. 45.3

If two angles of a triangle are unequal, the sides opposite these angles are also unequal and the greater side is opposite the greater angle.

Now, since angle B is twice angle A, we might be inclined to say, at first guess, that side b is also twice side a. However, this is not the case. The sides of a triangle do *not* have the same *ratio* as the opposite angles.

Instead, the ratio of side b to side a will always be the same as the ratio of the *sines* of the opposite angles. In other words,

$$\text{the ratio } \frac{b}{a} = \text{the ratio } \frac{\sin B}{\sin A}$$

This is the *sine law*. The law is usually stated in another form:

$$\text{Form 1.} \quad \frac{a}{\sin A} = \frac{b}{\sin B} = \frac{c}{\sin C}$$

$$\text{Form 2.} \quad \frac{\sin A}{a} = \frac{\sin B}{b} = \frac{\sin C}{c}$$

In words, the *sine law* may be stated as follows: *Any side of a triangle has the same ratio to the sine of the opposite angle as any other side has to the sine of its opposite angle.*

Either of the foregoing forms of the sine law may be used. In solving an oblique triangle by this law, one form is usually more convenient than the other, depending upon the information given in the problem.

The sine law is easily derived from a triangle. We draw any triangle ABC (Fig. 45.4) with sides a, b, and c. Draw a line segment from any angle, say, angle C, perpendicular to the opposite side, c. Then two right triangles are formed. We call the altitude h. From the definitions of the trigonometric

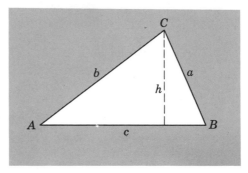

Fig. 45.4

functions we have

$$\frac{h}{b} = \sin A \qquad \text{and} \qquad \frac{h}{a} = \sin B$$

or

$$h = b \sin A \qquad \text{and} \qquad h = a \sin B$$

Here we have two values of h. Equating these values, we have

$$b \sin A = a \sin B$$

Dividing both sides of the equation by the quantity $\sin A \sin B$,

$$\frac{b}{\sin B} = \frac{a}{\sin A}$$

If, instead, we divide both sides of the equation by ab, we get the second form

$$\frac{\sin A}{a} = \frac{\sin B}{b}$$

Since angle A and angle B represent any two angles of the triangle, we can call one of them angle C and get the complete form of the sine law.

In using the sine law, we set up an equation between the two fractions that involve the given parts and the parts to be found. It is usually best to begin with the part to be found. It will be observed that in order to use this law at least one angle must be given.

Example 1. In a certain oblique triangle angle $A = 40.7°$, angle $C = 78.9°$, and $a = 14.2$ in. Find side c.

Solution. First we make a sketch of the triangle and label the parts (Fig. 45.5). Next, we set up a statement of the sine law involving the parts given and the part to

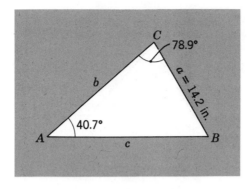

Fig. 45.5

be found. We begin with the part to be found.

$$\frac{c}{\sin C} = \frac{a}{\sin A}$$

Solving the equation for c, we get

$$c = \frac{a \sin C}{\sin A}$$

Substituting the given values,

$$c = \frac{(14.2)(\sin 78.9°)}{\sin 40.7°}$$

Taking sine values from the table, we get the equation involving numerical values:

$$c = \frac{(14.2)(0.9813)}{0.6521}$$

$$c = 21.37 \quad \text{or} \quad 21.4$$

The actual computation can be performed by means of logarithms, if desired.

Example 2. In an oblique triangle, $C = 73.4°$, $b = 21.3$ in., and $c = 27.6$ in. Solve the triangle completely. This means, find A, B, and a.

Solution. We make a sketch of the triangle (Fig. 45.6). Then we find angle B. Since angle C is given and angle B is to be found, we set up the sine law involving these angles. We begin with angle B, since it is unknown.

$$\frac{\sin B}{b} = \frac{\sin C}{c}$$

Then

$$\sin B = \frac{b \sin C}{c}$$

Substituting values, we have

$$\sin B = \frac{(21.3)(\sin 73.4°)}{27.6}$$

From this, we get

$$\sin B = \frac{(21.3)(0.9583)}{27.6} = 0.7396$$

$$\text{angle } B = 47.7°$$

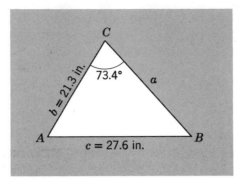

Fig. 45.6

Since we now know two angles of the triangle, we can find the third by use of the fact that the sum of the three angles of any triangle is 180°. Therefore, angle $A = 58.9°$.

To find side a, we write
$$\frac{a}{\sin A} = \frac{c}{\sin C}$$

Substituting values,
$$a = \frac{(27.6)(0.8563)}{0.9583} = 24.66 \quad \text{or} \quad 24.7$$

45.3 THE COSINE LAW

In some problems involving oblique triangles, we may not be able to use the sine law because of a lack of sufficient information. In such cases it may be possible to use the *cosine law*. This is another convenient method for solving some oblique triangles.

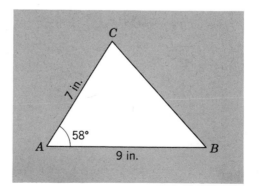

Fig. 45.7

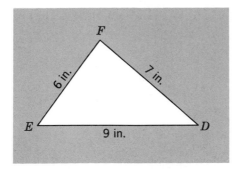

Fig. 45.8

For example, suppose we have the triangle shown in Fig. 45.7 in which we have given two sides and the included angle: $b = 7$ in., side $c = 9$ in., and angle $A = 58°$. If we try to use the sine law, we find that no matter how we set up the equation we shall have two unknowns. Therefore, the sine law cannot be used to solve the triangle.

As another example, suppose we have the three sides of a triangle *DEF* shown in Fig. 45.8: $d = 6$ in., $e = 7$ in., and $f = 9$ in. Here, again, we find that we cannot use the sine law because no angle is given. In such problems we can use the cosine law.

To derive the cosine law, we begin with a general triangle such as *ABC* in Fig. 45.9. Let us suppose that sides *b* and *c* are known and that angle *A* is also known. We draw a perpendicular from *C* to the opposite side at point *D*. Call the line segment *h*. The distance *AD* we may call *x*. Then the distance *DB* is $c - x$.

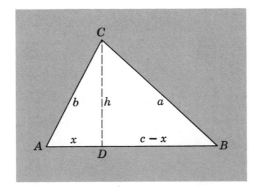

Fig. 45.9

We now write two equations involving h and then eliminate the h between the two equations. By the Pythagorean rule, we get the following equations:

$$b^2 = h^2 + x^2$$
$$a^2 = h^2 + (c - x)^2$$

Expanding the second equation, we get $a^2 = h^2 + c^2 - 2cx + x^2$

Rewriting the first equation, $b^2 = h^2 \qquad\qquad + x^2$

Subtracting (eliminating h), $a^2 - b^2 = c^2 - 2cx$

Transposing, $a^2 = b^2 + c^2 - 2cx$

The last of the foregoing equations is solved for a^2 and should enable us to find a. The right side of the equation involves only known quantities b and c, except for the factor x. If we can also eliminate this factor, all of the right side of the equation will be known.

If we look at the original figure, we see that

$$\frac{x}{b} = \cos A \qquad \text{or} \qquad x = b \cos A$$

In the final equation we replace x with its equivalent, $b \cos A$. The result is the *cosine law*:

$$a^2 = b^2 + c^2 - 2bc \cos A$$

In this formula every term and factor on the right side of the equation is known. Therefore, we can find a.

It should be understood that the letters a, b, and c refer to any of the sides of the triangle. Therefore, the formula may be stated in terms of the sides in any order:

$$a^2 = b^2 + c^2 - 2bc \cos A$$
$$b^2 = a^2 + c^2 - 2ac \cos B$$
$$c^2 = a^2 + b^2 - 2ab \cos C$$

The *cosine law* may be stated as follows: *The square of any side of a triangle is equal to the sum of the squares of the other two sides minus twice the product of those two sides times the cosine of the included angle. This is the cosine law.*

The student should try to show that the formula holds true when the included angle is an obtuse angle and also when it is a right angle.

The cosine law is used in two kinds of problems: (1) if we have given two sides and the included angle; (2) if we have given the three sides of a triangle.

Example 1. In a certain triangle, ABC, $a = 17.2$ in., $b = 21.4$ in., angle $C = 58.7°$. Find side c.

Solution. Since we are to find side c, we write the formula for c^2:

$$c^2 = a^2 + b^2 - 2ab \cos C$$

From the table, we find cos $C = 0.5195$. Substituting numerical values, we have

$$c^2 = (17.2)^2 + (21.4)^2 - 2(17.2)(21.4)(0.5195)$$

Expanding, $\quad c^2 = 295.84 + 457.96 - 382.44$

Combining, $\quad c^2 = 371.36$

Solving for c, $\quad c = 19.27 \quad$ or $\quad 19.3$

If we wish to find a particular angle in a triangle with three sides given, we set up the cosine law by using the form that includes the angle to be found.

Example 2. In a certain triangle, ABC, $a = 5$, $b = 7$, and $c = 8$. Find angle B.

Solution. Since we are to find angle B, we use the formula showing angle B.

$$b^2 = a^2 + c^2 - 2ac \cos B$$

The given numerical values may be substituted directly into this formula, or the formula may first be solved for angle B. If we use the formula as it appears here, we shall have the following results:

First Method. Substituting numerical values,

$$49 = 25 + 64 - 2(5)(8)(\cos B)$$

Combining, $\quad 49 = 89 - 80 \cos B$

Transposing, $\quad 80 \cos B = 89 - 49$

$$80 \cos B = 40$$

$$\cos B = 0.5000$$

$$B = 60°$$

Second Method. We may first solve the formula for B.

$$b^2 = a^2 + c^2 - 2ac \cos B$$

Transposing, $\quad 2ac \cos B = a^2 + c^2 - b^2$

Dividing both sides by $2ac$, $\quad \cos B = \dfrac{a^2 + c^2 - b^2}{2ac}$

Solving for B, $\quad B = \arccos \dfrac{a^2 + c^2 - b^2}{2ac}$

The given numerical values can now be substituted.

$$B = \arccos \frac{25 + 64 - 49}{2(5)(8)}$$

$$B = \arccos \frac{40}{80} = \arccos 0.5 = 60°$$

In some problems it may happen that the angle to be found is greater than 90°. The triangle is then an obtuse triangle. If the cosine of an angle happens to be negative, the angle is greater than 90°.

Example 3. In a certain triangle, ABC, $a = 25.8$ in., $b = 14.2$ in., $c = 17.3$ in. Find angle A.

Solution. We use the formula $a^2 = b^2 + c^2 - 2bc \cos A$. Solving the formula for A, we have

$$2bc \cos A = b^2 + c^2 - a^2$$

$$\cos A = \frac{b^2 + c^2 - a^2}{2bc}$$

$$A = \arccos \frac{b^2 + c^2 - a^2}{2bc}$$

Substituting known values,

$$A = \arccos \frac{(14.2)^2 + (17.3)^2 - (25.8)^2}{2(14.2)(17.3)}$$

$$A = \arccos \frac{201.64 + 299.29 - 665.64}{491.32}$$

$$A = \arccos \frac{-164.71}{491.32} = \arccos(-0.3352) = 109.6°$$

In Example 3, since the cosine is negative, the angle is greater than 90°. The triangle is an *obtuse* triangle.

Example 4. In a certain triangle, ABC, $a = 24.3$ ft, $b = 21.5$ ft, $B = 52.3°$. Find A.

Solution. Since we have two sides and the angle opposite one of the sides, we use the sine law. We begin with $\sin A$, since A is unknown.

$$\frac{\sin A}{a} = \frac{\sin B}{b}$$

Multiplying both sides by a, $\qquad \sin A = \frac{a \sin B}{b}$

Substituting known values, $\qquad \sin A = \frac{(24.3) \sin 52.3°}{21.5}$

Since $\sin 52.3° = 0.7912$, we have, $\sin A = \frac{(24.3)(0.7912)}{21.5}$

Solving, $\qquad\qquad\qquad\qquad\qquad \sin A = 0.8942$

$$A = 63.4° \text{ and } 116.6°$$

This problem is an illustration of what is known as the ambiguous case. There are two possible solutions to the problem, as shown in Fig. 45.10.

Note. The sine law or the cosine law should not be used for solving a *right triangle*. The formulas hold true for all triangles, but the work is simpler if these laws are not used in solving right triangles.

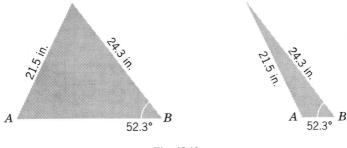

Fig. 45.10

Exercise 45.1

Solve the following triangles completely:

1. Given $A = 41.3°$, $B = 76.2°$, $b = 25.2$ in.
2. Given $B = 38.9°$, $C = 84.6°$, $a = 31.4$ ft
3. Given $A = 53.2°$, $b = 14$ in., $c = 18$ in.
4. Given $B = 48.1°$, $a = 23.1$ in., $c = 32.3$ in.
5. Given $C = 31.4°$, $a = 24.6$ ft, $b = 26.2$ ft
6. Given $C = 112.5°$, $b = 43.6$ ft, $c = 92.8$ ft
7. Given $a = 15.3$ in., $b = 19.4$ in., $c = 32.1$ in.   (first find $\angle C$)
8. Given $B = 86.2°$, $a = 18.2$ in., $b = 24.1$ in.
9. Given $a = 42.7$ cm, $b = 53.4$ cm, $c = 38.1$ cm
10. Given $B = 114.2°$, $a = 43.6$ cm, $c = 15.7$ cm
11. Given $B = 68.9°$, $a = 26.1$ cm $c = 32.4$ cm
12. Given $C = 35.8°$, $a = 23.6$ cm, $c = 17.2$ cm
13. Given $A = 39.1°$, $a = 15.5$ in., $c = 31.4$ in.
14. Given $A = 38.6°$, $B = 90°$, $b = 26.5$ ft
15. Given $C = 39.2°$, $a = 25$ cm, $c = 15.8$ cm
16. Try $a = 15.3$ in., $b = 23.4$ in., $c = 41.2$ in.

46

*Vectors**

46.1 ARITHMETIC ADDITION

Quantities may be added in various ways. When we first begin the process of addition of numbers and quantities in the first grade in school, we learn that 4 plus 3 equals 7; $4 added to $3 are $7; 4 miles plus 3 miles equals 7 miles.

In fact, all through the grades in school we never think of 4 added to 3 as being anything but 7. This is *arithmetic addition*.

46.2 ALGEBRAIC ADDITION

When we get to the study of algebra and positive and negative numbers, we learn that a distance of 4 miles added to a distance of 3 miles may not always result in 7 miles. For instance, if we walk 4 miles *east* and then 3 miles *west*, we are only 1 mile from our starting point. Here the result of our walking has been to take us only 1 mile.

In algebra we show direction by a plus sign ($+$) and a minus sign ($-$). Walking 4 miles *east* may be indicated by $+4$, and 3 miles *west* may be indicated by -3. The addition of a $+4$ to a -3 results in $+1$. *Algebraic addition is the addition involving positive and negative numbers.*

Algebraic addition of signed numbers may be understood even more clearly by considering two forces operating at the *same time*. Let us suppose we can row a boat at a rate of 4 miles per hour (mph) in still water. In 1 hour we row a distance of 4 miles.

Now, suppose we row with this same effort in a river in which the water flows at a rate of 3 mph. If we row *downstream*, our rate of travel with reference to the shore will be 7 mph. In 1 hour we row 4 miles and the river carries us 3 miles in the *same direction*. The result of the two forces and motions is that we shall move 7 miles downstream. This may be expressed as $(+4)$ plus $(+3)$ equals $+7$.

---

* In electrical engineering the word *phasor* is used in place of *vector* because a difference in time between two magnitudes such as voltages represents a difference in phase rather than in direction.

636

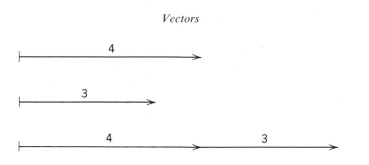

Fig. 46.1

Suppose we reverse our rowing and row upstream with the same force as before. That is, our rowing rate is still 4 mph. However, the force of the current has a downstream effect of 3 mph. The net result is that after 1 hour we shall have moved upstream only 1 mile. To add these two forces and motions, we use algebraic addition: $(+4) + (-3) = +1$.

The two forces, or distances, *rowing upstream* and being *carried downstream*, are called *vectors*. A *vector* is a force or velocity or distance of a certain size or magnitude operating in a particular direction. A vector has both *magnitude* and *direction*. In the example given one vector is 4 mph *upstream* and the other vector is 3 mph *downstream*. When we row downstream, the two vectors operate in the same direction.

46.3 REPRESENTATION OF VECTORS BY LINE SEGMENTS

A vector is often shown by a line segment. The direction of the line segment, shown by an arrowhead, indicates the *direction* of the vector. The length of the line segment represents the *magnitude* of the vector.

To be strictly accurate, the vector is the force or velocity or distance itself and is only represented by the arrow. However, the arrow is often called the vector, as when we say, "Draw a vector."

Let us represent by arrows the two vectors, 4 and 3 mph, operating in the same direction. We draw the arrows in the same direction (Fig. 46.1). The lengths of the arrows represent the magnitudes 4 and 3, respectively; that is, if one line is 4 units long, the other is 3 units long.

The addition of the two vectors may be represented by the sum of the two line segments. One arrow is drawn first, and the second arrow is drawn from the head of the first, in the proper direction and of proper length. The sum of the arrows is 7 units from the starting point, which represents 7 mph in the proper direction.

Two vectors operating in *opposite* directions, such as 4 mph upstream and 3 mph downstream, may be represented by arrows pointing in opposite directions (Fig. 46.2). The sum of the two vectors by algebraic addition is

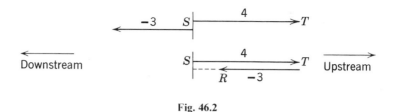

Fig. 46.2

+ 1, as we have seen. Algebraic addition may be shown here also by combining the two arrows. We first draw the arrow, ST, in the proper direction from the starting point. Then, from the head of the first arrow, T, we draw the second arrow in the proper direction and of correct length.

The head of the second arrow, R, represents the algebraic sum of the two vectors. It is one unit from the starting point. The result can be shown by a third vector, 1 unit long, representing the sum. This vector is shown by a broken line.

There is one point that must be clearly understood with reference to the addition of vectors. If we are rowing upstream at a rate of 4 mph and the current has a force of 3 mph downstream, our actual motion is somewhat different from that indicated by the two arrows. The arrows appear to indicate that, while we are rowing, the river remains still and waits for us to move 4 miles upstream in 1 hour. Then, when we have arrived at that point, we wait for the river to carry us 3 miles downstream. This does not happen.

Instead, we have the two forces operating at the *same time*. As a result, our actual motion is only 1 mile upstream in 1 hour. Yet it is proper to show the two motions by arrows correctly drawn; and the *result* of the two motions will be that indicated in the sketch, that is, 1 mile upstream.

46.4 GEOMETRIC ADDITION

As a third situation, suppose we row directly *across* the river. Let us suppose the river is 4 miles wide and the water runs downstream at 3 mph. Here we must use a different kind of addition. If we row directly across the river at *right angles to the current*, in one hour we shall have crossed the river but the current will have carried us 3 miles downstream. Again we can represent graphically by arrows the two vector forces operating at right angles to each other (Fig. 46.3). These forces are indicated in the diagram by the line segments ST and TR.

Our actual path of travel is represented by the arrow SR. This line segment represents our *direction* of travel and also the actual *distance* traveled.

Again, our actual travel is not exactly as indicated by the arrows, in the diagram. It is important to consider carefully just what happens in this case,

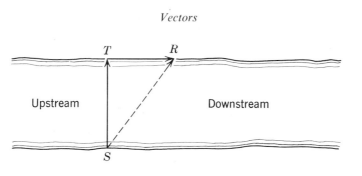

Fig. 46.3

since we have two forces operating at right angles to each other and at the *same time*. The arrows appear to indicate that the river waited one hour for us to go directly across and, after that, carried us downstream 3 miles. If this had happened, then the actual distance traveled would have been 7 miles. But such is not the case.

Our actual travel is represented by the diagonal line *SR*. By the Pythagorean rule, the length of this path is 5 miles. Here we cannot use arithmetic or algebraic addition. We must use *geometric* addition. The one vector, 4 miles in one direction, plus the second vector, 3 miles at right angles, equals a third vector, 5 miles in a diagonal direction. Again, we see that a vector has both magnitude and direction. Here, 4 miles + 3 miles = 5 miles.

Geometric addition is sometimes called *vectorial* addition. Geometric addition, or vectorial addition, can be done only by showing the vectors by arrows in a diagram.

46.5 RESULTANT AND COMPONENTS

A *resultant* vector is the vector that results from the addition of two or more vectors. In the diagram showing our path across the river we add the two vectors, 4 miles and 3 miles. The *resultant* is the sum of these two vectors. The *result* of the two forces is the *resultant* vector, 5 miles, in the *direction* indicated by the diagonal *SR* (Fig. 46.4).

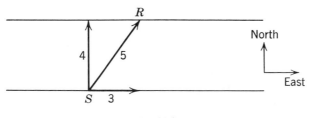

Fig. 46.4

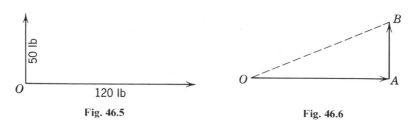

Fig. 46.5   Fig. 46.6

Component vectors are the vectors that are added to form the resultant. In the example given let us assume that the river runs *east* and our rowing is *north*. We can say that the two components are 4 miles *north* and 3 miles *east*. The *resultant* is 5 miles in a direction somewhat east of north. The *direction* can be indicated more accurately, as will be shown presently.

Let us consider another example. Suppose we have an object at point O (Fig. 46.5). Suppose that a force of, say, 140 pounds is required to move the object. Let us also suppose that a man pulls east with a force of 120 pounds and his son pulls north with a force of 50 pounds. The two forces, 120 pounds *east* and 50 pounds *north*, are the two component vectors. They contain both magnitude and direction. They are shown graphically by the arrows in the diagram.

Our question now is, "Will the object move, and, if so, in what direction?" The resultant of the two forces, 120 pounds and 50 pounds, is not 170 pounds.

In order to determine the resultant of the two forces, we add them graphically, or vectorially. There are two methods by which the resultant may be found. We may draw one arrow first, representing the proper direction and distance from the point O. Then we draw the second arrow from the head of the first, observing proper direction and distance (Fig. 46.6).

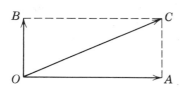

Fig. 46.7

By another method we draw each arrow in the proper direction and length from point O, such as OA and OB (Fig. 46.7). Then we complete a rectangle with these two line segments as sides. The diagonal OC of the rectangle represents the direction and magnitude of the resultant. By the Pythagorean rule, this diagonal is 130. The resultant force is therefore 130 pounds. The direction of the resultant force will also be indicated by the diagonal. The resultant shows that the object will not move.

We can now state the direction as being 22.6° north of east. This angle is found by reducing its tangent $\frac{50}{120}$ to the decimal 0.4167. The angle corresponding to this tangent is 22.6°.

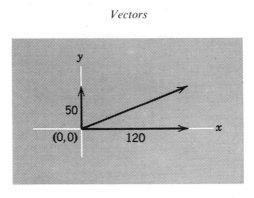

Fig. 46.8

The complete resultant vector has a magnitude of 130 pounds in a direction 22.6° north of east. The most compact way of indicating this resultant vector is by use of this notation:

$$130\underline{/22.6°}$$

46.6 VECTORS REPRESENTED ON THE COORDINATE SYSTEM

A set of component vectors and their resultant are often shown conveniently on the common system of rectangular coordinates. The two forces in the foregoing example are shown in Fig. 46.8.

Starting at the origin (0, 0), the 120-pound vector is shown by an arrow along the x-axis. The 50-pound vector is shown by an arrow along the positive y-axis. The two forces are thus represented by abscissa and ordinate, respectively. These two coordinates represent the component vectors. The vectorial sum of the two components is the resultant, which may be denoted by R.

46.7 FINDING THE RESULTANT OF TWO COMPONENTS

Let us suppose we have two component vectors represented by the abscissa and ordinate, respectively. We may call one vector the x-component and the other vector the y-component. Our problem now is to find the resultant. Remember, resultant means two things: *direction* and *magnitude*.

Suppose we have an x-component equal to -8, and a y-component equal to $+6$, shown on the coordinate system (Fig. 46.9). By the Pythagorean rule, the *magnitude* of the resultant is 10. If we indicate the magnitude by the small letter r, we have the formula

$$r = \sqrt{x^2 + y^2}$$

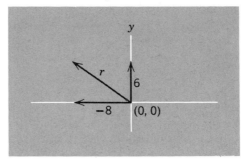

Fig. 46.9

In order to state the resultant completely, we must also tell its *direction*. Using the tangent value $\frac{6}{8}$ and disregarding the negative sign, we find the *reference* angle is 36.9°. However, this is not the angle of the resultant. The angle of the resultant, which must be measured from the right-hand direction of the *x*-axis, is 143.1°. The entire resultant can be written in this compact form:

$$R : 10\underline{/143.1°}$$

You will note that the angle of the resultant is arctan y/x.

46.8 FINDING THE COMPONENTS OF A GIVEN VECTOR

Let us suppose that we have given a particular vector that has been obtained as the sum of two components. If we know the resultant vector, including its magnitude and direction, our problem is to find the two components that will produce the given resultant vector.

Example. Suppose we have the given resultant vector $60\underline{/20°}$. Our problem is to find the components.

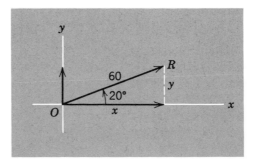

Fig. 46.10

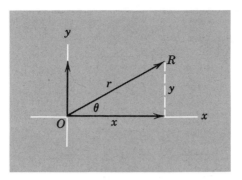

Fig. 46.11

Solution. Let us represent this vector on the coordinate system (Fig. 46.10). The magnitude is 60 units, and the angle is 20°. The given vector is represented by the arrow *OR*. We denote the components by *x* and *y*, respectively. In the diagram we see that

$$\frac{y}{60} = \sin 20°$$

Solving for *y*, we get
$$y = 60 \sin 20°$$
$$y = 60(0.3420)$$
$$y = 20.52$$

In the same way, we see that
$$\frac{x}{60} = \cos 20°$$

$$x = 60 \cos 20°$$
$$x = 60(0.9397)$$
$$x = 56.382$$

Now we have found the following components:

$$y = 20.52 \quad \text{and} \quad x = 56.38 \quad \text{(rounded off)}$$

To check the values for *x* and *y*, we can use the Pythagorean rule; that is, $x^2 + y^2$ should equal the square of 60. Since all the values are only approximate, the check will not show the two *exactly* equal.

The solution of this type of problem in more general terms may be shown by starting with a resultant stated in general terms (Fig. 46.11). If we have the given resultant $r\underline{/\theta}$, where *r* is the given distance and θ is the angle, our solution becomes

$$\frac{y}{r} = \sin \theta, \qquad \text{from which we get} \qquad \boxed{y = r \sin \theta}$$

$$\frac{x}{r} = \cos \theta, \qquad \text{from which we get} \qquad \boxed{x = r \cos \theta}$$

The two formulas, $y = r \sin \theta$ and $x = r \cos \theta$, can be used to find the components of any given vector, regardless of its magnitude or direction. We must be sure to observe the correct algebraic signs for the functions used.

Exercise 46.1

Find the resultant for each of the following sets of components. (Resultant includes both magnitude and direction.)

1. $x = 8$,	$y = 5$		**2.** $x = -15$,	$y = 11$
3. $x = -12$,	$y = -7$		**4.** $x = 5.2\,v$,	$y = -2.1\,v$
5. $x = -3.21\,v$,	$y = 5.32\,v$		**6.** $x = -23.2$,	$y = -4.13$
7. $x = 1.24$,	$y = -5.32$		**8.** $x = 2.45$,	$y = 5.13$
9. $x = 15\,ohms$,	$y = 5\,ohms$		**10.** $x = 0.5\,ohms$,	$y = 50\,ohms$
11. $x = 7.21$,	$y = 1.32$		**12.** $x = -32.4$,	$y = 124.0$
13. $x = 8.41$,	$y = -0.92$		**14.** $x = 5.31$,	$y = -5.12$
15. $x = 42.3$,	$y = -1.42$		**16.** $x = -2.46$,	$y = -9.40$

Find the components of each of the following:

17. $80/28.3°$	**18.** $32\,v/169.8°$
19. $50\,v/74.2°$	**20.** $4.2\,ohms/-38.4°$
21. $6\,amp/148.8°$	**22.** $23.4\,lb/58.1°$
23. $150\,v/204.9°$	**24.** $385\,miles/208.3°$
25. $70\,ohms/123.4°$	**26.** $57.4\,mph/152.8°$
27. $12/235.3°$	**28.** $42.6\,v/493°$
29. $15/287.6°$	**30.** $34.7/1432.6°$
31. $25/300.7°$	**32.** $1.65/73.2°$

33. If a plane is set to fly at 230 mph directly east and a wind is blowing from the north at 25 mph, find the direction of travel and the distance traveled in 1 hr.

34. If two forces of 360 and 155 lb, respectively, are exerted at right angles to each other, find the magnitude and direction of the resultant force. Show by diagram.

35. A motor boat is steered directly across a river at 12 mph. The speed of the river is 3.5 mph. What is the actual speed and direction of the boat through the water? Show by diagram.

36. What single force and direction would have the same effect as a pull of 25 lb east and 15 lb north?

37. A man pulls with a force of 160 lb in a direction of 41° north of east. What are the east and north components of the force?

38. A plane travels 220 miles in a direction south of east by 31°. What are the east and south components of the distance traveled?

39. A plane is headed due east; the wind is blowing from the north. At 12 noon the plane passes over town A, and at 1 P.M. it passes over town B. The towns are 295 miles apart. Town B is 10° south of east from A. Find the speed of the plane and the speed of the wind.

40. A pull of 52 lb is exerted in a direction 64° south of west. Find the west and south components of the force.

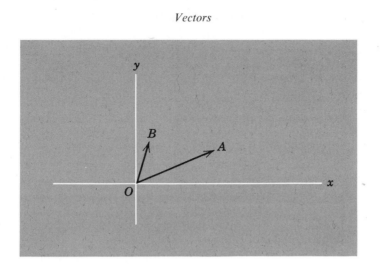

Fig. 46.12

46.9 GRAPHICAL ADDITION OF ANY TWO OR MORE VECTORS

It is often necessary to add vectors of any direction and magnitude. For instance, suppose we have the two vectors

$$A: 50\,\underline{/23.4°} \qquad \text{and} \qquad B: 20\,\underline{/71.2°}$$

These vectors can be represented graphically (Fig. 46.12).

If vector A is a force of 50 pounds in a direction indicated by 23.4° and vector B is a force of 20 pounds in a direction indicated by 71.2°, our problem

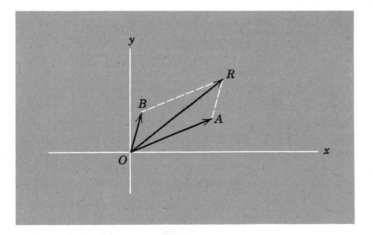

Fig. 46.13

then might be stated thus: what are the magnitude and the direction of the resultant force?

Graphically, we can add the vectors by completing a parallelogram on the two arrows, OA and OB (Fig. 46.13). The resultant vector is represented by the diagonal arrow, OR. This arrow shows the direction and magnitude of the resultant. If we make careful measurements of line segments and angles, we can also measure very closely the magnitude and direction of the resultant. This method is called *graphical* or *geometric* addition of vectors.

46.10   ADDITION OF VECTORS BY ALGEBRA AND TRIGONOMETRY

If we wish to obtain a more accurate measure of the sum of the two vectors, we add them by means of algebra and trigonometry. To add two or more vectors of any magnitude and direction, we follow this general procedure:

1. *Find the x-component and the y-component of each vector.*
2. *Add the x-components algebraically. The result will be the x-component of the resultant.*
3. *Add the y-components algebraically. The result will be the y-component resultant.*
4. *Combine the two components of the resultant by vectorial addition. Show the result as a magnitude and direction.*

Example.   Add the vectors $A: 50/\underline{23.4°}$ and $B: 20/\underline{71.2°}$.

Solution.   First we find the components of each vector. Let us indicate the components of A by x_1 and y_1 and the components of B by x_2 and y_2. By formula, $x = r \cos \theta$ and $y = r \sin \theta$. Then

$$\begin{aligned}
x_1 &= 50 \cos 23.4° & y_1 &= 50 \sin 23.4° \\
&= 50 \,(0.9178) & &= 50 \,(0.3971) \\
&= 45.890 & &= 19.855 \\
x_2 &= 20 \cos 71.2° & y_2 &= 20 \sin 71.2° \\
&= 20 \,(0.3223) & &= 20 \,(0.9466) \\
&= 6.446 & &= 18.932
\end{aligned}$$

The x-components are now added algebraically to form the x-component of the resultant. The y-components are added to form the y-component of the resultant. The subscript R indicates resultant.

$$\begin{aligned}
x_1 &= 45.890 & y_1 &= 19.855 \\
x_2 &= \underline{\;\;6.446} & y_2 &= \underline{18.932} \\
x_R &= 52.336, \text{ or } 52.34 & y_R &= 38.787, \text{ or } 38.79
\end{aligned}$$

We now find the magnitude of the resultant vector by the Pythagorean rule. By squaring the components, adding these squares, and finding the square root of the sum, we find that the magnitude of the resultant is

$$r = \sqrt{(52.34)^2 + (38.79)^2} = 65.15$$

The angle of the resultant is arctan $38.79/52.34 = 36.5°$. The resultant is written

$$65.15\underline{/36.5°}$$

46.11 VECTORS AS COMPLEX NUMBERS: OPERATOR-*j*

The components of a vector may be written in the form of a complex number: $a + bj$. The *x*-component becomes the real part of the complex number, and the *t*-component becomes the coefficient of *j*. The letter *j* is often placed before its coefficient, as *j*5. For instance, if the *x*-component of a vector is 17 and the *y*-component is -8, they may be written $17 - j8$. This form is known as "operator-*j*" notation. Such notation is common in the study of electric circuits.

If the components of vectors are written in operator-*j* notation, their addition becomes simply the addition of complex numbers (see Section 21.8). The procedure is shown in the following example.

Example 1. Add the vectors $A : 40\underline{/68.8°}$ and $60\underline{/205.7°}$.

Solution. We indicate the components by subscripts.

$$
\begin{array}{ll}
x_1 = 40 \cos 68.8° & y_1 = 40 \sin 68.8° \\
 = 40\,(0.3616) & = 40\,(0.9323) \\
 = 14.464 & = 37.292 \\
x_2 = 60 \cos 205.7° & y_2 = 60 \sin 205.7° \\
 = 60\,(-0.9011) & = 60\,(-0.4337) \\
 = -54.066 & = -26.22
\end{array}
$$

We now write these vectors as complex numbers.

$$
\begin{array}{ll}
A: & 14.464 + j37.292 \\
B: & -54.066 - j26.022 \\
\hline
R: & -39.602 + j11.270
\end{array}
$$

Resultant,

The magnitude and direction of the resultant are now computed.

$$r = \sqrt{(-39.602)^2 + (11.270)^2} = 41.17$$

The angle of the resultant is arctan $11.270/-39.602$. Disregarding the negative sign, we find the reference angle is $15.9°$. Since the resultant appears in the second quadrant, the angle of the resultant is $164.1°$. The resultant is written

$$41.17\underline{/164.1°}$$

The actual computation of the magnitude and direction of the resultant is usually most easily performed by logarithms. If the student is familiar with the use of a slide rule, the computation is easily done with that instrument.

Example 2. Add the following four vectors:

$$A:80\underline{/24.4°} \qquad B:50\underline{/131.4°} \qquad C:70\underline{/233.8°} \qquad D:60\underline{/317.9°}$$

Solution.

$$A:x_1 = 80 \cos\ 24.4° =\quad 72.856 \qquad y_1 = 80 \sin\ 24.4° =\quad 33.048$$
$$B:x_2 = 50 \cos 131.4° = -33.065 \qquad y_2 = 50 \sin 131.4° =\quad 37.505$$
$$C:x_3 = 70 \cos 233.8° = -41.342 \qquad y_3 = 70 \sin 233.8° = -56.490$$
$$D:x_4 = 60 \cos 317.9° =\quad 44.520 \qquad y_4 = 60 \sin 317.9° = -40.224$$

The vectors are now written in operator-j notation and added.

$$
\begin{array}{rl}
A: & 72.856 + j33.048 \\
B: & -33.065 + j37.505 \\
C: & -41.342 - j56.490 \\
D: & \underline{\quad 44.520 - j40.224} \\
R: & \quad 42.969 - j26.161
\end{array}
$$

We compute the magnitude and direction from the components of the resultant. By the Pythagorean rule, the magnitude is equal to $\sqrt{x^2 + y^2}$.

$$r = \sqrt{(42.97)^2 + (-26.16)^2}$$
$$= 50.31$$

To find the angle of the resultant, we first find the reference angle, which is arctan $26.16/42.97$. In finding the reference angle, we disregard the negative sign. The reference angle is $31.3°$. Since the resultant falls in the fourth quadrant, the angle of the resultant is $328.7°$.

In the case of a vector falling in the fourth quadrant, the angle is sometimes written as a negative angle. This should be done only in the case of a fourth-quadrant angle. The answer to the foregoing problem is

$$R:50.31\underline{/328.7°} \qquad \text{or} \qquad 50.31\underline{/-31.3°}$$

Exercise 46.2

Add the following sets of vectors:

1. $A:80\underline{/59.2°}$ $B:60\underline{/194.3°}$ $C:90\underline{/306.4°}$
2. $A:20\underline{/14.2°}$ $B:30\underline{/133.5°}$ $C:75\underline{/231.6°}$
3. $A:70\underline{/31.8°}$ $B:40\underline{/153.7°}$ $C:60\underline{/298.1°}$
4. $A:40\underline{/42.9°}$ $B:20\underline{/143.3°}$ $C:30\underline{/257.4°}$
5. $A:25\underline{/51.3°}$ $B:35\underline{/26.8°}$ $C:50\underline{/165.2°}$
6. $A:34\underline{/68.7°}$ $B:42\underline{/243.8°}$ $C:55\underline{/327.6°}$
7. $A:45\underline{/15.3°}$ $B:23\underline{/147.2°}$ $C:67\underline{/235°}$
     $D:54\underline{/312°}$

8. $A: 22.5\underline{/57.3°}$ $B: 31.2\underline{/114°}$ $C: 43\underline{/218°}$
   $D: 22.1\underline{/-13.2°}$

9. $A: 24\underline{/26.3°}$ $B: 36\underline{/116.7°}$ $C: 52\underline{/246°}$
   $D: 23\underline{/-23.6°}$

10. $A: 30\underline{/16.2°}$ $B: 50\underline{/72.6°}$ $C: 40\underline{/131.7°}$
   $D: 60\underline{/212°}$ $E: 10\underline{/293.1°}$

11. $A: 32\underline{/0°}$ $B: 14.3\underline{/42.3°}$ $C: 38\underline{/261°}$

12. $A: 65\underline{/90°}$ $B: 85\underline{/207.3°}$ $C: 72\underline{/-68°}$

13. $A: 52\underline{/35.2°}$ $B: 73\underline{/180°}$ $C: 54\underline{/297°}$

14. $A: 23\underline{/71.4°}$ $B: 31\underline{/158.2°}$ $C: 21\underline{/270°}$

15. $A: 36\underline{/0°}$ $B: 42\underline{/90°}$ $C: 27\underline{/-90°}$

47

Graphs of the Trigonometric Functions

47.1 SELECTION OF VALUES

We recall that in graphing an algebraic equation, $y = f(x)$, we find sets of values for x and y. As an example, consider the equation

$$y = x^2 - 3x - 4$$

In this equation we take any arbitrary value for x and find the corresponding value of y. For instance, if we take $x = 2$, then $y = -6$; if $x = 3$, $y = -4$; and so on. These pairs of values are plotted as the coordinates of points on the rectangular coordinate system.

If we have an equation involving a trigonometric function, we proceed in the same way. Suppose we wish to graph the equation

$$y = \sin x$$

We take any arbitrary values for x, such as 1, 2, 3, and so on, and find the corresponding values of y. These pairs of values are then plotted as points on the coordinate system.

However, in graphing the trigonometric functions, we run into difficulties not encountered in purely algebraic functions. For instance, in a trigonometric equation, such as $y = \sin x$, the values of x must be in *radians*. If we take the value $x = 1$, then we have $y = \sin 1$. Here the 1 must be taken as *1 radian*; that is,

$$y = \sin 1 = \sin 57.3° = 0.8415$$

In a trigonometric equation it is usually easier to take the values of x in terms of π radians. If this is done, the numbers of degrees can be rational numbers. For instance,

$$\sin \frac{\pi}{6} = \sin 30° = 0.5000$$

In plotting the points for the true trigonometric curves on the rectangular coordinate system, we must remember two things:

1. The units on the x-axis and the y-axis must be equal in length.
2. The units on the x-axis must represent radians.

650

It is true that we usually find the values of x by looking up the angle in degrees, since most tables give angles by degrees. However, if we are to get the true and proper shape of the curves, the scales on the axes must be laid off according to the foregoing rules. In actual practice, it will be somewhat easier to graph a trigonometric function if the scales are modified slightly; but if this is done, the result will not be the true shape of the curve.

47.2 THE SINE CURVE

To graph the equation $y = \sin x$, we first set up a table of pairs of values. The corresponding numbers of degrees are shown in parentheses.

	x	y		x	y
0	0	0	(210°)	$\frac{7\pi}{6}$	-0.5000
(30°)	$\frac{\pi}{6}$	0.5000	(225°)	$\frac{5\pi}{4}$	-0.7071
45°	$\frac{\pi}{4}$	0.7071	(240°)	$\frac{4\pi}{3}$	-0.8660
(60°)	$\frac{\pi}{3}$	0.8660	(270°)	$\frac{3\pi}{2}$	-1.0000
(90°)	$\frac{\pi}{2}$	1.0000	(300°)	$\frac{5\pi}{3}$	-0.8660
(120°)	$\frac{2\pi}{3}$	0.8660	(315°)	$\frac{7\pi}{4}$	-0.7071
(135°)	$\frac{3\pi}{4}$	0.7071	(330°)	$\frac{11\pi}{6}$	-0.5000
(150°)	$\frac{5\pi}{6}$	0.5000	(360°)	2π	0
(180°)	π	0			

All of the foregoing values of the sine can be found without a table by the method of special angles. If we wish to find the sine of angles at smaller intervals, such as 10° or 5°, we can use a table of values and plot as many values as desired.

To plot the foregoing values as points, we first show the x-axis and the y-axis on rectangular coordinate paper. Since most or all of the x-values are taken as positive, the y-axis can be located near the left side of the graph. We lay off equal units on the x-axis and the y-axis and number the points 1, 2, 3, and so on. For the sine curve the ordinate will never be greater than *one* (1).

Since the angles are usually found in terms of π radians, we locate the point π on the x-axis approximately $3\frac{1}{7}$ units to the right of the origin. This point represents an angle of π radians, or 180°. Using this point as a guide, we lay off the common fractional values of π, such as $\pi/6$, $\pi/4$, and $\pi/3$ (Fig. 47.1).

The values of x (that is, the angle in radians) and the corresponding values of y (that is, the sine values) are then plotted as points on the graph. If we join the points by a smooth curve, we get the true sine curve or the graph of the equation, $y = \sin x$.

47.3 CYCLE

In the equation $y = \sin x$, if we continue to find the sine values for angles greater than 360°, such as 390°, 420°, or 450°, we find that the curve repeats the same form or pattern. For the values of x from 0 to 360° we get one complete pattern of the curve. For the values of x from 360° to 720° we get an exact duplication of the same form we have from 0 to 360°. One complete pattern of any curve is called *one cycle*. For any angles beyond 2π, or 360°, the curve will repeat the same form. Such a curve is called a *periodic* curve. A periodic curve is one in which the same form or pattern is repeated indefinitely as the independent variable is increased without limit. Note especially that the curve of $y = \sin x$ has *one* cycle from 0 to 360°.

47.4 THE GRAPH OF THE EQUATION $y = \sin 2x$

In finding pairs of values for x and y in the equation $y = \sin 2x$, we must be careful to double the value of the angle x before finding the sine value. If we take the value of x as $\pi/6$, or 30°, then we must multiply this value by 2 before finding the value of y. To find the value of y, we have, for $x = 30°$, $y = \sin (2)(30°) = \sin 60° = 0.8660$.

In general, whenever a value of x is taken in this equation, this value must be multiplied by 2 before the sine value is found. Some of the angles from 0 to 2π and the corresponding sine values are shown in the table. The graph for the equation $y = \sin 2x$ is shown in Fig. 47.2. Note that there are two complete cycles of the curve for angles from 0 to 2π.

x	y ($\sin 2x$)
0	0
15°	0.5000
30°	0.8660
45°	1.0000
60°	0.8660
90°	0
120°	−0.8660
135°	−1.0000
150°	−0.8660
180°	0
210°	0.8660
225°	1.0000

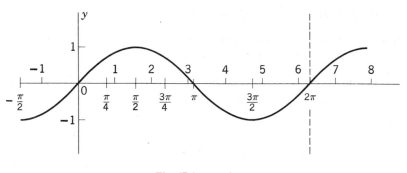

Fig. 47.1. $y = \sin x$.

47.5 FREQUENCY FACTOR

In graphing the equation $y = \sin 2x$, we get one complete cycle or pattern of the curve for angles from 0 to π, or 180°. If we take x values over the interval 0 to 2π, or 360°, we get *two* complete patterns or *cycles* of the curve. The form of the curve from 180° to 360° is identical with the form from 0 to 180°. In this case we say that the *frequency* of the cycle is 2. Note that in the interval covering angles from 0 to 2π there are two points at which the curve reaches its highest value and two points at which it reaches its lowest value.

If we were to graph the equation $y = \sin 3x$, we should get three complete cycles in the interval $x = 0$ to $x = 2\pi$. In general, if we graph the equation $y = \sin nx$, in which the n represents any numerical coefficient of x, then the number of cycles in the interval 0 to 360° will be n. For this reason, the n in this case, which is the coefficient of x, is called the *frequency factor*, since it indicates the number of cycles from 0 to 360°, or 2π. In the equation $y = \sin 10x$ the frequency factor is 10, which means that we get 10 cycles from $x = 0$ to $x = 2\pi$.

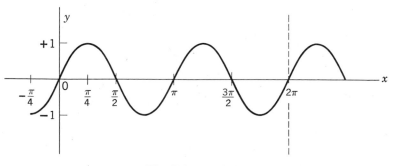

Fig. 47.2. $y = \sin 2x$.

47.6   THE GRAPH OF THE EQUATION $y = 2 \sin x$

In finding pairs of values for x and y in the equation $y = 2 \sin x$, we first take any value for x and find the sine of that angle. Then we multiply this sine value by 2. We do *not* double the angle. For instance, if we take $x = 30°$ (that is, $\pi/6$), we find that the sine of the angle is 0.5000. Then we multiply this value by 2 to find the value of y. When the angle is 90°, the sine value is 1, but this value is then doubled, so $y = 2$.

Some of the values of x and the corresponding values of y are shown in the table. The graph of the equation $y = 2 \sin x$ is shown in Fig. 47.3, with values of x from $x = 0$ to $x = 2\pi$.

x	y
0	0
30°	1.0000
45°	1.4142
60°	1.7320
90°	2.0000
120°	1.7320
135°	1.4142
150°	1.0000
180°	0
210°	− 1.0000
225°	− 1.4142

Note that in the interval from 0 to 2π there is only one complete cycle of the curve, since the frequency factor is 1. However, the curve has a greater distance from the x-axis. The ordinate y at one time reaches a value of 2.

47.7   AMPLITUDE FACTOR

In the equation $y = 2 \sin x$, whatever value we assign to x, we first find the sine value and then double this value. At every point on the curve the ordinate, or y-value, extends twice as far as that for the curve of $y = \sin x$. The height of the curve, or the greatest distance from the x-axis, is called the *amplitude* of the curve. The amplitude of $y = 2 \sin x$ is twice the amplitude of the sine curve, $y = \sin x$.

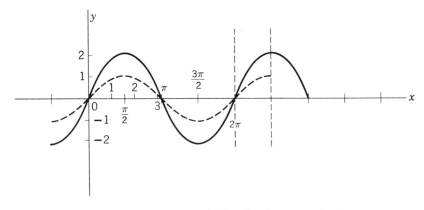

Fig. 47.3. $y = 2 \sin x$. (The broken line shows $y = \sin x$.)

If we were to graph the equation $y = 3 \sin x$, we should find that the amplitude is three times that of the sine curve. For this reason, the 3 is called the *amplitude factor*. In any equation of the form $y = m \sin x$ the coefficient m is the amplitude factor because it determines the greatest height or amplitude of the curve. Moreover, for any particular value of x, the curve has a y-value m times the y-value of the sine curve itself.

If we graph the equations $y = 3 \sin x$, $y = 4 \sin x$, or $y = m \sin x$, where m is any constant, we get only one complete cycle from $x = 0$ to $x = 2\pi$. Note that the frequency factor is 1 in each case. The frequency factor, that is, the coefficient of the angle, is not affected by the amplitude of the curve.

If we were to graph the equation $y = 30 \sin 20x$, we should get a curve of 20 cycles over a 360° interval. The amplitude factor is 30, which means that the curve reaches a point 30 units above and below the x-axis. Such a curve is called a *sinusoidal* curve, since it resembles the sine curve. For such curves it is often convenient to compress the scales in the y-direction.

47.8 THE COSINE CURVE

In finding pairs of values for x and y in the equation $y = \cos x$, we proceed as we do for the sine curve. We take any convenient values for x and then compute the values for y. Some of these values are shown in the table. Note especially the following values:

$$\cos 0 = 1$$
$$\cos \frac{\pi}{2} = 0$$
$$\cos \pi = -1$$

x	y
0	1.0000
30°	0.8660
45°	0.7071
60°	0.5000
90°	0
120°	−0.5000
135°	−0.7071
150°	−0.8660
180°	−1.0000

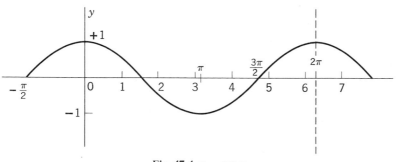

Fig. 47.4. $y = \cos x$.

If we take values of x from 0 to 2π and then plot these values carefully, the result is the cosine curve; it is the graph for the equation $y = \cos x$. The graph is shown in Fig. 47.4. Note that the amplitude is 1 and that the frequency is also 1. In general appearance, the cosine curve resembles the sine curve.

47.9   PHASE DIFFERENCE

In the graph of the equation $y = \cos x$ we get one cycle in the interval $x = 0$ to $x = 360°$. In the graph of the equation $y = \sin x$ we also get one cycle in the same interval. If we continue the sine and cosine curves beyond 360°, we find that the two curves have the same shape. However, their positions are separated by a 90° interval, or difference. This difference in position along the x-axis is called "phase difference." A phase difference between two curves represents a shift in a curve to the right or left.

47.10   OTHER TRIGONOMETRIC CURVES

In graphing the curves for the tangent, the cotangent, the secant, and the cosecant, we should note the following points:

1. For some values of x the function values do not exist. The function values increase or decrease without limit. The graphs in such cases approach straight lines but do not cross them. A straight line approached by a curve in this way is called an *asymptote*. For instance, the tangent of 90° does not exist. It can be said to be infinitely great. The tangent value continues to increase as x approaches 90°. Note these tangent values as the angle approaches 90°. The tangent of 89° is approximately 57.3; the tangent of 89° 59' is approximately 3438; the tangent of 89° 59' 59" is approximately 206,000. Just beyond 90° the tangent is a large *negative* number.

2. The tangent and cotangent curves cross the x-axis. The secant and cosecant curves do not cross the x-axis, since their smallest numerical value is 1.

3. The cosecant curve touches the sine curve at 90 and 270°, since the cosecant is the reciprocal of the sine. When the sine value is 0, the cosecant value is infinite.

4. The secant curve touches the cosine curve at 0, 180, and 360°, since the secant is the reciprocal of the cosine. When the cosine value is 0, the secant value is infinite.

47.11   COMPOUND CURVES

In some cases it is desirable to find the curve that represents the sum of two or more functions. For instance, we may want to find the curve for the equation

$$y = \sin x + \sin 2x$$

One way to graph this equation is to set up a table of values for y that correspond to the selected x values. Remember, in this instance the y values must represent the sum, $\sin x + \sin 2x$. For any particular value of x we must first find the sine of x, then the sine of $2x$, and then add these two to get the proper value of y. The pairs of corresponding values are plotted on the graph.

By another method that is somewhat simpler we add the values on the graph itself by means of a compass. To do this, we construct the graph of each function separately on the same form. Then with a compass, we measure the ordinate value of one curve at any point on the graph and then add this value to the ordinate value of the other curve.

Exercise 47.1

Graph the following equations on rectangular coordinate paper:

1. $y = \sin x$
2. $y = \cos x$
3. $y = \tan x$
4. $y = \cot x$
5. $y = \sec x$
6. $y = \csc x$
7. $y = \sin 3x$
8. $y = 3 \sin x$
9. $y = \cos 4x$
10. $y = 5 \cos x$
11. $y = 2 \sin 3x$
12. $y = \sin^2 x$
13. $y = \sin x + \cos x$
14. $y = \sin x + \sin 2x$
15. $y = \sin(90° + x)$
16. $y = 1 + \sin x$
17. $y = \sin x + \sin 2x + \sin 3x$
18. $y = (\sin x)(\cos x)$
19. $y = \tan^2 x + 1$
20. $y = \sec^2 x$
21. $y = \sin^2 x + \cos^2 x$
22. $y = (\sin^2 x)(\cos x)$
23. $y = (\sin^6 x)(\cos^5 x)$
24. $y = \sin x + \sin 3x + \sin 5x + \sin 7x$
25. Sketch the first six of these curves on the same graph.

Quiz No. 2. Trigonometry. Form A.

1. Express each of the following angles in radian measure:

   $225°$; $150°$; $300°$; $270°$; $15°$; $63°$; $750°$; $-45°$

2. Without using a table find the sine, cosine, and tangent of the following special angles. Leave answers in fractional and radical form. Sketch each angle.

   (a) $135°$ (b) $240°$ (c) $180°$ (d) $-30°$

3. Evaluate each of the following in numerical value:

   (a) $\cot 0.42$ (b) $1 + \sin 1$ (c) $\pi + \cos \pi$ (d) $3 + \tan 3$

4. Without using a table, find the value of each of the following:

  (a) sin 15°, using 30° and 45°   (b) tan 15°, using 60° and 45°.

5. In a certain right triangle, ABC, the sides are 7 inches, 24 inches, and 25 inches, respectively. Using the smallest angle, A, show that the following formula is true: $\sin 2A = 2 \sin A \cos A$.

6. In oblique triangle DEF, $D = 38.5°$, $E = 71.9°$, $d = 15$ inches. Find side e.

7. In oblique triangle ABC, $a = 12$ inches, $c = 15$ inches, $B = 58.4°$. Find side b.

8. In oblique triangle RST, $S = 41.7°$, $r = 30$ inches, $s = 24$ inches. Find angle R.

9. In oblique triangle DEF, $d = 7$ inches, $e = 9$ inches, $f = 10$ inches. Find angle E.

10. Find the rectangular components of the following vector and write the result as a complex number:

  73.4/291.6°

11. Write the following complex number as a vector in polar form, showing magnitude and direction of the vector:

  $5.4 - 4.1j$

12. Express each of the following vectors as a complex number in rectangular form. Then add the numbers and express the result as a vector showing magnitude and direction:

  $A : 90/\underline{123.8}$ $B : 50/\underline{223.5}$

13. Sketch the graph of the equation, $y = \sin 2x$, from $x = 0$ to $x = 360°$.

Quiz No. 2.   Trigonometry.   Form B.

1. Express each of the following angles in radian measure:

  210°;   330°;   135°;   180°;   12°;   44°;   765°;   −60°

2. Without using a table find the sine, cosine, and tangent of the following special angles. Leave answers in fractional and radical form. Sketch each angle.

  (a) 150°   (b) 225°   (c) 270°   (d) −60°

3. Evaluate each of the following in numerical value:

  (a) tan 0.31   (b) $1 + \cot 1$ (c) $\dfrac{\pi}{2} + \sin \dfrac{\pi}{2}$ (d) $4 + \cos 2$

4. Without using a table, find the value of each of the following:

  (a) cos 15°, using 60° and 45°   (b) tan 75°, using 45° and 30°

5. In a certain right triangle, ABC, the sides are 5 inches, 12 inches, and 13 inches, respectively. Using the smallest angle, A, show that the following formula is true: $\cos 2A = \cos^2 A - \sin^2 A$

6. In oblique triangle DEF, $D = 70.3°$, $E = 41.9°$; $e = 18$ inches. Find side d.

7. In oblique triangle ABC, $C = 55.6°$; $a = 15$ inches; $b = 18$ inches. Find side c.

8. In oblique triangle RST, $T = 62.4°$; $s = 20$ inches; $t = 24$ inches. Find angle S.

9. In oblique triangle DEF, $d = 6$ inches; $e = 8$ inches; $f = 5$ inches. Find angle F.

10. Find the rectangular components of the following vector and write the result as a complex number:

    $84.3/142.6°$

11. Write the following complex number as a vector in polar form, showing magnitude and direction of the vector:

    $-5.1 + 4.3j$

12. Express each of the following vectors as a complex number in rectangular form. Then add the numbers and express the result as a vector showing magnitude and direction:

    $A: 30/73.4°$ $B: 80/318.8°$

13. Sketch the graph of the equation, $y = 2 \cos x$, from $x = 0$ to $x = 360°$.

Answers to Odd-Numbered Exercises

Exercise 1.1, Page 9

1. 633; 1201; 1608; 1136; 1185; 1208; 1231 **3.** 1518; 1482; 1112; 1433; 1482; 1296; 1227 **5.** 46,179 **7.** 13,158 **9.** 74,267 **11.** 1375; 881; 7869; 4657; 626 **13.** 987; 2389; 1528; 2759; 3055 **15.** 8; 106; 134; 261; 348; 118; 89 **17.** 17 **19.** 68 **21.** 625; 403; 818; 339; 368; 127; 208

Exercise 1.2, Page 18

1. 140777; 344568; 287153; 428060; 450148 **3.** 3640472; 5498898; 4542531; 6285780; 4636989 **5.** 222222; 888888; 1244421; 44435556; 1030304 **7.** 30134 **9.** 10472 **11.** 100344 **13.** 104830 **15.** 437 **17.** 619 **19.** 762 **21.** 784 **23.** 568 **25.** 508 **27.** 706 **29.** 2909 (remainder 11) **31.** 12345679 **33.** 8081 **35.** almost 9 **37.** 6247 **39.** (approximate) 1423; 59; 1; 1 min. **41.** 1950–1960; 1930–1940: 244473; 1940–1950: 322115; 25,283,654 **43.** 120 ft **45.** 11 sec. **47.** 5,865,696,000,000 mi.

Exercise 2.1, Page 20

1. (a) **2.** (b) **3.** (a) **4.** (a) **5.** (b) **6.** (a) **7.** (a) **8.** (b) **9.** (b) **10.** (b) **11.** (b)
12. (a) **13.** (b) **14.** (a) **15.** (a) **16.** (b) **17.** (b) **18.** (b) **19.** (b) **20.** (b)

Exercise 2.2, Page 24

1. $\frac{14}{3}$ **3.** $\frac{17}{3}$ **5.** $\frac{46}{3}$ **7.** $\frac{107}{5}$ **9.** $\frac{105}{4}$ **11.** $\frac{171}{8}$ **13.** $\frac{81}{7}$ **15.** $\frac{64}{15}$ **17.** $\frac{100}{3}$ **19.** $\frac{75}{2}$ **21.** $\frac{40}{3}$
23. $\frac{145}{64}$ **25.** $\frac{65}{18}$ **27.** $\frac{173}{10}$ **29.** $3\frac{3}{4}$ **31.** $8\frac{2}{5}$ **33.** $6\frac{4}{5}$ **35.** $9\frac{3}{8}$ **37.** 27 **39.** $7\frac{4}{9}$ **41.** $16\frac{3}{4}$
43. $6\frac{8}{13}$ **45.** $15\frac{1}{8}$ **47.** $91\frac{3}{5}$ **49.** $52\frac{5}{6}$ **51.** $66\frac{6}{7}$ **53.** 33 **55.** $312\frac{5}{16}$ **57.** $103\frac{4}{17}$
59. $112\frac{3}{22}$

Exercise 2.3, Page 27

1. $\frac{1}{3}$ **3.** $\frac{5}{7}$ **5.** $\frac{3}{7}$ **7.** $\frac{7}{11}$ **9.** $\frac{3}{7}$ **11.** $\frac{7}{9}$ **13.** $\frac{5}{8}$ **15.** $\frac{5}{7}$ **17.** $\frac{4}{9}$ **19.** $\frac{3}{13}$ **21.** $\frac{3}{4}$ **23.** $\frac{5}{16}$
25. $\frac{5}{6}$ **27.** $\frac{3}{8}$ **29.** $\frac{5}{12}$ **31.** $\frac{21}{22}$ **33.** $\frac{3}{7}$ **35.** $\frac{5}{6}$ **37.** $\frac{18}{24}$; $\frac{16}{24}$; $\frac{9}{24}$; $\frac{14}{24}$ **39.** $\frac{70}{105}$; $\frac{90}{105}$; $\frac{84}{105}$; $\frac{56}{105}$
41. $\frac{168}{360}$; $\frac{220}{360}$; $\frac{255}{360}$; $\frac{189}{360}$

Exercise 2.4, Page 32

1. 24 **3.** 60 **5.** 60 **7.** 18 **9.** 420 **11.** 1260 **13.** 1800 **15.** 5040 **17.** 5400
19. 132,300 **21.** 2,047,500 **23.** 831,600 **25(a).** $64\frac{1}{4}$; $50\frac{3}{4}$; $484\frac{11}{16}$; $170\frac{5}{8}$; $70\frac{4}{5}$; $102\frac{4}{7}$
(b). $35\frac{1}{2}$; $13\frac{1}{2}$; $377\frac{13}{16}$; $75\frac{3}{8}$; $44\frac{4}{5}$; $22\frac{2}{5}$ **27.** $11\frac{19}{24}$ **29.** $11\frac{41}{48}$ **31.** $23\frac{43}{48}$ **33.** $21\frac{1669}{3285}$
35. $\frac{3}{40}$ **37.** $36\frac{9}{10}$ **39.** $47\frac{25}{36}$ **41.** $16\frac{17}{21}$ **43.** $25\frac{13}{16}$ **45.** $4\frac{7}{12}$ **47.** $192\frac{5}{8}$ **49.** $40\frac{7}{12}$ **51.** 1
53. $1\frac{1}{24}$ **55.** $31\frac{215}{288}$ **57.** $5\frac{193}{630}$ **59.** $14\frac{139}{180}$ **61.** $9\frac{1457}{1800}$ **63.** $\frac{43}{1200}$ **65.** $108\frac{35}{144}$

Exercise 2.5, Page 39

1. $\frac{8}{35}$ **3.** $1\frac{5}{7}$ **5.** 8   **7.** $63\frac{3}{8}$ **9.** $8\frac{4}{5}$ **11.** $46\frac{1}{2}$ **13.** $86\frac{1}{3}$ **15.** $62\frac{3}{14}$ **17.** $124\frac{1}{2}$ **19.** $1\frac{1}{5}$
21. $1\frac{1}{6}$ **23.** $6\frac{1}{2}$ **25.** $3\frac{7}{60}$ **27.** $\frac{25}{42}$ **29.** $127\frac{1}{2}$ **31.** $9\frac{89}{99}$ **33.** $2\frac{7}{10}$ **35.** $\frac{14}{129}$ **37.** $1726\frac{229}{720}$
39. $81\frac{459}{700}$ **41.** $52\frac{436}{567}$ **43.** $1842\frac{17}{24}$ **45.** $\frac{9}{140}$ **47.** $\frac{14}{15}$ **49.** 1   **51.** $\frac{812}{1355}$ **53.** $10\frac{3}{8}$ in.
55. 7   **57.** $2\frac{11}{64}$ in.   **59.** $18\frac{3}{8}$ in.   **61.** 5

Exercise 3.1, Page 45

1. 0.5   **3.** 0.625   **5.** 0.3636...   **7.** 3.1875   **9.** 6.875   **11.** 8.4   **13.** 7.833...
15. 1.09375   **17.** $9.888\frac{8}{9}$ **19.** $8.666\frac{2}{3}$ **21.** 9.15625   **23.** 1.28125   **25.** 8.4375   **27.** $\frac{1}{4}$
29. $\frac{4}{25}$ **31.** $1\frac{1}{5}$ **33.** $\frac{1}{3}$ **35.** $8\frac{1}{20}$ **37.** $3\frac{1}{40}$ **39.** $15\frac{3}{40}$ **41.** $5\frac{3}{80}$ **43.** $8\frac{1}{200}$ **45.** $\frac{601}{2000}$
47. $11\frac{2}{25}$ **49.** $\frac{1}{700}$

Exercise 3.2, Page 46

1. 1516.97   **3.** 295.535   **5.** 80683.18   **7.** 188.587   **9.** 758.9838   **11.** 41.06   **13.** 3550.53
15. 709.815   **17.** 188.968   **19.** 1.12086   **21.** 2.75   **23.** 1.61342   **25.** 0.93973
27. 0.57303   **29.** 1.36175   **31.** 221.6 mi.

Exercise 3.3, Page 49

1. 473530; 473500; 474000; 470000   **3.** 5081400; 5081000; 5080000; 5100000
5. 852.92; 852.9; 853; 850   **7.** 49.250; 49.25; 49.3; 49   **9.** 0·17397; 0·1740; 0.174; 0.17
11. 488540; 488500; 489000; 490000   **13.** 9270400; 9270000; 9270000; 9300000
15. 3.2581; 3.258; 3.26; 3.3   **17.** 0.0058404; 0.005840; 0.00584; 0.0058   **19.** 57.005;
57.00; 57.0; 57

Exercise 3.4, Page 50 (A plus sign or a minus sign after a number indicates that the true answer is a little more or a little less, respectively, than the answer shown.)

1. 440.16   **3.** 8.1528   **5.** 5.8875   **7.** 0.65504   **9.** 2.9172   **11.** 4.0866   **13.** 0.262006
15. 0.000713   **17.** 0.0015822   **19.** 0.85695   **21.** 28.77123   **23.** 6.50844   **25.** 9.0723764
27. 4.9913444   **29.** 284.71056   **31.** 0.05836572   **33.** 0.04364091   **35.** 1012.9008
37. 0.080938+   **39.** 0.0025787−   **41.** 0.055083−   **43.** 36.251+   **45.** 838.96+
47. 8.0779−   **49.** 0.6917−   **51.** 42.772−   **53.** 1.3709−   **55.** 29.633−   **57.** 680.85−
59. 0.000069191+

Exercise 3.5, Page 53 (No answers given for numbers 1–26.)

27. 42.955−   **29.** 0.036641−

Exercise 3.6, Page 54

1. 34.6; 41.3; 25.9; 58.3; 63.3; 233.4; 15.62 miles per gal.; $4.23   **3.** $6.46
5. 4.4226 sq in.; 8.50 in.   **7.** 992.25 sq in.; 126.0 in.   **9.** 4.43 in.   **11.** $3.96   **13.** 0.54 in.
15. 93   **17.** 10.88 in.   **19.** 5.035 in.   **21.** $19\frac{23}{32}$ in.   **23.** 15   **25.** 83.3 mph; 122.2 ft/sec
27. 76.2   **29.** 72.1   **31.** 107.76

Exercise 4.1, Page 58

1. $\frac{7}{20}$; 0.35   **3.** $\frac{7}{160}$; 0.04375   **5.** $\frac{1}{800}$; 0.00125   **7.** $\frac{3}{8}$; 0.375   **9.** $\frac{1}{7}$; 0.14286...   **11.** $1\frac{3}{4}$; 1.75
13. 10; 10   **15.** $\frac{1}{3}$; 0.3333   **17.** $\frac{3}{160}$; 0.01875   **19.** $\frac{1}{75}$; 0.01333   **21.** 80%   **23.** 10.9375%

25. 562.5%   **27.** 2.5%   **29.** 145.3%   **31.** $66\frac{2}{3}$%   **33.** $355\frac{5}{9}$%   **35.** 510%   **37.** 0.05%
39. 60%

Exercise 4.2, Page 61

1. $12.60   **3.** 37.5%   **5.** 50 mi.   **7.** 0.1212%   **9.** 125%   **11.** $1235; $559; $1170;
$845; $975; $409.50; $676; $630.50   **13.** 34,506   **15.** 0.0479; 50,300   **17.** $33\frac{1}{3}$%
19. $12; $60   **21.** (a) 12.5%; (b) $11\frac{1}{9}$%   **23.** 3.4%   **25.** 0.304   **27.** 160   **29.** $6800

Exercise 5.1, Page 68

1. 86.36   **3.** 879.26   **5.** 981.456   **7.** 3733.7   **9.** 162.15   **11.** 4633   **13.** 0.0235

Exercise 5.2, Page 68

1. 182.245   **3.** 3.1496   **5.** 1609.9   **7.** 339.1   **9.** 126.5   **11.** 4.51   **13.** 12.5 mils;
0.3175 mm   **15.** 12,408

Exercise 5.3, Page 73

1. 541.9   **3.** 12,102.8   **5.** 604.8   **7.** 1 hectare = 2.47 acres   **9.** 1260.3

Exercise 5.4, Page 74

1. 274.2 cm²; 68.58 cm   **3.** 14.021 by 8.534   **5.** 2.1 cm   **7.** 19 ft 2 in.   **9.** 1.2904 cm²
11. 1.8 lb   **13.** 254 sq in.   **15.** 2.273 kg   **17.** 0.9091 kg   **19.** 1.364 kg   **21.** 0.739 kg
23. 7.273 kg   **25.** 81.82 kg   **27.** 13.167 m   **29.** 211.7 m   **31.** 5.507 km   **33.** 3.048 m
35. 0.065 g   **37.** 0.454 kg   **39.** 2.54 cm   **41.** 45.72 m   **43.** 41.67 ft   **45.** 18.90 in.
47. 328.1 ft   **49.** 5468 yd   **57.** 329.2 m   **59.** 411 miles   **61.** 312.5 m

Exercise 6.1, Page 80

1. 42.7   **3.** 5.54   **5.** 523.3   **7.** 79.2   **9.** 904   **11.** 102.8   **13.** 0.7759   **15.** 30.80
17. 0.163   **19.** 264.6   **21.** 0.003873   **23.** 0.02052   **25.** 20 rd; 80 rd   **27.** 17.55 ft
29. 75.63 ft   **31.** 84.85 ft

Exercise 6.2, Page 83

1. 29.38   **3.** 5.356   **5.** 0.3142   **7.** 28460   **9.** 0.01365   **11.** 853.8   **13.** 4.5   **15.** 3.606
17. 1.225   **19.** 9.930   **21.** 2.562   **23.** 39.53   **25.** 1.414   **27.** 0.3162   **29.** 7.07
31. 9.898   **33.** 8.484   **35.** 8.66   **37.** 6.928   **39.** 13.86   **41.** 15.81   **43.** 60   **45.** 10.63
47. 17   **49.** 17.6; 17.6   **51.** 9.49 in.

Exercise 7.1, Page 89

1. 25043_6 **3.** 232213_4 **5.** 35204_6 **7.** 1201221_3 **9.** 320312_4 **11.** 30402_5
13. 100010   **15.** 100111   **17.** 101110   **19.** 110100   **21.** 111010   **23.** 100111010
25. 101100101   **27.** 111110111   **29.** 111010001   **31.** 1342   **33.** 1406   **35.** 722
37. 223   **39.** 9116   **41.** 53   **43.** 51   **45.** 43   **47.** 45   **49.** 59   **51.** 435   **53.** 453
55. 409   **57.** 367   **59.** 306   **61.** (a) 123; (b) 143; (c) 101   **63.** (a) 2112; (b) 2122;
(c) 103122   **65.** (a) 1001; (b) 100011; (c) 11001011

Exercise 8.1, Page 95

1. $a + b + c$ **3.** $3x + 4y$ **5.** $7 + x$ **7.** $y - 8$ **9.** $15 + n$ **11.** $10 - x$ **13.** $a - b$
15. m/n **17.** $(x + y)/xy$ **19.** $(a + b) - (x + y)$ **21.** $3(h - k)$ **23.** $(4a)(7b)$

Exercise 8.2, Page 99

1. $59; 41; -62; 32; -25; -59$ **3.** $24; -54; 48; -85; -89; 0$ **5.** $-57.996; 3.276;$
$-57.6; -41.39; -44.28; 0.065$ **7.** -1.87647 **9.** -2.0217

Exercise 8.3, Page 101

1. $14; 3; 5; 64; -73; -27$ **3.** $-43; -91; -25; 0; 25; -74$ **5.** $8; 212; -322; 322;$
$232; 1000$ **7.** $1.72; 4.128; -7.951; -8.897; -6.463; -3.5322$

Exercise 8.4, Page 103

1. 12 **3.** 1 **5.** 16 **7.** -23 **9.** 35 **11.** -23 **13.** 128 **15.** 376

Exercise 8.5, Page 105

1. -84 **3.** 40 **5.** -18.06 **7.** 2.88 **9.** -30.24 **11.** -96 **13.** 180 **15.** 120
17. -32 **19.** 540 **21.** $4650; 3402: -3844; -2254; 912; -1722; -1071$

Exercise 8.6, Page 106

1. 5 **3.** -8 **5.** 5 **7.** -16 **9.** -15 **11.** $2/3$ **13.** -2.6 **15.** $1\frac{1}{3}$ **17.** $-\frac{11}{14}$
19. $117; -14; -23; 17; -0.02$ **21.** $2\frac{1}{3}; -1.5; 0.00211; 0.8; -224$

Exercise 9.1, Page 112

1. Adding: $8x; -11x^2; -4st; 2n; -3xy; 4xy - 3x; -6x^2y$
   Subtracting: $-2x; 3x^2; -6st; 8n; 3xy; 4xy + 3x; -8x^2y$
3. Adding: $8xy^3; -11st^2; -xy; 0; -m^2n; -18x^2y; -12xy - 12xy^2$
   Subtracting: $-6xy^3; 5st^2; -13xy; -6xyz; -7m^2n; 0; -12xy + 12xy^2$
5. $4x^2y$ **7.** $-7x^2y^3$ **9.** $6a + 6b + 7c - ab$ **11.** $5x + 6y - z + 9$ **13.** $y^2 - 2xy$
15. $2x^2 - 5xy + 11y^2$ **17.** $6x^2 - 2xy + 3y^2$ **19.** $4x^2 + 5nx - 6n^2$
21. $y^2 + 8xy - x^2 + 5x$ **23.** $-2x^2 + 3xy - 2y^2 + 3x$ **25.** $5x^3 - 5x^2 + 9x$

Exercise 10.1, Page 120

1. $2^3x^4y^2$ **3.** 5^4x^3yz **5.** $10^4x^2y^2z^5$ **7.** $6x^2$ **9.** $-6x^3y^4$ **11.** $-7ax^4y^3$ **13.** $18x^9$
15. $15abcd$ **17.** $-60x^6y^4z^6$ **19.** $96a^3m^4n^6$ **21.** $189x^6y^3z^8$ **23.** $a^5b^4c^3$ **25.** $720abcde$
27. $12x^3 + 15x^2y - 6xy^2$ **29.** $8x^3yz - 10x^2y^2z - 14xy^3z$
31. $8a^4c^2 - 12a^3bc^3 + 20a^2b^2c^4 + 12ab^3c^6$
33. $8x^4y - 10x^3y^2 + 8x^2y^3 - 2xy^4 + 4x^2y + 2xy$ **35.** $-10x^5yz^4$ **37.** $2my$ **39.** -1
41. $-7x^2z$ **43.** $-6x^2y^3 + 5y^2 - 4xy$ **45.** $4r^2s^2t^3 - 3rs + 2t^2 - \frac{5}{2}r^3s^3t^4$

Exercise 10.2, Page 123

1. $6x^2 - xy - 15y^2$ **3.** $6x^3 - 7x^2y + y^3$ **5.** $2x^3 - 2x^2y - xy^2 - 14x^2 + 14xy + 7y^2$
7. $x^4 - 4x^3y + 6x^2y^2 - 4xy^3 + y^4$ **9.** $6x^3 - 5x^2 - 14x - 5$
11. $4x^4 - 7x^3y + 2x^2y^2 + y^4$ **13.** $3x^4 - 13x^3 - 4x^2 - 5x - 6$
15. $12x^5 - 6x^4 - 25x^3 + 14x^2 + 12x - 8$ **17.** $x^5 - 4x^4 + 6x^3 - 5x^2 - x - 3$
19. $2x^3 - 9x^2 - 11x + 60$ **21.** $8x^3 + 27y^3$ **23.** $a^4 + 2a^3b + a^2b^2 - b^4$
25. $x^5 - 8x^4 - x^3 + 92x^2 - 60x - 144$ **27.** $x^5 + y^5$ **29.** $8x^5 - 8x^4 + 25x^2 - 26x - 15$

Exercise 10.3, Page 126

1. $x + 5$ **3.** $3x - 2 + \dfrac{2}{x + 4}$ **5.** $3c + 2d - \dfrac{3d^2}{2c - 3d}$ **7.** $x^2 - 4x - 2 - \dfrac{5}{2x - 1}$

9. $2x^2 - 4x + 3 + \dfrac{6}{x + 2}$ **11.** $-3y^2 - 5y + 1 + \dfrac{15}{5 - 3y}$ **13.** $2x - 3$

15. $3x^2 + 4x - 2 - \dfrac{2}{4x - 1}$ **17.** $3n^2 - 5n + 4 - \dfrac{5}{2n - 3}$ **19.** $4h^2 - 7h + 5$

21. $2v^3 - 4v^2 + 3v - 5$ **23.** $6x^3 + 4x^2 + 7x - 3 - \dfrac{9}{3x - 2}$

25. $2x^3 + 4x^2 + 5x - 3 - \dfrac{4}{4x - 5}$ **27.** $8x^3 + 12x^2 - 18x - 27$ **29.** $5x^3 - 3x + 2$

31. $3x^2 + 3xy + \frac{7}{2}y^2 + \dfrac{45y^3}{4x - 6y}$ **33.** $3x^2 - 2x + 5 + \dfrac{37 - 30x}{2x^2 + 3x - 4}$

35. $4x^2 - 5xy - 3y^2$ **37.** $3x^3 + x^2 - \frac{3}{2}x - \frac{5}{4} - \dfrac{7}{4(2x - 3)}$

39. $2x^4 - 6x^3 - 4x^2 - 5x - \frac{11}{3} - \dfrac{52}{3(3x - 2)}$ **41.** $4x^2 + 3$

43. $x^4 + 2x^3 + 4x^2 + 8x + 16$

Exercise 10.4, Page 129 (Answers for 1, 5, 9, 13, 17, 21) (R denotes remainder).

1. $2x^2 - 4x - 1$, $R: 1$; $2x^2 - 8x + 11$, $R: -9$; $2x^2 - 2x - 1$, $R: 0$; $2x^2 + 3$, $R: 11$; $2x^2 - 10x + 23$, $R: -44$ **5.** $3x^3 - 4x^2 + 6x - 2$, $R: -14$; $3x^3 - 10x^2 + 20x - 28$, $R: 16$; $3x^3 - x^2 + 8x + 8$, $R: 4$; $3x^3 + 2x^2 + 16x + 40$, $R: 108$; $3x^3 + 5x^2 + 30x + 112$, $R: 436$ **9.** $3x^3 + x^2 + 2x + 1$, $R: -6$; $3x^3 - 5x^2 + 6x - 7$, $R: 0$; $3x^3 + 4x^2 + 9x + 17$, $R: 27$; $3x^3 - 8x^2 + 17x - 35$, $R: 63$; $3x^3 + 10x^2 + 41x + 163$, $R: 645$ **13.** $(x + 1)(x - 2)(x - 3)(x + 4)$ **17.** $x^6 - 2x^5 + 4x^4 - 8x^3 + 16x^2 - 32x + 64$ **21.** $x^3 + 2x^2 + 2x - 3$

Exercise 11.1, Page 133

1. 8   **3.** 8   **5.** identity   **7.** 2   **9.** 8   **11.** 12   **13.** identity   **15.** 5   **17.** -7 **19.** 1/2   **21.** 8   **23.** identity   **25.** 3   **27.** 12   **29.** identity

Exercise 11.2, Page 139

1. 4   **3.** -3 **5.** 10   **7.** 7/3   **9.** -1.6 **11.** -5 **13.** 3   **15.** 3.5   **17.** $-4\frac{2}{3}$ **19.** 2   **21.** 0   **23.** -7.5 **25.** 3.25   **27.** 0   **29.** $2\frac{1}{3}$ **31.** 3   **33.** -3 **35.** -1 **37.** -8.5 **39.** 0

Exercise 11.3, Page 141

1. 7   **3.** 2.2   **5.** 1.5   **7.** $1\frac{2}{3}$ **9.** -1.5 **11.** $2\frac{2}{9}$ **13.** 2.6   **15.** 12   **17.** -2 **19.** -2 **21.** 0.5   **23.** -1.5 **25.** -3 **27.** -4 **29.** identity   **31.** 1.5   **33.** 0   **35.** no solution   **37.** -7 **39.** 0.5   **41.** no solution

Exercise 12.1, Page 144

1. $2x + 3y$ **3.** $(5x)(7y)$ **5.** $2x + 13$ **7.** $2(x + 5x)$ **9.** $\dfrac{x + y}{xy}$ **11.** $x + 5$ **13.** $2x + 3$

15. $x - 5$ **17.** $(12)(7)$; $12x$; $12(20 - x)$ **19.** $5x + 12$ **21.** $(5)(23)$; $5x$; $5(62 - x)$
23. $25x + 10(37 - x)$ **25.** $8x + (16 - x)$ **27.** $x + 1$ **29.** $x + 2$ **31.** even; odd
33. even   **35.** $35t$ **37.** $(60)(5)$; $60x$; $60(3 - x)$ **39.** $x + 7$ **41.** $2x$ **43.** $x + (x + 19)$
45. $x + 800$; $x + 1600$; $x + 2400$; $x + 3200$

Exercise 12.2, Page 149

1. 17; 51   **3.** 23; 92   **5.** rule, \$15.50; drawing set, \$23.50   **7.** reel, \$10.50; rod, \$17.50
9. visitors, 19; home, 33   **11.** 13 free throws, 34 field goals   **13.** 176; 352; 292   **15.** 41 by
64 rd   **17.** 28 by 64 rd   **19.** $a = 19, b = 11, c = 15$

Exercise 12.3, Page 151

1. 9; 36   **3.** 8.5; 32.5   **5.** 10; 2   **7.** 12; 33   **9.** 1; 6   **11.** 9; 34

Exercise 12.4, Page 152

1. 48; 49; 50   **3.** 57; 59; 61; 63; 65; 67   **5.** 18; 22; 26; 30   **7.** 240   **9.** \$4700; \$5000;
\$5300; \$5600; \$5900

Exercise 12.5, Page 154

1. 41 nickels; 21 dimes   **3.** 33 quarters; 13 halves   **5.** 16 nickels; 14 dimes; 7 quarters
7. 42 ones; 30 threes   **9.** 72 children; 30 adults   **11.** 62.5; 37.5   **13.** 15072; 3768; 640
15. 250 pesos; 125 lempira; 50 sucres   **17.** 30; 60; 10

Exercise 12.6, Page 157

1. $5\frac{1}{3}$ hr   **3.** $5\frac{15}{17}$ hr   **5.** 54 mph   **7.** tr: 450; car: 225   **9.** 1:30 PM   **11.** 2100 mi

Exercise 12.7, Page 158

1. 19; 52   **3.** 32; 64   **5.** 43; 65   **7.** 11 free throws; 41 field goals   **9.** lot, \$2260;
house, \$18,440   **11.** 80; 75; 70; 65; 60   **13.** 3.75; 4.25; 4.75; 5.25; 5.75; 6.25
15. 5.7 ohms; 10 ohms   **17.** 11.3 ohms; 5.3 ohms; 33.9 ohms   **19.** 110; 330; 160
21. 13; 39   **23.** $7\frac{1}{2}$; 30   **25.** 9; 27   **27.** $8\frac{2}{3}$ by $20\frac{1}{3}$ **29.** 42.5°; 52.5°; 85°   **31.** 55.8;
55.8; 68.4   **33.** 8.75; 5.525; 9.725   **35.** 84; 86; 88   **37.** 47 nickels; 35 dimes
39. 13 nickels; 19 dimes; 18 quarters   **41.** 191 children; 69 adults   **43.** 426; 324
45. 37.4 at 40¢; 22.5 at 80¢   **47.** 4 hr 40 min   **49.** 50 mph

Exercise 13.1, Page 163

1. $24x^4 y^3 z$ **3.** $-60m^4 n^6$ **5.** $6x^5 y^4$ **7.** $-168a^7 b^3 c^6$ **9.** $-540x^{10} y^7$
11. $-1728a^9 b^3 x^3 yz$ **13.** $54r^6 s^3 t^2 x^3 y^6$

Exercise 13.2, Page 165

1. $6x - 10y + 4z$ **3.** $20x - 28y + 12$ **5.** $-30n^3 + 54n$ **7.** $-6x^2 y^2 + 8xy^3$
9. $-5x^5 y + 5x^2 y^3$ **11.** $4x^2 y + 8x^2 y^4 z - 12x^5 y^3$ **13.** $-8x^3 y^2 - 12x^4 y + 20x^2 y^4 + 4x^2 y$
15. $5x^5 y^2 z^3 + 4x^4 y^3 z^3 - x^2 yz^5 + x^2 yz^3$ **17.** $15h^3 k - 9h^3 k^2 - 12h^2 k^2$
19. $-2a^2 b^3 c^4 + 9a^2 b^3 c - 4ab^4 cx + 2abc$

Exercise 13.3, Page 166

1. $3(x + 4)$ **3.** $9(2 + x)$ **5.** $10x^2(3x - 2)$ **7.** $8(3x - y)$ **9.** $2n(3n - 16m)$
11. $7y^2(y - 2)$ **13.** $4x^3y(3x - 2y)$ **15.** $5st(7rs - 2)$ **17.** $\pi h(R^2 - r^2)$
19. $3(4x^2 - 3xy + 2y^2)$ **21.** $2x(3x^2 + 4x + 1)$ **23.** $5xy(1 - 2xy - 3x^2)$
25. $x(x^2 - x + 1 - x^3)$ **27.** $4xy(5x^3y^2 - x + 3y)$ **29.** $5n(2n + 3n^2 - 7)$
31. $pq(3p + 7q - 5)$ **33.** $3x^2y(2 + 4xy^2 - 5x^2y^4 + 3y)$ **35.** $a^2b^2(4a^3 - a^2b + 3ab^2 + b^3)$
37. $31r(4r - t + 2t^2 + 3r^2t^3)$ **39.** $2hk(9h^4k - 8h^2k^2 + 6h - 1)$ **41.** $m(a + b - c + 3)$
43. $(a + b)(7 + x)$ **45.** $(m + n)(m + n - 1)$

Exercise 13.4, Page 168

1. $x^2 - 9$ **3.** $16x^2 - 9y^2$ **5.** $9x^2 - 64a^2$ **7.** $25x^2 - 121y^2$ **9.** $49 - 36x^{10}$
11. $16x^2 - \frac{1}{9}$ **13.** $16x^2 - 25$ **15.** $9a^2 - 25b^2c^2$ **17.** $576n^2 - 289$ **19.** $8100 - 1$

Exercise 13.5, Page 169

1. $(x - 5)(x + 5)$ **3.** $(h + 6)(h - 6)$ **5.** $(3x - 7y)(3x + 7y)$ **7.** $(8x + 1)(8x - 1)$
9. $(3x + \frac{1}{2})(3x - \frac{1}{2})$ **11.** $(9z - 4y)(9z + 4y)$ **13.** $(xy - z)(xy + z)$ **15.** $9(x - 2)(x + 2)$
17. $2(3x + 5)(3x - 5)$ **19.** $(80 - 1)(80 + 1)$ **21.** $(a + b - c + d)(a + b + c - d)$
23. $(a - b - 5)(a - b + 5)$ **25.** $(x - \sqrt{5})(x + \sqrt{5})$ **27.** $(x - y - 4)(x + y + 2)$
29. $(3 - x + y)(7 - x - y)$

Exercise 13.6, Page 171

1. $x^2 + 14x + 49$ **3.** $4n^2 + 12n + 9$ **5.** $25r^2 - 60rs + 36s^2$ **7.** $9 - 60x + 100x^2$
9. $9x^4 - 6x^2 + 1$ **11.** $36x^2 + 6x + \frac{1}{4}$ **13.** $25a^2b^6 + ab^3 + 0.01$
15. $900 - 1140n + 361n^2$ **17.** $2500n^2 + 100n + 1$ **19.** $x^6y^4 + \frac{4}{3}x^3y^2 + \frac{4}{9}$
21. $400 - 40x^4 + x^8$ **23.** $(90 - 1)^2 = 8100 - 180 + 1$ **25.** $(a + b)^2 - 2c(a + b) + c^2$
27. $x^2 - 2x(y - 2) + (y - 2)^2$ **29.** $x^2 - 2x(3 - 2y) + (3 - 2y)^2$ **31.** $25x^2 - 70x + 49$
33. $9x^2 - 60x + 100$ **35.** $9c^2 + 6cd + d^2$ **37.** $x^6 + 2x^3y^5 + y^{10}$
39. $4a^4b^2 - 12a^2bc + 9c^2$ **41.** $9n^2 - n + 1/36$ **43.** $625 - 600xy + 144x^2y^2$
45. $25s^2 + st + 0.01t^2$ **47.** $6.25s^2 + s + 0.04$ **49.** $a^4b^6 - 2a^2b^3c^4 + c^8$
51. $x^2 = 4a^2 + 12a + 9$ **53.** $9x^2 - 30x + 25 = a^2m^2 - 12amn + 36n^2$
55. $x + 5 = 36$

Exercise 13.7, Page 172

1. $(3x + 8)^2$ **3.** no square   **5.** no square   **7.** no square   **9.** no square   **11.** no square
13. no square   **15.** no square   **17.** $(9 + x/2)^2$ **19.** $(12t - \frac{1}{3})^2$ **21.** $(xy + \frac{3}{2}c)^2$
23. $(xy^2 - 8z^3)^2$

Exercise 13.8, Page 173

1. $6x; (x + 3)^2$ **3.** $16n; (n - 8)^2$ **5.** $12x; (2x + 3)^2$ **7.** $10x; (5x + 1)^2$ **9.** $72x;$
$(4x + 9)^2$ **11.** $60x; (6x + 5)^2$ **13.** $2x; (3x - \frac{1}{3})^2$ **15.** $6ab^2; (ab^2 - 3)^2$ **17.** $x;$
$(x - \frac{1}{2})^2$ **19.** $3x; (3x - \frac{1}{2})^2$ **21.** $48x; (12 + 2x)^2$ **23.** $40F; (F + 20)^2$

Exercise 13.9, Page 174

1. $25; (x + 5)^2$ **3.** $49; (2x + 7)^2$ **5.** $64; (x + 8)^2$ **7.** $\frac{1}{4}; (x + \frac{1}{2})^2$ **9.** $16; (4x - 4)^2$
11. $\frac{169}{144}; (\frac{13}{12} + 6x)^2$ **13.** $\frac{1}{16}; (x + \frac{1}{4})^2$ **15.** $\frac{25}{16}; (2x - \frac{5}{4})^2$ **17.** $9; (7n + 3)^2$ **19.** $\frac{25}{4};$
$(10t - \frac{5}{2})^2$

Exercise 13.10, Page 175

1. $x^2 - 7x + 12$ **3.** $y^2 + 8y + 12$ **5.** $a^2 + a - 12$ **7.** $c^2 - 11c + 28$ **9.** $a^2 - 15a + 56$
11. $n^2 - 10n - 24$ **13.** $b^2 - 10b - 39$ **15.** $72 + x - x^2$ **17.** $x^2 - 25$ **19.** $n^6 - 4n^3 - 5$
21. $x^2 - 17x + 52$ **23.** $h^2 + h - 90$ **25.** $E^2 - 12E - 45$ **27.** $x^2 - 81$
29. $n^2 - 17n - 84$

Exercise 13.11, Page 176

1. $(x + 3)(x + 4)$ **3.** $(x - 6)(x + 1)$ **5.** $(y + 1)(y - 5)$ **7.** $(d + 2)(d - 7)$ **9.** $(x - 7)^2$
11. $(t + 8)(t - 2)$ **13.** $(n - 2)(n - 8)$ **15.** $(I + 2)(I + 42)$ **17.** $(4 - x)^2$
19. $(x + 4)(x - 12)$ **21.** $(n + 3)(n - 16)$ **23.** no factors **25.** no factors
27. $(E + 3)(E + 27)$ **29.** $(n + 2)(n - 18)$

Exercise 13.12, Page 178

1. $6x^2 + 17x + 12$ **3.** $12x^2 + x - 6$ **5.** $6x^2 - 7x - 10$ **7.** $5 + 11y - 36y^2$
9. $21b^2 - 16b - 16$ **11.** $20c^2 + 23c - 21$ **13.** $24a^2 + a - 10$ **15.** $4x^2 - 31x - 8$
17. $25x^2 - 70x + 49$ **19.** $33t^2 + t - 14$ **21.** $40 + 27xy - 4x^2y^2$ **23.** $6x^4 - 25x^2y - 9y^2$

Exercise 13.13, Page 179

1. $(2x + 3)(x - 4)$ **3.** $(3c + 2)(2c - 3)$ **5.** $(2n - 3)^2$ **7.** $(5x + 6)(x + 1)$
9. $(3p + 4)(4p - 5)$ **11.** $(2 + x)(1 - 4x)$ **13.** $(6n - 5)(3n + 2)$ **15.** $(3b - 4)(2b - 5)$
17. $(4k + 7)^2$ **19.** $(4 + 5x)(9 - 5x)$ **21.** $(3a - 2b)(8a + 3b)$ **23.** $(5x - 4y)^2$
25. $(9x - 4)(x - 1)$ **27.** $(8x + 9)(2x + 1)$

Exercise 13.14, Page 180

1. $(x - 2)(x^2 + 2x + 4)$ **3.** $(T + 10)(T^2 - 10T + 100)$ **5.** $(x^2 - 3)(x^4 + 3x^2 + 9)$
7. $(7t - 4)(49t^2 + 28t + 16)$ **9.** $(x - 1)(x^2 + x + 1)(x^6 + x^3 + 1)$
11. $(2y + 5)(4y^2 - 10y + 25)$ **13.** $(4n - 9)(16n^2 + 36n + 81)$
15. $[x + y - a + b][(x + y)^2 + (x + y)(a - b) + (a - b)^2]$

Exercise 13.15, Page 181

1. $(x^2 + y^2)(x + y)(x - y)$ **3.** $(x - y)(x^6 + x^5y + x^4y^2 + x^3y^3 + x^2y^4 + xy^5 + y^6)$
5. no factors **7.** no factors **9.** $(x - 2)(x + 2)(x^2 + 2x + 4)(x^2 - 2x + 4)$

Exercise 13.16, Page 182

1. $9(2x - 3)(2x + 3)$ **3.** $2y^2(2y - 1)(4y^2 + 2y + 1)$ **5.** $4n^2(8 - n)(8 + n)$
7. $(x^6 + 1)(x + 1)(x^2 - x + 1)(x - 1)(x^2 + x + 1)$ **9.** $4y^4(4 + y^2)(2 - y)(2 + y)$
11. $2y(5 + y)(25 - 5y + y^2)$ **13.** $n^2(n + 1)(n^6 - n^5 + n^4 - n^3 + n^2 - n + 1)$
15. $a^2(h - k)(h + k)$ **17.** $3x(x - 4)(x + 3)$ **19.** $4y^2(y + 12)(y - 1)$
21. $2x(x^2 - 9x - 12)$ **23.** $3x^2(5x - 3)(8x + 5)$ **25.** $2xy(x - 2)(x - 21)$
27. $4xy^2(x + 2)(x - 30)$ **29.** $xy^2(3x - 4y)(4x + 5y)$ **31.** $2xy(8x - 9)(x - 3)$
33. $y^2(24x - 45 + x^2)$ **35.** $6x(2x - 3)(3x + 10)$ **37.** $(a - 3b - x)(a - 3b + x)$
39. $(2y - x + 3)(2y + x - 3)$ **41.** $(x - y + 4)(x + y - 2)$ **43.** $(x - 3y + 4)(x + 3y)$
45. $(x - y + 2)(x^2 - 2xy + y^2 + 2x - 2y + 4)$ **47.** $(x + 1)(x - 1)(x + 2)(x^2 - 2x + 4)$

Exercise 14.1, Page 190

1. $\dfrac{3x}{5y^2}$ **3.** $\dfrac{2cx^4}{3n^2z}$ **5.** $\dfrac{3xz}{4aby}$ **7.** $\dfrac{3mn^2}{2a}$ **9.** 1   **11.** $\dfrac{1}{3abx}$ **13.** -1 **15.** $\dfrac{3x(x-5)}{2}$

17. $-(c+5)$ **19.** $\dfrac{x+3}{x-3}$ **21.** $\dfrac{x+4}{2(x+2)}$ **23.** $\dfrac{n+2}{n^2+2n+4}$ **25.** $\dfrac{1}{a+b}$

27. $\dfrac{2y(x-4)}{3(x-2)}$ **29.** $\dfrac{3x(n+6)}{2y(n+3)}$ **31.** $\dfrac{nx(2-5x)}{2(3x-2)}$ **33.** $\dfrac{x+y}{a-4}$ **35.** $\dfrac{c^2(c-2)}{c-4}$

37. $\dfrac{u^2+uv+v^2}{u(2u+v)}$ **39.** $\dfrac{3(6n-5)}{5(3n-2)}$ **41.** not reducible   **43.** $\dfrac{x+y}{x^4+x^3y+x^2y^2+xy^3+y^4}$

45. x^2+x+1 **47.** $\dfrac{(x-1)^2}{x^2+x+1}$ **49.** $\dfrac{y-x}{y+x}$

Exercise 14.2, Page 193

1. $\dfrac{acxy^2}{5b^3}$ **3.** $\dfrac{3ab^2}{10x}$ **5.** $\dfrac{x}{15cy}$ **7.** $\dfrac{a^2y}{6x^2}$ **9.** $\dfrac{3(x+3)}{x^2(x+5)}$ **11.** $\dfrac{x-2}{x+12}$

13. $\dfrac{x-2}{x(x+2)(x^2+3)}$ **15.** $\dfrac{2(a+2)}{a-1}$ **17.** $2x+1$ **19.** $\dfrac{(ab-1)(ab-2)}{6}$

21. $\dfrac{(x-1)^2}{(x-3)(x+3)^2}$ **23.** $\dfrac{(2r-3)(2r+3)}{(r-8)(r-9)}$ **25.** $\dfrac{n-9}{n-3}$ **27.** $\dfrac{(n-4)(n+3)^2}{(n-5)(n-2)(n+2)}$

Exercise 14.3, Page 199

1. $\dfrac{7x}{12}$ **3.** $\dfrac{19y-7}{12}$ **5.** $\dfrac{2x^2+5y+3x-2x^2y}{xy}$ **7.** $\dfrac{8a^2+6a-5}{2a^3}$

9. $\dfrac{2ab+9b^3-12a^3}{3a^2b^2}$ **11.** $\dfrac{3x-2}{8}$ **13.** $\dfrac{27x-43}{12}$ **15.** $\dfrac{6xy-x^2+x+y-3}{xy}$

17. $\dfrac{x-9}{x^2-9}$ **19.** $\dfrac{26x^2-3x^3+2x-40}{x(x+2)(x-5)}$ **21.** $\dfrac{-(5x+12)}{x(x+3)}$ **23.** $\dfrac{11x-20}{x(x-4)}$

25. $\dfrac{4x^2-3x^3+x-8}{x(x-2)}$ **27.** $\dfrac{2x^2-x^3+3x+3}{x(x-3)}$ **29.** $\dfrac{4x^2-3x^3+5x+15}{x(x-3)}$

31. $\dfrac{(4x-7)(2x+1)}{(x-5)(x+5)}$ **33.** $\dfrac{6x^2-5x^3+8x-8}{x^2(x+2)}$ **35.** $\dfrac{12x^2+25x-72}{(x+7)(x-3)}$

37. $\dfrac{3x^2-8x+16}{(2-x)(2+x)}$ **39.** $\dfrac{2x^3-15x^2+17x+37}{(x-4)(x+4)(x-3)}$

Exercise 14.4, Page 202

1. $\frac{14}{19}$ **3.** $\dfrac{33x^2}{60x-8}$ **5.** $2x-3$ **7.** $\dfrac{9(2x-5)}{25(2x+3)}$ **9.** $\dfrac{3(3-2x)}{3+2x}$ **11.** $\dfrac{4(7-5x)}{3(5-x)}$

13. $2-x$ **15.** $\dfrac{x+2y}{3y-2x}$

Exercise 15.1, Page 207

1. 18   **3.** 4   **5.** 5   **7.** 9   **9.** 30   **11.** −4   **13.** −3   **15.** 2/3   **17.** 6   **19.** −4   **21.** 12
23. 66   **25.** 10.5   **27.** 1200   **29.** 2400   **31.** 12 by 18

Exercise 15.2, Page 211

1. −6   **3.** 2/3   **5.** 1   **7.** −1   **9.** 1.6   **11.** −1   **13.** 8   **15.** 6   **17.** $6\frac{8}{9}$ **19.** −6
21. 0.5

Exercise 15.3, Page 212

1. 11   **3.** 1   **5.** 5.25   **7.** 4.5   **9.** 0.5   **11.** −280   **13.** 600   **15.** 3792   **17.** 450
19. 283

Exercise 15.4, Page 214

1. −3   **3.** 7   **5.** −8   **7.** 7   **9.** −18   **11.** −2   **13.** −10/11   **15.** −1   **17.** 15
19. 0.5   **21.** no solution   **23.** 4/9   **25.** 0   **27.** 5   **29.** 3   **31.** 0.5   **33.** 2/11   **35.** 9.5

Exercise 15.5, Page 217

1. $W = \dfrac{V}{LH}$ **3.** $r = \dfrac{d}{t}$ **5.** $x = \dfrac{y - B}{A}$ **7.** $r = \dfrac{A}{2\pi h}$ **9.** $r = \dfrac{E - IR}{I}$ **11.** $a = \dfrac{bf}{b - f}$

13. $P = \dfrac{A}{1 + rt}$ **15.** $M_1 = \dfrac{d^2 F}{K M_2}$ **17.** $A = \dfrac{2S - NL}{N}$ **19.** $b = \dfrac{ad}{c}$

21. $n = \dfrac{L - a + d}{d}$ **23.** $r = \dfrac{S - a}{S - L}$ **25.** $r = \dfrac{eR}{E - e}$ **27.** $x = \dfrac{b^2 + c^2 - a^2}{2b}$

29. $d = \dfrac{abc}{b - a}$ **31.** $t = \dfrac{g}{m - L}$ **33.** $h = \dfrac{A - 2\pi r^2}{2\pi r}$ **35.** $a = \dfrac{Cb}{Kb + C}$

37. $g = \dfrac{2S - 2Vt}{t^2}$ **39.** $r = \dfrac{x_1 - x}{x - x_2}$ **41.** $x_1 = \dfrac{mx_2 - y_2 + y_1}{m}$ **43.** $x = -2$

Exercise 15.6, Page 219

1. 12; 15   **3.** 51/54   **5.** $3\frac{3}{7}$ hr   **7.** 2.4 hr   **9.** 5 hr   **11.** 2 hr 21 min (approximate)
13. 18 by 30; perimeter 2 less   **15.** 2   **17.** 26   **19.** \$2500 at 3%; \$1500 at 7%
21. \$4800 at 4%; \$3000 at 6%   **23.** $9\frac{4}{19}$ gal   **25.** 7.5 qt   **27.** $523\frac{1}{3}$ **29.** 3   **31.** 150000;
12000   **33.** 180 mi   **35.** 42

Exercise 15.7, Page 222

1. 10   **3.** 4   **5.** −12   **7.** 2   **9.** −15   **11.** 5   **13.** 1   **15.** 24   **17.** 12   **19.** −7.8
21. $-4\frac{6}{7}$ **23.** 9   **25.** 1.9   **27.** 9   **29.** −2   **31.** $1\frac{7}{11}$

Exercise 16.1, Page 229 (Answers indicate ordered pairs; some as decimals.)

1. 3; −0.5   **3.** 3; 2   **5.** −1; −3   **7.** 1; −2   **9.** 1.5; −0.5   **11.** 0.5; −2.5   **13.** 61/13;
23/13   **15.** −61/29; −39/29   **17.** 30/7; 10/7   **19.** 41/23; 22/69   **21.** 1255/356;
140/89   **23.** 0.234...; −0.106...   **25.** 32/41; 112/41

27. $\dfrac{de - bf}{ad - bc}; \dfrac{af - ce}{ad - bc}$ **29.** $\dfrac{5cm + 3bn}{m^2 + n^2}; \dfrac{5cn - 3bm}{m^2 + n^2}$

Exercise 16.2, Page 231

1. -1; 5 **3.** -3; -1 **5.** 25/17; 7/17 **7.** $-14/5$; $-41/5$ **9.** 4; 1 **11.** 1.5; -0.5
13. 69/22; $-43/22$ **15.** 2; 0.5 **17.** 6; 7 **19.** 4; 5 **21.** $-20/7$; 95/28

Exercise 16.3, Page 232

1. -1; -4 **3.** $-9/43$; $-47/43$ **5.** 12/13; $-29/26$ **7.** 11; 5 **9.** -2; 7

Exercise 16.4, Page 234 (Answers in alphabetical order.)

1. 3; 1; -2 **3.** -1; 4; 1 **5.** 2; -2; -3 **7.** 0.5; 3; -0.5 **9.** 1; -4.2; -4.4 **11.** 4;
1; -1; -2 **13.** 3; -1; -3; -2 **15.** $\frac{834}{269}$; $\frac{409}{269}$; $\frac{170}{269}$; $\frac{152}{269}$ **17.** $\frac{27}{191}$; $\frac{478}{191}$; $-\frac{119}{191}$; $\frac{139}{191}$
19. -0.5; 2.75; 2.65; 3.75; -3.6 **21.** $\frac{937}{349}$; $\frac{1318}{349}$; $\frac{1537}{349}$ **23.** 1.884; 0.354; 0.722

Exercise 16.5, Page 237

1. 37/18; $-1/6$ **3.** 3; 0 **5.** Inconsistent **7.** Dependent **9.** 0; 3 **11.** Inconsistent
13. -12; -2; 9 **15.** -4; -1; -3

Exercise 16.6, Page 239

1. 61 nickels; 26 dimes **3.** \$2700 at 3%; \$4500 at 7% **5.** 30 gal of 15%; 20 gal of 40%
7. 43.75 at 50¢; 26.25 at 90¢ **9.** 37.5° and 52.5° **11.** 3.5 hr by car; 6.5 hr by train
13. plane: $234\frac{2}{3}$ mph; air: $21\frac{1}{3}$ mph **15.** plane: 420 mph; wind: 20 mph **17.** 7 q.;
14 d.; 16 n. **19.** 50¢: 60 lb; 80¢: 10 lb; 90¢: 30 lb **21.** \$6500 at 4%; \$3700 at 7%;
\$1800 at 9%

Exercise 17.3, Page 259 (Answers approximate to the nearest tenth.)

1. 4; 3 **3.** 3; 1 **5.** -3; -1 **7.** -7; 4 **9.** -3; 6 **11.** 4.4; -1.3 **13.** -1; -4
15. -2; 4 **17.** -3.5; 0 **19.** -2.6; 1.9 **21.** -1.2; -11.2

Exercise 18.1, Page 267

1. -343 **3.** 64/125 **5.** -64 **7.** 0.0001 **9.** 1.030301 **11.** y^6 **13.** n^{-8} **15.** y^{-5}
17. b^{4n+3} **19.** $x^{3.8}$ **21.** $x^{1/6}$ **23.** 10^7 **25.** x^{n+a+1} **27.** x^8 **29.** 10^5 **31.** $10^{-4.31724}$
33. x^{3n} **35.** $10^{0.81}$ **37.** x^6 **39.** x^7 **41.** x^{n-1} **43.** y^5 **45.** n^{20} **47.** y^{4n} **49.** $z^{2.7}$
51. $10^{1.27}$ **53.** $10^{4.07}$ **55.** y^{3m+8} **57.** $113\frac{7}{9}$ **59.** $-y^{15}$ **61.** m^{12} **63.** 1 **65.** y^{15}
67. a^4 **69.** 5^{9n} **71.** x^5 **73.** $10^{6.312}$ **75.** 10^{-6} **77.** $10^{1.78}$ **79.** $625x^{12}y^{-4}$
81. $-a^9b^{15}$ **83.** $-x^{12}y^{16}$ **85.** $256n^{16}$ **87.** $-a^0b^{12}$ **89.** $36a^{-6}b^8c^{-2}$
91. $125a^{-9}b^{12}c^{-3}$ **93.** $(400)(3^{-4})a^8n^{-8}$ **95.** $75x^{-1}$ **97.** $16x$ **99.** $x^{6y^2}y^{6y^3}$
101. $729x^3y^{-9/2}z^{-3/2}$ **103.** $64a^{-2}b$ **105.** $\dfrac{256x^8}{625y^{12}}$ **107.** $\dfrac{27a^{-6}}{64b^{15}}$ **109.** $\dfrac{x^8y^{12}}{a^{16}b^{-4}}$

111. $\dfrac{x^{4/3}}{y^{5/3}}$ **113.** $\dfrac{32x^{-10}y^{15}}{243a^{20}b^{-5}}$ **115.** $\dfrac{x^{24}y^{12}z^8t^4}{a^4b^8c^{12}}$

Exercise 18.2, Page 272

1. 1 **3.** 1 **5.** -1 **7.** 1 **9.** 1 **11.** 8 **13.** -3 **15.** 4 **17.** -1 **19.** 1/2 **21.** -5
23. 10 **25.** 3 **27.** $-8/3$ **29.** 343 **31.** $\dfrac{1}{x^4}$ **33.** $-\dfrac{y^2}{x^3z}$ **35.** $\dfrac{a^5d}{b^4c}$ **37.** $\dfrac{x^4}{h^2k^3}$ **39.** $\dfrac{y^3}{25xz^4}$

41. $-\dfrac{c}{9ab^3}$ **43.** $-\dfrac{by^3z}{ac^2x^4}$ **45.** $\dfrac{4cx^3z}{3a^2b^3y^4}$ **47.** $-\dfrac{1}{3ab^4x^3}$ **49.** $-ab$ **51.** $\dfrac{y-x}{xy}$

53. $\dfrac{ab(b-a)}{b^2-ba+a^2}$ **55.** $\dfrac{xy(y^2+yx+x^2)}{(y+x)(y^2+x^2)}$ **57.** $\dfrac{y^4+y^2x^2+x^4}{x^4y^4}$ **59.** $-3^{-2}a^{-1}b^{-3}c$

61. $-a^{-1}bc^{-2}x^{-4}y^3z$ **63.** $4(3^{-1})a^{-2}b^{-3}cx^3y^{-4}z$ **65.** $-3^{-1}a^{-1}b^{-4}x^{-3}$ **67.** 0.008

69. $4/9$ **71.** $9/16$ **73.** $-17/200$ **75.** $1/48$ **77.** $5/72$ **79.** $16/3$ **81.** $80/81$
83. $144/13$ **85.** 9 **87.** 9 **89.** 4 **91.** 12 **93.** 36 **95.** -36 **97.** 4 **99.** -216
101. -16 **103.** -16 **105.** -24 **107.** 36 **109.** 48 **111.** $5/6$ **113.** $2/45$
115. -288

Exercise 18.3, Page 277

1. $a^{1/2}$ **3.** $(29)^{1/2}$ **5.** $(x^2+y^2)^{1/2}$ **7.** $(x^3+5)^{1/5}$ **9.** $(x^3-8)^{3/2}$ **11.** $(x^2-a^2)^{1/2}$
13. 4 **15.** 9 **17.** 2 **19.** $5/7$ **21.** -2 **23.** 32 **25.** 243 **27.** 0.5 **29.** 0.125
31. $-16.$ **33.** 48 **35.** 0.008 **37.** 1000 **39.** 125 **41.** 16000

Exercise 18.4, Page 278

1. 1 **3.** 5 **5.** $1/3$ **7.** 243 **9.** -25 **11.** 1 **13.** 24 **15.** 1 **17.** x^{-2n} **19.** 2^{n+1}

21. $(x^2y^3)^n$ **23.** x^{-2} **25.** $1/3$ **27.** $-8x^6/27$ **29.** 64 **31.** 4 **33.** $1/y^2$ **35.** $\dfrac{1}{81x^4}$

37. $\dfrac{9y^4}{x^3}$ **39.** $\dfrac{6b^3x^4}{a^3}$ **41.** $\dfrac{81abx^2z}{25cy^3}$ **43.** $\dfrac{a^6bx^6y^{3/2}}{8c^{3/2}z^9}$

Exercise 18.5, Page 281

1. $(9.3)(10^7)$ **3.** $6.4(10^{-4})$ **5.** 10^{-7} **7.** $5(10^{-9})$ **9.** $1.8(10^{-8})$ **11.** $9.72(10^{12})$

Exercise 19.1, Page 287

1. x^4 **3.** $10^{2.8}$ **5.** 64 **7.** $4x^3$ **9.** $-4x^3$ **11.** $2x^2$ **13.** $3x^{10}$ **15.** $5a$ **17.** $5/7$
19. 0.25 **21.** $2x$ **23.** $x+y$ **25.** $n^{4/3}$ **27.** $-9x^3y^4z$ **29.** $x-2$

Exercise 19.2, Page 291

1. $4\sqrt{3}$ **3.** $7\sqrt{3}$ **5.** $5x^2\sqrt{x}$ **7.** $2x\sqrt[3]{2x}$ **9.** $\dfrac{\sqrt{6}}{4}$ **11.** $\dfrac{2\sqrt{3}}{9}$ **13.** $\dfrac{\sqrt{7ax}}{x^2}$ **15.** $2x^4\sqrt{2}$

17. $2x\sqrt[5]{2x}$ **19.** $16x^3\sqrt{x}$ **21.** $x^2\sqrt{x+1}$ **23.** $a\sqrt{x^3-x}$ **25.** no change
27. $10x^2y^2z^4\sqrt{5y}$ **29.** $6x\sqrt{2-x}$

Exercise 19.3, Page 293

1. 23.124 **3.** 2.1316 **5.** 65.7 **7.** 106.85 **9.** 53.64 **11.** 68.55 **13.** -10.857
15. 67.082 **17.** 0.432 **19.** 10.441

Exercise 19.4, Page 298

1. 37.95 **3.** 30 **5.** 144 **7.** 268.3 **9.** 272.2 **11.** 60 **13.** -31.205 **15.** 167.57
17. -98.38 **19.** -14.693 **21.** 2.679 **23.** 0.1255

Exercise 19.5, Page 300

1. $\dfrac{6\sqrt{2}}{5}$ 3. $\dfrac{\sqrt{3}}{3}$ 5. $\dfrac{3\sqrt{13}}{13}$ 7. $\dfrac{2\sqrt{15}}{15}$ 9. $\dfrac{2\sqrt{7}}{7}$ 11. $\dfrac{9+3\sqrt{5}}{4}$ 13. $16+8\sqrt{3}$

15. $\dfrac{6+\sqrt{15}}{7}$ 17. $2-\sqrt{3}$ 19. $7+4\sqrt{3}$ 21. $\dfrac{8\sqrt{5}+26\sqrt{3}+\sqrt{15}+25}{122}$

23. $4\sqrt{2}-3\sqrt{3}$ 25. $\dfrac{4\sqrt{5}-\sqrt{3}}{11}$ 27. $\dfrac{\sqrt{5}-18}{11}$ 29. $\dfrac{\sqrt{3}-39}{66}$

Exercise 19.6, Page 300

1. $16\sqrt{3}$ 3. $20\sqrt{2}$ 5. $28\sqrt{3}$ 7. $9\sqrt{3}$ 9. $-60\sqrt{2}$ 11. $-20\sqrt{3}$ 13. $12\sqrt{6}$

15. $\sqrt{6}$ 17. $\dfrac{3\sqrt{10}}{2}$ 19. $\dfrac{-2\sqrt{15}}{5}$ 21. $a\sqrt{a}$ 23. 30   25. $\sqrt{74}$ 27. $\sqrt{17}$

29. $3xy\sqrt{xz}$ 31. $x\sqrt{x^2-1}$ 33. $a+b$ 35. 23.01   37. 2.967   39. 0.392

41. -15.10 43. 0.02   45. 0.102   47. -0.651

Exercise 20.1, Page 305

1. ± 3 3. $\pm 5/2$ 5. $\pm\sqrt{5}$ 7. $\dfrac{\pm\sqrt{14}}{2}$ 9. $\pm\sqrt{-13}$ 11. $\pm 1/3$ 13. ± 1000

15. $\dfrac{\pm\sqrt{-10}}{2}$ 17. $\pm 4/3$ 19. $\dfrac{\pm\sqrt{6}}{4}$ 21. $\dfrac{\pm\sqrt{s}}{4}$ 23. $\sqrt{\dfrac{V}{\pi h}}$ 25. $\sqrt{\dfrac{Kab}{F}}$ 27. $\sqrt{\dfrac{Fr}{M}}$

Exercise 20.2, Page 309

1. $3; -2$ 3. $2; 3$ 5. $14; -6$ 7. $3/2; -2/3$ 9. ± 4 11. ± 3.5 13. $0; 0.4$
15. $\pm 10/3$ 17. $2/3; -1$ 19. no factors   21. $4/3; -1/2$

Exercise 20.3, Page 311

1. $9; -1$ 3. $3; -1/2$ 5. $3; 3/5$ 7. $\dfrac{-3\pm\sqrt{7}}{2}$ 9. $\dfrac{2\pm\sqrt{-6}}{2}$ (imaginary)   11. $0; -5/3$

13. $0; 3/7$ 15. $\dfrac{-5\pm\sqrt{37}}{2}$ 17. $2/3; -3/2$ 19. $\dfrac{2\pm\sqrt{-17}}{7}$ (imaginary)

Exercise 20.4, Page 314

1. $3\pm\sqrt{5}$ 3. $5/2; -1$ 5. $\dfrac{9\pm\sqrt{17}}{8}$ 7. $7/4; -1$ 9. $\dfrac{2\pm\sqrt{-68}}{6}$ (imaginary)

11. $1/2; 1/2$ 13. $1; -3/7$ 15. $2; -1/4$ 17. $\dfrac{1\pm\sqrt{11}}{5}$ 19. $-3\pm\sqrt{6}$ 21. $3; -1/2$

23. $\dfrac{-1\pm\sqrt{13}}{2}$ 25. $1; -1/5$ 27. $2; -3/4$ 29. $2; -2$ 31. $7; 1/2$ 33. $\dfrac{-1\pm\sqrt{313}}{4}$

35. $\dfrac{4\pm\sqrt{22}}{3}$

Exercise 20.5, Page 315

1. 6; 14 **3.** 8; −9 **5.** 12 and 14; −14 and −12 **7.** 5 by 9 in. **9.** 60 by 90 ft
11. 11.68 by 18.68 ft **13.** 45 mph; 30 mph **15.** 48 mph **17.** 15 ft **19.** 14·in.

Exercise 21.1, Page 323

1. $2i$ **3.** $7i$ **5.** $13j$ **7.** $4jx$ **9.** $8iy^3$ **11.** $2i\sqrt{2}$ **13.** $3i\sqrt{3}$ **15.** $i/2$ **17.** $\dfrac{i\sqrt{6}}{4}$

19. $5inr^2\sqrt{2nr}$ **21.** $10i$ **23.** $13j$ **25.** $10i$ **27.** -10 **29.** -5 **31.** -40 **33.** -18
35. -21 **37.** -7 **39.** $-j$ **41.** i **43.** 1 **45.** $-8i$ **47.** 1

Exercise 21.2, Page 325

1. $3 \pm 2i$ **3.** $-\frac{1}{4} \pm \frac{1}{4}\sqrt{7}i$ **5.** $2 \pm \sqrt{5}i$ **7.** $-3 \pm i$ **9.** $-2 \pm 2\sqrt{3}i$ **11.** $\frac{5}{2} \pm \frac{1}{2}\sqrt{183}i$
13. $2 \pm \frac{1}{2}\sqrt{2}i$ **15.** $10 \pm 20i$ **17.** $\pm 4\sqrt{2}i$ **19.** $\pm\frac{1}{4}\sqrt{6}i$ **21.** $\frac{3}{5} \pm \frac{1}{5}i$ **23.** $\frac{5}{2} \pm \frac{1}{2}i$

Exercise 21.3, Page 327

1. $8 - i$ **3.** $-2 - 8i$ **5.** $-2 - 2j$ **7.** $7 - 2i; 3 + j; -7 - 9i; -1 - j; 10 + 0i$
9. $-4 - 2i; -3 - 2j; -7 + 0i; -2 + j13; 5 - 11j$ Subtraction: (No. 7) $-1 + 6i;$
$-11 + 7j; -3 - 3i; 5 - 9j; 0 - 6i$ **11.** $10 - 15i$ **13.** $21 - 15j$ **15.** $14 + 5i$
17. 41 **19.** $-8 - 27i$ **21.** 29 **23.** $7 + 24j$ **25.** $-24 - 70i$ **27.** 8 **29.** -14
31. 6 **33.** 12 **35.** 0 **37.** $-6j$ **39.** $-14j$ **41.** $-12i$ **43.** $-8j$ **45.** 58 **47.** 58
49. 72 **51.** 16

Exercise 21.4, Page 330

1. $6 + 5i$ **3.** $-2 + 5j$ **5.** $8 + 3j$ **7.** $10 - 8j$ **9.** $-5 - 8j$ **11.** $-16 - 30i$ **13.** 50
15. 25 **17.** $-5 - 2i$ **19.** $5 + 2i$ **21(1).** $\frac{11}{10} - \frac{13}{10}i$ **21(3).** $-\frac{9}{34} - \frac{19}{34}j$ **21(5).** $\frac{5}{34} - \frac{31}{34}j$
21(7). 1 **21(9).** $\frac{21}{13} + \frac{1}{13}j$ **23.** $-\frac{10}{17} + \frac{6}{17}j$ **25.** $-\frac{5}{4}j$ **27.** (a) $\frac{3}{13} - \frac{2}{13}j$ (b) $\frac{5}{26} + \frac{1}{26}j$
(c) $-\frac{3}{34} + \frac{5}{34}j$ (d) $-\frac{1}{10} - \frac{1}{5}j$

Exercise 22.1, Page 341

1. $-1; -5/3$ **3.** $1/3; 1/3$ **5.** $\dfrac{1 \pm \sqrt{21}}{5}$ **7.** $\frac{5}{2}; \frac{5}{2}$ **9.** $2; 8$ **11.** $\frac{3}{4} \pm \frac{1}{4}\sqrt{7}i$

Exercise 22.2, Page 344

[Abbreviations: imag. (imaginary); eq. (equal); uneq. (unequal); ra. (rational); irra. (irrational).]

1. 9; real, uneq., ra. **3.** -16; imag., uneq. **5.** -100; imag., uneq. **7.** -100; imag., uneq. **9.** 0; real, eq., ra. **11.** -8; imag., uneq. **13.** 33; real, uneq., irra. **15.** 40; real, uneq., irra. **17.** 121; real, uneq., ra. **19.** -64; imag., uneq. **21.** 40; real, uneq., irra. **23.** 25; real, uneq., ra. **25.** 52; real, uneq., irra. **27.** -84; imag., uneq. **29.** 24; real, uneq., irra.

Exercise 22.3, Page 346

1. 9 **3.** $-1/8$ **5.** 9/32 **9.** no real value of m

Exercise 22.4, Page 348

1. $x^2 + 2x - 15 = 0$ **3.** $9x^2 + 3x - 2 = 0$ **5.** $x^2 - 4x + 13 = 0$
7. $9x^2 - 18x + 13 = 0$ **9.** $2x^2 - 8x + 9 = 0$ **11.** $x^2 + 3x = 0$ **13.** $x^3 - 7x + 6 = 0$
15. $2x^4 - 7x^3 - 2x^2 + 13x + 6 = 0$

Exercise 22.5, Page 351

1. $1; \pm 2$ **3.** $0; 2; -7$ **5.** $1; -3 \pm 2\sqrt{2}$ **7.** $2; -1 \pm \sqrt{3}i$ **9.** $\pm 1; \pm i$ **11.** $\pm 2; 3$
13. $0; -1; 2; 3$ **15.** $\pm 2; 4; 1/3$ **17.** $1; 2; 1 \pm \sqrt{10}$ **19.** $0; 1; -1; 2; -3$ **21.** ± 2;
$3; 3$ **23.** $1; 2; -\frac{3}{2} \pm \frac{3}{2}i$

Exercise 23.1, Page 368 (Only real points indicated.)

1. $(2, 1); (-4, 4)$ **3.** double point: $(1, -8)$ **5.** $(4, 0); (-1/2, -9/4)$ **7.** $(3, 0); (-5, -4)$
9. no real point **11.** $(0, 1); (8, 9)$ **13.** $(2, 4); (-76/13, -16/13)$ **15.** $(-3, \pm 4)$; and
double point $(-5, 0)$ **17.** $(2, \pm 1)$ **19.** $(3, 1); (-3, -1)$ **21.** $(2.6, 0.6); (-1, -3)$
23. no real point **25.** $(4, \pm 3)$ **27.** $(-4, \pm 3); (1, \pm\sqrt{24})$

Exercise 24.1, Page 374

1. 13 **3.** 6 **5.** 8 **7.** -2 **9.** -3 **11.** 16/25 **13.** 1; 2 **15.** 2 **17.** 7 **19.** 4
21. 1; 13/9 **23.** 7 **25.** 5; -3 **27.** none **29.** 512 **31.** 60 sq in. **33.** 60 in.

Exercise 25.1, Page 377

1. 2/3 **3.** 4/5 **5.** 5/12 **7.** 16 **9.** 1/5280 **11.** 2; 2; 4 **13.** $\frac{1}{3}; \frac{1}{3}; \frac{1}{9}$ **15.** 1/633600

Exercise 25.2, Page 380

1. 28 **3.** 2.8 **5.** ± 16 **7.** 23 **9.** 0; 8 **11.** 7 **13.** 80 **15.** 10.5 **17.** ± 14 **19.** $\pm 8i$
21. 3/5 **23.** 20/7

Exercise 25.3, Page 384

1. $C = Kp$ **3.** $L = Kw$ **5.** $W = KN$ **7.** $C = Kr$ **9.** $A = Kdh$ **11.** $r = Kt$
13. $W = Khr^2$ **15.** $W = Kr^3$

Exercise 25.4, Page 386

1. $t = K/r$ **3.** $F = K/d^2$ **5.** $R = K/d^2$ **7.** $V = K/p$ **9.** $L = K/\sqrt{s}$

Exercise 25.5, Page 388

1. 20 **3.** 2.5 **5.** $135 **7.** 800 lb **9.** 400 ft; 144 ft **11.** 33.75 **13.** 1080 gal
15. 405 watts **17.** $53\frac{1}{3}$ days **19.** 20 dynes **21.** four times as much light
23. 7.92 (Speed must be understood as 50 times per second instead of 1/50.)

Exercise 27.1, Page 419

1. 218.4 sq in.; 59.4 in. **3.** 177.8 cm² **5.** 187.7 sq in. **7.** 32.86 in.²; 27 in. **9.** 10.9 in.;
33.4 in. **11.** 7.2 in. **13.** $3.58 **15.** $168 **17.** 75 ft **19.** 72 rd; 384 rd **21.** 18.45
23. 23.87 in.; 10.5 in. **25.** 952 sq in. **27.** (a) 96; (b) 100; (c) 104; (d) 120; (e) 146;
(f) 160; (g) 204; (h) 296; (i) 390; (j) 580; (k) 1154; (l) 2305

Exercise 28.1, Page 429

1. 70.84 sq in.; 41.27 in.   **3.** 8.77 cm^2; 14.72 cm   **5.** 615.8 yd^2; 126.2 yd   **7.** 238.1 ft
9. 28.2 mi   **11.** 67.08 rd   **13.** 9.33 ft   **15.** (a) 18.67 in.; (b) 40.59 cm; (c) 4.98 m;
(d) 1414.2 m; (e) 6463 mm; (f) 7467 ft; (g) 509.1 rd; (h) 23.33 ft; (i) 7.778 yd; (j) 13.79 in.;
(k) 19.20 cm; (l) 4.667 mm; (m) 4.243 in.   **17.** (a) 140.3 sq in.; (b) 77.75 cm^2;
(c) 84.87 sq in.; (d) 26.34 cm^2; (e) 2270 ft^2

Exercise 29.1, Page 439

1. (a) 1385 in.^{2}; 131.95 in.; (b) 265.91 cm^2; 57.81 cm; (c) 15.904 ft^2; 14.137 ft; (d) 604.8 in.^{2};
87.179 in.; (e) 61.28 ft^2; 27.75 ft; (f) 8825 mm^2; 333 mm; (g) 11.310 ft^2; 377 ft;
(h) 706.9 mm^2; 94.25 mm   **3.** 6.156   **5.** 43.29 in.   **7.** 775.7   **9.** 47,180 ft^2 **11.** 4335 ft^2
13. 112.84 ft   **15.** 45.52 mph   **17.** 16π; 20π; 28π; 36π **19.** 8.485 in.   **21.** 16.97 in.
23. 1.5 amp   **25.** 6 in.; 44$\frac{2}{3}$ in.^{2} **27.** 44π ft; 228π ft^2 **29.** 12π

Exercise 30.1, Page 445

1. 130.5   **3.** 5.78   **5.** 32.3; 1455   **7.** 1131.5 lb   **9.** 615.47 in.^{3}; 105.2 in.   **11.** 503.6
13. 188.7 ft; 9,745,500,000,000 gal   **15.** 216 in.^{2} **17.** 252 in.^{2} **19.** 3,893,000,000,000

Exercise 31.1, Page 453

1. 34.48   **3.** 5.1 gal.   **5.** 15.96 in.   **7.** 1750; 556 lb   **9.** first, 16.55 gal; second, 10.46 gal
11. 125.7 ft^2 **13.** 1 ft^3; 8.5 ft^2; 6 ft^2; 192 ft^2 **15.** volume: first, 1399.8 cm^3; second,
982.3 cm^3; area: first, 710.3 cm^2; second, 584.8 cm^2 **17.** 226.89   **19.** 14.137

Exercise 32.1, Page 463

1. 20975; 6991.8   **3.** 3.81 in.   **5.** 798.7 lb   **7.** 297; 294.9   **9.** 11.17; 3.27 in.^{3} less
11. 9.83 ft^3 **13.** 18$\sqrt{2}$ in.^{3} **15.** 528 in.^{2} **17.** 5562.8 lb   **19.** 575.4

Exercise 33.1, Page 469

1. (a) 2144.7 in.^{3}; 804.25 in.^{2} (b) 14.137 in.^{3}; 28.274 in.^{2} (c) 9.48 in.^{3}; 21.66 in.^{2}
(d) 12.31 in.^{3}; 25.78 in.^{2} (e) 17.97 in.^{3}; 33.18 in.^{2} (f) 444.6 in.^{3}; 281.7 in.^{2} (g) 3305 in.^{3};
1063.6 in.^{2} **3.** 244.2 lb   **5.** 78.8 lb   **7.** 4.99 in.   **9.** 300 in.^{2}; 216 in.^{2}; 174.1 in.^{2}

Exercise 34.1, Page 475

1. 25; $\log_5 25 = 2$ **3.** 144; $\log_{12} 144 = 2$ **5.** 4096; $\log_8 4096 = 4$ **7.** 2048;
$\log_2 2048 = 11$ **9.** 256; $\log_4 256 = 4$ **11.** 729; $\log_9 729 = 3$ **13.** $\frac{1}{81}$; $\log_{1/3} \frac{1}{81} = 4$
15. $\frac{1}{32}$; $\log_2 \frac{1}{32} = -5$ **17.** 2; $\log_8 2 = 1/3$ **19.** 1; $\log_{10} 1 = 0$ **21.** $\log_N y = x$
23. $\log_5 z = x$ **25.** $\log_3 28 = x$ **27.** $\log_5 41.2 = z$ **29.** $\log_3 15.59 = 2.5$
31. $\log_{10} 31.63 = 1.5$ **33.** $8^3 = 512$ **35.** $2^9 = 512$ **37.** $4^{-1/2} = 1/2$ **39.** $10^0 = 1$
41. $b^c = A$ **43.** $x^y = a + b$ **45.** 3   **47.** 81   **49.** 2401   **51.** 6   **53.** 10

Exercise 34.2, Page 477

1. $\log 85 = 1.92942$ **3.** $\log 2500 = 3.39794$ **5.** $\log 812 = 2.90956$ **7.** $\log 340 = 2.53148$
9. $\log 18.4 = 1.26482$ **11.** $\log 60 = 1.77815$ **13.** $470 = 10^{2.67210}$ **15.** $59.2 = 10^{1.77232}$
17. $336 = 10^{2.52634}$ **19.** $61.7 = 10^{1.79029}$ **21.** $1.87 = 10^{0.27184}$ **23.** $24.8 = 10^{1.39445}$

Exercise 34.3, Page 478

1. $1.86(10^5)$ **3.** $2.53(10^{-3})$ **5.** $3.937(10^1)$ **7.** $3.1416(10^0)$ **9.** $6.34(10^{-7})$ **11.** 10^7
13. $3(10^8)$ **15.** $8.723(10^5)$ **17.** $4.378(10^0)$ **19.** $1.6534(10^1)$ **21.** $6.325(10^{-2})$
23. $2.54(10^7)$ **25.** $1.293(10^{-3})$ **27.** $3.665(10^{-3})$ **29.** 628 (16 zeros)

Exercise 34.4, Page 482

1. 5.25091 **3.** $0.54691 - 3$ **5.** 2.88001 **7.** 6.82776 **9.** $0.95012 - 1$ **11.** 2.84677
13. $0.70001 - 1$ **15.** $0.33041 - 5$ **17.** 6.15229 **19.** 0.52022 **21.** 0.98700
23. 4.17840 **25.** 8.71600 **27.** $0.87500 - 3$ **29.** 0.60293 **31.** $0.90309 - 1$

Exercise 34.5, Page 485

1. 1.44658 **3.** 0.38206 **5.** 4.06648 **7.** 4.47823 **9.** 1.68754 **11.** $0.70755 - 1$
13. 0.81200 **15.** 2.89085 **17.** 7.91747 **19.** $0.93122 - 4$ **21.** 0.49715 **23.** $0.50285 - 1$
25. $0.00436 - 1$ **27.** 0.82004 **29.** 133.24 **31.** 176.40 **33.** 16117 **35.** 0.19774
37. 0.00029589 **39.** 245720 **41.** 3162300 **43.** 4.1690 **45.** 0.61969 **47.** 87462
49. 0.00015849

Exercise 35.1, Page 489

1. 198840 **3.** 0.082272 **5.** 0.010186 **7.** 7716.0 **9.** 0.0041548 **11.** 0.96732
13. 8.0436 **15.** 3595.9

Exercise 35.2, Page 490

1. $-160,260$ **3.** $-61,533,000$ **5.** $-1.6604(10^9)$ **7.** $4.8958(10^{-6})$ **9.** $-14,562,000$
11. 3948 **13.** -161.71 **15.** -0.019651 **17.** -258.76 **19.** 4093.5 sq rd

Exercise 35.3, Page 498

1. 2684.8 **3.** 0.023259 **5.** $-5.1752(10^{-4})$ **7.** $4.5388(10^{-9})$ **9.** -2175.7 **11.** 2622.0
13. 306.52 **15.** 0.19492 **17.** -0.0022899 **19.** 0.0038891 **21.** -3944.2
23. $2.2422(10^{-5})$ **25.** 68593 **27.** 0.020903 **29.** $3.0155(10^8)$

Exercise 35.4, Page 499

1. $\log 5 + \log 7$ **3.** $\log 25 + \log 38 + \log 42$ **5.** $\log 47.2 + \log 68 + \log 3.9$
7. $\log p - \log q$ **9.** $\log 34 - \log 17$ **11.** $\log m + \log n - \log r - \log s$
13. $\log 4.7 + \log 72 - \log 1.3 - \log 31$ **15.** $\log 7.92 + \log 36.8 - \log 97 - \log 41.5$
17. $\log 60 + \log 6 + \log 8 + \log 7 - \log 14 - \log 12 - \log 40$ **19.** $\log (72)(36)$

21. $\log 20$ **23.** $\log 133,110$ **25.** $\log fghk$ **27.** $\log 16$ **29.** $\log \dfrac{16.83}{7.1}$ **31.** $\log 98$

33. $\log \dfrac{19.7}{6.3}$ **35.** $\log 40$ **37.** $\log \dfrac{acf}{bdg}$ **39.** $\log 1$

Exercise 35.5, Page 502

1. 3,195,900 **3.** 50969 **5.** $6.0615(10^{-9})$ **7.** $5.1582(10^{19})$ **9.** $6.3793(10^{-8})$ **11.** 63.83
13. 41,517,000 **15.** 272.17 **17.** $-1,193,900$ **19.** 8.453 **21.** 93662 **23.** 3883.0
25. 12277 **27.** $7.4737(10^{-8})$

Exercise 35.6, Page 510

1. 15.447 **3.** 9.1774 **5.** 0.17200 **7.** 0.037058 **9.** 0.97732 **11.** 23.150
13. $4.0322\,(10^{-4})$ **15.** $5.6424\,(10^{-9})$ **17.** 0.024820 **19.** 2.4170 **21.** 51.478
23. $6.376\,(10^{-7})$

Exercise 35.7, Page 510

1. $4\log x$ **3.** $\frac{1}{2}\log 58$ **5.** $2\log x + 3\log y$ **7.** $2\log 3.7 - 3\log 52$
9. $\log \pi + 2\log r + \log h - \log 7 - \log 33$ **11.** $\log \pi + 3\log r - \log 3$
13. $\frac{1}{2}\log 3.7 + \frac{1}{3}\log 52$ **15.** $\frac{1}{3}\log 0.012$ **17.** $\frac{1}{5}\log 4.32$ **19.** $\frac{1}{2}(\log a + \log b + \log c)$
21. $3\log 3.2 + \frac{1}{2}\log 42$ **23.** $\frac{1}{2}\log 67.3 - \log 4.38$ **25.** $\log 20^5$ **27.** $\log 8$ **29.** $\log 8$

31. $\log (5^2)(49^3)(3^4)$ **33.** $\log \dfrac{(40^3)\sqrt{81}}{25^2}$ **35.** $\log \dfrac{(2)(3)}{(2)(3)}$, or $\log 1$ **37.** $\log \dfrac{(8)(8)}{4}$, or $\log 16$

Exercise 35.8, Page 513

1. $\log 2 + \log 3$ **3.** $2\log 2$ **5.** $\log 10 - \log 2$ **7.** $3\log 2$ **9.** $5\log 2$ **11.** $3\log 3$
13. $\log 27 + \log 2$ **15.** $4\log 3$ **17.** $\log 81 + \log 4$ **19.** $10\log 2 + 2\log 3$
21. $\log 3 - \log 2$ **23.** $\log 10 + 2\log 3 - 3\log 2$ **25.** $7^4 = 2400$ (approximate);
$7^4 = (100)(4)(6)$; $\log 7^4 = \log 100 + \log 4 + \log 6$; then

$$\log 7 = \frac{\log 100 + \log 4 + \log 6}{4} = \frac{2 + 0.60206 + 0.77815}{4} = 0.8451 \text{ (approximate)}$$

Exercise 36.1, Page 519

1. 483.4 **3.** 832.3 **5.** 836.8 **7.** 48.91 **9.** 834.7 sq in. **11.** 10.72 in. **13.** 38.91 in.
15. 22.98 cm; 307.9 cm^2 **17.** 104.24 ft **19.** 4132.3 **21.** 46.51 **23.** 10.98 in.
25. 2,413,900 **27.** 256.1 in.^{2} **29.** 5.25 in. **31.** 91.365 in.^{2} **33.** 36,325 ft **35.** 1.253

Exercise 36.2, Page 522

1. 3.41554 **3.** 38.645 **5.** 0.50668 **7.** 3.60475 **9.** 2.75700 **11.** 6.32163 **13.** 1.64708
15. 1.76999 **17.** 1.901 **19.** 0.08990 **21.** 61.71 **23.** 0.68763 **25.** 0.69481
27. 10.11689 **29.** 2.178

Exercise 36.3, Page 525

1. 10 **3.** 376.78 **5.** 14.556 **7.** 229.60 **9.** $2/7$ **11.** 3.4022 **13.** 1.9462 **15.** 1.7384
17. 3.2809 **19.** 2.2436 **21.** 0.7993 **23.** 0.61278 **25.** 0.3059 **27.** 7.5812

Exercise 36.4, Page 529

1. 3.4567 **3.** 7.300 **5.** 5.551 **7.** 10.638 **9.** -3.079 **11.** 14.446 **13.** 63.2 **15.** 562
17. 947 **19.** 0.703 **21.** 0.154 **23.** 189.3 **25.** 3.161 **27.** 78.1 **29.** $M = 0.0660$
31. $K = 11070$ **33.** $Y = 0.005332$

Exercise 37.2, Page 544 (Answers are given in the order : sine, cosine, tangent, cotangent,
secant, cosecant ; some are expressed in decimal form.)

A. $\frac{3}{5}; \frac{4}{5}; \frac{3}{4}; \frac{4}{3}; \frac{5}{4}; \frac{5}{3}$ **C.** $-\frac{3}{5}; \frac{4}{5}; -\frac{3}{4}; -\frac{4}{3}; \frac{5}{4}; -\frac{5}{3}$ **E.** $-\frac{12}{13}; \frac{5}{13}; -\frac{12}{5}; -\frac{5}{12}; \frac{13}{5}$ **G.** $\frac{7}{25};$
$-\frac{24}{25}; -\frac{7}{24}; -\frac{24}{7}; -\frac{25}{24}; \frac{25}{7}$ **I.** $\dfrac{1}{\sqrt{17}}; \dfrac{4}{\sqrt{17}}; \frac{1}{4}; 4; \dfrac{\sqrt{17}}{4}; \sqrt{17}$ **K.** $\dfrac{1}{\sqrt{2}}; \dfrac{1}{\sqrt{2}}; 1; 1; \sqrt{2}; \sqrt{2}$

M. $-\dfrac{1}{\sqrt{2}}$; $\dfrac{1}{\sqrt{2}}$; -1; -1; $\sqrt{2}$; $-\sqrt{2}$ **O.** -0.394; 0.919; -0.429; -2.333; 1.088;

-2.539 **Q.** -0.555; -0.832; 0.667; 1.5; -1.202; -1.803 **S.** 0.5145; -0.8575;

-0.6; -1.667; -1.166; 1.944 **U.** $\frac{1}{2}$; $\dfrac{\sqrt{3}}{2}$; $\dfrac{\sqrt{3}}{3}$; $\sqrt{3}$; $\dfrac{2\sqrt{3}}{3}$; 2 **W.** $\dfrac{\sqrt{11}}{6}$; $\frac{5}{6}$; $\dfrac{\sqrt{11}}{5}$;

$\dfrac{5\sqrt{11}}{11}$; $\frac{6}{5}$; $\dfrac{6\sqrt{11}}{11}$ **Y.** $-\dfrac{1}{\sqrt{5}}$; $\dfrac{2}{\sqrt{5}}$; $-\frac{1}{2}$; -2; $\dfrac{\sqrt{5}}{2}$; $-\sqrt{5}$ **α.** $\dfrac{5}{\sqrt{41}}$; $\dfrac{4}{\sqrt{41}}$; $\frac{5}{4}$; $\frac{4}{5}$; $\dfrac{\sqrt{41}}{4}$; $\dfrac{\sqrt{41}}{5}$

θ. $\dfrac{\sqrt{5}}{3}$; $\frac{2}{3}$; $\dfrac{\sqrt{5}}{2}$; $\dfrac{2}{\sqrt{5}}$; $\frac{3}{2}$; $\dfrac{3}{\sqrt{5}}$

Exercise 38.1, Page 548

1. 0.3971   **3.** 0.7159   **5.** 0.17021   **7.** 0.9923   **9.** 0.2905   **11.** 1.5577   **13.** 0.13744
15. 0.01571   **17.** 0.9999   **19.** 0.5736   **21.** 2.605   **23.** 1.0000   **25.** 0.31593   **27.** 0.60761
29. 0.84151   **31.** 0.21469   **33.** 0.81647   **35.** 0.23599   **37.** 0.23485   **39.** 0.12447
41. 0.62183   **43.** 2.6581   **45.** 0.97529   **47.** 0.99307   **49.** 1.0280   **51.** 1.4774
53. 2.7778   **55.** 10.4°   **57.** 16.2°   **59.** 63.5°   **61.** 74.2°   **63.** 78.9°   **65.** 38.81°
67. 81.85°   **69.** 67.67°   **71.** 27.46°

Exercise 38.2, Page 550

1. 19.6°   **3.** 29.7°   **5.** 63.7°   **7.** 73.2°   **9.** 39.22°   **11.** 26.53°   **13.** 78.23°   **15.** 68.8°
17. 36.87°   **19.** 67.38°

Exercise 39.1, Page 555 (Answers for questions 1, 2, and 3.)

A. $3\sqrt{13}$; $\dfrac{2}{\sqrt{13}}$; $\dfrac{3}{\sqrt{13}}$; $\frac{2}{3}$; 33.7°   **C.** $\sqrt{40}$; $\dfrac{\sqrt{40}}{7}$; $\frac{3}{7}$; $\dfrac{\sqrt{40}}{3}$; 64.6°   **E.** $9\sqrt{2}$; $\dfrac{\sqrt{2}}{2}$; $\dfrac{\sqrt{2}}{2}$; 1; 45°

G. $\sqrt{31}$; $\frac{15}{16}$; $\dfrac{\sqrt{31}}{16}$; $\dfrac{15}{\sqrt{31}}$; 69.64°   **I.** $\sqrt{1090}$; $\dfrac{19}{\sqrt{1090}}$; $\dfrac{27}{\sqrt{1090}}$; $\frac{19}{27}$; 35° 8′

Exercise 39.2, Page 557

1. $B = 55.6°$; $b = 24.54$; $c = 29.73$ **3.** $B = 27.5°$; $a = 41.11$; $c = 46.35$ **5.** $A = 60.4°$;
$a = 186.6$; $c = 214.6$ **7.** $A = 32.3°$; $B = 57.7°$; $c = 6.044$ **9.** $A = 45.4°$; $B = 44.6°$;
$b = 87.8$ **11.** $B = 51.8°$; $a = 69.4$; $b = 88.3$ **13.** $A = 36.6°$; $a = 146.1$; $b = 196.7$
15. $A = 37.3°$; $B = 52.7°$; $c = 64.86$ **17.** $A = 38.5°$; $B = 51.5°$; $a = 25.2$
19. $A = 56.8°$; $B = 33.2°$; $c = 38.7$ **21.** $B = 70.8°$; $b = 93.04$; $c = 98.52$
23. $A = 84.3°$; $b = 4.554$; $c = 45.86$ **25.** $A = 58.17°$; $B = 31.83°$; $b = 33.0$
27. $B = 68.1°$; $a = 17.08$; $b = 42.5$ **29.** $A = 85.2°$; $a = 994$; $c = 997$

Exercise 39.3, Page 560

1. $B = 73.7°$; $a = 7.252$; $c = 25.84$ **3.** $A = 51.8°$; $b = 9.91$; $c = 16.03$ **5.** $B = 38.1°$;
$b = 25.25$; $c = 40.92$ **7.** $B = 16.5°$; $a = 1418$; $c = 1482$ **9.** $A = 20.1°$; $B = 69.9°$;
$c = 767.8$ **11.** $A = 71° 19′$; $B = 18° 41′$; $a = 171.6$

Exercise 39.4, Page 563

1. 30.53 ft; 9.57 ft   **3.** 142.6 ft   **5.** 622.2 ft   **7.** 17.5°   **9.** 622.9 ft   **11.** 75.8°; 23.3 ft
13. 155.4 ft   **15.** 52.4 ft   **17.** 120.4 ft

Exercise 40.1, Page 572 (Answers in the order: sine, cosine, tangent, cotangent.)

1. 0.4019; −0.9157; −0.4390; −2.278   **3.** −0.8980; −0.4399; 2.041; 0.4899
5. 0.9932; −0.11667; −8.513; −0.11747   **7.** −0.6225; 0.7826; −0.7954; −1.2572
9. −0.6574; 0.7536; −0.8724; −1.1463   **11.** −0.2198; −0.9755; 0.2254; 4.437
13. −0.4462; −0.8949; 0.4986; 2.006   **15.** −0.4879; −0.8729; 0.5589; 1.789
17. −0.6665; −0.7455; 0.8941; 1.1184   **19.** −0.4352; 0.9003; −0.4834; −2.069
21. 0.2990; 0.9542; 0.3134; 3.191   **23.** 0.5693; −0.8221; −0.6924; −1.4442
25. 0.5621; 0.8271; 0.6796; 1.4715   **27.** 0.8221; −0.5693; −1.4442; −0.6924
29. 0.4586; 0.8886; 0.5161; 1.937   **31.** 0.79618; −0.60506; −1.3159; −0.75996
33. −0.51877; −0.85491; 0.60681; 1.6479   **35.** −0.96456; 0.26387; −3.6554; −0.27357
37. 0.78387; −0.62092; −1.2624; −0.79212   **39.** 0.90802; −0.41892; −2.1675;
−0.46136   **41.** −107.68   **43.** −3.297   **45.** −9.90   **47.** −11.788   **49.** −43.82

Exercise 40.2, Page 574

1. 204.9°; 335.1°   **3.** 147.3°; 327.3°   **5.** 151.2°; 208.8°   **7.** 64.4°; 295.6°   **9.** 55.2°;
235.2°

Exercise 40.3, Page 576 (Answers in the order: sine, cosine, tangent, cotangent, secant, cosecant. Given values are omitted.)

1. $\frac{3}{5}; \frac{4}{5}; \frac{4}{3}; \frac{5}{4}; \frac{5}{3}$ **3.** $\frac{4}{5}; \frac{4}{5}; \frac{3}{4}; \frac{5}{3}; \frac{5}{4}$ **5.** $\frac{15}{17}; \frac{8}{15}; \frac{15}{8}; \frac{17}{15}; \frac{17}{8}$ **7.** $\frac{1}{\sqrt{2}}; \frac{1}{\sqrt{2}}; 1; \sqrt{2}; \sqrt{2}$

9. $\frac{\sqrt{3}}{2}$ $\frac{1}{2}$; $\sqrt{3}$; $\frac{1}{\sqrt{3}}$; $\frac{2}{\sqrt{3}}$ **11.** $\frac{\sqrt{16-x^2}}{4}$; $\frac{x}{\sqrt{16-x^2}}$; $\frac{\sqrt{16-x^2}}{x}$; $\frac{4}{\sqrt{16-x^2}}$; $\frac{4}{x}$

13. $\frac{v}{\sqrt{v^2+9}}$; $\frac{3}{\sqrt{v^2+9}}$; $\frac{3}{v}$; $\frac{\sqrt{v^2+9}}{3}$; $\sqrt{v^2+9}$ **15.** 0.745; 0.667; 1.118; 0.894; 1.342

17. $\frac{\sqrt{3}}{2}$; $\frac{1}{\sqrt{3}}$; $\sqrt{3}$; $\frac{2}{\sqrt{3}}$; 2.0   **19.** 0.7927; 0.6097; 0.7692; 1.64; 1.262   **21.** $\frac{4}{5}$ **23.** 1.6

25. 60°

Exercise 41.2, Page 582

1. 52.1°   **3.** 77.2°   **5.** 47.4°   **7.** 90° − θ   **9.** 90° − φ   **11.** 0°   **13.** cot   **15.** 15°
17. 90° − M   **19.** csc X   **21.** cot φ   **23.** sec 17°   **25.** 85.7°   **27.** −180°   **29.** tan

Exercise 41.4, Page 586

17. csc x   **19.** sec² φ csc φ   **21.** sin² M cos M   **23.** cot² A csc A   **25.** tan A sin² A
27. cot Z csc² Z   **27.** csc³ φ   **31.** tan² θ sin³ θ

Exercise 42.1, Page 592

1. 540°   **3.** 90°   **5.** 30°   **7.** 1800°   **9.** 270°   **11.** 3π/4   **13.** π/10   **15.** 4π

Exercise 42.2, Page 595

1. $\pi/4$ **3.** $5\pi/4$ **5.** $11\pi/6$ **7.** $-\pi/2$ **9.** $5\pi/36$ **11.** 2.653   **13.** 120π **15.** -1.2968
17. $3\pi/2$ **19.** $5\pi/8$ **21.** 900°   **23.** 194.8°   **25.** 75.63°   **27.** 418.3°   **29.** 6876°
31. 360°   **33.** 1   **35.** 0.8660   **37.** 1   **39.** -1 **41.** 0.0548   **43.** 0.3624   **45.** 2.5708
47. 0.815   **49.** 15.601

Exercise 42.3, Page 603

1. 386 deg.^{2} **3.** 108.3 deg.^{2} **5.** 228 deg.^{2} **7.** 364 deg.^{2} **9.** 69.7 ft   **11.** 67.6 in.

Exercise 43.1, Page 610 (Some values shown as decimals.)

25. 1   **27.** 0   **29.** $\frac{1}{2}\sqrt{3}$ **31.** 1/4   **33.** $-\sqrt{3}$ **35.** 1   **37.** 1   **39.** not defined   **41.** 1
43. -12.32 **45.** not defined   **47.** 2   **49.** $2 + \sqrt{6}$ **51.** 240°; 300°   **53.** 1.09861
55. 1.24245

Exercise 43.2, Page 613

1. 30°; 150°   **3.** 0; 90°; 180°; 270°   **5.** 60°; 120°; 240°; 300°   **7.** 30°; 90°; 150°; 210°;
270°; 330°   **9.** 27°; 45°; 99°; 117°; 171°; 189°; 243°; 261°; 315°; 333°   **11.** 30°; 150°;
210°; 330°   **13.** 60°; 240°   **15.** 10°; 50°; 70°; 110°; 130°; 170° 190°; 230°; 250°; 290°;
310°; 350°   **17.** 0; 180°   **19.** 90°

Exercise 45.1, Page 635

1. $C = 62.5°$; $a = 17.13$; $c = 23.02$ **3.** $B = 49.4°$; $C = 77.4°$; $a = 14.8$ **5.** $A = 67.9°$;
$B = 80.7°$; $c = 13.83$ **7.** $A = 19.7°$; $B = 25.3°$; $C = 135°$ **9.** $A = 52.5°$; $B = 82.5°$;
$C = 45.0°$ **11.** $A = 46°\ 37.7'$; $C = 64°\ 28.3'$; $b = 33.498$ **13.** impossible case
15. $A = 90.0°$; $B = 50.8°$; $b = 19.37$

Exercise 46.1, Page 644

1. $\sqrt{89}\ \underline{/32.0°}$ **3.** $13.89\ \underline{/210.25°}$ **5.** $6.213\ \underline{/121.1°}$ **7.** $5.463\ \underline{/283°\ 7'}$ **9.** $5\sqrt{10}\ \underline{/18.43°}$
11. $7.33\ \underline{/10.4°}$ **13.** $8.46\ \underline{/-6.24°}$ **15.** $42.32\ \underline{/-1.92°}$ **17.** $x = 70.44$; $y = 37.93$
19. $x = 13.615$; $y = 48.11$ **21.** $x = -5.13$; $y = 3.11$ **23.** $x = -136.05$; $y = -63.15$
25. $x = -38.54$; $y = 58.44$ **27.** $x = -6.83$; $y = -9.87$ **29.** $x = 4.54$; $y = -14.30$
31. $x = 12.76$; $y = -21.50$ **33.** 231.35 mi east by 6.2° south   **35.** 12.5 mph, across by
16.3° downstream   **37.** 120.8 lb east; 105 lb north   **39.** plane 290.5 mph; wind 51.2 mph

Exercise 46.2, Page 648

1. $40.7\ \underline{/-27.1°}$ **3.** $51.92\ \underline{/1°\ 1'}$ **5.** $48.09\ \underline{/91°\ 45'}$ **7.** $73.96\ \underline{/-72.9°}$ **9.** $14.88\ \underline{/-69.25°}$
11. $46.05\ \underline{/-37.3°}$ **13.** $19.106\ \underline{/251.72°}$ **15.** $39\ \underline{/22.62°}$

APPENDIX

Tables

Table I. Five-Place Common Logarithms of Numbers

N	0	1	2	3	4	5	6	7	8	9
100	00 000	043	087	130	173	217	260	303	346	389
01	432	475	518	561	604	647	689	732	775	817
02	00 860	903	945	988	*030	*072	*115	*157	*199	*242
03	01 284	326	368	410	452	494	536	578	620	662
04	01 703	745	787	828	870	912	953	995	*036	*078
05	02 119	160	202	243	284	325	366	407	449	490
06	531	572	612	653	694	735	776	816	857	898
07	02 938	979	*019	*060	*100	*141	*181	*222	*262	*302
08	03 342	383	423	463	503	543	583	623	663	703
09	03 743	782	822	862	902	941	981	*021	*060	*100
110	04 139	179	218	258	297	336	376	415	454	493
11	532	571	610	650	689	727	766	805	844	883
12	04 922	961	999	*038	*077	*115	*154	*192	*231	*269
13	05 308	346	385	423	461	500	538	576	614	652
14	05 690	729	767	805	843	881	918	956	994	*032
15	06 070	108	145	183	221	258	296	333	371	408
16	446	483	521	558	595	633	670	707	744	781
17	06 819	856	893	930	967	*004	*041	*078	*115	*151
18	07 188	225	262	298	335	372	408	445	482	518
19	555	591	628	664	700	737	773	809	846	882
120	07 918	954	990	*027	*063	*099	*135	*171	*207	*243
21	08 279	314	350	386	422	458	493	529	565	600
22	636	672	707	743	778	814	849	884	920	955
23	08 991	*026	*061	*096	*132	*167	*202	*237	*272	*307
24	09 342	377	412	447	482	517	552	587	621	656
25	09 691	726	760	795	830	864	899	934	968	*003
26	10 037	072	106	140	175	209	243	278	312	346
27	380	415	449	483	517	551	585	619	653	687
28	10 721	755	789	823	857	890	924	958	992	*025
29	11 059	093	126	160	193	227	261	294	327	361
130	394	428	461	494	528	561	594	628	661	694
31	11 727	760	793	826	860	893	926	959	992	*024
32	12 057	090	123	156	189	222	254	287	320	352
33	385	418	450	483	516	548	581	613	646	678
34	12 710	743	775	808	840	872	905	937	969	*001
35	13 033	066	098	130	162	194	226	258	290	322
36	354	386	418	450	481	513	545	577	609	640
37	672	704	735	767	799	830	862	893	925	956
38	13 988	*019	*051	*082	*114	*145	*176	*208	*239	*270
39	14 301	333	364	395	426	457	489	520	551	582
140	613	644	675	706	737	768	799	829	860	891
41	14 922	953	983	*014	*045	*076	*106	*137	*168	*198
42	15 229	259	290	320	351	381	412	442	473	503
43	534	564	594	625	655	685	715	746	776	806
44	15 836	866	897	927	957	987	*017	*047	*077	*107
45	16 137	167	197	227	256	286	316	346	376	406
46	435	465	495	524	554	584	613	643	673	702
47	16 732	761	791	820	850	879	909	938	967	997
48	17 026	056	085	114	143	173	202	231	260	289
49	319	348	377	406	455	464	493	522	551	580
150	17 609	638	667	696	725	754	782	811	840	869
N	0	1	2	3	4	5	6	7	8	9

Prop. Parts

	44	43	42
1	4.4	4.3	4.2
2	8.8	8.6	8.4
3	13.2	12.9	12.6
4	17.6	17.2	16.8
5	22.0	21.5	21.0
6	26.4	25.8	25.2
7	30.8	30.1	29.4
8	35.2	34.4	33.6
9	39.6	38.7	37.8

	41	40	39
1	4.1	4	3.9
2	8.2	8	7.8
3	12.3	12	11.7
4	16.4	16	15.6
5	20.5	20	19.5
6	24.6	24	23.4
7	28.7	28	27.3
8	32.8	32	31.2
9	36.9	36	35.1

	38	37	36
1	3.8	3.7	3.6
2	7.6	7.4	7.2
3	11.4	11.1	10.8
4	15.2	14.8	14.4
5	19.0	18.5	18.0
6	22.8	22.2	21.6
7	26.6	25.9	25.2
8	30.4	29.6	28.8
9	34.2	33.3	32.4

	35	34	33
1	3.5	3.4	3.3
2	7.0	6.8	6.6
3	10.5	10.2	9.9
4	14.0	13.6	13.2
5	17.5	17.0	16.5
6	21.0	20.4	19.8
7	24.5	23.8	23.1
8	28.0	27.2	26.4
9	31.5	30.6	29.7

	32	31	30
1	3.2	3.1	3
2	6.4	6.2	6
3	9.6	9.3	9
4	12.8	12.4	12
5	16.0	15.5	15
6	19.2	18.6	18
7	22.4	21.7	21
8	25.6	24.8	24
9	28.8	27.9	27

Table I. Five-Place Common Logarithms of Numbers (*Continued*)

N	0	1	2	3	4	5	6	7	8	9
150	17 609	638	667	696	725	754	782	811	840	869
51	17 898	926	955	984	*013	*041	*070	*099	*127	*156
52	18 184	213	241	270	298	327	355	384	412	441
53	469	498	526	554	583	611	639	667	696	724
54	18 752	780	808	837	865	893	921	949	977	*005
55	19 033	061	089	117	145	173	201	229	257	285
56	312	340	368	396	424	451	479	507	535	562
57	590	618	645	673	700	728	756	783	811	838
58	19 866	893	921	948	976	*003	*030	*058	*085	*112
59	20 140	167	194	222	249	276	303	330	358	385
160	412	439	466	493	520	548	575	602	629	656
61	683	710	737	763	790	817	844	871	898	925
62	20 952	978	*005	*032	*059	*085	*112	*139	*165	*192
63	21 219	245	272	299	325	352	378	405	431	458
64	484	511	537	564	590	617	643	669	696	722
65	21 748	775	801	827	854	880	906	932	958	985
66	22 011	037	063	089	115	141	167	194	220	246
67	272	298	324	350	376	401	427	453	479	505
68	531	557	583	608	634	660	686	712	737	763
69	22 789	814	840	866	891	917	943	968	994	*019
170	23 045	070	096	121	147	172	198	223	249	274
71	300	325	350	376	401	426	452	477	502	528
72	553	578	603	629	654	679	704	729	754	779
73	23 805	830	855	880	905	930	955	980	*005	*030
74	24 055	080	105	130	155	180	204	229	254	279
75	304	329	353	378	403	428	452	477	502	527
76	551	576	601	625	650	674	699	724	748	773
77	24 797	822	846	871	895	920	944	969	993	*018
78	25 042	066	091	115	139	164	188	212	237	261
79	285	310	334	358	382	406	431	455	479	503
180	527	551	575	600	624	648	672	696	720	744
81	25 768	792	816	840	864	888	912	935	959	983
82	26 007	031	055	079	102	126	150	174	198	221
83	245	269	293	316	340	364	387	411	435	458
84	482	505	529	553	576	600	623	647	670	694
85	717	741	764	788	811	834	858	881	905	928
86	26 951	975	998	*021	*045	*068	*091	*114	*138	*161
87	27 184	207	231	254	277	300	323	346	370	393
88	416	439	462	485	508	531	554	577	600	623
89	646	669	692	715	738	761	784	807	830	852
190	27 875	898	921	944	967	989	*012	*035	*058	*081
91	28 103	126	149	171	194	217	240	262	285	307
92	330	353	375	398	421	443	466	488	511	533
93	556	578	601	623	646	668	691	713	735	758
94	28 780	803	825	847	870	892	914	937	959	981
95	29 003	026	048	070	092	115	137	159	181	203
96	226	248	270	292	314	336	358	380	403	425
97	447	469	491	513	535	557	579	601	623	645
98	667	688	710	732	754	776	798	820	842	863
99	29 885	907	929	951	973	994	*016	*038	*060	*081
200	30 103	125	146	168	190	211	233	255	276	298

Prop. Parts

	29	28
1	2.9	2.8
2	5.8	5.6
3	8.7	8.4
4	11.6	11.2
5	14.5	14.0
6	17.4	16.8
7	20.3	19.6
8	23.2	22.4
9	26.1	25.2

	27	26
1	2.7	2.6
2	5.4	5.2
3	8.1	7.8
4	10.8	10.4
5	13.5	13.0
6	16.2	15.6
7	18.9	18.2
8	21.6	20.8
9	24.3	23.4

	25
1	2.5
2	5.0
3	7.5
4	10.0
5	12.5
6	15.0
7	17.5
8	20.0
9	22.5

	24	23
1	2.4	2.3
2	4.8	4.6
3	7.2	6.9
4	9.6	9.2
5	12.0	11.5
6	14.4	13.8
7	16.8	16.1
8	19.2	18.4
9	21.6	20.7

	22	21
1	2.2	2.1
2	4.4	4.2
3	6.6	6.3
4	8.8	8.4
5	11.0	10.5
6	13.2	12.6
7	15.4	14.7
8	17.6	16.8
9	19.8	18.9

Table I.   Five-Place Common Logarithms of Numbers (*Continued*)

N	0	1	2	3	4	5	6	7	8	9
200	30 103	125	146	168	190	211	233	255	276	298
01	320	341	363	384	406	428	449	471	492	514
02	535	557	578	600	621	643	664	685	707	728
03	750	771	792	814	835	856	878	899	920	942
04	30 963	984	*006	*027	*048	*069	*091	*112	*133	*154
05	31 175	197	218	239	260	281	302	323	345	366
06	387	408	429	450	471	492	513	534	555	576
07	597	618	639	660	681	702	723	744	765	785
08	31 806	827	848	869	890	911	931	952	973	994
09	32 015	035	056	077	098	118	139	160	181	201
210	222	243	263	284	305	325	346	366	387	408
11	428	449	469	490	510	531	552	572	593	613
12	634	654	675	695	715	736	756	777	797	818
13	32 838	858	879	899	919	940	960	980	*001	*021
14	33 041	062	082	102	122	143	163	183	203	224
15	244	264	284	304	325	345	365	385	405	425
16	445	465	486	506	526	546	566	586	606	626
17	646	666	686	706	726	746	766	786	806	826
18	33 846	866	885	905	925	945	965	985	*005	*025
19	34 044	064	084	104	124	143	163	183	203	223
220	242	262	282	301	321	341	361	380	400	420
21	439	459	479	498	518	537	557	577	596	616
22	635	655	674	694	713	733	753	772	792	811
23	34 830	850	869	889	908	928	947	967	986	*005
24	35 025	044	064	083	102	122	141	160	180	199
25	218	238	257	276	295	315	334	353	372	392
26	411	430	449	468	488	507	526	545	564	583
27	603	622	641	660	679	698	717	736	755	774
28	793	813	832	851	870	889	908	927	946	965
29	35 984	*005	*021	*040	*059	*078	*097	*116	*135	*154
230	36 173	192	211	229	248	267	286	305	324	342
31	361	380	399	418	436	455	474	493	511	530
32	549	568	586	605	624	642	661	680	698	717
33	736	754	773	791	810	829	847	866	884	903
34	36 922	940	959	977	996	*014	*033	*051	*070	*088
35	37 107	125	144	162	181	199	218	236	254	273
36	291	310	328	346	365	383	401	420	438	457
37	475	493	511	530	548	566	585	603	621	639
38	658	676	694	712	731	749	767	785	803	822
39	37 840	858	876	894	912	931	949	967	985	*003
240	38 021	039	057	075	093	112	130	148	166	184
41	202	220	238	256	274	292	310	328	346	364
42	382	399	417	435	453	471	489	507	525	543
43	561	578	596	614	632	650	668	686	703	721
44	739	757	775	792	810	828	846	863	881	899
45	38 917	934	952	970	987	*005	*023	*041	*058	*076
46	39 094	111	129	146	164	182	199	217	235	252
47	270	287	305	322	340	358	375	393	410	428
48	445	463	480	498	515	533	550	568	585	602
49	620	637	655	672	690	707	724	742	759	777
250	39 794	811	829	846	863	881	898	915	933	950
N	0	1	2	3	4	5	6	7	8	9

Prop. Parts

	22	21
1	2.2	2.1
2	4.4	4.2
3	6.6	6.5
4	8.8	8.4
5	11.0	10.5
6	13.2	12.6
7	15.4	14.7
8	17.6	16.8
9	19.8	18.9

	20
1	2
2	4
3	6
4	8
5	10
6	12
7	14
8	16
9	18

	19
1	1.9
2	3.8
3	5.7
4	7.6
5	9.5
6	11.4
7	13.3
8	15.2
9	17.1

	18
1	1.8
2	3.6
3	5.4
4	7.2
5	9.0
6	10.8
7	12.6
8	14.4
9	16.2

	17
1	1.7
2	3.4
3	5.1
4	6.8
5	8.5
6	10.2
7	11.9
8	13.6
9	15.3

Table I. Five-Place Common Logarithms of Numbers (*Continued*)

N	0	1	2	3	4	5	6	7	8	9
250	39 794	811	829	846	863	881	898	915	933	950
51	39 967	985	*002	*019	*037	*054	*071	*088	*106	*123
52	40 140	157	175	192	209	226	243	261	278	295
53	312	329	346	364	381	398	415	432	449	466
54	483	500	518	535	552	569	586	603	620	637
55	654	671	688	705	722	739	756	773	790	807
56	824	841	858	875	892	909	926	943	960	976
57	40 993	*010	*027	*044	*061	*078	*095	*111	*128	*145
58	41 162	179	196	212	229	246	263	280	296	313
59	330	347	363	380	397	414	430	447	464	481
260	497	514	531	547	564	581	597	614	631	647
61	664	681	697	714	731	747	764	780	797	814
62	830	847	863	880	896	913	929	946	963	979
63	41 996	*012	*029	*045	*062	*078	*095	*111	*127	*144
64	42 160	177	193	210	226	243	259	275	292	308
65	325	341	357	374	390	406	423	439	455	472
66	488	504	521	537	553	570	586	602	619	635
67	651	667	684	700	716	732	749	765	781	797
68	813	830	846	862	878	894	911	927	943	959
69	42 975	991	*008	*024	*040	*056	*072	*088	*104	*120
270	43 136	152	169	185	201	217	233	249	265	281
71	297	313	329	345	361	377	393	409	425	441
72	457	473	489	505	521	537	553	569	584	600
73	616	632	648	664	680	696	712	727	743	759
74	775	791	807	823	838	854	870	886	902	917
75	43 933	949	965	981	996	*012	*028	*044	*059	*075
76	44 091	107	122	138	154	170	185	201	217	232
77	248	264	279	295	311	326	342	358	373	389
78	404	420	436	451	467	483	498	514	529	545
79	560	576	592	607	623	638	654	669	685	700
280	716	731	747	762	778	793	809	824	840	855
81	44 871	886	902	917	932	948	963	979	994	*010
82	45 025	040	056	071	086	102	117	133	148	163
83	179	194	209	225	240	255	271	286	301	317
84	332	347	362	378	393	408	423	439	454	469
85	484	500	515	530	545	561	576	591	606	621
86	637	652	667	682	697	712	728	743	758	773
87	788	803	818	834	849	864	879	894	909	924
88	45 939	954	969	984	*000	*015	*030	*045	*060	*075
89	46 090	105	120	135	150	165	180	195	210	225
290	240	255	270	285	300	315	330	345	359	374
91	389	404	419	434	449	464	479	494	509	523
92	538	553	568	583	598	613	627	642	657	672
93	687	702	716	731	746	761	776	790	805	820
94	835	850	864	879	894	909	923	938	953	967
95	46 982	997	*012	*026	*041	*056	*070	*085	*100	*114
96	47 129	144	159	173	188	202	217	232	246	261
97	276	290	305	319	334	349	363	378	392	407
98	422	436	451	465	480	494	509	524	538	553
99	567	582	596	611	625	640	654	669	683	698
300	47 712	727	741	756	770	784	799	813	828	842

Prop. Parts

18		17		16		15		14	
1	1.8	1	1.7	1	1.6	1	1.5	1	1.4
2	3.6	2	3.4	2	3.2	2	3.0	2	2.8
3	5.4	3	5.1	3	4.8	3	4.5	3	4.2
4	7.2	4	6.8	4	6.4	4	6.0	4	5.6
5	9.0	5	8.5	5	8.0	5	7.5	5	7.0
6	10.8	6	10.2	6	9.6	6	9.0	6	8.4
7	12.6	7	11.9	7	11.2	7	10.5	7	9.8
8	14.4	8	13.6	8	12.8	8	12.0	8	11.2
9	16.2	9	15.3	9	14.4	9	13.5	9	12.6

Table I. Five-Place Common Logarithms of Numbers (*Continued*)

N	0	1	2	3	4	5	6	7	8	9
300	47 712	727	741	756	770	784	799	813	828	842
01	47 857	871	885	900	914	929	943	958	972	986
02	48 001	015	029	044	058	073	087	101	116	130
03	144	159	173	187	202	216	230	244	259	273
04	287	302	316	330	344	359	373	387	401	416
05	430	444	458	473	487	501	515	530	544	558
06	572	586	601	615	629	643	657	671	686	700
07	714	728	742	756	770	785	799	813	827	841
08	855	869	883	897	911	926	940	954	968	982
09	48 996	*010	*024	*038	*052	*066	*080	*094	*108	*122
310	49 136	150	164	178	192	206	220	234	248	262
11	276	290	304	318	332	346	360	374	388	402
12	415	429	443	457	471	485	499	513	527	541
13	554	568	582	596	610	624	638	651	665	679
14	693	707	721	734	748	762	776	790	803	817
15	831	845	859	872	886	900	914	927	941	955
16	49 969	982	996	*010	*024	*037	*051	*065	*079	*092
17	50 106	120	133	147	161	174	188	202	215	229
18	243	256	270	284	297	311	325	338	352	365
19	379	393	406	420	433	447	461	474	488	501
320	515	529	542	556	569	583	596	610	623	637
21	651	664	678	691	705	718	732	745	759	772
22	786	799	813	826	840	853	866	880	893	907
23	50 920	934	947	961	974	987	*001	*014	*028	*041
24	51 055	068	081	095	108	121	135	148	162	175
25	188	202	215	228	242	255	268	282	295	308
26	322	335	348	362	375	388	402	415	428	441
27	455	468	481	495	508	521	534	548	561	574
28	587	601	614	627	640	654	667	680	693	706
29	720	733	746	759	772	786	799	812	825	838
330	851	865	878	891	904	917	930	943	957	970
31	51 983	996	*009	*022	*035	*048	*061	*075	*088	*101
32	52 114	127	140	153	166	179	192	205	218	231
33	244	257	270	284	297	310	323	336	349	362
34	375	388	401	414	427	440	453	466	479	492
35	504	517	530	543	556	569	582	595	608	621
36	634	647	660	673	686	699	711	724	737	750
37	763	776	789	802	815	827	840	853	866	879
38	52 892	905	917	930	943	956	969	982	994	*007
39	53 020	033	046	058	071	084	097	110	122	135
340	148	161	173	186	199	212	224	237	250	263
41	275	288	301	314	326	339	352	364	377	390
42	403	415	428	441	453	466	479	491	504	517
43	529	542	555	567	580	593	605	618	631	643
44	656	668	681	694	706	719	732	744	757	769
45	782	794	807	820	832	845	857	870	882	895
46	53 908	920	933	945	958	970	983	995	*008	*020
47	54 033	045	058	070	083	095	108	120	133	145
48	158	170	183	195	208	220	233	245	258	270
49	283	295	307	320	332	345	357	370	382	394
350	54 407	419	432	444	456	469	481	494	506	518
N	0	1	2	3	4	5	6	7	8	9

Prop. Parts

	15
1	1.5
2	3.0
3	4.5
4	6.0
5	7.5
6	9.0
7	10.5
8	12.0
9	13.5

	14
1	1.4
2	2.8
3	4.2
4	5.6
5	7.0
6	8.4
7	9.8
8	11.2
9	12.6

	13
1	1.3
2	2.6
3	3.9
4	5.2
5	6.5
6	7.8
7	9.1
8	10.4
9	11.7

	12
1	1.2
2	2.4
3	3.6
4	4.8
5	6.0
6	7.2
7	8.4
8	9.6
9	10.8

Table I. Five-Place Common Logarithms of Numbers (*Continued*)

N	0	1	2	3	4	5	6	7	8	9
350	54 407	419	432	444	456	469	481	494	506	518
51	531	543	555	568	580	593	605	617	630	642
52	654	667	679	691	704	716	728	741	753	765
53	777	790	802	814	827	839	851	864	876	888
54	54 900	913	925	937	949	962	974	986	998	*011
55	55 023	035	047	060	072	084	096	108	121	133
56	145	157	169	182	194	206	218	230	242	255
57	267	279	291	303	315	328	340	352	364	376
58	388	400	413	425	437	449	461	473	485	497
59	509	522	534	546	558	570	582	594	606	618
360	630	642	654	666	678	691	703	715	727	739
61	751	763	775	787	799	811	823	835	847	859
62	871	883	895	907	919	931	943	955	967	979
63	55 991	*003	*015	*027	*038	*050	*062	*074	*086	*098
64	56 110	122	134	146	158	170	182	194	205	217
65	229	241	253	265	277	289	301	312	324	336
66	348	360	372	384	396	407	419	431	443	455
67	467	478	490	502	514	526	538	549	561	573
68	585	597	608	620	632	644	656	667	679	691
69	703	714	726	738	750	761	773	785	797	808
370	820	832	844	855	867	879	891	902	914	926
71	56 937	949	961	972	984	996	*008	*019	*031	*043
72	57 054	066	078	089	101	113	124	136	148	159
73	171	183	194	206	217	229	241	252	264	276
74	287	299	310	322	334	345	357	368	380	392
75	403	415	426	438	449	461	473	484	496	507
76	519	530	542	553	565	576	588	600	611	623
77	634	646	657	669	680	692	703	715	726	738
78	749	761	772	784	795	807	818	830	841	852
79	864	875	887	898	910	921	933	944	955	967
380	57 978	990	*001	*013	*024	*035	*047	*058	*070	*081
81	58 092	104	115	127	138	149	161	172	184	195
82	206	218	229	240	252	263	274	286	297	309
83	320	331	343	354	365	377	388	399	410	422
84	433	444	456	467	478	490	501	512	524	535
85	546	557	569	580	591	602	614	625	636	647
86	659	670	681	692	704	715	726	737	749	760
87	771	782	794	805	816	827	838	850	861	872
88	883	894	906	917	928	939	950	961	973	984
89	58 995	*006	*017	*028	*040	*051	*062	*073	*084	*095
390	59 106	118	129	140	151	162	173	184	195	207
91	218	229	240	251	262	273	284	295	306	318
92	329	340	351	362	373	384	395	406	417	428
93	439	450	461	472	483	494	506	517	528	539
94	550	561	572	583	594	605	616	627	638	649
95	660	671	682	693	704	715	726	737	748	759
96	770	780	791	802	813	824	835	846	857	868
97	879	890	901	912	923	934	945	956	966	977
98	59 988	999	*010	*021	*032	*043	*054	*065	*076	*086
99	60 097	108	119	130	141	152	163	173	184	195
400	60 206	217	228	239	249	260	271	282	293	304

Prop. Parts | N | 0 | 1 | 2 | 3 | 4 | 5 | 6 | 7 | 8 | 9

Prop. Parts

13		12		11		10	
1	1.3	1	1.2	1	1.1	1	1.0
2	2.6	2	2.4	2	2.2	2	2.0
3	3.9	3	3.6	3	3.3	3	3.0
4	5.2	4	4.8	4	4.4	4	4.0
5	6.5	5	6.0	5	5.5	5	5.0
6	7.8	6	7.2	6	6.6	6	6.0
7	9.1	7	8.4	7	7.7	7	7.0
8	10.4	8	9.6	8	8.8	8	8.0
9	11.7	9	10.8	9	9.9	9	9.0

Table I. Five-Place Common Logarithms of Numbers (*Continued*)

N	0	1	2	3	4	5	6	7	8	9	Prop. Parts
400	60 206	217	228	239	249	260	271	282	293	304	
01	314	325	336	347	358	369	379	390	401	412	
02	423	433	444	455	466	477	487	498	509	520	
03	531	541	552	563	574	584	595	606	617	627	
04	638	649	660	670	681	692	703	713	724	735	
05	746	756	767	778	788	799	810	821	831	842	
06	853	863	874	885	895	906	917	927	938	949	
07	60 959	970	981	991	*002	*013	*023	*034	*045	*055	
08	61 066	077	087	098	109	119	130	140	151	162	
09	172	183	194	204	215	225	236	247	257	268	
410	278	289	300	310	321	331	342	352	363	374	
11	384	395	405	416	426	437	448	458	469	479	
12	490	500	511	521	532	542	553	563	574	584	
13	595	606	616	627	637	648	658	669	679	690	
14	700	711	721	731	742	752	763	773	784	794	
15	805	815	826	836	847	857	868	878	888	899	
16	61 909	920	930	941	951	962	972	982	993	*003	
17	62 014	024	034	045	055	066	076	086	097	107	
18	118	128	138	149	159	170	180	190	201	211	
19	221	232	242	252	263	273	284	294	304	315	
420	325	335	346	356	366	377	387	397	408	418	
21	428	439	449	459	469	480	490	500	511	521	
22	531	542	552	562	572	583	593	603	613	624	
23	634	644	655	665	675	685	696	706	716	726	
24	737	747	757	767	778	788	798	808	818	829	
25	839	849	859	870	880	890	900	910	921	931	
26	62 941	951	961	972	982	992	*002	*012	*022	*033	
27	63 043	053	063	073	083	094	104	114	124	134	
28	144	155	165	175	185	195	205	215	225	236	
29	246	256	266	276	286	296	306	317	327	337	
430	347	357	367	377	387	397	407	417	428	438	
31	448	458	468	478	488	498	508	518	528	538	
32	548	558	568	579	589	599	609	619	629	639	
33	649	659	669	679	689	699	709	719	729	739	
34	749	759	769	779	789	799	809	819	829	839	
35	849	859	869	879	889	899	909	919	929	939	
36	63 949	959	969	979	988	998	*008	*018	*028	*038	
37	64 048	058	068	078	088	098	108	118	128	137	
38	147	157	167	177	187	197	207	217	227	237	
39	246	256	266	276	286	296	306	316	326	335	
440	345	355	365	375	385	395	404	414	424	434	
41	444	454	464	473	483	493	503	513	523	532	
42	542	552	562	572	582	591	601	611	621	631	
43	640	650	660	670	680	689	699	709	719	729	
44	738	748	758	768	777	787	797	807	816	826	
45	836	846	856	865	875	885	895	904	914	924	
46	64 933	943	953	963	972	982	992	*002	*011	*021	
47	65 031	040	050	060	070	079	089	099	108	118	
48	128	137	147	157	167	176	186	196	205	215	
49	225	234	244	254	263	273	283	292	302	312	
450	65 321	331	341	350	360	369	379	389	398	408	
N	0	1	2	3	4	5	6	7	8	9	Prop. Parts

Prop. Parts

11

1	1.1
2	2.2
3	3.3
4	4.4
5	5.5
6	6.6
7	7.7
8	8.8
9	9.9

10

1	1.0
2	2.0
3	3.0
4	4.0
5	5.0
6	6.0
7	7.0
8	8.0
9	9.0

9

1	0.9
2	1.8
3	2.7
4	3.6
5	4.5
6	5.4
7	6.3
8	7.2
9	8.1

Table I.   Five-Place Common Logarithms of Numbers (*Continued*)

Proportional Parts:

10		9		8	
1	1.0	1	0.9	1	0.8
2	2.0	2	1.8	2	1.6
3	3.0	3	2.7	3	2.4
4	4.0	4	3.6	4	3.2
5	5.0	5	4.5	5	4.0
6	6.0	6	5.4	6	4.8
7	7.0	7	6.3	7	5.6
8	8.0	8	7.2	8	6.4
9	9.0	9	8.1	9	7.2

N	0	1	2	3	4	5	6	7	8	9
450	65 321	331	341	350	360	369	379	389	398	408
51	418	427	437	447	456	466	475	485	495	504
52	514	523	533	543	552	562	571	581	591	600
53	610	619	629	639	648	658	667	677	686	696
54	706	715	725	734	744	753	763	772	782	792
55	801	811	820	830	839	849	858	868	877	887
56	896	906	916	925	935	944	954	963	973	982
57	65 992	*001	*011	*020	*030	*039	*049	*058	*068	*077
58	66 087	096	106	115	124	134	143	153	162	172
59	181	191	200	210	219	229	238	247	257	266
460	276	285	295	304	314	323	332	342	351	361
61	370	380	389	398	408	417	427	436	445	455
62	464	474	483	492	502	511	521	530	539	549
63	558	567	577	586	596	605	614	624	633	642
64	652	661	671	680	689	699	708	717	727	736
65	745	755	764	773	783	792	801	811	820	829
66	839	848	857	867	876	885	894	904	913	922
67	66 932	941	950	960	969	978	987	997	*006	*015
68	67 025	034	043	052	062	071	080	089	099	108
69	117	127	136	145	154	164	173	182	191	201
470	210	219	228	237	247	256	265	274	284	293
71	302	311	321	330	339	348	357	367	376	385
72	394	403	413	422	431	440	449	459	468	477
73	486	495	504	514	523	532	541	550	560	569
74	578	587	596	605	614	624	633	642	651	660
75	669	679	688	697	706	715	724	733	742	752
76	761	770	779	788	797	806	815	825	834	843
77	852	861	870	879	888	897	906	916	925	934
78	67 943	952	961	970	979	988	997	*006	*015	*024
79	68 034	043	052	061	070	079	088	097	106	115
480	124	133	142	151	160	169	178	187	196	205
81	215	224	233	242	251	260	269	278	287	296
82	305	314	323	332	341	350	359	368	377	386
83	395	404	413	422	431	440	449	458	467	476
84	485	494	502	511	520	529	538	547	556	565
85	574	583	592	601	610	619	628	637	646	655
86	664	673	681	690	699	708	717	726	735	744
87	753	762	771	780	789	797	806	815	824	833
88	842	851	860	869	878	886	895	904	913	922
89	68 931	940	949	958	966	975	984	993	*002	*011
490	69 020	028	037	046	055	064	073	082	090	099
91	108	117	126	135	144	152	161	170	179	188
92	197	205	214	223	232	241	249	258	267	276
93	285	294	302	311	320	329	338	346	355	364
94	373	381	390	399	408	417	425	434	443	452
95	461	469	478	487	496	504	513	522	531	539
96	548	557	566	574	583	592	601	609	618	627
97	636	644	653	662	671	679	688	697	705	714
98	723	732	740	749	758	767	775	784	793	801
99	810	819	827	836	845	854	862	871	880	888
500	69 897	906	914	923	932	940	949	958	966	975

Prop. Parts	N	0	1	2	3	4	5	6	7	8	9

Table I.   Five-Place Common Logarithms of Numbers (*Continued*)

N	0	1	2	3	4	5	6	7	8	9
500	69 897	906	914	923	932	940	949	958	966	975
01	69 984	992	*001	*010	*018	*027	*036	*044	*053	*062
02	70 070	079	088	096	105	114	122	131	140	148
03	157	165	174	183	191	200	209	217	226	234
04	243	252	260	269	278	286	295	303	312	321
05	329	338	346	355	364	372	381	389	398	406
06	415	424	432	441	449	458	467	475	484	492
07	501	509	518	526	535	544	552	561	569	578
08	586	595	603	612	621	629	638	646	655	663
09	672	680	689	697	706	714	723	731	740	749
510	757	766	774	783	791	800	808	817	825	834
11	842	851	859	868	876	885	893	902	910	919
12	70 927	935	944	952	961	969	978	986	995	*003
13	71 012	020	029	037	046	054	063	071	079	088
14	096	105	113	122	130	139	147	155	164	172
15	181	189	198	206	214	223	231	240	248	257
16	265	273	282	290	299	307	315	324	332	341
17	349	357	366	374	383	391	399	408	416	425
18	433	441	450	458	466	475	483	492	500	508
19	517	525	533	542	550	559	567	575	584	592
520	600	609	617	625	634	642	650	659	667	675
21	684	692	700	709	717	725	734	742	750	759
22	767	775	784	792	800	809	817	825	834	842
23	850	858	867	875	883	892	900	908	917	925
24	71 933	941	950	958	966	975	983	991	999	*008
25	72 016	024	032	041	049	057	066	074	082	090
26	099	107	115	123	132	140	148	156	165	173
27	181	189	198	206	214	222	230	239	247	255
28	263	272	280	288	296	304	313	321	329	337
29	346	354	362	370	378	387	395	403	411	419
530	428	436	444	452	460	469	477	485	493	501
31	509	518	526	534	542	550	558	567	575	583
32	591	599	607	616	624	632	640	648	656	665
33	673	681	689	697	705	713	722	730	738	746
34	754	762	770	779	787	795	803	811	819	827
35	835	843	852	860	868	876	884	892	900	908
36	916	925	933	941	949	957	965	973	981	989
37	72 997	*006	*014	*022	*030	*038	*046	*054	*062	*070
38	73 078	086	094	102	111	119	127	135	143	151
39	159	167	175	183	191	199	207	215	223	231
540	239	247	255	263	272	280	288	296	304	312
41	320	328	336	344	352	360	368	376	384	392
42	400	408	416	424	432	440	448	456	464	472
43	480	488	496	504	512	520	528	536	544	552
44	560	568	576	584	592	600	608	616	624	632
45	640	648	656	664	672	679	687	695	703	711
46	719	727	735	743	751	759	767	775	783	791
47	799	807	815	823	830	838	846	854	862	870
48	878	886	894	902	910	918	926	933	941	949
49	73 957	965	973	981	989	997	*005	*013	*020	*028
550	74 036	044	052	060	068	076	084	092	099	107
N	**0**	**1**	**2**	**3**	**4**	**5**	**6**	**7**	**8**	**9**

Prop. Parts

9		8		7	
1	0.9	1	0.8	1	0.7
2	1.8	2	1.6	2	1.4
3	2.7	3	2.4	3	2.1
4	3.6	4	3.2	4	2.8
5	4.5	5	4.0	5	3.5
6	5.4	6	4.8	6	4.2
7	6.3	7	5.6	7	4.9
8	7.2	8	6.4	8	5.6
9	8.1	9	7.2	9	6.3

Table I. Five-Place Common Logarithms of Numbers (*Continued*)

N	0	1	2	3	4	5	6	7	8	9
550	74 036	044	052	060	068	076	084	092	099	107
51	115	123	131	139	147	155	162	170	178	186
52	194	202	210	218	225	233	241	249	257	265
53	273	280	288	296	304	312	320	327	335	343
54	351	359	367	374	382	390	398	406	414	421
55	429	437	445	453	461	468	476	484	492	500
56	507	515	523	531	539	547	554	562	570	578
57	586	593	601	609	617	624	632	640	648	656
58	663	671	679	687	695	702	710	718	726	733
59	741	749	757	764	772	780	788	796	803	811
560	819	827	834	842	850	858	865	873	881	889
61	896	904	912	920	927	935	943	950	958	966
62	74 974	981	989	997	*005	*012	*020	*028	*035	*043
63	75 051	059	066	074	082	089	097	105	113	120
64	128	136	143	151	159	166	174	182	189	197
65	205	213	220	228	236	243	251	259	266	274
66	282	289	297	305	312	320	328	335	343	351
67	358	366	374	381	389	397	404	412	420	427
68	435	442	450	458	465	473	481	488	496	504
69	511	519	526	534	542	549	557	565	572	580
570	587	595	603	610	618	626	633	641	648	656
71	664	671	679	686	694	702	709	717	724	732
72	740	747	755	762	770	778	785	793	800	808
73	815	823	831	838	846	853	861	868	876	884
74	891	899	906	914	921	929	937	944	952	959
75	75 967	974	982	989	997	*005	*012	*020	*027	*035
76	76 042	050	057	065	072	080	087	095	103	110
77	118	125	133	140	148	155	163	170	178	185
78	193	200	208	215	223	230	238	245	253	260
79	268	275	283	290	298	305	313	320	328	335
580	343	350	358	365	373	380	388	395	403	410
81	418	425	433	440	448	455	462	470	477	485
82	492	500	507	515	522	530	537	545	552	559
83	567	574	582	589	597	604	612	619	626	634
84	641	649	656	664	671	678	686	693	701	708
85	716	723	730	738	745	753	760	768	775	782
86	790	797	805	812	819	827	834	842	849	856
87	864	871	879	886	893	901	908	916	923	930
88	76 938	945	953	960	967	975	982	989	997	*004
89	77 012	019	026	034	041	048	056	063	070	078
590	085	093	100	107	115	122	129	137	144	151
91	159	166	173	181	188	195	203	210	217	225
92	232	240	247	254	262	269	276	283	291	298
93	305	313	320	327	335	342	349	357	364	371
94	379	386	393	401	408	415	422	430	437	444
95	452	459	466	474	481	488	495	503	510	517
96	525	532	539	546	554	561	568	576	583	590
97	597	605	612	619	627	634	641	648	656	663
98	670	677	685	692	699	706	714	721	728	735
99	743	750	757	764	772	779	786	793	801	808
600	77 815	822	830	837	844	851	859	866	873	880

Prop. Parts

8
1 | 0.8
2 | 1.6
3 | 2.4
4 | 3.2
5 | 4.0
6 | 4.8
7 | 5.6
8 | 6.4
9 | 7.2

7
1 | 0.7
2 | 1.4
3 | 2.1
4 | 2.8
5 | 3.5
6 | 4.2
7 | 4.9
8 | 5.6
9 | 6.3

Table I. Five-Place Common Logarithms of Numbers (*Continued*)

N	0	1	2	3	4	5	6	7	8	9	Prop. Parts
600	77 815	822	830	837	844	851	859	866	873	880	
01	887	895	902	909	916	924	931	938	945	952	
02	77 960	967	974	981	988	996	*003	*010	*017	*025	
03	78 032	039	046	053	061	068	075	082	089	097	
04	104	111	118	125	132	140	147	154	161	168	
05	176	183	190	197	204	211	219	226	233	240	
06	247	254	262	269	276	283	290	297	305	312	**8**
07	319	326	333	340	347	355	362	369	376	383	1 0.8
08	390	398	405	412	419	426	433	440	447	455	2 1.6
09	462	469	476	483	490	497	504	512	519	526	3 2.4
610	533	540	547	554	561	569	576	583	590	597	4 3.2
											5 4.0
											6 4.8
11	604	611	618	625	633	640	647	654	661	668	7 5.6
12	675	682	689	696	704	711	718	725	732	739	8 6.4
13	746	753	760	767	774	781	789	796	803	810	9 7.2
14	817	824	831	838	845	852	859	866	873	880	
15	888	895	902	909	916	923	930	937	944	951	
16	78 958	965	972	979	986	993	*000	*007	*014	*021	
17	79 029	036	043	050	057	064	071	078	085	092	
18	099	106	113	120	127	134	141	148	155	162	
19	169	176	183	190	197	204	211	218	225	232	
620	239	246	253	260	267	274	281	288	295	302	
21	309	316	323	330	337	344	351	358	365	372	
22	379	386	393	400	407	414	421	428	435	442	
23	449	456	463	470	477	484	491	498	505	511	**7**
24	518	525	532	539	546	553	560	567	574	581	1 0.7
25	588	595	602	609	616	623	630	637	644	650	2 1.4
26	657	664	671	678	685	692	699	706	713	720	3 2.1
27	727	734	741	748	754	761	768	775	782	789	4 2.8
28	796	803	810	817	824	831	837	844	851	858	5 3.5
29	865	872	879	886	893	900	906	913	920	927	6 4.2
630	79 934	941	948	955	962	969	975	982	989	996	7 4.9
											8 5.6
31	80 003	010	017	024	030	037	044	051	058	065	9 6.3
32	072	079	085	092	099	106	113	120	127	134	
33	140	147	154	161	168	175	182	188	195	202	
34	209	216	223	229	236	243	250	257	264	271	
35	277	284	291	298	305	312	318	325	332	339	
36	346	353	359	366	373	380	387	393	400	407	
37	414	421	428	434	441	448	455	462	468	475	
38	482	489	496	502	509	516	523	530	536	543	
39	550	557	564	570	577	584	591	598	604	611	**6**
640	618	625	632	638	645	652	659	665	672	679	1 0.6
											2 1.2
41	686	693	699	706	713	720	726	733	740	747	3 1.8
42	754	760	767	774	781	787	794	801	808	814	4 2.4
43	821	828	835	841	848	855	862	868	875	882	5 3.0
44	889	895	902	909	916	922	929	936	943	949	6 3.6
45	80 956	963	969	976	983	990	996	*003	*010	*017	7 4.2
46	81 023	030	037	043	050	057	064	070	077	084	8 4.8
47	090	097	104	111	117	124	131	137	144	151	9 5.4
48	158	164	171	178	184	191	198	204	211	218	
49	224	231	238	245	251	258	265	271	278	285	
650	81 291	298	305	311	318	325	331	338	345	351	
N	0	1	2	3	4	5	6	7	8	9	Prop. Parts

Table I. Five-Place Common Logarithms of Numbers (*Continued*)

Prop. Parts	N	0	1	2	3	4	5	6	7	8	9
	650	81 291	298	305	311	318	325	331	338	345	351
	51	358	365	371	378	385	391	398	405	411	418
	52	425	431	438	445	451	458	465	471	478	485
	53	491	498	505	511	518	525	531	538	544	551
	54	558	564	571	578	584	591	598	604	611	617
	55	624	631	637	644	651	657	664	671	677	684
	56	690	697	704	710	717	723	730	737	743	750
	57	757	763	770	776	783	790	796	803	809	816
	58	823	829	836	842	849	856	862	869	875	882
	59	889	895	902	908	915	921	928	935	941	948
	660	81 954	961	968	974	981	987	994	*000	*007	*014
	61	82 020	027	033	040	046	053	060	066	073	079
	62	086	092	099	105	112	119	125	132	138	145
7	63	151	158	164	171	178	184	191	197	204	210
1 0.7	64	217	223	230	236	243	249	256	263	269	276
2 1.4	65	282	289	295	302	308	315	321	328	334	341
3 2.1	66	347	354	360	367	373	380	387	393	400	406
4 2.8	67	413	419	426	432	439	445	452	458	465	471
5 3.5	68	478	484	491	497	504	510	517	523	530	536
6 4.2	69	543	549	556	562	569	575	582	588	595	601
7 4.9 **8** 5.6 **9** 6.3	**670**	607	614	620	627	633	640	646	653	659	666
	71	672	679	685	692	698	705	711	718	724	730
	72	737	743	750	756	763	769	776	782	789	795
	73	802	808	814	821	827	834	840	847	853	860
	74	866	872	879	885	892	898	905	911	918	924
	75	930	937	943	950	956	963	969	975	982	988
	76	82 995	*001	*008	*014	*020	*027	*033	*040	*046	*052
	77	83 059	065	072	078	085	091	097	104	110	117
	78	123	129	136	142	149	155	161	168	174	181
	79	187	193	200	206	213	219	225	232	238	245
	680	251	257	264	270	276	283	289	296	302	308
	81	315	321	327	334	340	347	353	359	366	372
	82	378	385	391	398	404	410	417	423	429	436
	83	442	448	455	461	467	474	480	487	493	499
6	84	506	512	518	525	531	537	544	550	556	563
1 0.6	85	569	575	582	588	594	601	607	613	620	626
2 1.2	86	632	639	645	651	658	664	670	677	683	689
3 1.8	87	696	702	708	715	721	727	734	740	746	753
4 2.4	88	759	765	771	778	784	790	797	803	809	816
5 3.0	89	822	828	835	841	847	853	860	866	872	879
6 3.6 **7** 4.2 **8** 4.8 **9** 5.4	**690**	885	891	897	904	910	916	923	929	935	942
	91	83 948	954	960	967	973	979	985	992	998	*004
	92	84 011	017	023	029	036	042	048	055	061	067
	93	073	080	086	092	098	105	111	117	123	130
	94	136	142	148	155	161	167	173	180	186	192
	95	198	205	211	217	223	230	236	242	248	255
	96	261	267	273	280	286	292	298	305	311	317
	97	323	330	336	342	348	354	361	367	373	379
	98	386	392	398	404	410	417	423	429	435	442
	99	448	454	460	466	473	479	485	491	497	504
	700	84 510	516	522	528	535	541	547	553	559	566
Prop. Parts	N	0	1	2	3	4	5	6	7	8	9

Table I.   Five-Place Common Logarithms of Numbers (*Continued*)

N	0	1	2	3	4	5	6	7	8	9
700	84 510	516	522	528	535	541	547	553	559	566
01	572	578	584	590	597	603	609	615	621	628
02	634	640	646	652	658	665	671	677	683	689
03	696	702	708	714	720	726	733	739	745	751
04	757	763	770	776	782	788	794	800	807	813
05	819	825	831	837	844	850	856	862	868	874
06	880	887	893	899	905	911	917	924	930	936
07	84 942	948	954	960	967	973	979	985	991	997
08	85 003	009	016	022	028	034	040	046	052	058
09	065	071	077	083	089	095	101	107	114	120
710	126	132	138	144	150	156	163	169	175	181
11	187	193	199	205	211	217	224	230	236	242
12	248	254	260	266	272	278	285	291	297	303
13	309	315	321	327	333	339	345	352	358	364
14	370	376	382	388	394	400	406	412	418	425
15	431	437	443	449	455	461	467	473	479	485
16	491	497	503	509	516	522	528	534	540	546
17	552	558	564	570	576	582	588	594	600	606
18	612	618	625	631	637	643	649	655	661	667
19	673	679	685	691	697	703	709	715	721	727
720	733	739	745	751	757	763	769	775	781	788
21	794	800	806	812	818	824	830	836	842	848
22	854	860	866	872	878	884	890	896	902	908
23	914	920	926	932	938	944	950	956	962	968
24	85 974	980	986	992	998	*004	*010	*016	*022	*028
25	86 034	040	046	052	058	064	070	076	082	088
26	094	100	106	112	118	124	130	136	141	147
27	153	159	165	171	177	183	189	195	201	207
28	213	219	225	231	237	243	249	255	261	267
29	273	279	285	291	297	303	308	314	320	326
730	332	338	344	350	356	362	368	374	380	386
31	392	398	404	410	415	421	427	433	439	445
32	451	457	463	469	475	481	487	493	499	504
33	510	516	522	528	534	540	546	552	558	564
34	570	576	581	587	593	599	605	611	617	623
35	629	635	641	646	652	658	664	670	676	682
36	688	694	700	705	711	717	723	729	735	741
37	747	753	759	764	770	776	782	788	794	800
38	806	812	817	823	829	835	841	847	853	859
39	864	870	876	882	888	894	900	906	911	917
740	923	929	935	941	947	953	958	964	970	976
41	86 982	988	994	999	*005	*011	*017	*023	*029	*035
42	87 040	046	052	058	064	070	075	081	087	093
43	099	105	111	116	122	128	134	140	146	151
44	157	163	169	175	181	186	192	198	204	210
45	216	221	227	233	239	245	251	256	262	268
46	274	280	286	291	297	303	309	315	320	326
47	332	338	344	349	355	361	367	373	379	384
48	390	396	402	408	413	419	425	431	437	442
49	448	454	460	466	471	477	483	489	495	500
750	87 506	512	518	523	529	535	541	547	552	558
N	0	1	2	3	4	5	6	7	8	9

Prop. Parts

7	
1	0.7
2	1.4
3	2.1
4	2.8
5	3.5
6	4.2
7	4.9
8	5.6
9	6.3

6	
1	0.6
2	1.2
3	1.8
4	2.4
5	3.0
6	3.6
7	4.2
8	4.8
9	5.4

5	
1	0.5
2	1.0
3	1.5
4	2.0
5	2.5
6	3.0
7	3.5
8	4.0
9	4.5

Table I.   Five-Place Common Logarithms of Numbers (*Continued*)

Prop. Parts	N	0	1	2	3	4	5	6	7	8	9
	750	87 506	512	518	523	529	535	541	547	552	558
	51	564	570	576	581	587	593	599	604	610	616
	52	622	628	633	639	645	651	656	662	668	674
	53	679	685	691	697	703	708	714	720	726	731
	54	737	743	749	754	760	766	772	777	783	789
	55	795	800	806	812	818	823	829	835	841	846
	56	852	858	864	869	875	881	887	892	898	904
	57	910	915	921	927	933	938	944	950	955	961
	58	87 967	973	978	984	990	996	*001	*007	*013	*018
	59	88 024	030	036	041	047	053	058	064	070	076
	760	081	087	093	098	104	110	116	121	127	133
	61	138	144	150	156	161	167	173	178	184	190
	62	195	201	207	213	218	224	230	235	241	247
	63	252	258	264	270	275	281	287	292	298	304
	64	309	315	321	326	332	338	343	349	355	360
	65	366	372	377	383	389	395	400	406	412	417
	66	423	429	434	440	446	451	457	463	468	474
	67	480	485	491	497	502	508	513	519	525	530
	68	536	542	547	553	559	564	570	576	581	587
	69	593	598	604	610	615	621	627	632	638	643
	770	649	655	660	666	672	677	683	689	694	700
	71	705	711	717	722	728	734	739	745	750	756
	72	762	767	773	779	784	790	795	801	807	812
	73	818	824	829	835	840	846	852	857	863	868
	74	874	880	885	891	897	902	908	913	919	925
	75	930	936	941	947	953	958	964	969	975	981
	76	88 986	992	997	*003	*009	*014	*020	*025	*031	*037
	77	89 042	048	053	059	064	070	076	081	087	092
	78	098	104	109	115	120	126	131	137	143	148
	79	154	159	165	170	176	182	187	193	198	204
	780	209	215	221	226	232	237	243	248	254	260
	81	265	271	276	282	287	293	298	304	310	315
	82	321	326	332	337	343	348	354	360	365	371
	83	376	382	387	393	398	404	409	415	421	426
	84	432	437	443	448	454	459	465	470	476	481
	85	487	492	498	504	509	515	520	526	531	537
	86	542	548	553	559	564	570	575	581	586	592
	87	597	603	609	614	620	625	631	636	642	647
	88	653	658	664	669	675	680	686	691	697	702
	89	708	713	719	724	730	735	741	746	752	757
	790	763	768	774	779	785	790	796	801	807	812
	91	818	823	829	834	840	845	851	856	862	867
	92	873	878	883	889	894	900	905	911	916	922
	93	927	933	938	944	949	955	960	966	971	977
	94	89 982	988	993	998	*004	*009	*015	*020	*026	*031
	95	90 037	042	048	053	059	064	069	075	080	086
	96	091	097	102	108	113	119	124	129	135	140
	97	146	151	157	162	168	173	179	184	189	195
	98	200	206	211	217	222	227	233	238	244	249
	99	255	260	266	271	276	282	287	293	298	304
	800	90 309	314	320	325	331	336	342	347	352	358
Prop. Parts	N	0	1	2	3	4	5	6	7	8	9

Prop. Parts

	6
1	0.6
2	1.2
3	1.8
4	2.4
5	3.0
6	3.6
7	4.2
8	4.8
9	5.4

	5
1	0.5
2	1.0
3	1.5
4	2.0
5	2.5
6	3.0
7	3.5
8	4.0
9	4.5

Table I.   Five-Place Common Logarithms of Numbers (*Continued*)

N	0	1	2	3	4	5	6	7	8	9	Prop. Parts
800	90 309	314	320	325	331	336	342	347	352	358	
01	363	369	374	380	385	390	396	401	407	412	
02	417	423	428	434	439	445	450	455	461	466	
03	472	477	482	488	493	499	504	509	515	520	
04	526	531	536	542	547	553	558	563	569	574	
05	580	585	590	596	601	607	612	617	623	628	
06	634	639	644	650	655	660	666	671	677	682	
07	687	693	698	703	709	714	720	725	730	736	
08	741	747	752	757	763	768	773	779	784	789	
09	795	800	806	811	816	822	827	832	838	843	
810	849	854	859	865	870	875	881	886	891	897	
11	902	907	913	918	924	929	934	940	945	950	
12	90 956	961	966	972	977	982	988	993	998	*004	
13	91 009	014	020	025	030	036	041	046	052	057	
14	062	068	073	078	084	089	094	100	105	110	
15	116	121	126	132	137	142	148	153	158	164	
16	169	174	180	185	190	196	201	206	212	217	
17	222	228	233	238	243	249	254	259	265	270	
18	275	281	286	291	297	302	307	312	318	323	
19	328	334	339	344	350	355	360	365	371	376	
820	381	387	392	397	403	408	413	418	424	429	
21	434	440	445	450	455	461	466	471	477	482	
22	487	492	498	503	508	514	519	524	529	535	
23	540	545	551	556	561	566	572	577	582	587	
24	593	598	603	609	614	619	624	630	635	640	
25	645	651	656	661	666	672	677	682	687	693	
26	698	703	709	714	719	724	730	735	740	745	
27	751	756	761	766	772	777	782	787	793	798	
28	803	808	814	819	824	829	834	840	845	850	
29	855	861	866	871	876	882	887	892	897	903	
830	908	913	918	924	929	934	939	944	950	955	
31	91 960	965	971	976	981	986	991	997	*002	*007	
32	92 012	018	023	028	033	038	044	049	054	059	
33	065	070	075	080	085	091	096	101	106	111	
34	117	122	127	132	137	143	148	153	158	163	
35	169	174	179	184	189	195	200	205	210	215	
36	221	226	231	236	241	247	252	257	262	267	
37	273	278	283	288	293	298	304	309	314	319	
38	324	330	335	340	345	350	355	361	366	371	
39	376	381	387	392	397	402	407	412	418	423	
840	428	433	438	443	449	454	459	464	469	474	
41	480	485	490	495	500	505	511	516	521	526	
42	531	536	542	547	552	557	562	567	572	578	
43	583	588	593	598	603	609	614	619	624	629	
44	634	639	645	650	655	660	665	670	675	681	
45	686	691	696	701	706	711	716	722	727	732	
46	737	742	747	752	758	763	768	773	778	783	
47	788	793	799	804	809	814	819	824	829	834	
48	840	845	850	855	860	865	870	875	881	886	
49	891	896	901	906	911	916	921	927	932	937	
850	92 942	947	952	957	962	967	973	978	983	988	
N	0	1	2	3	4	5	6	7	8	9	Prop. Parts

Prop. Parts:

6
1 | 0.6
2 | 1.2
3 | 1.8
4 | 2.4
5 | 3.0
6 | 3.6
7 | 4.2
8 | 4.8
9 | 5.4

5
1 | 0.5
2 | 1.0
3 | 1.5
4 | 2.0
5 | 2.5
6 | 3.0
7 | 3.5
8 | 4.0
9 | 4.5

Table I.   Five-Place Common Logarithms of Numbers (*Continued*)

Prop. Parts	N	0	1	2	3	4	5	6	7	8	9
	850	92 942	947	952	957	962	967	973	978	983	988
	51	92 993	998	*003	*008	*013	*018	*024	*029	*034	*039
	52	93 044	049	054	059	064	069	075	080	085	090
	53	095	100	105	110	115	120	125	131	136	141
	54	146	151	156	161	166	171	176	181	186	192
	55	197	202	207	212	217	222	227	232	237	242
	56	247	252	258	263	268	273	278	283	288	293
	57	298	303	308	313	318	323	328	334	339	344
	58	349	354	359	364	369	374	379	384	389	394
	59	399	404	409	414	420	425	430	435	440	445
	860	450	455	460	465	470	475	480	485	490	495
	61	500	505	510	515	520	526	531	536	541	546
	62	551	556	561	566	571	576	581	586	591	596
	63	601	606	611	616	621	626	631	636	641	646
	64	651	656	661	666	671	676	682	687	692	697
	65	702	707	712	717	722	727	732	737	742	747
	66	752	757	762	767	772	777	782	787	792	797
	67	802	807	812	817	822	827	832	837	842	847
	68	852	857	862	867	872	877	882	887	892	897
	69	902	907	912	917	922	927	932	937	942	947
	870	93 952	957	962	967	972	977	982	987	992	997
	71	94 002	007	012	017	022	027	032	037	042	047
	72	052	057	062	067	072	077	082	086	091	096
	73	101	106	111	116	121	126	131	136	141	146
	74	151	156	161	166	171	176	181	186	191	196
	75	201	206	211	216	221	226	231	236	240	245
	76	250	255	260	265	270	275	280	285	290	295
	77	300	305	310	315	320	325	330	335	340	345
	78	349	354	359	364	369	374	379	384	389	394
	79	399	404	409	414	419	424	429	433	438	443
	880	448	453	458	463	468	473	478	483	488	493
	81	498	503	507	512	517	522	527	532	537	542
	82	547	552	557	562	567	571	576	581	586	591
	83	596	601	606	611	616	621	626	630	635	640
	84	645	650	655	660	665	670	675	680	685	689
	85	694	699	704	709	714	719	724	729	734	738
	86	743	748	753	758	763	768	773	778	783	787
	87	792	797	802	807	812	817	822	827	832	836
	88	841	846	851	856	861	866	871	876	880	885
	89	890	895	900	905	910	915	919	924	929	934
	890	939	944	949	954	959	963	968	973	978	983
	91	94 988	993	998	*002	*007	*012	*017	*022	*027	*032
	92	95 036	041	046	051	056	061	066	071	075	080
	93	085	090	095	100	105	109	114	119	124	129
	94	134	139	143	148	153	158	163	168	173	177
	95	182	187	192	197	202	207	211	216	221	226
	96	231	236	240	245	250	255	260	265	270	274
	97	279	284	289	294	299	303	308	313	318	323
	98	328	332	337	342	347	352	357	361	366	371
	99	376	381	386	390	395	400	405	410	415	419
	900	95 424	429	434	439	444	448	453	458	463	468
Prop. Parts	N	0	1	2	3	4	5	6	7	8	9

Prop. Parts

	6
1	0.6
2	1.2
3	1.8
4	2.4
5	3.0
6	3.6
7	4.2
8	4.8
9	5.4

	5
1	0.5
2	1.0
3	1.5
4	2.0
5	2.5
6	3.0
7	3.5
8	4.0
9	4.5

	4
1	0.4
2	0.8
3	1.2
4	1.6
5	2.0
6	2.4
7	2.8
8	3.2
9	3.6

Table I.   Five-Place Common Logarithms of Numbers (*Continued*)

N	0	1	2	3	4	5	6	7	8	9	Prop. Parts
900	95 424	429	434	439	444	448	453	458	463	468	
01	472	477	482	487	492	497	501	506	511	516	
02	521	525	530	535	540	545	550	554	559	564	
03	569	574	578	583	588	593	598	602	607	612	
04	617	622	626	631	636	641	646	650	655	660	
05	665	670	674	679	684	689	694	698	703	708	
06	713	718	722	727	732	737	742	746	751	756	
07	761	766	770	775	780	785	789	794	799	804	
08	809	813	818	823	828	832	837	842	847	852	
09	856	861	866	871	875	880	885	890	895	899	
910	904	909	914	918	923	928	933	938	942	947	
11	952	957	961	966	971	976	980	985	990	995	
12	95 999	*004	*009	*014	*019	*023	*028	*033	*038	*042	**5**
13	96 047	052	057	061	066	071	076	080	085	090	1 0.5
14	095	099	104	109	114	118	123	128	133	137	2 1.0 3 1.5
15	142	147	152	156	161	166	171	175	180	185	4 2.0
16	190	194	199	204	209	213	218	223	227	232	5 2.5 6 3.0
17	237	242	246	251	256	261	265	270	275	280	7 3.5
18	284	289	294	298	303	308	313	317	322	327	8 4.0
19	332	336	341	346	350	355	360	365	369	374	9 4.5
920	379	384	388	393	398	402	407	412	417	421	
21	426	431	435	440	445	450	454	459	464	468	
22	473	478	483	487	492	497	501	506	511	515	
23	520	525	530	534	539	544	548	553	558	562	
24	567	572	577	581	586	591	595	600	605	609	
25	614	619	624	628	633	638	642	647	652	656	
26	661	666	670	675	680	685	689	694	699	703	
27	708	713	717	722	727	731	736	741	745	750	
28	755	759	764	769	774	778	783	788	792	797	
29	802	806	811	816	820	825	830	834	839	844	
930	848	853	858	862	867	872	876	881	886	890	
31	895	900	904	909	914	918	923	928	932	937	
32	942	946	951	956	960	965	970	974	979	984	
33	96 988	993	997	*002	*007	*011	*016	*021	*025	*030	**4**
34	97 035	039	044	049	053	058	063	067	072	077	1 0.4
35	081	086	090	095	100	104	109	114	118	123	2 0.8 3 1.2
36	128	132	137	142	146	151	155	160	165	169	4 1.6
37	174	179	183	188	192	197	202	206	211	216	5 2.0 6 2.4
38	220	225	230	234	239	243	248	253	257	262	7 2.8
39	267	271	276	280	285	290	294	299	304	308	8 3.2
940	313	317	322	327	331	336	340	345	350	354	9 3.6
41	359	364	368	373	377	382	387	391	396	400	
42	405	410	414	419	424	428	433	437	442	447	
43	451	456	460	465	470	474	479	483	488	493	
44	497	502	506	511	516	520	525	529	534	539	
45	543	548	552	557	562	566	571	575	580	585	
46	589	594	598	603	607	612	617	621	626	630	
47	635	640	644	649	653	658	663	667	672	676	
48	681	685	690	695	699	704	708	713	717	722	
49	727	731	736	740	745	749	754	759	763	768	
950	97 772	777	782	786	791	795	800	804	809	813	
N	0	1	2	3	4	5	6	7	8	9	Prop. Parts

Table I. Five-Place Common Logarithms of Numbers (*Continued*)

Prop. Parts	N	0	1	2	3	4	5	6	7	8	9
	950	97 772	777	782	786	791	795	800	804	809	813
	51	818	823	827	832	836	841	845	850	855	859
	52	864	868	873	877	882	886	891	896	900	905
	53	909	914	918	923	928	932	937	941	946	950
	54	97 955	959	964	968	973	978	982	987	991	996
	55	98 000	005	009	014	019	023	028	032	037	041
	56	046	050	055	059	064	068	073	078	082	087
	57	091	096	100	105	109	114	118	123	127	132
	58	137	141	146	150	155	159	164	168	173	177
	59	182	186	191	195	200	204	209	214	218	223
	960	227	232	236	241	245	250	254	259	263	268
	61	272	277	281	286	290	295	299	304	308	313
	62	318	322	327	331	336	340	345	349	354	358
	63	363	367	372	376	381	385	390	394	399	403
	64	408	412	417	421	426	430	435	439	444	448
	65	453	457	462	466	471	475	480	484	489	493
	66	498	502	507	511	516	520	525	529	534	538
	67	543	547	552	556	561	565	570	574	579	583
	68	588	592	597	601	605	610	614	619	623	628
	69	632	637	641	646	650	655	659	664	668	673
	970	677	682	686	691	695	700	704	709	713	717
	71	722	726	731	735	740	744	749	753	758	762
	72	767	771	776	780	784	789	793	798	802	807
	73	811	816	820	825	829	834	838	843	847	851
	74	856	860	865	869	874	878	883	887	892	896
	75	900	905	909	914	918	923	927	932	936	941
	76	945	949	954	958	963	967	972	976	981	985
	77	98 989	994	998	*003	*007	*012	*016	*021	*025	*029
	78	99 034	038	043	047	052	056	061	065	069	074
	79	078	083	087	092	096	100	105	109	114	118
	980	123	127	131	136	140	145	149	154	158	162
	81	167	171	176	180	185	189	193	198	202	207
	82	211	216	220	224	229	233	238	242	247	251
	83	255	260	264	269	273	277	282	286	291	295
	84	300	304	308	313	317	322	326	330	335	339
	85	344	348	352	357	361	366	370	374	379	383
	86	388	392	396	401	405	410	414	419	423	427
	87	432	436	441	445	449	454	458	463	467	471
	88	476	480	484	489	493	498	502	506	511	515
	89	520	524	528	533	537	542	546	550	555	559
	990	564	568	572	577	581	585	590	594	599	603
	91	607	612	616	621	625	629	634	638	642	647
	92	651	656	660	664	669	673	677	682	686	691
	93	695	699	704	708	712	717	721	726	730	734
	94	739	743	747	752	756	760	765	769	774	778
	95	782	787	791	795	800	804	808	813	817	822
	96	826	830	835	839	843	848	852	856	861	865
	97	870	874	878	883	887	891	896	900	904	909
	98	913	917	922	926	930	935	939	944	948	952
	99	99 957	961	965	970	974	978	983	987	991	996
	1000	00 000	004	009	013	017	022	026	030	035	039
Prop. Parts	N	0	1	2	3	4	5	6	7	8	9

Proportional Parts (left margin):

5
1	0.5
2	1.0
3	1.5
4	2.0
5	2.5
6	3.0
7	3.5
8	4.0
9	4.5

4
1	0.4
2	0.8
3	1.2
4	1.6
5	2.0
6	2.4
7	2.8
8	3.2
9	3.6

700

Table II. Natural Trigonometric Functions for Decimal Fractions of a Degree

Deg.	Sin	Tan	Cot	Cos	Deg.	Deg.	Sin	Tan	Cot	Cos	Deg.
0.0	0.00000	0.00000	∞	1.0000	90.0	.5	.07846	.07870	12.706	.9969	.5
.1	.00175	.00175	573.0	1.0000	.9	.6	.08020	.08046	12.429	.9968	.4
.2	.00349	.00349	286.5	1.0000	.8	.7	.08194	.08221	12.163	.9966	.3
.3	.00524	.00524	191.0	1.0000	.7	.8	.08368	.08397	11.909	.9965	.2
.4	.00698	.00698	143.24	1.0000	.6	.9	.08542	.08573	11.664	.9963	.1
.5	.00873	.00873	114.59	1.0000	.5	5.0	0.08716	0.08749	11.430	0.9962	85.0
.6	.01047	.01047	95.49	0.9999	.4	.1	.08889	.08925	11.205	.9960	.9
.7	.01222	.01222	81.85	.9999	.3	.2	.09063	.09101	10.988	.9959	.8
.8	.01396	.01396	71.62	.9999	.2	.3	.09237	.09277	10.780	.9957	.7
.9	.01571	.01571	63.66	.9999	.1	.4	.09411	.09453	10.579	.9956	.6
1.0	0.01745	0.01746	57.29	0.9998	89.0	.5	.09585	.09629	10.385	.9954	.5
.1	.01920	.01920	52.08	.9998	.9	.6	.09758	.09805	10.199	.9952	.4
.2	.02094	.02095	47.74	.9998	.8	.7	.09932	.09981	10.019	.9951	.3
.3	.02269	.02269	44.07	.9997	.7	.8	.10106	.10158	9.845	.9949	.2
.4	.02443	.02444	40.92	.9997	.6	.9	.10279	.10334	9.677	.9947	.1
.5	.02618	.02619	38.19	.9997	.5	6.0	0.10453	0.10510	9.514	0.9945	84.0
.6	.02792	.02793	35.80	.9996	.4	.1	.10626	.10687	9.357	.9943	.9
.7	.02967	.02968	33.69	.9996	.3	.2	.10800	.10863	9.205	.9942	.8
.8	.03141	.03143	31.82	.9995	.2	.3	.10973	.11040	9.058	.9940	.7
.9	.03316	.03317	30.14	.9995	.1	.4	.11147	.11217	8.915	.9938	.6
2.0	0.03490	0.03492	28.64	0.9994	88.0	.5	.11320	.11394	8.777	.9936	.5
.1	.03664	.03667	27.27	.9993	.9	.6	.11494	.11570	8.643	.9934	.4
.2	.03839	.03842	26.03	.9993	.8	.7	.11667	.11747	8.513	.9932	.3
.3	.04013	.04016	24.90	.9992	.7	.8	.11840	.11924	8.386	.9930	.2
.4	.04188	.04191	23.86	.9991	.6	.9	.12014	.12101	8.264	.9928	.1
.5	.04362	.04366	22.90	.9990	.5	7.0	0.12187	0.12278	8.144	0.9925	83.0
.6	.04536	.04541	22.02	.9990	.4	.1	.12360	.12456	8.028	.9923	.9
.7	.04711	.04716	21.20	.9989	.3	.2	.12533	.12633	7.916	.9921	.8
.8	.04885	.04891	20.45	.9988	.2	.3	.12706	.12810	7.806	.9919	.7
.9	.05059	.05066	19.74	.9987	.1	.4	.12880	.12988	7.700	.9917	.6
3.0	0.05234	0.05241	19.081	0.9986	87.0	.5	.13053	.13165	7.596	.9914	.5
.1	.05408	.05416	18.464	.9985	.9	.6	.13226	.13343	7.495	.9912	.4
.2	.05582	.05591	17.886	.9984	.8	.7	.13399	.13521	7.396	.9910	.3
.3	.05756	.05766	17.343	.9983	.7	.8	.13572	.13698	7.300	.9907	.2
.4	.05931	.05941	16.832	.9982	.6	.9	.13744	.13876	7.207	.9905	.1
.5	.06105	.06116	16.350	.9981	.5	8.0	0.13917	0.14054	7.115	0.9903	82.0
.6	.06279	.06291	15.895	.9980	.4	.1	.14090	.14232	7.026	.9900	.9
.7	.06453	.06467	15.464	.9979	.3	.2	.14263	.14410	6.940	.9898	.8
.8	.06627	.06642	15.056	.9978	.2	.3	.14436	.14588	6.855	.9895	.7
.9	.06802	.06817	14.669	.9977	.1	.4	.14608	.14767	6.772	.9893	.6
4.0	0.06976	0.06993	14.301	0.9976	86.0	.5	.14781	.14945	6.691	.9890	.5
.1	.07150	.07168	13.951	.9974	.9	.6	.14954	.15124	6.612	.9888	.4
.2	.07324	.07344	13.617	.9973	.8	.7	.15126	.15302	6.535	.9885	.3
.3	.07498	.07519	13.300	.9972	.7	.8	.15299	.15481	6.460	.9882	.2
.4	.07672	.07695	12.996	.9971	85.6	.9	.15471	.15660	6.386	.9880	81.1
Deg.	Cos	Cot	Tan	Sin	Deg.	Deg.	Cos	Cot	Tan	Sin	Deg.

701

Table II. Natural Trigonometric Functions for Decimal Fractions of a Degree
(*Continued*)

Deg.	Sin	Tan	Cot	Cos	Deg.	Deg.	Sin	Tan	Cot	Cos	Deg.
9.0	0.15643	0.15838	6.314	0.9877	81.0	.5	.2334	.2401	4.165	.9724	.5
.1	.15816	.16017	6.243	.9874	.9	.6	.2351	.2419	4.134	.9720	.4
.2	.15988	.16196	6.174	.9871	.8	.7	.2368	.2438	4.102	.9715	.3
.3	.16160	.16376	6.107	.9869	.7	.8	.2385	.2456	4.071	.9711	.2
.4	.16333	.16555	6.041	.9866	.6	.9	.2402	.2475	4.041	.9707	.1
.5	.16505	.16734	5.976	.9863	.5	14.0	0.2419	0.2493	4.011	0.9703	76.0
.6	.16677	.16914	5.912	.9860	.4	.1	.2436	.2512	3.981	.9699	.9
.7	.16849	.17093	5.850	.9857	.3	.2	.2453	.2530	3.952	.9694	.8
.8	.17021	.17273	5.789	.9854	.2	.3	.2470	.2549	3.923	.9690	.7
.9	.17193	.17453	5.730	.9851	.1	.4	.2487	.2568	3.895	.9686	.6
10.0	0.1736	0.1763	5.671	0.9848	80.0	.5	.2504	.2586	3.867	.9681	.5
.1	.1754	.1781	5.614	.9845	.9	.6	.2521	.2605	3.839	.9677	.4
.2	.1771	.1799	5.558	.9842	.8	.7	.2538	.2623	3.812	.9673	.3
.3	.1788	.1817	5.503	.9839	.7	.8	.2554	.2642	3.785	.9668	.2
.4	.1805	.1835	5.449	.9836	.6	.9	.2571	.2661	3.758	.9664	.1
.5	.1822	.1853	5.396	.9833	.5	15.0	0.2588	0.2679	3.732	0.9659	75.0
.6	.1840	.1871	5.343	.9829	.4	.1	.2605	.2698	3.706	.9655	.9
.7	.1857	.1890	5.292	.9826	.3	.2	.2622	.2717	3.681	.9650	.8
.8	.1874	.1908	5.242	.9823	.2	.3	.2639	.2736	3.655	.9646	.7
.9	.1891	.1926	5.193	.9820	.1	.4	.2656	.2754	3.630	.9641	.6
11.0	0.1908	0.1944	5.145	0.9816	79.0	.5	.2672	.2773	3.606	.9636	.5
.1	.1925	.1962	5.097	.9813	.9	.6	.2689	.2792	3.582	.9632	.4
.2	.1942	.1980	5.050	.9810	.8	.7	.2706	.2811	3.558	.9627	.3
.3	.1959	.1998	5.005	.9806	.7	.8	.2723	.2830	3.534	.9622	.2
.4	.1977	.2016	4.959	.9803	.6	.9	.2740	.2849	3.511	.9617	.1
.5	.1994	.2035	4.915	.9799	.5	16.0	0.2756	0.2867	3.487	0.9613	74.0
.6	.2011	.2053	4.872	.9796	.4	.1	.2773	.2886	3.465	.9608	.9
.7	.2028	.2071	4.829	.9792	.3	.2	.2790	.2905	3.442	.9603	.8
.8	.2045	.2089	4.787	.9789	.2	.3	.2807	.2924	3.420	.9598	.7
.9	.2062	.2107	4.745	.9785	.1	.4	.2823	.2943	3.398	.9593	.6
12.0	0.2079	0.2126	4.705	0.9781	78.0	.5	.2840	.2962	3.376	.9588	.5
.1	.2096	.2144	4.665	.9778	.9	.6	.2857	.2981	3.354	.9583	.4
.2	.2113	.2162	4.625	.9774	.8	.7	.2874	.3000	3.333	.9578	.3
.3	.2130	.2180	4.586	.9770	.7	.8	.2890	.3019	3.312	.9573	.2
.4	.2147	.2199	4.548	.9767	.6	.9	.2907	.3038	3.291	.9568	.1
.5	.2164	.2217	4.511	.9763	.5	17.0	0.2924	0.3057	3.271	0.9563	73.0
.6	.2181	.2235	4.474	.9759	.4	.1	.2940	.3076	3.251	.9558	.9
.7	.2198	.2254	4.437	.9755	.3	.2	.2957	.3096	3.230	.9553	.8
.8	.2215	.2272	4.402	.9751	.2	.3	.2974	.3115	3.211	.9548	.7
.9	.2233	.2290	4.366	.9748	.1	.4	.2990	.3134	3.191	.9542	.6
13.0	0.2250	0.2309	4.331	0.9744	77.0	.5	.3007	.3153	3.172	.9537	.5
.1	.2267	.2327	4.297	.9740	.9	.6	.3024	.3172	3.152	.9532	.4
.2	.2284	.2345	4.264	.9736	.8	.7	.3040	.3191	3.133	.9527	.3
.3	.2300	.2364	4.230	.9732	.7	.8	.3057	.3211	3.115	.9521	.2
.4	.2317	.2382	4.198	.9728	76.6	.9	.3074	.3230	3.096	.9516	72.1
Deg.	Cos	Cot	Tan	Sin	Deg.	Deg.	Cos	Cot	Tan	Sin	Deg.

Table II. Natural Trigonometric Functions for Decimal Fractions of a Degree
(*Continued*)

Deg.	Sin	Tan	Cot	Cos	Deg.	Deg.	Sin	Tan	Cot	Cos	Deg.
18.0	0.3090	0.3249	3.078	0.9511	72.0	.5	.3827	.4142	2.414	.9239	.5
.1	.3107	.3269	3.060	.9505	.9	.6	.3843	.4163	2.402	.9232	.4
.2	.3123	.3288	3.042	.9500	.8	.7	.3859	.4183	2.391	.9225	.3
.3	.3140	.3307	3.024	.9494	.7	.8	.3875	.4204	2.379	.9219	.2
.4	.3156	.3327	3.006	.9489	.6	.9	.3891	.4224	2.367	.9212	.1
.5	.3173	.3346	2.989	.9483	.5	23.0	0.3907	0.4245	2.356	0.9205	67.0
.6	.3190	.3365	2.971	.9478	.4	.1	.3923	.4265	2.344	.9198	.9
.7	.3206	.3385	2.954	.9472	.3	.2	.3939	.4286	2.333	.9191	.8
.8	.3223	.3404	2.937	.9466	.2	.3	.3955	.4307	2.322	.9184	.7
.9	.3239	.3424	2.921	.9461	.1	.4	.3971	.4327	2.311	.9178	.6
19.0	0.3256	0.3443	2.904	0.9455	71.0	.5	.3987	.4348	2.300	.9171	.5
.1	.3272	.3463	2.888	.9449	.9	.6	.4003	.4369	2.289	.9164	.4
.2	.3289	.3482	2.872	.9444	.8	.7	.4019	.4390	2.278	.9157	.3
.3	.3305	.3502	2.856	.9438	.7	.8	.4035	.4411	2.267	.9150	.2
.4	.3322	.3522	2.840	.9432	.6	.9	.4051	.4431	2.257	.9143	.1
.5	.3338	.3541	2.824	.9426	.5	24.0	0.4067	0.4452	2.246	0.9135	66.0
.6	.3355	.3561	2.808	.9421	.4	.1	.4083	.4473	2.236	.9128	.9
.7	.3371	.3581	2.793	.9415	.3	.2	.4099	.4494	2.225	.9121	.8
.8	.3387	.3600	2.778	.9409	.2	.3	.4115	.4515	2.215	.9114	.7
.9	.3404	.3620	2.762	.9403	.1	.4	.4131	.4536	2.204	.9107	.6
20.0	0.3420	0.3640	2.747	0.9397	70.0	.5	.4147	.4557	2.194	.9100	.5
.1	.3437	.3659	2.733	.9391	.9	.6	.4163	.4578	2.184	.9092	.4
.2	.3453	.3679	2.718	.9385	.8	.7	.4179	.4599	2.174	.9085	.3
.3	.3469	.3699	2.703	.9379	.7	.8	.4195	.4621	2.164	.9078	.2
.4	.3486	.3719	2.689	.9373	.6	.9	.4210	.4642	2.154	.9070	.1
.5	.3502	.3739	2.675	.9367	.5	25.0	0.4226	0.4663	2.145	0.9063	65.0
.6	.3518	.3759	2.660	.9361	.4	.1	.4242	.4684	2.135	.9056	.9
.7	.3535	.3779	2.646	.9354	.3	.2	.4258	.4706	2.125	.9048	.8
.8	.3551	.3799	2.633	.9348	.2	.3	.4274	.4727	2.116	.9041	.7
.9	.3567	.3819	2.619	.9342	.1	.4	.4289	.4748	2.106	.9033	.6
21.0	0.3584	0.3839	2.605	0.9336	69.0	.5	.4305	.4770	2.097	.9026	.5
.1	.3600	.3859	2.592	.9330	.9	.6	.4321	.4791	2.087	.9018	.4
.2	.3616	.3879	2.578	.9323	.8	.7	.4337	.4813	2.078	.9011	.3
.3	.3633	.3899	2.565	.9317	.7	.8	.4352	.4834	2.069	.9003	.2
.4	.3649	.3919	2.552	.9311	.6	.9	.4368	.4856	2.059	.8996	.1
.5	.3665	.3939	2.539	.9304	.5	26.0	0.4384	0.4877	2.050	0.8988	64.0
.6	.3681	.3959	2.526	.9298	.4	.1	.4399	.4899	2.041	.8980	.9
.7	.3697	.3979	2.513	.9291	.3	.2	.4415	.4921	2.032	.8973	.8
.8	.3714	.4000	2.500	.9285	.2	.3	.4431	.4942	2.023	.8965	.7
.9	.3730	.4020	2.488	.9278	.1	.4	.4446	.4964	2.014	.8957	.6
22.0	0.3746	0.4040	2.475	0.9272	68.0	.5	.4462	.4986	2.006	.8949	.5
.1	.3762	.4061	2.463	.9265	.9	.6	.4478	.5008	1.997	.8942	.4
.2	.3778	.4081	2.450	.9259	.8	.7	.4493	.5029	1.988	.8934	.3
.3	.3795	.4101	2.438	.9252	.7	.8	.4509	.5051	1.980	.8926	.2
.4	.3811	.4122	2.426	.9245	67.6	.9	.4524	.5073	1.971	.8918	63.1
Deg.	Cos	Cot	Tan	Sin	Deg.	Deg.	Cos	Cot	Tan	Sin	Deg.

Deg.	Sin	Tan	Cot	Cos	Deg.	Deg.	Sin	Tan	Cot	Cos	Deg.
27.0	0.4540	0.5095	1.963	0.8910	63.0	.5	.5225	.6128	1.6319	.8526	.5
.1	.4555	.5117	1.954	.8902	.9	.6	.5240	.6152	1.6255	.8517	.4
.2	.4571	.5139	1.946	.8894	.8	.7	.5255	.6176	1.6191	.8508	.3
.3	.4586	.5161	1.937	.8886	.7	.8	.5270	.6200	1.6128	.8499	.2
.4	.4602	.5184	1.929	.8878	.6	.9	.5284	.6224	1.6066	.8490	.1
.5	.4617	.5206	1.921	.8870	.5	32.0	0.5299	0.6249	1.6003	0.8480	58.0
.6	.4633	.5228	1.913	.8862	.4	.1	.5314	.6273	1.5941	.8471	.9
.7	.4648	.5250	1.905	.8854	.3	.2	.5329	.6297	1.5880	.8462	.8
.8	.4664	.5272	1.897	.8846	.2	.3	.5344	.6322	1.5818	.8453	.7
.9	.4679	.5295	1.889	.8838	.1	.4	.5358	.6346	1.5757	.8443	.6
28.0	0.4695	0.5317	1.881	0.8829	62.0	.5	.5373	.6371	1.5697	.8434	.5
.1	.4710	.5340	1.873	.8821	.9	.6	.5388	.6395	1.5637	.8425	.4
.2	.4726	.5362	1.865	.8813	.8	.7	.5402	.6420	1.5577	.8415	.3
.3	.4741	.5384	1.857	.8805	.7	.8	.5417	.6445	1.5517	.8406	.2
.4	.4756	.5407	1.849	.8796	.6	.9	.5432	.6469	1.5458	.8396	.1
.5	.4772	.5430	1.842	.8788	.5	33.0	0.5446	0.6494	1.5399	0.8387	57.0
.6	.4787	.5452	1.834	.8780	.4	.1	.5461	.6519	1.5340	.8377	.9
.7	.4802	.5475	1.827	.8771	.3	.2	.5476	.6544	1.5282	.8368	.8
.8	.4818	.5498	1.819	.8763	.2	.3	.5490	.6569	1.5224	.8358	.7
.9	.4833	.5520	1.811	.8755	.1	.4	.5505	.6594	1.5166	.8348	.6
29.0	0.4848	0.5543	1.804	0.8746	61.0	.5	.5519	.6619	1.5108	.8339	.5
.1	.4863	.5566	1.797	.8738	.9	.6	.5534	.6644	1.5051	.8329	.4
.2	.4879	.5589	1.789	.8729	.8	.7	.5548	.6669	1.4994	.8320	.3
.3	.4894	.5612	1.782	.8721	.7	.8	.5563	.6694	1.4938	.8310	.2
.4	.4909	.5635	1.775	.8712	.6	.9	.5577	.6720	1.4882	.8300	.1
.5	.4924	.5658	1.767	.8704	.5	34.0	0.5592	0.6745	1.4826	0.8290	56.0
.6	.4939	.5681	1.760	.8695	.4	.1	.5606	.6771	1.4770	.8281	.9
.7	.4955	.5704	1.753	.8686	.3	.2	.5621	.6796	1.4715	.8271	.8
.8	.4970	.5727	1.746	.8678	.2	.3	.5635	.6822	1.4659	.8261	.7
.9	.4985	.5750	1.739	.8669	.1	.4	.5650	.6847	1.4605	.8251	.6
30.0	0.5000	0.5774	1.7321	0.8660	60.0	.5	.5664	.6873	1.4550	.8241	.5
.1	.5015	.5797	1.7251	.8652	.9	.6	.5678	.6899	1.4496	.8231	.4
.2	.5030	.5820	1.7182	.8643	.8	.7	.5693	.6924	1.4442	.8221	.3
.3	.5045	.5844	1.7113	.8634	.7	.8	.5707	.6950	1.4388	.8211	.2
.4	.5060	.5867	1.7045	.8625	.6	.9	.5721	.6976	1.4335	.8202	.1
.5	..5075	.5890	1.6977	.8616	.5	35.0	0.5736	0.7002	1.4281	0.8192	55.0
.6	.5090	.5914	1.6909	.8607	.4	.1	.5750	.7028	1.4229	.8181	.9
.7	.5105	.5938	1.6842	.8599	.3	.2	.5764	.7054	1.4176	.8171	.8
.8	.5120	.5961	1.6775	.8590	.2	.3	.5779	.7080	1.4124	.8161	.7
.9	.5135	.5985	1.6709	.8581	.1	.4	.5793	.7107	1.4071	.8151	.6
31.0	0.5150	0.6009	1.6643	0.8572	59.0	.5	.5807	.7133	1.4019	.8141	.5
.1	.5165	.6032	1.6577	.8563	.9	.6	.5821	.7159	1.3968	.8131	.4
.2	.5180	.6056	1.6512	.8554	.8	.7	.5835	.7186	1.3916	.8121	.3
.3	.5195	.6080	1.6447	.8545	.7	.8	.5850	.7212	1.3865	.8111	.2
.4	.5210	.6104	1.6383	.8536	58.6	.9	.5864	.7239	1.3814	.8100	54.1
Deg.	Cos	Cot	Tan	Sin	Deg.	Deg.	Cos	Cot	Tan	Sin	Deg.

Table II. Natural Trigonometric Functions for Decimal Fractions of a Degree
(*Continued*)

Deg.	Sin	Tan	Cot	Cos	Deg.	Deg.	Sin	Tan	Cot	Cos	Deg.
36.0	0.5878	0.7265	1.3764	0.8090	54.0	.5	.6494	.8541	1.1708	.7604	.5
.1	.5892	.7292	1.3713	.8080	.9	.6	.6508	.8571	1.1667	.7593	.4
.2	.5906	.7319	1.3663	.8070	.8	.7	.6521	.8601	1.1626	.7581	.3
.3	.5920	.7346	1.3613	.8059	.7	.8	.6534	.8632	1.1585	.7570	.2
.4	.5934	.7373	1.3564	.8049	.6	.9	.6547	.8662	1.1544	.7559	.1
.5	.5948	.7400	1.3514	.8039	.5	41.0	0.6561	0.8693	1.1504	0.7547	49.0
.6	.5962	.7427	1.3465	.8028	.4	.1	.6574	.8724	1.1463	.7536	.9
.7	.5976	.7454	1.3416	.8018	.3	.2	.6587	.8754	1.1423	.7524	.8
.8	.5990	.7481	1.3367	.8007	.2	.3	.6600	.8785	1.1383	.7513	.7
.9	.6004	.7508	1.3319	.7997	.1	.4	.6613	.8816	1.1343	.7501	.6
37.0	0.6018	0.7536	1.3270	0.7986	53.0	.5	.6626	.8847	1.1303	.7490	.5
.1	.6032	.7563	1.3222	.7976	.9	.6	.6639	.8878	1.1263	.7478	.4
.2	.6046	.7590	1.3175	.7965	.8	.7	.6652	.8910	1.1224	.7466	.3
.3	.6060	.7618	1.3127	.7955	.7	.8	.6665	.8941	1.1184	.7455	.2
.4	.6074	.7646	1.3079	.7944	.6	.9	.6678	.8972	1.1145	.7443	.1
.5	.6088	.7673	1.3032	.7934	.5	42.0	0.6691	0.9004	1.1106	0.7431	48.0
.6	.6101	.7701	1.2985	.7923	.4	.1	.6704	.9036	1.1067	.7420	.9
.7	.6115	.7729	1.2938	.7912	.3	.2	.6717	.9067	1.1028	.7408	.8
.8	.6129	.7757	1.2892	.7902	.2	.3	.6730	.9099	1.0990	.7396	.7
.9	.6143	.7785	1.2846	.7891	.1	.4	.6743	.9131	1.0951	.7385	.6
38.0	0.6157	0.7813	1.2799	0.7880	52.0	.5	.6756	.9163	1.0913	.7373	.5
.1	.6170	.7841	1.2753	.7869	.9	.6	.6769	.9195	1.0875	.7361	.4
.2	.6184	.7869	1.2708	.7859	.8	.7	.6782	.9228	1.0837	.7349	.3
.3	.6198	.7898	1.2662	.7848	.7	.8	.6794	.9260	1.0799	.7337	.2
.4	.6211	.7926	1.2617	.7837	.6	.9	.6807	.9293	1.0761	.7325	.1
.5	.6225	.7954	1.2572	.7826	.5	43.0	0.6820	0.9325	1.0724	0.7314	47.0
.6	.6239	.7983	1.2527	.7815	.4	.1	.6833	.9358	1.0686	.7302	.9
.7	.6252	.8012	1.2482	.7804	.3	.2	.6845	.9391	1.0649	.7290	.8
.8	.6266	.8040	1.2437	.7793	.2	.3	.6858	.9424	1.0612	.7278	.7
.9	.6280	.8069	1.2393	.7782	.1	.4	.6871	.9457	1.0575	.7266	.6
39.0	0.6293	0.8098	1.2349	0.7771	51.0	.5	.6884	.9490	1.0538	.7254	.5
.1	.6307	.8127	1.2305	.7760	.9	.6	.6896	.9523	1.0501	.7242	.4
.2	.6320	.8156	1.2261	.7749	.8	.7	.6909	.9556	1.0464	.7230	.3
.3	.6334	.8185	1.2218	.7738	.7	.8	.6921	.9590	1.0428	.7218	.2
.4	.6347	.8214	1.2174	.7727	.6	.9	.6934	.9623	1.0392	.7206	.1
.5	.6361	.8243	1.2131	.7716	.5	44.0	0.6947	0.9657	1.0355	0.7193	46.0
.6	.6374	.8273	1.2088	.7705	.4	.1	.6959	.9691	1.0319	.7181	.9
.7	.6388	.8302	1.2045	.7694	.3	.2	.6972	.9725	1.0283	.7169	.8
.8	.6401	.8332	1.2002	.7683	.2	.3	.6984	.9759	1.0247	.7157	.7
.9	.6414	.8361	1.1960	.7672	.1	.4	.6997	.9793	1.0212	.7145	.6
40.0	0.6428	0.8391	1.1918	0.7660	50.0	.5	.7009	.9827	1.0176	.7133	.5
.1	.6441	.8421	1.1875	.7649	.9	.6	.7022	.9861	1.0141	.7120	.4
.2	.6455	.8451	1.1833	.7638	.8	.7	.7034	.9896	1.0105	.7108	.3
.3	.6468	.8481	1.1792	.7627	.7	.8	.7046	.9930	1.0070	.7096	.2
.4	.6481	.8511	1.1750	.7615	49.6	.9	.7059	.9965	1.0035	.7083	.1
						45.0	0.7071	1.0000	1.0000	0.7071	45.0
Deg.	Cos	Cot	Tan	Sin	Deg.	Deg.	Cos	Cot	Tan	Sin	Deg.

Table III.   Secants and Cosecants for Decimal Fractions of a Degree

Deg.	Sec	Csc	Deg.	Deg.	Sec	Csc	Deg.	Deg.	Sec	Csc	Deg.
0.0	1.0000		90.0	5.0	1.0038	11.474	85.0	10.0	1.0154	5.7588	80.0
.1	1.0000	572.96	.9	.1	1.0040	11.249	.9	.1	1.0157	5.7023	.9
.2	1.0000	286.48	.8	.2	1.0041	11.034	.8	.2	1.0161	5.6470	.8
.3	1.0000	190.99	.7	.3	1.0043	10.826	.7	.3	1.0164	5.5928	.7
.4	1.0000	143.24	.6	.4	1.0045	10.626	.6	.4	1.0167	5.5396	.6
.5	1.0000	114.59	.5	.5	1.0046	10.433	.5	.5	1.0170	5.4874	.5
.6	1.0001	95.495	.4	.6	1.0048	10.248	.4	.6	1.0174	5.4362	.4
.7	1.0001	81.853	.3	.7	1.0050	10.068	.3	.7	1.0177	5.3860	.3
.8	1.0001	71.622	.2	.8	1.0051	9.8955	.2	.8	1.0180	5.3367	.2
.9	1.0001	63.665	.1	.9	1.0053	9.7283	·1	.9	1.0184	5.2883	.1
1.0	1.0002	57.299	89.0	6.0	1.0055	9.5668	84.0	11.0	1.0187	5.2408	79.0
.1	1.0002	52.090	.9	.1	1.0057	9.4105	.9	.1	1.0191	5.1942	.9
.2	1.0002	47.750	.8	.2	1.0059	9.2593	.8	.2	1.0194	5.1484	.8
.3	1.0003	44.077	.7	.3	1.0061	9.1129	.7	.3	1.0198	5.1034	.7
.4	1.0003	40.930	.6	.4	1.0063	8.9711	.6	.4	1.0201	5.0593	.6
.5	1.0003	38.202	.5	.5	1.0065	8.8337	.5	.5	1.0205	5.0159	.5
.6	1.0004	38.815	.4	.6	1.0067	8.7004	.4	.6	1.0209	4.9732	.4
.7	1.0004	33.708	.3	.7	1.0069	8.5711	.3	.7	1.0212	4.9313	.3
.8	1.0005	31.836	.2	.8	1.0071	8.4457	.2	.8	1.0216	4.8901	.2
.9	1.0006	30.161	.1	.9	1.0073	8.3238	.1	.9	1.0220	4.8496	.1
2.0	1.0006	28.654	88.0	7.0	1.0075	8.2055	83.0	12.0	1.0023	4.8097	78.0
.1	1.0007	27.290	.9	.1	1.0077	8.0905	.9	.1	1.0227	4.7706	.9
.2	1.0007	26.050	.8	.2	1.0079	7.9787	.8	.2	1.0231	4.7321	.8
.3	1.0008	24.918	.7	.3	1.0082	7.8700	.7	.3	1.0235	4.6942	.7
.4	1.0009	23.880	.6	.4	1.0084	7.7642	.6	.4	1.0239	4.6569	.6
.5	1.0010	22.926	.5	.5	1.0086	7.6613	.5	.5	1.0243	4.6202	.5
.6	1.0010	22.044	.4	.6	1.0089	7.5611	.4	.6	1.0247	4.5841	.4
.7	1.0011	21.229	.3	.7	1.0091	7.4635	.3	.7	1.0251	4.5486	.3
.8	1.0012	20.471	.2	.8	1.0093	7.3684	.2	.8	1.0255	4.5137	.2
.9	1.0013	19.766	.1	.9	1.0096	7.2757	.1	.9	1.0259	4.4793	.1
3.0	1.0014	19.107	87.0	8.0	1.0098	7.1853	82.0	13.0	1.0263	4.4454	77.0
.1	1.0015	18.492	.9	.1	1.0101	7.0972	.9	.1	1.0267	4.4121	.9
.2	1.0016	17.914	.8	.2	1.0103	7.0112	.8	.2	1.0271	4.3792	.8
.3	1.0017	17.372	.7	.3	1.0106	6.9275	.7	.3	1.0276	4.3469	.7
.4	1.0018	16.862	.6	.4	1.0108	6.8454	.6	.4	1.0280	4.3150	.6
.5	1.0019	16.380	.5	.5	1.0111	6.7655	.5	.5	1.0284	4.2837	.5
.6	1.0020	15.926	.4	.6	1.0114	6.6874	.4	.6	1.0288	4.2527	.4
.7	1.0021	15.496	.3	.7	1.0116	6.6111	.3	.7	1.0293	4.2223	.3
.8	1.0022	15.089	.2	.8	1.0119	6.5366	.2	.8	1.0297	4.1923	.2
.9	1.0023	14.703	.1	.9	1.0122	6.4637	.1	.9	1.0302	4.1627	.1
4.0	1.0024	14.336	86.0	9.0	1.0125	6.3925	81.0	14.0	1.0306	4.1336	76.0
.1	1.0026	13.987	.9	.1	1.0127	6.3228	.9	.1	1.0311	4.1048	.9
.2	1.0027	13.654	.8	.2	1.0130	6.2546	.8	.2	1.0315	4.0765	.8
.3	1.0028	13.337	.7	.3	1.0133	6.1880	.7	.3	1.0320	4.0486	.7
.4	1.0030	13.035	.6	.4	1.0136	6.1227	.6	.4	1.0324	4.0211	.6
.5	1.0031	12.745	.5	.5	1.0139	6.0589	.5	.5	1.0329	3.9939	.5
.6	1.0032	12.469	.4	.6	1.0142	5.9963	.4	.6	1.0334	3.9672	.4
.7	1.0034	12.204	.3	.7	1.0145	5.9351	.3	.7	1.0338	3.9408	.3
.8	1.0035	11.951	.2	.8	1.0148	5.8751	.2	.8	1.0343	3.9147	.2
.9	1.0037	11.707	.1	.9	1.0151	5.8164	.1	.9	1.0348	3.8890	.1
5.0	1.0038	11.474	85.0	10.0	1.0154	5.7588	80.0	15.0	1.0353	3.8637	75.0
Deg.	Csc	Sec	Deg.	Deg.	Csc	Sec	Deg.	Deg.	Csc	Sec	Deg.

Table III. Secants and Cosecants for Decimal Fractions of a Degree (*Continued*)

Deg.	Sec	Csc	Deg.	Deg.	Sec	Csc	Deg.	Deg.	Sec	Csc	Deg.
15.0	1.0353	3.8637	75.0	20.0	1.0642	2.9238	70.0	25.0	1.1034	2.3662	65.0
.1	1.0358	3.8387	.9	.1	1.0649	2.9099	.9	.1	1.1043	2.3574	.9
.2	1.0363	3.8140	.8	.2	1.0655	2.8960	.8	.2	1.1052	2.3486	.8
.3	1.0367	3.7897	.7	.3	1.0662	2.8824	.7	.3	1.1061	2.3400	.7
.4	1.0372	3.7657	.6	.4	1.0669	2.8688	.6	.4	1.1070	2.3314	.6
.5	1.0377	3.7420	.5	.5	1.0676	2.8555	.5	.5	1.1079	2.3228	.5
.6	1.0382	3.7186	.4	.6	1.0683	2.8422	.4	.6	1.1089	2.3144	.4
.7	1.0388	3.6955	.3	.7	1.0690	2.8291	.3	.7	1.1098	2.3060	.3
.8	1.0393	3.6727	.2	.8	1.0697	2.8161	.2	.8	1.1107	2.2976	.2
.9	1.0398	3.6502	.1	.9	1.0704	2.8032	.1	.9	1.1117	2.2894	.1
16.0	1.0403	3.6280	74.0	21.0	1.0711	2.7904	69.0	26.0	1.1126	2.2812	64.0
.1	1.0408	3.6060	.9	.1	1.0719	2.7778	.9	.1	1.1136	2.2730	.9
.2	1.0413	3.5843	.8	.2	1.0726	2.7653	.8	.2	1.1145	2.2650	.8
.3	1.0419	3.5629	.7	.3	1.0733	2.7529	.7	.3	1.1155	2.2570	.7
.4	1.0424	3.5418	.6	.4	1.0740	2.7407	.6	.4	1.1164	2.2490	.6
.5	1.0429	3.5209	.5	.5	1.0748	2.7285	.5	.5	1.1174	2.2412	.5
.6	1.0435	3.5003	.4	.6	1.0755	2.7165	.4	.6	1.1184	2.2333	.4
.7	1.0440	3.4799	.3	.7	1.0763	2.7046	.3	.7	1.1194	2.2256	.3
.8	1.0446	3.4598	.2	.8	1.0770	2.6927	.2	.8	1.1203	2.2179	.2
.9	1.0451	3.4399	.1	.9	1.0778	2.6811	.1	.9	1.1213	2.2103	.1
17.0	1.0457	3.4203	73.0	22.0	1.0785	2.6695	68.0	27.0	1.1223	2.2027	63.0
.1	1.0463	3.4009	.9	.1	1.0793	2.6580	.9	.1	1.1233	2.1952	.9
.2	1.0468	3.3817	.8	.2	1.0801	2.6466	.8	.2	1.1243	2.1877	.8
.3	1.0474	3.3628	.7	.3	1.0808	2.6354	.7	.3	1.1253	2.1803	.7
.4	1.0480	3.3440	.6	.4	1.0816	2.6242	.6	.4	1.1264	2.1730	.6
.5	1.0485	3.3255	.5	.5	1.0824	2.6131	.5	.5	1.1274	2.1657	.5
.6	1.0491	3.3072	.4	.6	1.0832	2.6022	.4	.6	1.1284	2.1584	.4
.7	1.0497	3.2891	.3	.7	1.0840	2.5913	.3	.7	1.1294	2.1513	.3
.8	1.0503	3.2712	.2	.8	1.0848	2.5805	.2	.8	1.1305	2.1441	.2
.9	1.0509	3.2535	.1	.9	1.0856	2.5699	.1	.9	1.1315	2.1371	.1
18.0	1.0515	3.2361	72.0	23.0	1.0864	2.5593	67.0	28.0	1.1326	2.1301	62.0
.1	1.0521	3.2188	.9	.1	1.0872	2.5488	.9	.1	1.1336	2.1231	.9
.2	1.0527	3.2017	.8	.2	1.0880	2.5384	.8	.2	1.1347	2.1162	.8
.3	1.0533	3.1848	.7	.3	1.0888	2.5282	.7	.3	1.1357	2.1093	.7
.4	1.0539	3.1681	.6	.4	1.0896	2.5180	.6	.4	1.1368	2.1025	.6
.5	1.0545	3.1515	.5	.5	1.0904	2.5078	.5	.5	1.1379	2.0957	.5
.6	1.0551	3.1352	.4	.6	1.0913	2.4978	.4	.6	1.1390	2.0890	.4
.7	1.0557	3.1190	.3	.7	1.0921	2.4879	.3	.7	1.1401	2.0824	.3
.8	1.0564	3.1030	.2	.8	1.0929	2.4780	.2	.8	1.1412	2.0757	.2
˙.9	1.0570	3.0872	.1	.9	1.0938	2.4683	.1	.9	1.1423	2.0692	.1
19.0	1.0576	3.0716	71.0	24.0	1.0946	2.4586	66.0	29.0	1.1434	2.0627	61.0
.1	1.0583	3.0561	.9	.1	1.0955	2.4490	.9	.1	1.1445	2.0562	.9
.2	1.0589	3.0407	.8	.2	1.0963	2.4395	.8	.2	1.1456	2.0498	.8
.3	1.0595	3.0256	.7	.3	1.0972	2.4300	.7	.3	1.1467	2.0434	.7
.4	1.0602	3.0106	.6	.4	1.0981	2.4207	.6	.4	1.1478	2.0371	.6
.5	1.0608	2.9957	.5	.5	1.0989	2.4114	.5	.5	1.1490	2.0308	.5
.6	1.0615	2.9811	.4	.6	1.0998	2.4022	.4	.6	1.1501	2.0245	.4
.7	1.0622	2.9665	.3	.7	1.1007	2.3931	.3	.7	1.1512	2.0183	.3
.8	1.0628	2.9521	.2	.8	1.1016	2.3841	.2	.8	1.1524	2.0122	.2
.9	1.0635	2.9379	.1	.9	1.1025	2.3751	.1	.9	1.1535	2.0061	.1
20.0	1.0642	2.9238	70.0	25.0	1.1034	2.3662	65.0	30.0	1.1547	2.0000	60.0
Deg.	Csc	Sec	Deg.	Deg.	Csc	Sec	Deg.	Deg.	Csc	Sec	Deg.

Table III. Secants and Cosecants for Decimal Fractions of a Degree (*Continued*)

Deg.	Sec	Csc	Deg.	Deg.	Sec	Csc	Deg.	Deg.	Sec	Csc	Deg.
30.0	1.1547	2.0000	60.0	35.0	1.2208	1.7434	55.0	40.0	1.3054	1.5557	50.0
.1	1.1559	1.9940	.9	.1	1.2223	1.7391	.9	.1	1.3073	1.5525	.9
.2	1.1570	1.9880	.8	.2	1.2238	1.7348	.8	.2	1.3093	1.5493	.8
.3	1.1582	1.9821	.7	.3	1.2253	1.7305	.7	.3	1.3112	1.5461	.7
.4	1.1594	1.9762	.6	.4	1.2268	1.7263	.6	.4	1.3131	1.5429	.6
.5	1.1606	1.9703	.5	.5	1.2283	1.7221	.5	.5	1.3151	1.5398	.5
.6	1.1618	1.9645	.4	.6	1.2299	1.7179	.4	.6	1.3171	1.5366	.4
.7	1.1630	1.9587	.3	.7	1.2314	1.7137	.3	.7	1.3190	1.5335	.3
.8	1.1642	1.9530	.2	.8	1.2329	1.7095	.2	.8	1.3210	1.5304	.2
.9	1.1654	L.9473	.1	.9	1.2345	1.7054	.1	.9	1.3230	1.5273	.1
31.0	1.1666	1.9416	59.0	36.0	1.2361	1.7013	54.0	41.0	1.3250	1.5243	49.0
.1	1.1679	1.9360	.9	.1	1.2376	1.6972	.9	.1	1.3270	1.5212	.9
.2	1.1691	1.9304	.8	.2	1.2392	1.6932	.8	.2	1.3291	1.5182	.8
.3	1.1703	1.9249	.7	.3	1.2408	1.6892	.7	.3	1.3311	1.5151	.7
.4	1.1716	1.9194	.6	.4	1.2424	1.6852	.6	.4	1.3331	1.5121	.6
.5	1.1728	1.9139	.5	.5	1.2440	1.6812	.5	.5	1.3352	1.5092	.5
.6	1.1741	1.9084	.4	.6	1.2456	1.6772	.4	.6	1.3373	1.5062	.4
.7	1.1753	1.9031	.3	.7	1.2472	1.6733	.3	.7	1.3393	1.5032	.3
.8	1.1766	1.8977	.2	.8	1.2489	1.6694	.2	.8	1.3414	1.5003	.2
.9	1.1779	1.8924	.1	.9	1.2505	1.6655	.1	.9	1.3435	1.4974	.1
32.0	1.1792	1.8871	58.0	37.0	1.2521	1.6616	53.0	42.0	1.3456	1.4945	48.0
.1	1.1805	1.8818	.9	.1	1.2538	1.6578	.9	.1	1.3478	1.4916	.9
.2	1.1818	1.8766	.8	.2	1.2554	1.6540	.8	.2	1.3499	1.4887	.8
.3	1.1831	1.8714	.7	.3	1.2571	1.6502	.7	.3	1.3520	1.4859	.7
.4	1.1844	1.8663	.6	.4	1.2588	1.6464	.6	.4	1.3542	1.4830	.6
.5	1.1857	1.8612	.5	.5	1.2605	1.6427	.5	.5	1.3563	1.4802	.5
.6	1.1870	1.8561	.4	.6	1.2622	1.6390	.4	.6	1.3585	1.4774	.4
.7	1.1883	1.8510	.3	.7	1.2639	1.6353	.3	.7	1.3607	1.4746	.3
.8	1.1897	1.8460	.2	.8	1.2656	1.6316	.2	.8	1.3629	1.4718	.2
.9	1.1910	1.8410	.1	.9	1.2673	1.6279	.1	.9	1.3651	1.4690	.1
33.0	1.1924	1.8361	57.0	38.0	1.2690	1.6243	52.0	43.0	1.3673	1.4663	47.0
.1	1.1937	1.8312	.9	.1	1.2708	1.6207	.9	.1	1.3696	1.4635	.9
.2	1.1951	1.8263	.8	.2	1.2725	1.6171	.8	.2	1.3718	1.4608	.8
.3	1.1964	1.8214	.7	.3	1.2742	1.6135	.7	.3	1.3741	1.4581	.7
.4	1.1978	1.8166	.6	.4	1.2760	1.6099	.6	.4	1.3763	1.4554	.6
.5	1.1992	1.8118	.5	.5	1.2778	1.6064	.5	.5	1.3786	1.4527	.5
.6	1.2006	1.8070	.4	.6	1.2796	1.6029	.4	.6	1.3809	1.4501	.4
.7	1.2020	1.8023	.3	.7	1.2813	1.5994	.3	.7	1.3832	1.4474	.3
.8	1.2034	1.7976	.2	.8	1.2831	1.5959	.2	.8	1.3855	1.4448	.2
.9	1.2048	1.7929	.1	.9	1.2849	1.5925	.1	.9	1.3878	1.4422	.1
34.0	1.2062	1.7883	56.0	39.0	1.2868	1.5890	51.0	44.0	1.3902	1.4396	46.0
.1	1.2076	1.7837	.9	.1	1.2886	1.5856	.9	.1	1.3925	1.4370	.9
.2	1.2091	1.7791	.8	.2	1.2904	1.5822	.8	.2	1.3949	1.4344	.8
.3	1.2105	1.7745	.7	.3	1.2923	1.5788	.7	.3	1.3972	1.4318	.7
.4	1.2120	1.7700	.6	.4	1.2941	1.5755	.6	.4	1.3996	1.4293	.6
.5	1.2134	1.7655	.5	.5	1.2960	1.5721	.5	.5	1.4020	1.4267	.5
.6	1.2149	1.7610	.4	.6	1.2978	1.5688	.4	.6	1.4044	1.4242	.4
.7	1.2163	1.7566	.3	.7	1.2997	1.5655	.3	.7	1.4069	1.4217	.3
.8	1.2178	1.7522	.2	.8	1.3016	1.5622	.2	.8	1.4093	1.4192	.2
.9	1.2193	1.7478	.1	.9	1.3035	1.5590	.1	.9	1.4118	1.4167	.1
35.0	1.2208	1.7434	55.0	40.0	1.3054	1.5557	50.0	45.0	1.4142	1.4142	45.0

Deg.	Csc	Sec	Deg.	Deg.	Csc	Sec	Deg.	Deg.	Csc	Sec	Deg.

Index